Fourth Edition

Contemporary Business Mathematics

with Canadian Applications

S.A. HUMMELBRUNNER

Fourth Edition

Contemporary Business Mathematics

with Canadian Applications

S.A. HUMMELBRUNNER

PRENTICE HALL CANADA INC.
SCARBOROUGH, ONTARIO

Canadian Cataloguing in Publication Data

Hummelbrunner, S. A. (Siegfried August)
Contemporary business mathematics with Canadian applications

4th ed.
ISBN 0-13-287582-9

1. Business mathematics. I. Title.

HF5691.H85 1994 650′.01′513 C93-095092-5

Prentice-Hall, Inc., Englewood Cliffs, New Jersey
Prentice-Hall International (UK) Limited, London
Prentice-Hall of Australia, Pty. Limited, Sydney
Prentice-Hall Hispanoamericana, S.A., Mexico City
Prentice-Hall of India Private Limited, New Delhi
Prentice-Hall of Japan, Inc., Tokyo
Simon & Schuster Asia Private Limited, Singapore
Editora Prentice-Hall do Brasil, Ltda., Rio de Janeiro

ISBN 0-13-287582-9

Acquisitions Editor: Jacqueline Wood
Developmental Editor: Maurice Esses
Copy Editor: Mia London
Production Editor: Valerie Adams
Production Coordinator: Anna Orodi
Cover Design & Image: Pronk & Associates
Page Layout: Compeer Typographic Services Ltd.

4 5 RRD 97 96

Printed and bound in USA.

Contents

Preface

Contemporary Business Mathematics is intended for use in introductory mathematics of finance courses in business administration programs. In more general application it also provides a comprehensive basis for those who wish to review and extend their understanding of business mathematics.

The primary objective of the text is to increase the student's knowledge and skill in the solution of practical financial and mathematical problems encountered in the business community. It also provides a supportive base for mathematical topics in finance, accounting and marketing.

Contemporary Business Mathematics is essentially a teaching text using the objectives approach. The systematic and sequential development of the material is supported by carefully selected and worked examples. These detailed step-by-step solutions presented in a clear and uncluttered layout are particularly helpful in allowing students, in either independent studies or in the traditional classroom setting, to carefully monitor their own progress.

Each topic in each chapter is followed by an exercise containing numerous drill questions and application problems. The review exercise and self-test at the end of each chapter and the case studies are designed to assist in the integration of the material studied. The computer programs contained in the Solutions Manual provide samples of those text problems most suited to solution by computer.

The first four chapters and Appendix I (Review of basic algebra) are intended for students with little or no background in algebra and provide an opportunity to review arithmetic and algebraic processes.

The text is based on Canadian practice, and reflects current trends utilizing available technology — specifically the availability of reasonably priced electronic pocket calculators.

Students using this book should have access to calculating equipment having a power function and a natural logarithm function. The use of such calculators eliminates the arithmetic constraints often associated with financial problems and frees the student from reliance on financial tables.

The power function and the natural logarithm function are often needed to determine values which will be used for forther computation. Such values should not be rounded and all available digits should be retained. The student is encouraged to use the memory to retain such values.

When using the memory the student needs to be aware that the number of digits retained in the registers of the calculator is greater than the number of digits displayed. Depending on whether the memory or the displayed digits are used, slight differences may occur. Such differences will undoubtedly be encountered when working the examples presented in the text. However, they are insignificant and should not be of concern. In most cases the final answers will agree, whichever method is used.

Students are encouraged to use preprogrammed financial calculators though this is not essential. The use of preprogrammed calculators facilitates the solving of most financial problems and is demonstrated extensively in chapters 9 to 17.

The fourth edition of the text has taken into account the suggestions, comments and criticisms received from reviewers, publisher's representatives and users of the first three editions including students. In this regard I wish to give special thanks to all those who responded to a questionnaire about ways to improve the previous edition. I would also like to thank those instructors who participated in a special focus group for this edition: Elaine Hales, Georgian College; Sharyn Jeffries, Centennial College; Colleen Quinn, Seneca College; Ishwar Dean, George Brown College; Rick Law, Humber College; Tom Quinn, Humber College; and Debbie Kirwin, Sheridan College (Brampton). Thanks are also due to Jim Gowland of Conestoga College who prepared the case studies.

SIEG HUMMELBRUNNER

Mississauga
December 1993

PART ONE

Mathematics fundamentals

1 *Review of arithmetic*

Introduction

Electronic calculators are now in general use in business to perform arithmetic computations. The fundamental operations of addition, subtraction, multiplication, and division with whole numbers and decimal fractions can be done with any model on the market. However, to use a calculator as a tool in solving problems requires skill in using the basic order of operations, converting mixed numbers and common fractions into decimal form, and rounding answers to the desired number of decimal positions.

Objectives

Upon completing this chapter, you will be able to

1. simplify arithmetic expressions involving the basic order of operations;
2. solve basic problems, including arithmetic averages, involving the fundamental operations;
3. determine gross earnings for employees remunerated by the payment of salaries, hourly wages, or commissions.

1.1 *Basics of arithmetic*

A. The basic order of operations

To ensure that operations are performed consistently, we must follow the *order of operations*.

If an arithmetic expression contains brackets as well as any or all of powers, multiplication, division, addition, and subtraction, we use the following procedure:

1. perform all operations *inside* a bracket first (the operations inside the bracket must be performed in proper order);
2. perform powers;

3. perform multiplications and divisions in order;
4. perform addition and subtraction.

Example **1.1a**

(i) $9 - 4 \times 2 = 9 - 8 = 1$ ← do multiplication before subtraction

(ii) $(9 - 4) \times 2 = 5 \times 2 = 10$ ← work inside the bracket first

(iii) $(13 + 5) \div 6 - 3 = 18 \div 6 - 3$ ← work inside the bracket first, then do division before subtraction
$= 3 - 3$
$= 0$

(iv) $18 \div 6 + 3 \times 2 = 3 + 6 = 9$ ← do multiplication and division before adding

(v) $18 \div (6 + 3) \times 2 = 18 \div 9 \times 2$ ← work inside the bracket first, then do division and multiplication in order
$= 2 \times 2$
$= 4$

(vi) $18 \div (3 \times 2) + 3 = 18 \div 6 + 3$ ← work inside bracket first, then divide before adding
$= 3 + 3$
$= 6$

(vii) $8(9 - 4) - 4(12 - 5) = 8(5) - 4(7)$ ← work inside brackets first, then multiply before subtracting
$= 40 - 28$
$= 12$

(viii) $\frac{12 - 4}{6 - 2} = (12 - 4) \div (6 - 2)$ ← the fraction line indicates brackets as well as division
$= 8 \div 4$
$= 2$

B. *Converting common fractions into decimal fractions*

Common fractions are converted into decimal fractions by performing the indicated division to the desired number of decimal places or until the decimal terminates.

Example **1.1b**

(i) $\frac{9}{8} = 9 \div 8 = 1.125$

(ii) $\frac{1}{3} = 1 \div 3 = 0.33333\ldots$

(iii) $\frac{7}{6} = 7 \div 6 = 1.16666\ldots$

C. *Converting mixed decimals to decimal form*

Mixed decimals, such as $0.33\frac{1}{3}$, are a convenient way of representing repeating decimals in abbreviated form.

Example **1.1c**

(i) $0.33\dfrac{1}{3} = 0.333333\ldots$ ⟵ divide 1 by 3 and replace $\frac{1}{3}$ by the resulting decimal digits

(ii) $0.55\dfrac{5}{9} = 0.555555\ldots$ ⟵ divide 5 by 9 and replace $\frac{5}{9}$ by the resulting decimal digits

(iii) $0.72\dfrac{5}{12} = 0.7241666\ldots$ ⟵ divide 5 by 12 and replace $\frac{5}{12}$ by the resulting decimal digits

D. *Converting mixed numbers to decimal fractions*

Mixed numbers are numbers consisting of a whole number and a fraction, such as $5\frac{3}{4}$. Such numbers represent the *sum* of a whole number and a common fraction and can be converted into decimal form by changing the common fraction into a decimal fraction.

Example **1.1d**

(i) $5\dfrac{3}{4} = 5 + \dfrac{3}{4} = 5 + 0.75 = 5.75$

(ii) $6\dfrac{2}{3} = 6 + \dfrac{2}{3} = 6 + 0.66666\ldots = 6.66666\ldots$

(iii) $7\dfrac{1}{12} = 7 + \dfrac{1}{12} = 7 + 0.083333\ldots = 7.083333\ldots$

E. *Rounding*

Answers to problems, particularly when obtained with the help of a calculator, often need to be rounded to a desired number of decimal places. In most business problems involving money values, the rounding needs to be done to the nearest cent, that is, to two decimal positions.

While different methods of rounding are used, for most business purposes the following procedure is suitable.

1. If the first digit in the group of decimal digits that is to be dropped is the digit 5 or 6 or 7 or 8 or 9, the last digit retained is *increased* by 1.
2. If the first digit in the group of decimal digits that is to be dropped is the digit 0 or 1 or 2 or 3 or 4, the last digit is left *unchanged.*

Example **1.1e** Round each of the following to two decimals.

(i) 7.384 ⟶ 7.38 ⟵ drop the digit 4

(ii) 7.385 ⟶ 7.39 ⟵ round the digit 8 up to 9

(iii) 12.9448 ⟶ 12.94 ⟵ discard 48

(iv) 9.32838 ⟶ 9.33 ⟵ round the digit 2 up to 3

(v) 24.8975 ⟶ 24.90 ⟵ round the digit 9 up to 0; this requires rounding 89 to 90

(vi) 1.996 ⟶ 2.00 ⟵ round the second digit 9 up to 0; this requires rounding 1.99 to 2.00

(vii) 3199.99833 ⟶ 3200.00 ⟵ round the second digit 9 up to 0; this requires rounding 3199.99 to 3200.00

F. Complex fractions

Complex fractions are mathematical expressions containing one or more fractions in the numerator or denominator or both. Certain formulae used in simple interest and simple discount calculations result in complex fractions. When you encounter such fractions, take care to use the order of operations properly, whether computing manually or with the help of a calculator.

Example **1.1f**

(i) $$\frac{420}{1600 \times \frac{315}{360}} = \frac{420}{1600 \times 0.875} = \frac{420}{1400} = 0.3$$

(ii) $$\frac{450}{3600 \times 0.16\frac{2}{3}} = \frac{450}{3600 \times 0.166666\ldots} = \frac{450}{600} = 0.75$$

(iii) $$500\left(1 + 0.16 \times \frac{225}{360}\right)$$

$= 500(1 + 0.10)$ ⟵ multiply 0.16 by 225 and divide by 360

$= 500(1.10)$ ⟵ add inside bracket

$= 550$

(iv) $$1000\left(1 - 0.18 \times \frac{288}{360}\right) = 1000(1 - 0.144)$$

$$= 1000(0.856)$$

$$= 856$$

(v) $$\frac{824}{1 + 0.15 \times \frac{73}{365}} = \frac{824}{1 + 0.03} = \frac{824}{1.03} = 800$$

(vi) $$\frac{1755}{1 - 0.21 \times \frac{210}{360}} = \frac{1755}{1 - 0.1225} = \frac{1755}{0.8775} = 2000$$

Exercise 1.1

A. Simplify each of the following.

1. $12 + 6 \div 3$
2. $(12 + 6) \div 3$
3. $(7 + 4) \times 5 - 2$
4. $7 + 4 \times 5 - 2$
5. $5 \times 3 + 2 \times 4$
6. $5(3 + 2) - 12 \div 3$
7. $6(7 - 2) - 3(5 - 3)$
8. $8(9 - 6) + 4(6 + 5)$
9. $\dfrac{16 - 8}{8 - 2}$
10. $\dfrac{20 - 16}{15 + 9}$

B. Convert each of the following fractions into a decimal fraction. Write your answer as shown in the display of your calculator set for the maximum number of decimals.

1. $\dfrac{11}{8}$
2. $\dfrac{7}{4}$
3. $\dfrac{5}{3}$
4. $\dfrac{5}{6}$
5. $\dfrac{11}{6}$
6. $\dfrac{7}{9}$
7. $\dfrac{13}{12}$
8. $\dfrac{19}{15}$

C. Convert each of the following mixed decimals correct to 7 decimal positions.

1. $0.66\frac{2}{3}$
2. $0.16\frac{2}{3}$
3. $0.08\frac{1}{3}$
4. $0.03\frac{1}{3}$
5. $1.33\frac{1}{3}$
6. $2.83\frac{1}{3}$
7. $0.55\frac{5}{9}$
8. $2.22\frac{2}{9}$

D. Convert each of the following mixed numbers into decimal form.

1. $3\frac{3}{8}$
2. $3\frac{2}{5}$
3. $8\frac{1}{3}$
4. $16\frac{2}{3}$
5. $33\frac{1}{3}$
6. $83\frac{1}{3}$
7. $7\frac{7}{9}$
8. $7\frac{1}{12}$

E. Round each of the following to two decimal places.

1. 5.633
2. 17.449
3. 18.0046
4. 253.4856
5. 57.69875
6. 3.09475
7. 12.995
8. 39.999

F. Simplify each of the following.

1. $\dfrac{54}{0.12 \times \frac{225}{360}}$
2. $\dfrac{264}{4400 \times \frac{146}{365}}$
3. $620\left(1 + 0.14 \times \dfrac{45}{360}\right)$
4. $375\left(1 + 0.16 \times \dfrac{292}{365}\right)$
5. $2100\left(1 - 0.135 \times \dfrac{240}{360}\right)$
6. $8500\left(1 - 0.17 \times \dfrac{216}{360}\right)$
7. $\dfrac{250\,250}{1 + 0.15 \times \frac{330}{360}}$
8. $\dfrac{2358}{1 + 0.12 \times \frac{146}{365}}$
9. $\dfrac{3460}{1 - 0.18 \times \frac{270}{360}}$
10. $\dfrac{2901}{1 - 0.165 \times \frac{73}{365}}$

1.2 *Applications—averages*

A. Basic problems

When electronic calculators are used to solve problems, the accuracy of the final answer is often influenced by the number of decimal positions used for intermediate values. To avoid introducing rounding errors, keep intermediate values unrounded.

Example **1.2a** The local cooperative received $36\frac{3}{4}$ tonnes of feed at \$240 per tonne. Sales for the following five days were

$$3\tfrac{5}{8} \text{ tonnes}, 4\tfrac{3}{4} \text{ tonnes}, 7\tfrac{2}{3} \text{ tonnes}, 5\tfrac{1}{2} \text{ tonnes, and } 6\tfrac{3}{8} \text{ tonnes.}$$

What was the value of inventory at the end of Day 5?

Solution

$$\text{Total sales (in tonnes)} = 3\frac{5}{8} + 4\frac{3}{4} + 7\frac{2}{3} + 5\frac{1}{2} + 6\frac{3}{8}$$

$$= 3.625 + 4.75 + 7.6666667 + 5.5 + 6.375$$

$$= 27.9166667$$

$$\text{Inventory (in tonnes)} = 36.75 - 27.9166667 = 8.8333333$$

$$\text{Value of inventory} = 8.8333333 \times 240 = 2119.999992 = \$2120.00$$

Example **1.2b** Complete the following excerpt from an invoice.

Quantity	*Unit Price*	*Amount*
72	\$0.875	\$______
45	$0.66\frac{2}{3}$	______
54	$0.83\frac{1}{3}$	______
42	$1.33\frac{1}{3}$	______
32	1.375	______
	TOTAL	\$______

Solution

$$72 \times 0.875 = \quad \$\ 63.00$$

$$45 \times 0.66\frac{2}{3} = 45 \times 0.6666667 = \quad 30.00$$

$$54 \times 0.83\frac{1}{3} = 54 \times 0.8333333 = \quad 45.00$$

$$42 \times 1.33\frac{1}{3} = 42 \times 1.3333333 = \quad 56.00$$

$$32 \times 1.375 = \quad 44.00$$

$$\$238.00$$

B. Problems involving simple arithmetic average

The *arithmetic mean* of a set of values is a widely used average found by adding the values in the set and dividing by the number of those values.

Example **1.2c** The marks obtained by Jim Pearson for the seven tests comprising Section 1 of his Mathematics of Finance course were 82, 68, 88, 72, 78, 96, and 83.

(i) If all tests count equally, what was his average mark for Section 1?

(ii) If his marks for Section 2 and Section 3 of the course were 72.4 and 68.9 respectively and all section marks have equal value, what was his course average?

Solution

(i) $$\text{Section Average} = \frac{\text{Sum of the Test Marks for the Section}}{\text{Number of Tests}} = \frac{82 + 68 + 88 + 72 + 78 + 96 + 83}{7} = \frac{567}{7} = 81.0$$

(ii) $$\text{Course Average} = \frac{\text{Sum of the Section Marks}}{\text{Number of Sections}} = \frac{81.0 + 72.4 + 68.9}{3} = \frac{222.3}{3} = 74.1$$

Example **1.2d** Monthly sales of Sheridan Service for last year were

January	\$13 200	July	\$13 700
February	11 400	August	12 800
March	14 600	September	13 800
April	13 100	October	15 300
May	13 600	November	14 400
June	14 300	December	13 900

What were Sheridan's average monthly sales for the year?

Solution

Total sales = 164 100

$$\text{Average Monthly Sales} = \frac{\text{Total Sales}}{\text{Number of Months}} = \frac{164\,100}{12} = \$13\,675$$

C. Weighted average

If the items to be included in computing an arithmetic mean are arranged in groups or if the items are not equally important, a *weighted arithmetic average* should be obtained. Multiply each item by the numbers involved or by a weighting factor representing its importance.

Example 1.2e During last season, Fairfield Farms sold strawberries as follows: 800 boxes at \$1.25 per box in the early part of the season; 1600 boxes at \$0.90 per box and 2000 boxes at \$0.75 per box at the height of the season; and 600 boxes at \$1.10 per box during the late season.

(i) What was the average price charged?

(ii) What was the average price per box?

Solution

(i) The average price charged is a simple average of the four different prices charged during the season.

$$\text{Average Price} = \frac{1.25 + 0.90 + 0.75 + 1.10}{4} = \frac{4.00}{4} = \$1.00$$

(ii) To obtain the average price per box, the number of boxes sold at each price must be taken into account; that is, a weighted average must be computed.

800 boxes @ \$1.25 per box	⟶	\$1000.00
1600 boxes @ \$0.90 per box	⟶	1440.00
2000 boxes @ \$0.75 per box	⟶	1500.00
600 boxes @ \$1.10 per box	⟶	660.00
5000 boxes	⟵ TOTALS ⟶	\$4600.00

$$\text{Average Price per Box} = \frac{\text{Total Value}}{\text{Number of Boxes}} = \frac{4600.00}{5000} = \$0.92$$

Example 1.2f The Dutch Cheese Shop creates its house brand by mixing 13 kg of coffee priced at \$7.50 per kg, 16 kg of coffee priced at \$6.25 per kg, and 11 kg of coffee priced at \$5.50 per kg. At what price should the store sell its house blend to realize the same revenue as it could make by selling the three types of coffee separately?

Solution

13 kg @ \$7.50 per kg	⟶	\$ 97.50
16 kg @ \$6.25 per kg	⟶	100.00
11 kg @ \$5.50 per kg	⟶	60.50
40 kg	⟵ TOTALS ⟶	\$258.00

$$\text{Average Value} = \frac{\text{Total Value}}{\text{Number of Units}} = \frac{258.00}{40} = \$6.45$$

The house blend should sell for \$6.45 per kg.

***Example* 1.2g** The credit hours and grades for Dana's first term courses are listed here.

Course	*Credit Hours*	*Grade*
Accounting	5	A
Economics	3	B
English	4	C
Law	2	D
Marketing	4	A
Mathematics	3	A
Elective	2	D

According to the grading system A's, B's, C's, and D's are worth 4, 3, 2, and 1 quality points respectively. Based on this information, determine

(i) Dana's average course grade;

(ii) Dana's grade-point average (average per credit hour).

Solution

(i) The average course grade is the average quality points obtained:

$$\frac{4+3+2+1+4+4+1}{7} = \frac{19}{7} = 2.71$$

(ii) The average obtained in part (i) is misleading since the credit hours of the courses are not equal. The grade-point average is a more appropriate average because it is a weighted average allowing for the number of credit hours per course.

Course	*Credit Hours*	×	*Quality Points*	=	*Weighted Points*
Accounting	5	×	4	=	20
Economics	3	×	3	=	9
English	4	×	2	=	8
Law	2	×	1	=	2
Marketing	4	×	4	=	16
Mathematics	3	×	4	=	12
Elective	2	×	1	=	2
	23	⟵	TOTALS	⟶	69

$$\text{Grade-Point Average} = \frac{\text{Total Weighted Points}}{\text{Total Credit Hours}} = \frac{69}{23} = 3.00$$

Example **1.2h** A partnership agreement provides for the distribution of the yearly profit or loss on the basis of the partners' average monthly investment balance. The investment account of one of the partners shows the following entries.

Balance, January 1	$25 750
April 1, withdrawal	3 250
June 1, investment	4 000
November 1, investment	2 000

Determine the partner's average monthly balance in his investment account.

Solution

To determine the average monthly investment, determine the balance in the investment account after each change and weigh this balance by the number of months invested.

Date	*Change*	*Balance*	×	*Number of Months Invested*	=	*Weighted Value*
January 1		25 750	×	3	=	77 250
April 1	−3250	22 500	×	2	=	45 000
June 1	+4000	26 500	×	5	=	132 500
November 1	+2000	28 500	×	2	=	57 000
		TOTALS		12		311 750

$$\text{Average Monthly Investment} = \frac{\text{Weighted Value}}{\text{Number of Months}} = \frac{311\ 750}{12} = \$25\ 979.17$$

Example **1.2i** Several shoe stores in the city carry the same make of shoes. The number of pairs of shoes sold and the price charged by each store are shown below.

Store	*Number of Pairs Sold*	*Price per Pair*
A	60	$43.10
B	84	38.00
C	108	32.00
D	72	40.50

(i) What was the average number of pairs of shoes sold per store?

(ii) What was the average price per store?

(iii) What was the average sales revenue per store?

(iv) What was the average price per pair of shoes?

Solution

(i) The average number of pairs of shoes sold per store

$$= \frac{60 + 84 + 108 + 72}{4} = \frac{324}{4} = 81$$

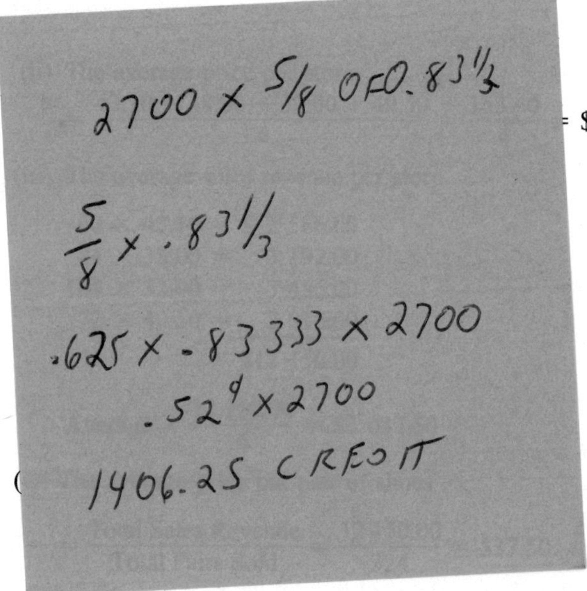

= $38.40

Exercise 1.2

A. Answer each of the following questions.

1. Heart Lake Developments sold four lakefront lots for $27 500 per hectare. If the size of the lots in hectares was $3\frac{3}{4}$, $2\frac{2}{3}$, $3\frac{5}{8}$, and $4\frac{5}{6}$ respectively, what was the total sales revenue of the four lots?

2. Five carpenters worked $15\frac{1}{2}$, $13\frac{3}{4}$, $18\frac{1}{2}$, $21\frac{1}{4}$, and $22\frac{3}{4}$ hours respectively. What was the total cost of labour if the carpenters were each paid $12.75 per hour?

3. A piece of property valued at $56 100 is assessed for property tax purposes at $\frac{6}{11}$ of its value. If the property tax rate is $3.75 on each $100 of assessed value, what is the amount of tax levied on the property?

4. A retailer returned 2700 defective items to the manufacturer and received a credit for the retail price of $0.83\frac{1}{3}$ per item less a discount of $\frac{3}{8}$ of the retail price. What was the amount of the credit received by the retailer?

5. Extend the following invoice.

Quantity	*Description*	*Unit Price*	*$*
64	A	$0.75	______
54	B	$0.83\frac{1}{3}$	______
72	C	0.375	______
42	D	$1.33\frac{1}{3}$	______
		TOTAL	______

6. Complete the following inventory sheet.

Item	*Quantity*	*Cost per Unit*	*Total*
1	96	\$0.875	______
2	330	$0.16\frac{2}{3}$	______
3	144	1.75	______
4	240	$1.66\frac{2}{3}$	______
		TOTAL	______

B. Solve each of the following problems involving an arithmetic average.

1. Records of Sheridan Service's fuel oil consumption for the last six-month period show that Sheridan paid 38.5 cents per litre for the first 1100 litres, 41.5 cents per litre for the next 1600 litres, and 42.5 cents per litre for the last delivery of 1400 litres. Determine the average cost of fuel oil per litre for the six-month period.

2. On a trip, a motorist purchased gasoline as follows: 56 litres at 49.0 cents per litre; 64 litres at 60.5 cents per litres; 70 litres at 51.5 cents per litre; and 54 litres at 54.5 cents per litre.
   (i) What was the average number of litres per purchase?
   (ii) What was the average cost per litre?
   (iii) If the motorist averaged 8.75 km per litre, what was her average cost of gasoline per kilometre?

3. The course credit hours and grades for Bill's fall semester are given below. At his college, an A is worth six quality points, a B four points, a C two points, and a D one point.

Credit hours:	3	5	2	4	4	2
Grade:	B	C	A	C	D	A

   What is Bill's grade-point average?

4. Kim Blair invested \$7500 in a business on January 1. She withdrew \$900 on March 1, reinvested \$1500 on August 1, and withdrew \$300 on September 1. What is Kim's average monthly investment balance for the year?

1.3 *Applications—payroll*

Employees can be remunerated for their services in a variety of ways. The main methods of remuneration are salaries, hourly wage rates, and commission. While the computations involved in preparing a payroll are fairly simple, utmost care is needed to assure that all calculations are accurate.

A. Salaries

Compensation of employees by **salary** is usually on a monthly or a yearly basis. Monthly salaried personnel get paid either monthly or semi-monthly. Personnel on a yearly salary basis may get paid monthly, semi-monthly, every two weeks, or weekly, or according to special schedules such as those used by some Boards of Education to pay their teachers. If salary is paid weekly or every two weeks, the year is assumed to consist of exactly 52 weeks.

Calculations of **gross earnings** per pay period is fairly simple. Computing overtime for salaried personnel can be problematic since overtime is usually paid based on an hourly rate.

***Example* 1.3a** An employee with an annual salary of \$23 296.00 is paid every two weeks. The regular workweek is 40 hours.

(i) What is the gross pay per pay period?

(ii) What is the hourly rate of pay?

(iii) What are the gross earnings for a pay period in which the employee worked six hours of overtime and is paid one-and-a-half times the regular hourly rate of pay?

Solution

(i) An employee paid every two weeks receives the annual salary over 26 pay periods.

$$\text{Gross pay per two-week period} = \frac{23\,296.00}{26} = \$896.00$$

(ii) Given a 40-hour week, the employee's compensation for two weeks covers 80 hours.

$$\text{Hourly rate of pay} = \frac{896.00}{80} = \$11.20$$

(iii) Regular gross earnings for two-week period \$896.00
Overtime pay
6 hours @ \$11.20 × 1.5 = 6 × 11.20 × 1.5 100.80
Total gross earnings for pay period \$996.80

***Example* 1.3b** Mike Paciuc receives a monthly salary of \$2080.00 paid semi-monthly. Mike's regular workweek is 37.5 hours. Any hours worked over 37.5 hours in a week are overtime and are paid at time-and-a-half regular pay. During the first half of October, Mike worked 7.5 hours overtime.

(i) What is Mike's hourly rate of pay?

(ii) What are his gross earnings for the pay period ending October 15?

Solution

(i) When computing the hourly rate of pay for personnel employed on a monthly salary basis, the correct approach requires that the yearly salary be determined first. The hourly rate of pay may then be computed on the basis of 52 weeks per year.

$$\text{Yearly gross earnings} = 2080.00 \times 12 = \$24\,960.00$$

$$\text{Weekly gross earnings} = \frac{24\,960.00}{52} = \$480.00$$

$$\text{Hourly rate of pay} = \frac{480.00}{37.5} = \$12.80$$

(ii) Regular semi-monthly gross earnings $= \dfrac{2080.00}{2} = \$1040.00$

Overtime pay $= 7.5 \times 12.80 \times 1.5 \qquad = \underline{144.00}$

Total gross earnings for pay period $\qquad \underline{\underline{\$1184.00}}$

Example **1.3c** Teachers with the Northern Mississagi Board of Education are under contract for 200 teaching days per year. They are paid according to the following schedule:

8% of annual salary on the first day of school;
4% of annual salary for each of 20 two-week pay periods;
12% of annual salary at the end of the last pay period in June.

Fern Brooks, a teacher employed by the board, is paid an annual salary of $51 240.00.

(i) What is Fern's daily rate of pay?

(ii) What is Fern's gross pay?
  (a) for the first pay period?
  (b) for the last pay period?
  (c) for all other pay periods?

(iii) If Fern takes an unpaid leave of absence for three days during a pay period ending in April, what is her gross pay for that pay period?

Solution

(i) Daily rate of pay $= \dfrac{51\,240.00}{200} = \$256.20$

(ii) **(a)** First gross pay $= 0.08 \times 51\,240.00 = \$4099.20$
  (b) Last gross pay $= 0.12 \times 51\,240.00 = \$6148.80$
  (c) All other gross pay $= 0.04 \times 51\,240.00 = \$2049.60$

(iii) Gross pay for pay period ending in April $= \$2049.60$
  Less 3 days of pay $= \frac{3}{200}$ of \$51 240.00 $= \underline{768.60}$

Gross pay $\underline{\underline{\$1281.00}}$

B. *Commission*

Persons engaged in the buying and selling functions of a business are often compensated by a **commission**. Of the various types of commission designed to meet the specific circumstances of a particular business, the most commonly encountered are straight commission, graduated (or sliding-scale) commission, and base salary plus commission.

Straight commission is usually calculated as a percent of net sales for a given time period. Net sales are the difference between the gross sales for the time period and any sales returns and allowances.

Graduated commission usually involves paying an increasing percent for increasing sales levels during a given time period.

Salary plus commission is a method that guarantees a minimum income per pay period to the salesperson. However, the rate of commission in such cases is either at a lower rate or is not paid until a minimum sales level (called a **quota**) for a time period has been reached.

Sales personnel on commission often have a drawing account with their employer. The salesperson may withdraw funds from such an account in advance to meet business and personal expenses. However, any money advanced is deducted from the commission earned when the salesperson is paid.

***Example* 1.3d** Robin Thomas receives a commission of 11.5% on his net sales and is entitled to drawings of up to \$1000.00 per month. During August, Robin's gross sales amounted to \$15 540.00 and sales returns and allowances were \$360.00.

(i) What are Robin's net sales for August?

(ii) How much is his commission for August?

(iii) If Robin drew \$875.00 in August, what is the amount due to him?

Solution

(i) Gross sales	\$15 540.00
Less sales returns and allowances	360.00
Net sales	\$15 180.00

(ii) Commission = 11.5% of net sales
= $0.115 \times 15\ 180.00$
= \$1745.70

(iii) Gross commission earned	\$1745.70
Less drawings	875.00
Amount due	\$ 870.70

***Example* 1.3e** Valerie works as a salesperson for the local Minutemen Press. She receives a commission of 7.5% on monthly sales up to \$8000.00, 9.25% on the next \$7000.00, and 11% on any additional sales during the month. If Valerie's September sales amounted to \$18 750.00, what is her gross commission for the month?

Solution

Commission on the first \$8000.00 = 0.075 × 8000.00	=	\$ 600.00
Commission on the next \$7000.00 = 0.0925 × 7000.00	=	647.50
Commission on sales over \$15 000 = 0.11 × 3750.00	=	412.50
Total commission for September		\$1660.00

Example **1.3f** Rita is employed as a salesclerk in a fabric store. She receives a weekly salary of \$575.00 plus a commission of $6\frac{1}{4}\%$ on all weekly sales subject to a weekly sales quota of \$5000.00. Derek works in the shoe store located next door. He receives a minimum of \$500.00 per week or a commission of 12.5% on all sales for the week, whichever is the greater. If both Rita and Derek had sales of \$5960.00 last week, how much compensation does each receive for the week?

Solution

Rita's compensation

Base salary	\$575.00
Plus commission = $6\frac{1}{4}\%$ on sales over \$5000.00	
= 0.0625 × 960.00	60.00
Total compensation	\$635.00

Derek's compensation

Minimum weekly pay	\$500.00
Commission = 12.5% of \$5960.00 = 0.125 × 5960.00 =	\$745.00

Since the commission is greater than the guaranteed minimum pay of \$500.00, Derek's compensation is \$745.00.

C. *Wages*

The term **wages** usually applies to compensation paid to *hourly* rated employees. Their gross earnings are calculated by multiplying the number of hours worked by the hourly rate of pay plus any overtime pay. Overtime is most often paid at time and one-half the regular hourly rate for any hours exceeding an established number of regular hours per week or per day. The number of regular hours is often established by agreement between the employer and employees. The most common regular workweek is 40 hours. If no agreement exists, federal or provincial employment standards legislation provides for a maximum number of hours per week, such as 44 hours for most employers in Ontario. Any hours over the set maximum must be paid at least at time and one-half of the regular hourly rate.

When overtime is involved, gross earnings can be calculated by either one of two methods.

Method A

The most common method, and the easiest method for the wage earner to understand, determines total gross earnings by adding overtime pay to the gross pay for a regular workweek.

Method B

In the second method, the overtime excess (or **overtime premium**) is computed separately and added to gross earnings for all hours (including the overtime hours) at the regular rate of pay. Computation of the excess labor cost due to overtime emphasizes the additional expense due to overtime and provides management with information that is useful to cost control.

Example **1.3g** Mario is a machinist with Scott Tool and Die and is paid \$14.40 per hour. The regular workweek is 40 hours and overtime is paid at time and one-half the regular hourly rate. If Mario worked $46\frac{1}{2}$ hours last week, what were his gross earnings?

Solution

Method A

Gross earnings for a regular workweek = 40 × 14.40	=	\$576.00
Overtime pay = 6.5 × 14.40 × 1.5	=	140.40
Gross pay		\$716.40

Method B

Earnings at the regular hourly rate = 46.5 × 14.40	=	\$669.60
Overtime premium = $6.5 \times \left(\frac{1}{2} \text{ of } 14.40\right) = 6.5 \times 7.20$	=	46.80
Gross pay		\$716.40

Example **1.3h** Gloria works for \$8.44 an hour under a union contract that provides for daily overtime for all hours worked over eight hours. Overtime includes hours worked on Saturdays and is paid at time and one-half the regular rate of pay. Hours worked on Sundays or holidays are paid at double the regular rate of pay. Use both methods to determine Gloria's gross earnings for a week in which she worked the following hours:

Monday	9 hours	Tuesday	$10\frac{1}{2}$ hours
Wednesday	7 hours	Thursday	$9\frac{1}{2}$ hours
Friday	8 hours	Saturday	6 hours
Sunday	6 hours		

Solution

Day	*Mo*	*Tu*	*We*	*Thu*	*Fr*	*Sat*	*Su*	*Total*
Regular hours	8	8	7	8	8			39
Overtime at time and one-half	1	2.5		1.5		6		11
Overtime at double time							6	6
Total hours worked	9	10.5	7	9.5	8	6	6	56

Method A

Gross earnings for regular hours	= 39 × 8.44 =		$329.16
Overtime pay			
at time and one-half	= 11 × 8.44 × 1.5 =	$139.26	
at double time	= 6 × 8.44 × 2 =	101.28	240.54
	Total gross pay		$569.70

Method B

Earnings at regular hourly rate	= 56 × 8.44 =		$472.64
Overtime pay			
at time and one-half	$= 11\left(\frac{1}{2} \text{ of } \$8.44\right)$		
	= 11 × 4.22 =	$46.42	
at double time	= 6 × 8.44 =	$50.64	97.06
	Total gross pay		$569.70

Exercise 1.3

A. Answer each of the following questions.

1. R. Burton is employed at an annual salary of $22 932.00 paid semi-monthly. The regular workweek is 36 hours.
   - **(a)** What is the regular salary per pay period?
   - **(b)** What is the hourly rate of pay?
   - **(c)** What is the gross pay for a pay period in which the employee worked 11 hours overtime at time and one-half regular pay?
2. C. Hall receives a yearly salary of $23 868.00. She is paid bi-weekly and her regular workweek is 37.5 hours.
   - **(a)** What is the gross pay per pay period?
   - **(b)** What is the hourly rate of pay?
   - **(c)** What is the gross pay for a pay period in which she works $8\frac{1}{2}$ hours overtime at time and one-half regular pay?
3. Carole is paid a monthly salary of $1101.10. Her regular workweek is 35 hours.
   - **(a)** What is Carole's hourly rate of pay?
   - **(b)** What is Carole's gross pay for May if she worked $7\frac{3}{4}$ hours overtime during the month at time and one-half regular pay?
4. Herb receives a semi-monthly salary of $863.20 and works a regular workweek of 40 hours.
   - **(a)** What is Herb's hourly rate of pay?
   - **(b)** If Herb's gross earnings in one pay period were $990.19, for how many hours of overtime was he paid at time and one-half regular pay?

5. An employee of a Board of Education is paid an annual salary in twenty-two bi-weekly payments of \$1123.00 each. If the employee is under contract for 200 workdays of $7\frac{1}{2}$ hours each,

(a) what is the hourly rate of pay?

(b) what is the gross pay for a pay period in which the employee was away for two days at no pay?

6. Geraldine Moog is paid a commission of $9\frac{3}{4}\%$ on her net sales and is authorized to draw up to \$800.00 a month. What is the amount due to Geraldine at the end of a month in which she drew \$720.00, had sales of \$12 660.00, and sales returns were \$131.20?

7. What is a salesperson's commission on net sales of \$16 244.00 if the commission is paid on a sliding scale of $8\frac{1}{4}\%$ on the first \$6000.00, $9\frac{3}{4}\%$ on the next \$6000.00, and 11.5% on any additional sales?

8. A sales representative selling auto parts receives a commission of 4.5% on net sales up to \$10 000.00, 6% on the next \$5000.00, and 8% on any further sales. If his sales for a month were \$24 250.00 and sales returns were \$855.00, what was his commission for the month?

9. A salesclerk at a local boutique receives a weekly base salary of \$225.00 on a quota of \$4500.00 per week plus a commission of $6\frac{1}{2}\%$ on sales exceeding the quota.

(a) What are the gross earnings for a week if sales are \$4125.00?

(b) What are the gross earnings for a week if sales amount to \$6150.00?

10. A clothing store salesperson is paid a weekly salary of \$250.00 or a commission of 12.5% of his sales, whichever is the greater. What is his salary for a week in which his sales were

(a) \$1780.00? **(b)** \$2780.00?

11. For October, Monique Lemay earned a commission of \$1884.04 on gross sales of \$21 440.00. If returns and allowances were 5% of gross sales, what is her rate of commission based on net sales?

12. Jim Scott had gross earnings of \$354.30 for last week. Jim earns a base salary of \$270.00 on a weekly quota of \$4000.00. If his sales for the week were \$5124.00, what is his commission rate?

13. Doug Wilson earned a commission of \$2036.88 for March. If his rate of commission is 11.25% of net sales, and returns and allowances were 8% of gross sales, what were Doug's gross sales for the month?

14. Corrie Daley had gross earnings of \$337.50 for the week. If she receives a base salary of \$264.00 on a quota of \$4800.00 and a commission of 8.75% on sales exceeding the quota, what were Corrie's sales for the week?

15. Carlos Shastri is employed at an hourly rate of \$8.42. The regular workweek is 40 hours and overtime is paid at time and one-half regular pay. Using the two methods illustrated earlier, compute Carlos's gross earnings for a week in which he worked 47 hours.

16. Kim Ferrill earns \$10.60 per hour. Overtime from Monday to Friday is paid at time and one-half regular pay for any hours over $7\frac{1}{2}$ per day. Overtime on weekends is paid at double the regular rate of pay. Last week Kim worked regular hours on Monday, Wednesday, and Friday, 9 hours on Tuesday, $10\frac{1}{2}$ hours on Thursday, and 6 hours on Saturday. Determine Kim's gross wages by each of the two methods.

17. An employee of a repair shop receives a gross pay of \$261.80 for a regular workweek of 44 hours. What is the hourly rate of pay?

18. A wage statement shows gross earnings of \$361.00 for 45 hours of work. What is the hourly rate of pay if the regular workweek is 40 hours and overtime is paid at time and one-half the regular rate of pay?

Review exercise

1. Simplify each of the following.

(a) $32 - 24 \div 8$

(b) $(48 - 18) \div 15 - 10$

(c) $(8 \times 6 - 4) \div (16 - 4 \times 3)$

(d) $9(6 - 2) - 4(3 + 4)$

(e) $\dfrac{108}{0.18 \times \frac{216}{360}}$

(f) $\dfrac{288}{2400 \times \frac{292}{365}}$

(g) $320\left(1 + 0.10 \times \dfrac{225}{360}\right)$

(h) $1000\left(1 - 0.12 \times \dfrac{150}{360}\right)$

(i) $\dfrac{660}{1 + 0.14 \times \frac{144}{360}}$

(j) $\dfrac{1120.00}{1 - 0.13 \times \frac{292}{365}}$

2. Sales of a particular make and size of nails during a day were $4\frac{1}{3}$ kg, $3\frac{3}{4}$ kg, $5\frac{1}{2}$ kg, and $6\frac{5}{8}$ kg.

(a) How many kilograms of nails were sold?

(b) What is the total sales value at \$1.20 per kilogram?

(c) What was the average weight per sale?

(d) What was the average sales value per sale?

3. Extend and total the following invoice.

Quantity	*Description*	*Unit Price*	*Total*
56	Item A	\$0.625	________
180	Item B	$0.83\frac{1}{3}$	________
126	Item C	$1.16\frac{2}{3}$	________
144	Item D	1.75	________
		TOTAL	________

4. The basic pay categories, hourly rates of pay, and the number of employees in each category for the machining department of a company are shown below.

Category	*Hourly Pay*	*Number of Employees*
Supervisors	$15.45	2
Machinists	12.20	6
Assistants	9.60	9
Helpers	7.50	13

(a) What is the average rate of pay per category?

(b) What is the average rate of pay per employee?

5. Hélène Gauthier invested $15 000 on January 1 in a partnership. She withdrew $2000 on June 1, withdrew a further $1500 on August 1, and reinvested $4000 on November 1. What was her average monthly investment balance for the year?

6. Brent DeCosta invested $12 000 in a business on January 1 and an additional $2400 on April 1. He withdrew $1440 on June 1 and invested $2880 on October 1. What was Brent's average monthly investment balance for the year?

7. Maria is paid a semi-monthly salary of $800.80. Her regular workweek is 40 hours. Overtime is paid at time and one-half regular pay.

(a) What is Maria's hourly rate of pay?

(b) What is Maria's gross pay if she worked $8\frac{1}{2}$ hours overtime in one pay period?

8. Casey receives an annual salary of $17 472.00, is paid monthly, and works 35 regular hours per week.

(a) What is Casey's gross remuneration per pay period?

(b) What is his hourly rate of pay?

(c) How many hours overtime did Casey work during a month for which his gross pay was $1693.60?

9. Tim is employed at an annual salary of $20 292.48. His regular workweek is 36 hours and he is paid semi-monthly.

(a) What is Tim's gross pay per period?

(b) What is his hourly rate of pay?

(c) What is his gross pay for a period in which he worked $12\frac{1}{2}$ hours overtime at time and one-half regular pay?

10. Artemis is paid a weekly commission of 4% on net sales of $3000.00, 8% on the next $1500.00, and 12.5% on all further sales. Her sales for a week were $5580.00 and sales returns and allowances were $60.00.

(a) What were her gross earnings for the week?

(b) What was her average hourly rate of pay for the week if she worked 43 hours?

11. Last week June worked 44 hours. She is paid $8.20 per hour for a regular workweek of 37.5 hours and overtime at time and one-half regular pay.

(a) What were June's gross wages for last week?

(b) What is the amount of the overtime premium?

12. Vacek is paid a monthly commission on a graduated basis of $7\frac{1}{2}\%$ on net sales of \$7000.00, 9% on the next \$8000.00, and 11% on any additional sales. If sales for April were \$21 500.00 and sales returns were \$325.00, what were his gross earnings for the month?

13. Margit is paid on a weekly commission basis. She is paid a base salary of \$240.00 on a weekly quota of \$8000.00 and a commission of 4.75% on any sales in excess of the quota.
    (a) If Margit's sales for last week were \$11 340.00, what were her gross earnings?
    (b) What are Margit's average hourly earnings if she worked 35 hours?

14. Last week Lisa had gross earnings of \$321.30. Lisa receives a base salary of \$255.00 and a commission on sales exceeding her quota of \$5000.00. What is her rate of commission if her sales were \$6560.00?

15. John earned a gross commission of \$2101.05 during July. What were his sales if his rate of commission is 10.5% of net sales and sales returns and allowances for the month were 8% of his sales?

16. Edith worked 47 hours during a week for which her gross remuneration was \$426.22. Based on a regular workweek of 40 hours and overtime payment at time and one-half regular pay, what is Edith's hourly rate of pay?

17. Norm is paid a semi-monthly salary of \$682.50. Regular hours are $37\frac{1}{2}$ per week and overtime is paid at time and one-half regular pay.
    (a) What is Norm's hourly rate of pay?
    (b) How many hours overtime did Norm work in a pay period for which his gross pay was \$846.30?

18. Silvio's gross earnings for last week were \$328.54. His remuneration consists of a base salary of \$280.00 plus a commission of 6% on net sales exceeding his weekly quota of \$5000.00. What were Silvio's sales for the week if sales returns and allowances were \$136.00?

19. Sean's gross wages for a week were \$541.20. His regular workweek is 40 hours and overtime is paid at time and one-half regular pay. What is Sean's regular hourly wage if he worked $47\frac{1}{2}$ hours?

20. Aviva's pay stub shows gross earnings of \$304.30 for a week. Her regular rate of pay is \$6.80 per hour for a 35-hour week and overtime is paid at time and one-half regular pay. How many hours did she work?

Self-test

1. Evaluate each of the following.
    (a) $4320\left(1 + 0.18 \times \frac{45}{360}\right)$
    (b) $2160\left(0.15 \times \frac{105}{360}\right)$
    (c) $2880\left(1 - 0.12 \times \frac{285}{360}\right)$
    (d) $\frac{410.40}{0.24 \times \frac{135}{360}}$
    (e) $\frac{5124}{1 + 0.09 \times \frac{270}{360}}$

2. The following information is shown in your investment account for last year: balance on January 1 was \$7200; a withdrawal of \$480 on March 1; deposits of \$600 on August 1 and \$120 on October 1. What was the account's average monthly balance for the year?

3. Extend each of the following and determine the total.

Quantity	*Unit Price*
72	1.25
84	$0.16\frac{2}{3}$
40	0.875
48	$1.33\frac{1}{3}$

4. Purchases of an inventory item during the last accounting period were as follows:

No. of Items	*Unit Price*
5	9
6	7
3	8
6	6

What was the average price per item?

5. Ace Realty sold lots for \$15 120 per hectare. What is the total sales value if the lot sizes, in hectares, were $5\frac{1}{4}$, $6\frac{1}{3}$, $4\frac{3}{8}$, and $3\frac{5}{6}$?

6. Property valued at \$130 000 is assessed at $\frac{2}{13}$ of its value. What is the amount of tax due for this year if the tax rate is \$3.25 per \$100 of assessed value?

7. A salesperson earned a commission of \$806.59 for last week on gross sales of \$5880. If returns and allowances were 11.5% of gross sales, what is his rate of commission based on net sales?

8. A.Y. receives an annual salary of \$26 478.40. She is paid monthly on a 38-hour workweek. What is the gross pay for a pay period in which she works 8.75 hours overtime at time and one-half regular pay?

9. J.B. earns \$16.60 an hour with time and one-half for hours worked over 8 a day. His hours for a week are 8.25, 8.25, 9.5, 11.5, and 7.25. Determine his gross earnings for a week.

10. A wage earner receives a gross pay of \$513.98 for 52.5 hours of work. What is his hourly rate of pay if a regular workweek is 42 hours and overtime is paid at time and one-half the regular rate of pay?

11. A salesperson receives a weekly base salary of \$200.00 on a quota of \$2500. On the next \$2000, she receives a commission of 11%. On any additional sales, the commission rate is 15%. Find her gross earnings for a week in which her sales total \$6280.

12. C.D. is paid a semi-monthly salary of \$780.00. If her regular workweek is 40 hours, what is her hourly rate of pay?

CASE STUDY

Johnson Leather is a small, family-operated manufacturing business that specializes in producing leather-wrapped steering wheels for the auto industry. Competition is strong and the success or failure of the company can depend on its price quotation for a large order. If the quote is too high, the company may not get the contract. If the quote is too low, it may lose money. One of the large car manufacturers has asked Johnson Leather to quote on an order for 125 000 leather-covered steering wheels. Determine the price quotation for the order. Round costs to the nearest hundredth. (Leather is sold in imperial measurements, not in metric.)

1. The steering wheel has a diameter of $13\frac{1}{2}$ inches. Three seams join the leather pieces around the wheel circumference. Each seam requires one-half inch of leather to sew. How much leather is needed for each wheel? (Circumference = πd. Round to the nearest tenth of an inch. $\pi = \frac{22}{7}$.)

2. Leather is sold by the square foot. Previous production figures show that $13\frac{1}{3}$ steering wheels can be wrapped with 10 square feet of leather. How many square feet of leather should be bought for this order (to the nearest square foot)?

3. Two leather suppliers bid on the contract to supply Johnson Leather. Ajax Leather sells its leather at $127.50 for 100 square feet. Beta Leather prices its leather at $55 for 40 square feet. Beta has supplied excellent quality in previous years while Ajax is a new supplier.
   (a) Which company provides the lower quotation?
   (b) What would be the total extra cost to buy from the more expensive supplier?
   (c) What can the purchasing agent at Johnson's do in this situation?
   (d) Suggest the advantages and disadvantages of buying from each supplier.

4. Determine the total cost of leather for one steering wheel. Assume Johnson Leather has decided to pay for the better quality leather.

5. Producing and installing the leather wrap requires cutting, sewing, and fitting. The cutters earn $8.50/hour and can match and cut the leather for 120 wheels in one hour. The sewers earn $9.75/hour and can sew 70 covers in one hour. The fitters earn $7.60/hour and can fit 40 covers to the wheel in one hour. What is the total labour cost per wheel?

6. The different shipping routes required for the different assembly plants means the shipping costs vary. Each carton contains 50 wheels. The destinations and rates are
   Windsor: 50 000 wheels at $17.70 per carton;
   Oshawa: 40 000 wheels at $18.25 per carton;
   Ste-Thérèse: 35 000 wheels at $21.00 per carton.
   Determine the average shipping cost per wheel.

7. The salesperson receives a commission for securing this contract. The graduated commission scale is
   $0.10 per wheel for the first 50 000;
   $0.12 per wheel for the next 50 000;
   $0.14 per wheel for the remainder.
   Determine the average cost of commission for each wheel.
8. The plastic steering wheel is bought from a plastics company for $11.73. Calculate the total production, selling, and shipping costs for one complete wheel.
9. Johnson Leather would like to make a total profit of $600 000 on this contract. What is the necessary quote per heel to achieve this figure?
10. If competition forces the company to quote $10.75 per wheel, what is the total profit or loss?

Glossary of terms used

Complex fractions mathematical expressions containing one or more fractions in the numerator or the denominator or both

Commission the term applied to remuneration of sales personnel based on their sales performance

Graduated commission remuneration paid as an increasing percent for increasing sales levels for a fixed period of time

Gross earnings the amount of an employee's remuneration before deductions

Mixed decimals decimals consisting of a decimal and a fraction, such as $0.33\frac{1}{3}$

Mixed numbers numbers consisting of a whole number and a fraction, such as $3\frac{3}{4}$

Overtime premium extra labor cost due to overtime

Quota a sales level required before the commission percent is paid; usually associated with remuneration by base salary and commission

Salary the term usually applied to monthly or annual remuneration of personnel

Salary plus commission a method of remunerating sales personnel that guarantees a minimum income per pay period

Wages the term usually applied to the remuneration of hourly rated employees

2 *Review of basic algebra*

Introduction

The use of letter symbols helps establish relationships between variables and permits generalizations that are helpful in solving mathematical problems.

Many problems in business and finance can be solved by using predetermined formulae generally applicable to similar problems. When formulae are used, the student needs manipulative skills, such as being able to do algebraic substitution and simplification.

For other problems, no predetermined formulae may be available. However, such problems can often be solved by setting up and solving an algebraic equation.

An equation is a statement of equality between two algebraic expressions. If an equation contains only one letter symbol (variable) and if that variable occurs with power '1' only, the equation is a linear or first-degree equation in one unknown. Equations of this type may be set up for many types of business problems, and solving the equation gives the solution to a particular problem.

Objectives

Upon completing this chapter, you will be able to

1. simplify algebraic expressions using the fundamental operations and evaluate algebraic expressions by substitution;
2. simplify and evaluate powers with positive exponents, negative exponents, and exponent zero;
3. use an electronic calculator equipped with a power function to compute the numerical value of arithmetic expressions involving fractional exponents;
4. write exponential equations in logarithmic form and use an electronic calculator equipped with a natural logarithm function to determine the value of natural logarithms;
5. solve basic equations using addition, subtraction, multiplication, and division;
6. solve equations involving algebraic simplification;
7. solve word problems by creating equations.

2.1 *Simplification of algebraic expressions*

A. Addition and subtraction

1. *Simplification Involving Addition and Subtraction*

In algebra, only **like terms** may be added or subtracted. This is done by *adding* or *subtracting* the **numerical coefficients** of the like terms according to the rules used for adding and subtracting signed numbers, and *retaining* the common **literal coefficient**. The process of adding and subtracting like terms is called **combining like terms** or **collecting like terms**.

Example **2.1a**

(i) $6x + 3x + 7x$ ← all three terms are like terms
$= (6 + 3 + 7)x$ ← add the numerical coefficients
$= 16x$ ← retain the common literal coefficient

(ii) $9a - 5a - 7a + 4a$
$= (9 - 5 - 7 + 4)a$
$= a$

(iii) $-5m - (-3m) - (+6m)$
$= -5m + (+3m) + (-6m)$ ← change the subtraction to addition
$= -5m + 3m - 6m$
$= (-5 + 3 - 6)m$
$= -8m$

(iv) $7x - 4y - 3x - 6y$ ← the two sets of like terms are $7x$, $-3x$, and $-4y$, $-6y$, and are collected separately
$= (7 - 3)x + (-4 - 6)y$
$= 4x - 10y$

(v) $5x^2 - 3x - 4 + 2x - 5 + x^2$
$= (5 + 1)x^2 + (-3 + 2)x + (-4 - 5)$
$= 6x^2 - x - 9$

2. *Simplification Involving Brackets*

When simplifying **algebraic expressions** involving brackets, remove the brackets according to the following rules and collect like terms.

(a) If the brackets are preceded by a (+) sign or no sign,
drop the brackets and retain the terms inside the brackets with their signs unchanged:
$(-7a + 5b - c)$ becomes $-7a + 5b - c$.

(b) If the brackets are preceded by a (−) sign,
drop the brackets and change the sign of every term inside the brackets:
$-(-7a + 5b - c)$ becomes $7a - 5b + c$.

Example **2.1b**

(i) $(7a - 3b) - (4a + 3b)$
$= 7a - 3b - 4a - 3b$ ⟵ $(7a - 3b)$ becomes $7a - 3b$; $-(4a + 3b)$ becomes $-4a - 3b$
$= 3a - 6b$

(ii) $-(3x^2 - 8x - 5) + (2x^2 - 5x + 4)$
$= -3x^2 + 8x + 5 + 2x^2 - 5x + 4$
$= -x^2 + 3x + 9$

(iii) $4b - (3a - 4b - c) - (5c + 2b)$
$= 4b - 3a + 4b + c - 5c - 2b$
$= -3a + 6b - 4c$

B. *Multiplication*

1. *Multiplication of Monomials*

The product of two or more **monomials** is the product of their numerical coefficients multiplied by the product of their literal coefficients.

Example **2.1c**

(i) $5(3a)$
$= (5 \times 3)a$ ⟵ obtain the product of the numerical coefficients
$= 15a$

(ii) $(-7a)(4b)$
$= (-7 \times 4)(a \times b)$ ⟵ obtain the product of the numerical coefficients, -7 and 4, and the product of the literal coefficients, a and b
$= -28ab$

(iii) $(-3)(4x)(-5x)$
$= [(-3)(4)(-5)][(x)(x)]$
$= 60x^2$

2. *Multiplication of Monomials with Polynomials*

The product of a **polynomial** and a monomial is obtained by multiplying each term of the polynomial by the monomial.

Example **2.1d**

(i) $5(a - 3)$
$= 5(a) + 5(-3)$ ⟵ multiply 5 by a and 5 by (-3)
$= 5a - 15$

(ii) $-4(3x^2 - 2x - 1)$
$= -4(3x^2) + (-4)(-2x) + (-4)(-1)$ ⟵ multiply each term of the trinomial by (-4)
$= (-12x^2) + (+8x) + (+4)$
$= -12x^2 + 8x + 4$

(iii) $3a(4a - 5b - 2c)$
$= (3a)(4a) + (3a)(-5b) + (3a)(-2c)$
$= (12a^2) + (-15ab) + (-6ac)$
$= 12a^2 - 15ab - 6ac$

3. *Simplification Involving Brackets and Multiplication*

Example **2.1e**

(i) $3(x - 5) - 2(x - 7)$
$= 3x - 15 - 2x + 14$ ← carry out the multiplication
$= x - 1$ ← collect like terms

(ii) $a(3a - 1) - 4(2a + 3)$
$= 3a^2 - a - 8a - 12$
$= 3a^2 - 9a - 12$

(iii) $5(m - 7) - 8(3m - 2) - 3(7 - 3m)$
$= 5m - 35 - 24m + 16 - 21 + 9m$
$= -10m - 40$

(iv) $-4(5a - 3b - 2c) + 5(-2a - 4b + c)$
$= -20a + 12b + 8c - 10a - 20b + 5c$
$= -30a - 8b + 13c$

4. *Multiplication of a Polynomial by a Polynomial*

The product of two polynomials is obtained by multiplying each term of one polynomial by each term of the other polynomial and collecting like terms.

Example **2.1f**

(i) $(3a + 2b)(4c - 3d)$
$= 3a(4c - 3d) + 2b(4c - 3d)$ ← each term of the first polynomial is multiplied by the second polynomial
$= 12ac - 9ad + 8bc - 6bd$ ← carry out the multiplication

(ii) $(5x - 2)(3x + 4)$
$= 5x(3x + 4) - 2(3x + 4)$
$= 15x^2 + 20x - 6x - 8$
$= 15x^2 + 14x - 8$

C. Division

1. *Division of Monomials*

The quotient of two monomials is the quotient of their numerical coefficients multiplied by the quotient of their literal coefficients.

***Example* 2.1g**

(i) $32ab \div 8b = \dfrac{32ab}{8b} = \left(\dfrac{32}{8}\right)\left(\dfrac{ab}{b}\right) = 4a$

(ii) $24x^2 \div (-6x) = \left(\dfrac{24}{-6}\right)\left(\dfrac{x^2}{x}\right) = -4x$

2. *Division of a Polynomial by a Monomial*

To determine the quotient of a polynomial divided by a monomial, divide each term of the polynomial by the monomial.

***Example* 2.1h**

(i) $(12a + 8) \div 4 = \dfrac{12a + 8}{4} = \dfrac{12a}{4} + \dfrac{8}{4} = 3a + 2$

(ii) $(18x - 12) \div 6 = \dfrac{18x - 12}{6} = \dfrac{18x}{6} - \dfrac{12}{6} = 3x - 2$

(iii) $(12a^3 - 15a^2 - 9a) \div (-3a)$

$= \dfrac{12a^3 - 15a^2 - 9a}{-3a}$

$= \dfrac{12a^3}{-3a} + \dfrac{-15a^2}{-3a} + \dfrac{-9a}{-3a}$

$= -4a^2 + 5a + 3$

D. Substitution

Evaluating algebraic expressions for given values of the variables requires replacing the variables with the given values. The replacement or substitution of the variables by the given values takes place each time the variables appear in the expression.

***Example* 2.1i**

(i) Evaluate $7x - 3y - 5$ for $x = -2$, $y = 3$

Solution

$7x - 3y - 5$
$= 7(-2) - 3(3) - 5$ ⟵ replace x by (-2) and y by 3
$= -14 - 9 - 5$
$= -28$

(ii) Evaluate $\dfrac{2NC}{P(n + 1)}$ for N = 12, C = 220, P = 1500, n = 15

Solution

$$\frac{2NC}{P(n + 1)} = \frac{2(12)(220)}{1500(15 + 1)} = 0.22$$

(iii) Evaluate $\frac{I}{RT}$ for $I = 126$, $R = 0.125$, $T = \frac{324}{360}$

Solution

$$\frac{I}{RT} = \frac{126}{0.125 \times \frac{324}{360}} = 1120$$

(iv) Evaluate $P(1 + RT)$ for $P = 900$, $R = 0.15$, $T = \frac{240}{360}$

Solution

$$\begin{aligned} P(1 + RT) &= 900\left(1 + 0.15 \times \frac{240}{360}\right) \\ &= 900(1 + 0.10) \\ &= 900(1.10) \\ &= 990 \end{aligned}$$

(v) Evaluate $A(1 - dt)$ for $A = 800$, $d = 0.135$, $t = \frac{288}{360}$

Solution

$$\begin{aligned} A(1 - dt) &= 800\left(1 - 0.135 \times \frac{288}{360}\right) \\ &= 800(1 - 0.108) \\ &= 800(0.892) \\ &= 713.60 \end{aligned}$$

(vi) Evaluate $\frac{A}{1 + RT}$ for $A = 1644$, $R = 0.16$, $T = \frac{219}{365}$

Solution

$$\frac{A}{1 + RT} = \frac{1644}{1 + 0.16 \times \frac{219}{365}} = \frac{1644}{1 + 0.096} = \frac{1644}{1.096} = 1500$$

(vii) Evaluate $\frac{P}{1 - dt}$ for $P = 1002$, $d = 0.18$, $t = \frac{330}{360}$

Solution

$$\frac{P}{1 - dt} = \frac{1002}{1 - 0.18 \times \frac{330}{360}} = \frac{1002}{1 - 0.165} = \frac{1002}{0.835} = 1200$$

Exercise 2.1

A. Simplify.

1. $9a + 3a + 7a$
2. $6m - 2m - m$
3. $-4a - 8 + 3a - 2$
4. $2x - 3y - 4x - y$
5. $x - 0.2x$
6. $x + 0.06x$
7. $x + 0.4x$
8. $x - 0.02x$
9. $x^2 - 2x - 5 + x - 3 - 2x^2$
10. $3ax - 2x + 1 - 3 + 3x - 4ax$
11. $(2x - 3y) - (x + 4y)$
12. $-(4 - 5a) - (-2 + 3a)$
13. $(a^2 - ab + b^2) - (3a^2 + 5ab - 4b^2)$
14. $-(3m^2 - 4m - 5) - (4 - 2m - 2m^2)$
15. $6 - (4x - 3y + 1) - (5x + 2y - 9)$
16. $(7a - 5b) - (-3a + 4b) - 5b$

B. Simplify.

1. $3(-4x)$
2. $-7(8a)$
3. $-5x(2a)$
4. $-9a(-3b)$
5. $-x(2x)$
6. $-6m(-4m)$
7. $-4(5x)(-3y)$
8. $2a(-3b)(-4c)(-1)$
9. $-2(x - 2y)$
10. $5(2x - 4)$
11. $a(2x^2 - 3x - 1)$
12. $-6x(4 - 2b - b^2)$
13. $4(5x - 6) - 3(2 - 5x)$
14. $-3(8a - b) - 2(-7a + 9b)$
15. $-3a(5x - 1) + a(5 - 2x) - 3a(x + 1)$
16. $8(3y - 4) - 2(2y - 1) - (1 - y)$
17. $(3x - 1)(x + 2)$
18. $(5m - 2n)(m - 3n)$
19. $(x + y)(x^2 - xy + y^2)$
20. $(a - 1)(a^2 - 2a + 1)$
21. $(5x - 4)(2x - 1) - (x + 7)(3x + 5)$
22. $2(a - 1)(2a - 3) - 3(3a - 2)(a + 1)$

C. Simplify.

1. $20ab \div 5$
2. $30xy \div (-6x)$
3. $(-12x^2) \div (-3x)$
4. $(-42ab) \div (7ab)$
5. $(20m - 8) \div 2$
6. $(14x - 21) \div (-7)$
7. $(10x^2 - 15x - 30) \div (-5)$
8. $(-a^3 - 4a^2 - 3a) \div (-a)$

D. Evaluate each of the following for the values given.

1. $3x - 2y - 3$ for $x = -4, y = -5$
2. $\frac{1}{2}(3x^2 - x - 1) - \frac{1}{4}(5 - 2x - x^2)$ for $x = -3$
3. $\frac{RP(n + 1)}{2N}$ for $R = 0.21, P = 1200, n = 77, N = 26$
4. $\frac{I}{PT}$ for $I = 63, P = 840, T = \frac{216}{360}$
5. $\frac{I}{RT}$ for $I = 198, R = 0.165, T = \frac{146}{365}$
6. $\frac{2NC}{P(n + 1)}$ for $N = 52, C = 60, P = 1800, n = 25$
7. $P(1 + RT)$ for $P = 880, R = 0.12, T = \frac{75}{360}$
8. $A(1 - RT)$ for $A = 1200, R = 0.175, T = \frac{252}{360}$
9. $\frac{P}{1 - dt}$ for $P = 1253, d = 0.135, t = \frac{280}{360}$
10. $\frac{A}{1 + RT}$ for $A = 1752, R = 0.152, T = \frac{225}{360}$

2.2 *Integral exponents*

A. Basic concept and definition

If a number is to be used as a **factor** several times, the mathematical expression can be written more efficiently by using exponents:

$$5 \times 5 \times 5 \times 5 \text{ may be written as } 5^4.$$

Note: In the expression 5^4 ⟶ 5 is called the **base**
⟶ 4 is called the **exponent**
⟶ 5^4 is called the **power**

Example 2.2a

(i) $7 \times 7 \times 7 \times 7 \times 7 = 7^5$

(ii) $(-4)(-4)(-4) = (-4)^3$

(iii) $(1.01)(1.01)(1.01)(1.01) = (1.01)^4$

(iv) $(a)(a)(a)(a)(a)(a)(a) = a^7$

(v) $(1 + i)(1 + i)(1 + i)(1 + i)(1 + i)(1 + i) = (1 + i)^6$

Definition: When 'n' is a positive integer, 'a^n' represents the product of 'n' equal factors whose value is 'a'.

$$a^n = (a)(a)(a)(a)\ldots(a) \text{ to } n \text{ factors}$$

a is called the **base**
n is called the **exponent**
a^n is called the **power**

$$\text{POWER} = \text{BASE}^{\text{to the EXPONENT}}$$

Note: If a number is raised to the exponent '1', the power equals the base.

$5^1 = 5$ and $a^1 = a$;
conversely, $6 = 6^1$ and $x = x^1$.

B. *Numerical evaluation of powers with positive integral exponents*

1. *Evaluation when the Base is a Positive Integer*

To evaluate a power, we may rewrite the power in factored form and obtain the product by multiplication.

Example **2.2b**

(i) 2^5 ← means that 2 is a factor 5 times
$= (2)(2)(2)(2)(2)$ ← power rewritten in factored form
$= 32$ ← product

(ii) $(5)^3$ ← 5 is a factor 3 times
$= (5)(5)(5)$
$= 125$

(iii) 1^7 ← 1 is a factor 7 times
$= (1)(1)(1)(1)(1)(1)(1)$
$= 1$

(iv) a^n if $a = 4$, $n = 6$
$a^n = 4^6$
$= (4)(4)(4)(4)(4)(4)$
$= 4096$

2. *Evaluation when the Base is a Negative Integer*

If a power has a negative base, the number of equal factors shown by the exponent determines the sign of the product.

(a) If the exponent is an even positive integer, the product is positive.

(b) If the exponent is an odd positive integer, the product is negative.

Example 2.2c

(i) $(-4)^3 \longleftarrow$ (-4) is a factor 3 times
$= (-4)(-4)(-4)$
$= -64 \longleftarrow$ the answer is negative (n is odd)

(ii) $(-2)^8 \longleftarrow$ (-2) is a factor 8 times
$= (-2)(-2)(-2)(-2)(-2)(-2)(-2)(-2)$
$= 256 \longleftarrow$ the answer is positive (n is even)

Note: -2^8 means $-(2)^8 = -(2)(2)(2)(2)(2)(2)(2)(2) = -256$

(iii) $(-1)^{55}$
$= (-1)(-1)(-1)(-1)\ldots$ to 55 factors
$= -1$

(iv) $3a^n$ for $a = -5$, $n = 4$
$3a^n = 3(-5)^4$
$= 3(-5)(-5)(-5)(-5)$
$= 3(625)$
$= 1875$

3. *Evaluation when the Base is a Common Fraction or Decimal*

Example 2.2d

(i) $\left(\frac{3}{2}\right)^5 \longleftarrow$ $\frac{3}{2}$ is a factor 5 times

$= \left(\frac{3}{2}\right)\left(\frac{3}{2}\right)\left(\frac{3}{2}\right)\left(\frac{3}{2}\right)\left(\frac{3}{2}\right)$

$= \frac{(3)(3)(3)(3)(3)}{(2)(2)(2)(2)(2)}$

$= \frac{243}{32}$

(ii) $(0.1)^4 \longleftarrow$ 0.1 is a factor 4 times
$= (0.1)(0.1)(0.1)(0.1)$
$= 0.0001$

(iii) $\left(-\frac{1}{3}\right)^3 \longleftarrow$ $\left(-\frac{1}{3}\right)$ is a factor 3 times

$= \left(-\frac{1}{3}\right)\left(-\frac{1}{3}\right)\left(-\frac{1}{3}\right)$

$= \frac{(-1)(-1)(-1)}{(3)(3)(3)}$

$= \frac{-1}{27}$

(iv) $(1.02)^2$
$= (1.02)(1.02)$
$= 1.0404$

(v) $(1 + i)^n$ for $i = 0.03$, $n = 4$
$(1 + i)^n = (1 + 0.03)^4$
$= (1.03)(1.03)(1.03)(1.03)$
$= 1.12550881$

C. Operations with Powers

1. *Multiplication of Powers*

To multiply powers that have the same base, retain the common base and add the exponents.

$$a^m \times a^n = a^{m+n}$$ ← *Formula* **2.1A**

$$a^m \times a^n \times a^p = a^{m+n+p}$$ ← *Formula* **2.1B**

Example 2.2e

(i) $3^5 \times 3^2$
$= 3^{5+2}$ ← retain the common base 3 and add the exponents 5 and 2
$= 3^7$

(ii) $(-4)^3(-4)^7(-4)^5$
$= (-4)^{3+7+5}$ ← retain the common base (-4) and add the exponents 3, 7, and 5
$= (-4)^{15}$

(iii) $\left(\frac{1}{8}\right)^5\left(\frac{1}{8}\right) = \left(\frac{1}{8}\right)^{5+1} = \left(\frac{1}{8}\right)^6$

(iv) $(x^3)(x^5)(x) = x^{3+5+1} = x^9$

(v) $(1.06)^{16}(1.06)^{14} = (1.06)^{16+14} = 1.06^{30}$

(vi) $(1 + i)(1 + i)^5(1 + i)^{20} = (1 + i)^{1+5+20} = (1 + i)^{26}$

2. *Division of Powers*

To divide powers that have the same base, retain the common base and subtract the exponent of the divisor from the exponent of the dividend.

$$a^m \div a^n = a^{m-n}$$ ← *Formula* **2.2**

Example 2.2f

(i) $2^8 \div 2^5$
$= 2^{8-5}$ ⟵ retain the common base 2 and subtract the exponent of the divisor, 5, from the exponent of the dividend, 8
$= 2^3$

(ii) $(-10)^8 \div (-10)^7$
$= (-10)^{8-7}$ ⟵ retain the common base (-10) and subtract the exponents
$= (-10)^1$ or -10

(iii) $\left(-\frac{2}{5}\right)^6 \div \left(-\frac{2}{5}\right)^2 = \left(-\frac{2}{5}\right)^{6-2} = \left(-\frac{2}{5}\right)^4$

(iv) $a^{15} \div a^{10} = a^{15-10} = a^5$

(v) $(1.10)^{24} \div 1.10 = (1.10)^{24-1} = 1.10^{23}$

(vi) $(1+i)^{80} \div (1+i)^{60} = (1+i)^{80-60} = (1+i)^{20}$

3. *Raising a Power to a Power*

To raise a power to a power, retain the base and multiply the exponents.

$(a^m)^n = a^{mn}$ ⟵ ***Formula* 2.3**

Example 2.2g

(i) $(3^2)^5$
$= 3^{2\times 5}$ ⟵ retain the base 3 and multiply the exponents 2 and 5
$= 3^{10}$

(ii) $[(-4)^5]^3$
$= (-4)^{5\times 3}$ ⟵ retain the base and multiply the exponents
$= (-4)^{15}$

(iii) $= \left[\left(\frac{4}{3}\right)^6\right]^{10} = \left(\frac{4}{3}\right)^{6\times 10} = \left(\frac{4}{3}\right)^{60}$

(iv) $(a^7)^3 = a^{7\times 3} = a^{21}$

(v) $[(1.005)^{50}]^4 = (1.005)^{50\times 4} = 1.005^{200}$

(vi) $[(1+i)^{75}]^2 = (1+i)^{75\times 2} = (1+i)^{150}$

4. *Power of a Product and Power of a Quotient*

The power of a product, written in factored form, is the product of the individual factors raised to the exponent.

$$(ab)^m = a^m b^m$$ ⟵ ***Formula* 2.4**

Note: ab^2 is not the same as $(ab)^2$ since ab^2 means $(a)(b)(b)$ while $(ab)^2 = (ab)(ab) = (a)(a)(b)(b) = a^2b^2$.

The power of a quotient is the quotient of the dividend and the divisor raised to the exponent.

$$\left(\frac{a}{b}\right)^m = \frac{a^m}{b^m}$$ ⟵ ***Formula* 2.5**

Example 2.2h

(i) $(2 \times 3)^5 = 2^5 \times 3^5$

(ii) $(6 \times 2^7)^4 = 6^4 \times (2^7)^4 = 6^4 \times 2^{28}$

(iii) $\left(-\frac{5}{7}\right)^3 = \frac{(-5)^3}{7^3}$

(iv) $(a^3b)^4 = (a^3)^4 \times b^4 = a^{12}b^4$

(v) $\left[\frac{(1+i)}{i}\right]^3 = \frac{(1+i)^3}{i^3}$

D. Zero exponent

A zero exponent results when using the law of division of powers on powers with equal exponents.

$$\begin{aligned} &3^5 \div 3^5 \\ &= 3^{5-5} \\ &= 3^0 \end{aligned}$$

The result may be interpreted as follows.

$$3^5 \div 3^5 = \frac{3^5}{3^5} = \frac{3 \times 3 \times 3 \times 3 \times 3}{3 \times 3 \times 3 \times 3 \times 3} = 1$$

$$\boxed{3^0 = 1}$$

Similarly, $a^6 \div a^6 = a^{6-6} = a^0$

and since $a^6 \div a^6 = \frac{a^6}{a^6} = \frac{(a)(a)(a)(a)(a)(a)}{(a)(a)(a)(a)(a)(a)} = 1,$

$$\boxed{a^0 = 1}$$

In general, *any number raised to the exponent zero is 1*, except zero itself. The expression 0^0 has no meaning and is said to be *undefined.*

E. Negative exponents

A negative exponent results when the exponent of the divisor is greater than the exponent of the dividend.

$$\begin{aligned} &4^3 \div 4^5 \\ &= 4^{3-5} \\ &= 4^{-2} \end{aligned}$$

The result may be interpreted as follows.

$$4^3 \div 4^5 = \frac{4^3}{4^5} = \frac{4 \times 4 \times 4}{4 \times 4 \times 4 \times 4 \times 4} = \frac{1}{4 \times 4} = \frac{1}{4^2}$$

$$\boxed{4^{-2} = \frac{1}{4^2}}$$

Similarly, $a^5 \div a^8 = a^{5-8} = a^{-3}$

and since $a^5 \div a^8 = \frac{a^5}{a^8} = \frac{(a)(a)(a)(a)(a)}{(a)(a)(a)(a)(a)(a)(a)(a)}$

$$= \frac{1}{(a)(a)(a)} = \frac{1}{a^3},$$

$$\boxed{a^{-3} = \frac{1}{a^3}}$$

$$\boxed{a^{-m} = \frac{1}{a^m}} \longleftarrow \textit{Formula 2.6}$$

In general, a base raised to a negative exponent is equivalent to '1' divided by the same base raised to the corresponding positive exponent.

Example 2.2i

(i) $2^{-3} = \frac{1}{2^3} = \frac{1}{8}$

(ii) $(-3)^{-2} = \frac{1}{(-3)^2} = \frac{1}{9}$

(iii) $\left(\frac{1}{4}\right)^{-4} = \frac{1}{\left(\frac{1}{4}\right)^4} = \frac{1}{\frac{1}{256}} = \frac{1}{1} \times \frac{256}{1} = 256$

(iv) $\left(-\frac{3}{5}\right)^{-3} = \frac{1}{\left(-\frac{3}{5}\right)^3} = \frac{1}{\frac{-27}{125}} = \frac{-125}{27}$

Note: Since $\frac{-125}{27} = \frac{(-5)^3}{3^3} = \left(-\frac{5}{3}\right)^3 \longrightarrow \left(-\frac{3}{5}\right)^{-3} = \left(-\frac{5}{3}\right)^3$

$$\left(\frac{y}{x}\right)^{-m} = \left(\frac{x}{y}\right)^{m}$$ ⟵ **Formula 2.7**

(v) $(-4)^0 = 1$

(vi) $(1.05)^{-2} = \frac{1}{1.05^2} = \frac{1}{1.1025} = 0.9070295$

(vii) $(1 + i)^{-10} = \frac{1}{(1 + i)^{10}}$

(viii) $(1 + i)^{-1} = \frac{1}{1 + i}$

(ix) $(1 + i)^0 = 1$

Exercise 2.2

A. Evaluate each of the following.

1. 3^4
2. 1^5
3. $(-2)^4$
4. $(-1)^{12}$
5. $\left(\frac{2}{3}\right)^4$
6. $\left(-\frac{1}{4}\right)^3$
7. $(0.5)^2$
8. $(-0.1)^3$
9. $(-4)^0$
10. m^0
11. 3^{-2}
12. $(-5)^{-3}$
13. $\left(\frac{1}{5}\right)^{-3}$
14. $\left(\frac{2}{3}\right)^{-4}$
15. 1.01^{-1}
16. $(1.05)^0$

B. Simplify.

1. $2^5 \times 2^3$
2. $(-4)^3 \times (-4)$
3. $4^7 \div 4^4$
4. $(-3)^9 \div (-3)^7$
5. $(2^3)^5$
6. $[(-4)^3]^6$
7. $a^4 \times a^{10}$
8. $m^{12} \div m^7$
9. $3^4 \times 3^6 \times 3$
10. $(-1)^3(-1)^7(-1)^5$
11. $\frac{6^7 \times 6^3}{6^9}$
12. $\frac{(x^4)(x^5)}{x^7}$
13. $\left(\frac{3}{5}\right)^4\left(\frac{3}{5}\right)^7$
14. $\left(\frac{1}{6}\right)^5 \div \left(\frac{1}{6}\right)^3$
15. $\left(-\frac{3}{2}\right)\left(-\frac{3}{2}\right)^6\left(-\frac{3}{2}\right)^4$
16. $\left(-\frac{3}{4}\right)^8 \div \left(-\frac{3}{4}\right)^7$
17. $(1.025^{80})(1.025^{70})$
18. $1.005^{240} \div 1.005^{150}$
19. $[1.04^{20}]^4$
20. $\left[\left(-\frac{3}{7}\right)^5\right]^3$

21. $(1 + i)^{100}(1 + i)^{100}$

22. $(1 - r)^2(1 - r)^2(1 - r)^2$

23. $[(1 + i)^{80}]^2$

24. $[(1 - r)^{40}]^3$

25. $(ab)^5$

26. $(2xy)^4$

27. $(m^3n)^8$

28. $\left(\frac{a^3b^2}{x}\right)^4$

29. $2^3 \times 2^5 \times 2^{-4}$

30. $5^2 \div 5^{-3}$

31. $\left(\frac{a}{b}\right)^{-8}$

32. $\left(\frac{1+i}{i}\right)^{-n}$

2.3 *Fractional exponents*

A. Radicals

When the product of two or more equal factors is expressed in exponential form, one of the equal factors is called the **root of the product**. The exponent indicates the number of equal factors, that is, the **power of the root**.

For example,

$25 = 5^2 \longrightarrow$ 5 is the second power root (square root) of 25
$8 = 2^3 \longrightarrow$ 2 is the third power root (cube root) of 8
$81 = 3^4 \longrightarrow$ 3 is the fourth (power) root of 81
$a^5 \longrightarrow$ a is the fifth root of a^5
$7^n \longrightarrow$ 7 is the nth root of 7^n
$x^n \longrightarrow$ x is the nth root of x^n

The operational symbol for finding the root of an expression is $\sqrt{\ }$. This symbol represents the *positive* root only. If the negative root is desired, a minus sign is placed in front of the symbol; that is, the negative root is represented by $-\sqrt{\ }$.

The power of a root is written at the upper left of the symbol as in $\sqrt[3]{\ }$ or $\sqrt[n]{\ }$.

The indicated root is called a **radical**, the power indicated is called the **index**, and the number under the symbol is called the **radicand**.

In $\sqrt[5]{32}$, the index is 5,
the radicand is 32, and
the radical is $\sqrt[5]{32}$.

When the square root is to be found, it is customary to omit the index 2. The symbol $\sqrt{\ }$ is understood to mean the positive square root of the radicand.

$$\sqrt{49} \text{ means } \sqrt[2]{49} \text{ or } 7.$$

In special cases, the radicand is an integral power of the root. The root can readily be found by expressing the radicand in exponential form; the index of the root and the exponent are the same.

Example **2.3a**

(i) $\sqrt{64} = \sqrt{8^2}$ ← the radicand 64 is expressed in exponential form as a square

$= 8$ ← one of the two equal factors 8 is the root

(ii) $\sqrt[5]{32} = \sqrt[5]{2^5}$ ← express the radicand 32 as the fifth power of 2

$= 2$ ← one of the five equal factors 2 is the root

(iii) $\sqrt[3]{0.125} = \sqrt[3]{0.5^3} = 0.5$

In most cases, however, the radicand cannot be easily rewritten in exponential form. The arithmetic determination of the numerical value of these roots is a laborious process. But computating the root is easily accomplished using electronic calculators equipped with a power function. The problems in Example 2.3b are intended to ensure that students are able to use the power function. They should be done using an electronic calculator.

Example **2.3b**

(i) $\sqrt{1425} = 37.7492$ **Check** $37.7492^2 = 1425$

(ii) $\sqrt[5]{12\,960} = 6.6454$ **Check** $6.6454^5 = 12\,960$

(iii) $\sqrt[15]{40\,000} = 2.0268$ **Check** $2.0268^{15} = 40\,009$ (due to rounding)

(iv) $\sqrt[20]{1\,048\,576} = 2$ **Check** $2^{20} = 1\,048\,576$

(v) $\sqrt{0.005184} = 0.072$ **Check** $0.072^2 = 0.005184$

(vi) $\sqrt[7]{0.038468} = 0.6279$ **Check** $0.6279^7 = 0.032848$ (due to rounding)

(vii) $\sqrt[45]{1.954213} = 1.015$ **Check** $1.015^{45} = 1.954213$

(viii) $\sqrt[36]{0.0225284} = 0.9$ **Check** $0.9^{36} = 0.0225284$

(ix) $\sqrt{2^6} = \sqrt{64} = 8$

(x) $\sqrt[3]{5^6} = \sqrt[3]{15\,625} = 25$

B. *Fractional exponents*

Radicals may be written in exponential form and fractional exponents may be represented in radical form according to the following definitions.

(a) The exponent is a positive fraction with numerator 1.

$$a^{\frac{1}{n}} = \sqrt[n]{a} \quad \longleftarrow \textit{Formula 2.8}$$

$$4^{\frac{1}{2}} = \sqrt{4} = 2$$

$$27^{\frac{1}{3}} = \sqrt[3]{27} = \sqrt[3]{3^3} = 3$$

$$625^{\frac{1}{4}} = \sqrt[4]{625} = \sqrt[4]{5^4} = 5$$

(b) The exponent is a negative fraction with numerator 1.

$$a^{-\frac{1}{n}} = \frac{1}{a^{\frac{1}{n}}} = \frac{1}{\sqrt[n]{a}} \quad \longleftarrow \textit{Formula 2.9}$$

$$8^{-\frac{1}{3}} = \frac{1}{8^{\frac{1}{3}}} = \frac{1}{\sqrt[3]{8}} = \frac{1}{\sqrt[3]{2^3}} = \frac{1}{2}$$

$$243^{-\frac{1}{5}} = \frac{1}{243^{\frac{1}{5}}} = \frac{1}{\sqrt[5]{243}} = \frac{1}{\sqrt[5]{3^5}} = \frac{1}{3}$$

(c) The exponent is a positive or negative fraction with numerator other than 1.

$$a^{\frac{m}{n}} = \sqrt[n]{a^m} = (\sqrt[n]{a})^m \quad \longleftarrow \textit{Formula 2.10}$$

$$a^{-\frac{m}{n}} = \frac{1}{a^{\frac{m}{n}}} = \frac{1}{\sqrt[n]{a^m}} \quad \longleftarrow \textit{Formula 2.11}$$

$$16^{\frac{3}{4}} = \sqrt[4]{16^3} = (\sqrt[4]{16})^3 = (\sqrt[4]{2^4})^3 = (2)^3 = 8$$

$$27^{\frac{4}{3}} = \sqrt[3]{27^4} = (\sqrt[3]{27})^4 = (\sqrt[3]{3^3})^4 = (3)^4 = 81$$

$$36^{-\frac{3}{2}} = \frac{1}{(\sqrt[2]{36})^3} = \frac{1}{(\sqrt[2]{6^2})^3} = \frac{1}{6^3} = \frac{1}{216}$$

For calculators, convert fractional exponents into decimals and compute the answer using the power function.

Example 2.3c

(i) $36^{\frac{3}{2}} = 36^{1.5} = 216$

(ii) $3^{\frac{5}{4}} = 3^{1.25} = 3.948222$

(iii) $\sqrt[5]{12} = 12^{\frac{1}{5}} = 12^{0.2} = 1.6437518$

(iv) $\sqrt[8]{325^5} = 325^{\frac{5}{8}} = 325^{0.625} = 37.147287$

(v) $\sqrt[6]{1.075} = 1.075^{\frac{1}{6}} = 1.075^{0.1666667} = 1.0121264$

Exercise 2.3

A. Use an electronic calculator equipped with a power function to compute each of the following, correct to four decimals.

1. $\sqrt{5184}$
2. $\sqrt{205.9225}$
3. $\sqrt[7]{2187}$
4. $\sqrt[10]{1.1046221}$
5. $\sqrt[20]{4.3184}$
6. $\sqrt[16]{0.00001526}$
7. $\sqrt[6]{1.0825}$
8. $\sqrt[12]{1.15}$

B. Compute each of the following.

1. $3025^{\frac{1}{2}}$
2. $2401^{\frac{1}{4}}$
3. $525.21875^{\frac{2}{5}}$
4. $21.6^{\frac{4}{3}}$
5. $\sqrt[12]{1.125^7}$
6. $\sqrt[6]{1.095}$
7. $4^{-\frac{1}{3}}$
8. $1.06^{-\frac{1}{12}}$
9. $\dfrac{1.03^{60} - 1}{0.03}$
10. $\dfrac{1 - 1.05^{-36}}{0.05}$

2.4 *Logarithms—basic aspects*

A. The concept of logarithm

In Chapter 2, Section 2.2 and Section 2.3, the exponential form of writing numbers was discussed.

$64 = 2^6$ ⟶ the number 64 is represented as a power of 2
$243 = 3^5$ ⟶ the number 243 is represented as a power of 3
$10\,000 = 10^4$ ⟶ the number 10 000 is represented as a power of 10
$5 = 125^{\frac{1}{3}}$ ⟶ the number 5 is represented as a power of 125
$0.001 = 10^{-3}$ ⟶ the number 0.001 is represented as a power of 10

In general, when a number is represented as a base raised to an exponent, the exponent is called a logarithm. A **logarithm** is defined as the *exponent* to which a base must be raised to produce a given number.

Accordingly,

in $64 = 2^6$, 6 is the logarithm of 64 to the base 2, written $6 = \log_2 64$;
in $243 = 3^5$, 5 is the logarithm of 243 to the base 3, written $5 = \log_3 243$;
in $10\,000 = 10^4$, 4 is the logarithm of 10 000 to the base 10, written $4 = \log_{10} 10\,000$;
in $5 = 125^{\frac{1}{3}}$, $\frac{1}{3}$ is the logarithm of 5 to the base 125, written $\frac{1}{3} = \log_{125} 5$;
in $0.001 = 10^{-3}$, -3 is the logarithm of 0.001 to the base 10, written $-3 = \log_{10} 0.001$.

In general, if $N = b^y$ ⟵ *exponential* form
then $y = \log_b N$ ⟵ *logarithmic* form

***Example* 2.4a** Write each of the following numbers in exponential form and in logarithmic form using the base indicated.

(i) 32 base 2 (ii) 81 base 3

(iii) 256 base 4 (iv) 100 000 base 10

(v) 6 base 36 (vi) 3 base 27

(vii) 0.0001 base 10 (viii) $\frac{1}{8}$ base 2

Solution

Exponential Form	*Logarithmic Form*
(i) Since $32 = 2 \times 2 \times 2 \times 2 \times 2$ $32 = 2^5$	$5 = \log_2 32$
(ii) Since $81 = 3 \times 3 \times 3 \times 3$ $81 = 3^4$	$4 = \log_3 81$
(iii) Since $256 = 4 \times 4 \times 4 \times 4$ $256 = 4^4$	$4 = \log_4 256$
(iv) Since $100\ 000 = 10 \times 10 \times 10 \times 10 \times 10$ $100\ 000 = 10^5$	$5 = \log_{10} 100\ 000$
(v) Since $6 = \sqrt{36}$ $6 = 36^{\frac{1}{2}}$	$\frac{1}{2} = \log_{36} 6$
(vi) Since $3 = \sqrt[3]{27}$ $3 = 27^{\frac{1}{3}}$	$\frac{1}{3} = \log_{27} 3$
(vii) Since $0.0001 = \frac{1}{10\ 000} = \frac{1}{10^4}$ $0.0001 = 10^{-4}$	$-4 = \log_{10} 0.0001$
(viii) Since $\frac{1}{8} = \frac{1}{2^3}$ $\frac{1}{8} = 2^{-3}$	$-3 = \log_2 \frac{1}{8}$

B. *Common logarithms*

While the base b may be any positive number other than 1, only the numbers 10 and e are used in practice.

Logarithms with base 10 are called **common logarithms**. Obtained from the exponential function $x = 10^y$, the notation used to represent common logarithms is $y = \log x$. (The base 10 is understood and so is not written.)

By definition then, the common logarithm of a number is the exponent to which the base 10 must be raised to give that number.

log 1000 = 3 since 1000 = 10^3
log 1 000 000 = 6 since 1 000 000 = 10^6
log 0.01 = −2 since 0.01 = 10^{-2}
log 0.0001 = −4 since 0.0001 = 10^{-4}
log 1 = 0 since 1 = 10^0

Historically, common logarithms were used for numerical calculations that were required in problems involving compound interest. However, with the availability of electronic calculators equipped with a power function, the need for common logarithms as a computational tool has disappeared. Accordingly, this text gives no further consideration to common logarithms.

C. Natural logarithms

The most common exponential function is $y = e^x$

where $e = \lim_{n \to \infty} (1 + \frac{1}{n})^n = 2.7182818285$ approximately.

The logarithmic form of this function is $x = \log_e y$ but is always written as $x = \ln y$ and called the **natural logarithm.**

Electronic calculators equipped with the universal power function are generally equipped as well with the e^x function and the *ln x* function (natural logarithm function). This latter function eliminates any need for common logarithms and should be used to solve certain problems involving compound interest.

D. Useful relationships

The following relationships are helpful when using natural logarithms:

1. The logarithm of a product of two or more positive numbers is the sum of the logarithms of the factors.

$$\ln(ab) = \ln a + \ln b$$ ⟵ ***Formula* 2.12A**

$$\ln(abc) = \ln a + \ln b + \ln c$$ ⟵ ***Formula* 2.12B**

2. The logarithm of the quotient of two positive numbers is equal to the logarithm of the dividend (numerator) minus the logarithm of the divisor (denominator).

$$\ln\left(\frac{a}{b}\right) = \ln a - \ln b$$ ⟵ ***Formula* 2.13**

3. The logarithm of a power of a positive number is the exponent of the power multiplied by the logarithm of the number.

$$\ln(a^k) = k(\ln a)$$ ⟵ ***Formula* 2.14**

4. (i) $\ln e = 1$ since $e = e^1$
(ii) $\ln 1 = 0$ since $1 = e^0$

***Example* 2.4b** Use an electronic calculator equipped with a natural logarithm function to find n in each of the following.

(i) $2000 = 1500(1.05^n)$

(ii) $10\,000(1.0125^{-n}) = 8057.32$

(iii) $2.00 = 1.00e^{0.1n}$

Solution

(i)

$$
\begin{aligned}
2000 &= 1500(1.05^n) \\
\ln 2000 &= \ln 1500(1.05^n) \longleftarrow \text{take the natural logarithm of each side} \\
\ln 2000 &= \ln 1500 + \ln 1.05^n \longleftarrow \text{using Formula 2.12A} \\
\ln 2000 &= \ln 1500 + n \ln 1.05 \longleftarrow \text{using Formula 2.14} \\
7.6009025 &= 7.3132204 + n(0.04879016) \longleftarrow \text{using the } \ln x \text{ function} \\
0.2876821 &= 0.04879016n \\
n &= \frac{0.2876821}{0.04879016} \\
n &= 5.896 \text{ (approximately)}
\end{aligned}
$$

Alternatively (and more efficiently)

$$
\begin{aligned}
2000 &= 1500(1.05^n) \\
1.05^n &= \frac{2000}{1500} \longleftarrow \text{divide by 1500 to isolate the term containing } n \\
1.05^n &= 1.3333333 \longleftarrow \text{simplify} \\
n \ln 1.05 &= \ln 1.3333333 \longleftarrow \text{using Formula 2.14} \\
n(0.04879016) &= 0.2876821 \\
n &= \frac{0.2876821}{0.04879016} \\
n &= 5.896
\end{aligned}
$$

(ii)

$$
\begin{aligned}
10\,000(1.0125^{-n}) &= 8057.32 \\
1.0125^{-n} &= 0.805732 \\
(-n)(\ln 1.0125) &= \ln 0.805732 \\
(-n)(0.0124225) &= -0.2160041 \\
n &= \frac{0.2160041}{0.0124225} \\
n &= 17.388 \text{ (approximately)}
\end{aligned}
$$

(iii)

$$
\begin{aligned}
2.00 &= 1.00e^{0.1n} \\
e^{0.1n} &= 2.00 \\
(0.1n)(\ln e) &= \ln 2.00 \\
(0.1n)(1) &= \ln 2.00 \longleftarrow \ln e = 1 \\
0.1n &= 0.6931472 \\
n &= 6.93
\end{aligned}
$$

Exercise 2.4

A. Express each of the following in logarithmic form.

1. $2^9 = 512$
2. $3^7 = 2187$
3. $5^{-3} = \frac{1}{125}$
4. $10^{-5} = 0.00001$
5. $e^{2j} = 18$
6. $e^{-3x} = 12$

B. Write each of the following in exponential form.

1. $\log_2 32 = 5$
2. $\log_3 \frac{1}{81} = -4$
3. $\log_{10} 10 = 1$
4. $\ln e^2 = 2$

C. Use an electronic calculator equipped with a natural logarithm function to evaluate each of the following.

1. ln 2
2. ln 200
3. ln 0.105
4. ln 0.01
5. $6500.00 = 575.00(1.01)\left[\frac{(1.01^n - 1)}{0.01}\right]$
6. $5400.00 = 600.00\left(\frac{1 - 1.035^{-n}}{0.035}\right)$

2.5 *Solving basic equations*

A. Basic terms and concepts

1. An **equation** is a statement of equality between two algebraic expressions.

$$7x = 35$$
$$3a - 4 = 11 - 2a$$
$$5(2k - 4) = -3(k + 2)$$

2. If an equation contains only one *variable* and the variable occurs with power 1 only, the equation is said to be a **linear** or **first-degree equation** in one unknown. The three equations listed above are linear equations in one unknown.

3. The two expressions that are equated are called the sides or **members of the equation**. Every equation has a left side (left member) and a right side (right member).

In the equation $3a - 4 = 11 - 2a$,

$3a - 4$ is the left side (left member) and

$11 - 2a$ is the right side (right member).

4. The process of finding a replacement value (number) for the variable, which when substituted into the equation makes the two members of the equation equal, is called *solving the equation*. The replacement value that makes the two members equal is called a *solution* or **root of the equation.** A linear or first-degree equation has only one root and the root, when substituted into the equation, is said to *satisfy* the equation.

The root (solution) of the equation
$3a - 4 = 11 - 2a$ is 3 because when
3 is substituted for a
the left side $3a - 4 = 3(3) - 4 = 9 - 4 = 5$ and
the right side $11 - 2a = 11 - 2(3) = 11 - 6 = 5$.
Thus, for $a = 3$, Left Side = Right Side and 3 satisfies the equation.

5. Equations which have the same root are called **equivalent equations.**

$$6x + 5 = 4x + 17$$
$$6x = 4x + 12$$
$$2x = 12$$
$$x = 6$$

are equivalent equations because the root of all four equations is 6; that is, when 6 is substituted for x, each of the equations is satisfied.

Equivalent equations are useful in solving equations. They may be obtained

(a) by multiplying or dividing both sides of the equation by a number other than zero; and

(b) by adding or subtracting the same number on both sides of the equation.

6. When solving an equation, the basic aim in choosing the operations that will generate useful equivalent equations is to

(a) isolate the terms containing the variable on one side of the equation (this is achieved by addition or subtraction);

(b) make the numerical coefficient of the single term containing the variable equal +1 (this is achieved by multiplication or division).

B. *Solving equations using division*

If each side of an equation is divided by the same non-zero number, the resulting equation is equivalent to the original equation.

$$15x = 45 \quad \longleftarrow \text{original equation}$$

$$\begin{array}{lrl} \text{divide by 3} \longrightarrow & 5x = 15 & \\ \text{or divide by 5} \longrightarrow & 3x = 9 & \Big\} \longleftarrow \text{equivalent equations} \\ \text{or divide by 15} \longrightarrow & x = 3 & \end{array}$$

Division is used in solving equations when the numerical coefficient of the single term containing the variable is an integer or a decimal fraction.

Example 2.5a

(i)

$$12x = 36 \longleftarrow \text{original equation}$$

$$\frac{12x}{12} = \frac{36}{12} \longleftarrow \text{divide each side by the numerical coefficient 12}$$

$$x = 3 \longleftarrow \text{solution}$$

(ii)

$$-7x = 42$$

$$\frac{-7x}{-7} = \frac{42}{-7} \longleftarrow \text{divide each side by the numerical coefficient } -7$$

$$x = -6$$

(iii)

$$0.2x = 3$$

$$\frac{0.2x}{0.2} = \frac{3}{0.2}$$

$$x = 15$$

(iv)

$$x - 0.3x = 14$$

$$0.7x = 14$$

$$\frac{0.7x}{0.7} = \frac{14}{0.7}$$

$$x = 20$$

C. *Solving equations using multiplication*

If each side of an equation is multiplied by the same non-zero number, the resulting equation is equivalent to the original equation.

$$-3x = 6 \longleftarrow \text{original equation}$$

$$\left.\begin{array}{ll} \text{multiply by 2} \longrightarrow & -6x = 12 \\ \text{or multiply by } -1 \longrightarrow & 3x = -6 \end{array}\right\} \longleftarrow \text{equivalent equations}$$

Multiplication is used in solving equations containing common fractions to eliminate the denominator or denominators.

Example 2.5b

(i)

$$\frac{1}{2}x = 3 \longleftarrow \text{original equation}$$

$$2\left(\frac{1}{2x}\right) = 2(3) \longleftarrow \text{multiply each side by 2 to eliminate the denominator}$$

$$x = 6 \longleftarrow \text{solution}$$

(ii)

$$-\frac{1}{4}x = 2 \longleftarrow \text{original equation}$$

$$4\left(-\frac{1}{4}x\right) = 4(2) \longleftarrow \text{multiply each side by 4 to eliminate the denominator}$$

$$-1x = 8$$

$$(-1)(-x) = (-1)(8) \longleftarrow \text{multiply by } (-1) \text{ to make the coefficient of the term in } x \text{ positive}$$

$$x = -8$$

(iii) $-\frac{1}{7}x = -2$

$(-7)\left(-\frac{1}{7}x\right) = (-7)(-2)$ ⟵ multiply by (-7) to eliminate the denominator and to make the coefficient of x equal to $+1$

$x = 14$

D. Solving equations using addition

If the same number is added to each side of an equation, the resulting equation is equivalent to the original equation.

$x - 5 = 4$ ⟵ original equation

add 3 ⟶ $x - 5 + 3 = 4 + 3$
or add 5 ⟶ $x - 5 + 5 = 4 + 5$ } ⟵ equivalent equations

Addition is used to isolate the term or terms containing the variable when terms that have a negative coefficient appear in the equation.

Example 2.5c

(i) $x - 6 = 4$

$x - 6 + 6 = 4 + 6$ ⟵ add 6 to each side of the equation to eliminate the term -6 on the left side of the equation

$x = 10$

(ii) $-2x = -3 - 3x$

$-2x + 3x = -3 - 3x + 3x$ ⟵ add $3x$ to each side to eliminate the term in x on the right side

$x = -3$

(iii) $-x - 5 = 8 - 2x$

$-x - 5 + 5 = 8 - 2x + 5$ ⟵ add 5 to eliminate the constant -5 on the left side

$-x = 13 - 2x$ ⟵ combine like terms

$-x + 2x = 13 - 2x + 2x$ ⟵ add $2x$ to eliminate the term in x on the right side

$x = 13$

E. Solving equations using subtraction

If the same number is subtracted from each side of an equation, the resulting equation is equivalent to the original equation.

$x + 8 = 9$ ⟵ original equation

subtract 4 ⟶ $x + 8 - 4 = 9 - 4$
or subtract 8 ⟶ $x + 8 - 8 = 9 - 8$ } ⟵ equivalent equations

Subtraction is used to isolate the term or terms containing the variable when terms having a positive numerical coefficient appear in the equation.

Example **2.5d**

(i)

$$x + 10 = 6$$
$$x + 10 - 10 = 6 - 10 \longleftarrow \text{subtract 10 from each side of the equation}$$
$$x = -4$$

(ii)

$$7x = 9 + 6x$$
$$7x - 6x = 9 + 6x - 6x \longleftarrow \text{subtract } 6x \text{ from each side to eliminate the term } 6x \text{ on the right side}$$
$$x = 9$$

(iii)

$$6x + 4 = 5x - 3$$
$$6x + 4 - 4 = 5x - 3 - 4 \longleftarrow \text{subtract 4 from each side to eliminate the term 4 on the left side}$$
$$6x = 5x - 7 \longleftarrow \text{combine like terms}$$
$$6x - 5x = 5x - 7 - 5x \longleftarrow \text{subtract } 5x \text{ from each side of the equation to eliminate the term } 5x \text{ on the right side}$$
$$x = -7$$

F. *Using two or more operations to solve equations*

When more than one operation is needed to solve an equation, the operations are usually applied as follows.

(a) First, use addition and subtraction to isolate the terms containing the variable on one side of the equation (usually the left side).

(b) Second, after combining like terms, use multiplication and division to make the coefficient of the term containing the variable equal to +1.

Example **2.5e**

(i)

$$\left(-\frac{3}{5}\right)x = 12$$
$$5\left(-\frac{3}{5}\right)x = 5(12) \longleftarrow \text{multiply by 5 to eliminate the denominator}$$
$$-3x = 60$$
$$\frac{-3x}{-3} = \frac{60}{-3} \longleftarrow \text{divide by } -3$$
$$x = -20$$

(ii)

$$7x - 5 = 15 + 3x$$
$$7x - 5 + 5 = 15 + 3x + 5 \longleftarrow \text{add 5}$$
$$7x = 20 + 3x \longleftarrow \text{combine like terms}$$
$$7x - 3x = 20 + 3x - 3x \longleftarrow \text{subtract } 3x$$
$$4x = 20$$
$$x = 5 \longleftarrow \text{divide by 4}$$

(iii)
$$\begin{aligned} 3x + 9 - 7x &= 24 - x - 3 \\ 9 - 4x &= 21 - x \leftarrow \text{combine like terms} \\ 9 - 4x - 9 &= 21 - x - 9 \\ -4x &= 12 - x \\ -4x + x &= 12 - x + x \\ -3x &= 12 \\ x &= -4 \end{aligned}$$

G. *Checking equations*

To check the solution to an equation, substitute the solution into each side of the equation and determine the value of each side.

Example 2.5f

(i) For $-\frac{3}{5}x = 12$, the solution shown is $x = -20$.

Check

Left Side $= -\frac{3}{5}x = \left(-\frac{3}{5}\right)(-20) = -3(-4) = 12$

Right Side $= 12$

Since the Left Side = Right Side, -20 is the solution to the equation.

(ii) For $7x - 5 = 15 + 3x$, the solution shown is $x = 5$.

Check

$LS = 7x - 5 = 7(5) - 5 = 35 - 5 = 30$

$RS = 15 + 3x = 15 + 3(5) = 15 + 15 = 30$

Since the LS = RS, 5 is the solution.

(iii) For $3x + 9 - 7x = 24 - x - 3$, the solution shown is $x = -4$.

Check

$LS = 3(-4) + 9 - 7(-4) = -12 + 9 + 28 = 25$

$RS = 24 - (-4) - 3 = 24 + 4 - 3 = 25$

Since LS = RS, -4 is the solution.

Exercise 2.5

A. Solve each of the following equations.

1. $15x = 45$ **2.** $-7x = 35$ **3.** $0.9x = 72$

4. $0.02x = 13$ **5.** $\frac{1}{6}x = 3$ **6.** $-\frac{1}{8}x = 7$

7. $\frac{3}{5}x = -21$ 8. $-\frac{4}{3}x = -32$ 9. $x - 3 = -7$

10. $-2x = 7 - 3x$ 11. $x + 6 = -2$ 12. $3x = 9 + 2x$

13. $4 - x = 9 - 2x$ 14. $2x + 7 = x - 5$ 15. $x + 0.6x = 32$

16. $x - 0.3x = 210$ 17. $x - 0.04x = 192$ 18. $x + 0.07x = 64.20$

B. Solve each of the following equations and check your solution.

1. $3x + 5 = 7x - 11$ 2. $5 - 4x = -4 - x$

3. $2 - 3x - 9 = 2x - 7 + 3x$ 4. $4x - 8 - 9x = 10 + 2x - 4$

2.6 *Equation solving involving algebraic simplification*

A. Solving linear equations involving the product of integral constants and binomials

To solve this type of equation, multiply first, then simplify.

Example **2.6a**

(i) $3(2x - 5) = -5(7 - 2x)$

$6x - 15 = -35 + 10x$ ⟵ expand

$6x - 10x = -35 + 15$ ⟵ isolate the terms in x

$-4x = -20$

$x = 5$

Check

LS $= 3[2(5) - 5] = 3(10 - 5) = 3(5) = 15$

RS $= -5[7 - 2(5)] = -5(7 - 10) = -5(-3) = 15$

Since LS = RS, 5 is the solution.

(ii) $x - 4(3x - 7) = 3(9 - 5x) - (x - 11)$

$x - 12x + 28 = 27 - 15x - x + 11$ ⟵ expand

$-11x + 28 = 38 - 16x$ ⟵ combine like terms

$-11x + 16x = 38 - 28$ ⟵ isolate the terms in x

$5x = 10$

$x = 2$

Check

LS $= 2 - 4[3(2) - 7]$
$= 2 - 4(6 - 7)$
$= 2 - 4(-1)$
$= 2 + 4$
$= 6$

RS $= 3[9 - 5(2)] - (2 - 11)$
$= 3(9 - 10) - (-9)$
$= 3(-1) + 9$
$= -3 + 9$
$= 6$

Since LS = RS, 2 is the solution.

B. *Solving linear equations containing common fractions*

The best approach when solving equations containing common fractions is to first create an equivalent equation without common fractions. Multiply each term of the equation by the **lowest common denominator (LCD)** of the fractions.

Example 2.6b

(i)

$$\frac{4}{5}x - \frac{3}{4} = \frac{7}{12} + \frac{11}{15}x \longleftarrow \text{LCD} = 60$$

$$60\left(\frac{4}{5}x\right) - 60\left(\frac{3}{4}\right) = 60\left(\frac{7}{12}\right) + 60\left(\frac{11}{15}x\right) \longleftarrow \text{multiply each term by 60}$$

$$12(4x) - 15(3) = 5(7) + 4(11x) \longleftarrow \text{reduce to eliminate the fractions}$$

$$48x - 45 = 35 + 44x$$

$$48x - 44x = 35 + 45$$

$$4x = 80$$

$$x = 20$$

Check

$$\text{LS} = \frac{4}{5}(20) - \frac{3}{4} = 16 - 0.75 = 15.25$$

$$\text{RS} = \frac{7}{12} + \frac{11}{15}(20) = 0.5833333 + 14.6666667 = 15.25$$

Since LS = RS, 20 is the solution.

(ii)

$$\frac{5}{8}x - 3 = \frac{3}{4} + \frac{5x}{6} \longleftarrow \text{LCD} = 24$$

$$24\left(\frac{5x}{8}\right) - 24(3) = 24\left(\frac{3}{4}\right) + 24\left(\frac{5x}{6}\right)$$

$$3(5x) - 72 = 6(3) + 4(5x)$$

$$15x - 72 = 18 + 20x$$

$$-5x = 90$$

$$x = -18$$

Check

$$\text{LS} = \frac{5}{8}(-18) - 3 = -11.25 - 3 = -14.25$$

$$\text{RS} = \frac{3}{4} + \frac{5}{6}(-18) = 0.75 - 15.00 = -14.25$$

Since LS = RS, the solution is −18.

C. *Solving linear equations involving fractional constants and multiplication*

When solving this type of equation, the best approach is first to eliminate the fractions and then to expand.

Example **2.6c**

(i)

$$\frac{3}{2}(x-2)-\frac{2}{3}(2x-1)=5 \longleftarrow \text{LCD} = 6$$

$$6\left(\frac{3}{2}\right)(x-2)-6\left(\frac{2}{3}\right)(2x-1)=6(5) \longleftarrow \text{multiply each side by 6}$$

$$3(3)(x-2)-2(2)(2x-1)=30 \longleftarrow \text{reduce to eliminate fractions}$$

$$9(x-2)-4(2x-1)=30$$

$$9x-18-8x+4=30$$

$$x-14=30$$

$$x=44$$

Check

$$\text{LS} = \frac{3}{2}(44-2)-\frac{2}{3}(2\times 44-1)=\frac{3}{2}(42)-\frac{2}{3}(87)=63-58=5$$

$$\text{RS} = 5$$

Since LS = RS, 44 is the solution.

(ii)

$$-\frac{3}{5}(4x-1)+\frac{5}{8}(4x-3)=\frac{-11}{10} \longleftarrow \text{LCD} = 40$$

$$40\left(\frac{-3}{5}\right)(4x-1)+40\left(\frac{5}{8}\right)(4x-3)=40\left(\frac{-11}{10}\right)$$

$$8(-3)(4x-1)+5(5)(4x-3)=4(-11)$$

$$-24(4x-1)+25(4x-3)=-44$$

$$-96x+24+100x-75=-44$$

$$4x-51=-44$$

$$4x=7$$

$$x=\frac{7}{4}$$

Check

$$\text{LS} = -\frac{3}{5}\left[4\left(\frac{7}{4}\right)-1\right]+\frac{5}{8}\left[4\left(\frac{7}{4}\right)-3\right]$$

$$= -\frac{3}{5}(7-1)+\frac{5}{8}(7-3)$$

$$= -\frac{18}{5}+\frac{5}{2}=-\frac{36}{10}+\frac{25}{10}=-\frac{11}{10}$$

$$\text{RS} = -\frac{11}{10}$$

Since LS = RS, the solution is $\frac{7}{4}$.

Exercise 2.6

A. Solve each of the following equations and check your solutions.

1. $12x - 4(9x - 20) = 320$
2. $5(x - 4) - 3(2 - 3x) = -54$
3. $3(2x - 5) - 2(2x - 3) = -15$
4. $17 - 3(2x - 7) = 7x - 3(2x - 1)$

B. Solve each of the following equations.

1. $x - \frac{1}{4}x = 15$
2. $x + \frac{5}{8}x = 26$
3. $\frac{2}{3}x - \frac{1}{4} = -\frac{7}{4} - \frac{5}{6}x$
4. $\frac{5}{3} - \frac{2}{5}x = \frac{1}{6}x - \frac{1}{30}$
5. $\frac{3}{4}x + 4 = \frac{113}{24} - \frac{2}{3}x$
6. $2 - \frac{3}{2}x = \frac{2}{3}x + \frac{31}{9}$

C. Solve each of the following equations.

1. $\frac{3}{4}(2x - 1) - \frac{1}{3}(5 - 2x) = -\frac{55}{12}$
2. $\frac{4}{5}(4 - 3x) + \frac{53}{40} = \frac{3}{10}x - \frac{7}{8}(2x - 3)$
3. $\frac{2}{3}(2x - 1) - \frac{3}{4}(3 - 2x) = 2x - \frac{20}{9}$
4. $\frac{4}{3}(3x - 2) - \frac{3}{5}(4x - 3) = \frac{11}{60} + 3x$

2.7 *Solving Problems*

Many business problems may be solved by means of a linear equation in one unknown. To solve problems by means of an algebraic equation, follow the systematic procedure outlined below.

STEP 1 *Introduce the variable* to be used by means of a complete sentence. This ensures a clear understanding and a record of what the variable is intended to represent.

STEP 2 *Translate* the information in the problem statement in terms of the variable.

STEP 3 *Set up* an algebraic equation. This usually means matching the algebraic expressions developed in Step 2 to a specific number.

STEP 4 *Solve* the equation, state a conclusion, and check the conclusion against the problem statement.

***Example* 2.7a** A TV set was sold during a sale for \$575. What is the regular selling price of the set if the price of the set was reduced by $\frac{1}{6}$ of the regular price?

Solution

STEP 1 *Introduce the variable.* Let the regular selling price be represented by \$$x$.

STEP 2 *Translate.* The reduction in price is \$$\frac{1}{6}x$, and the reduced price is \$$(x - \frac{1}{6}x)$.

STEP 3 *Set up an equation.* Since the reduced price is given as \$575,

$$x - \frac{1}{6}x = 575$$

STEP 4 *Solve* the equation, state a conclusion, and check.

$$\frac{5}{6}x = 575$$

$$x = \frac{6(575)}{5}$$

$$x = 690$$

The regular selling price is \$690.

Check		
	Regular selling price	\$690
	Reduction: $\frac{1}{6}$ of 690	115
	Reduced price	\$575

***Example* 2.7b** The material cost of a product is \$4 less than twice the cost of the direct labour, and the overhead is $\frac{5}{6}$ of the direct labour cost. If the total cost of the product is \$157, what is the amount of each of the three elements of cost?

Solution

Three values are needed, and the variable could represent any of the three. However, problems of this type can be solved most easily by representing the proper item by the variable rather than by selecting any of the other items. The *proper* item is the one to which the other item or items are *directly related.* In this problem, direct labour is that item.

Let the cost of direct labour be represented by $\$x$; then the cost of direct material is $\$(2x - 4)$ and the cost of overhead is $\$\frac{5}{6}x$.

The total cost is $\$(x + 2x - 4 + \frac{5}{6}x)$.

Since the total cost is given as \$157,

$$x + 2x - 4 + \frac{5}{6}x = 157$$
$$3x + \frac{5}{6}x = 161$$
$$18x + 5x = 966$$
$$23x = 966$$
$$x = 42$$

Material cost is \$80, direct labour cost is \$42, and overhead is \$35.

Check Material cost: $2x - 4 = 2(42) - 4 =$ \$80
Direct labour cost: x = \$42
Overhead cost: $\frac{5}{6}x = \frac{5}{6}(42)$ = \$35
Total cost \$157

Example **2.7c** Sheridan Service paid \$240 for heat and power during January. If heat was \$40 less than three times the cost of power, how much was the cost of heat for January?

Solution

Although the cost of heat is required, it is more convenient to represent the cost of power by the variable since heat cost is expressed in terms of power cost.

Let the cost of power be represented by $\$x$; then the cost of heat is $\$(3x - 40)$ and the total cost is $\$(x + 3x - 40)$. Since the total cost is given as \$240,

$$x + 3x - 40 = 240$$
$$4x = 280$$
$$x = 70$$

The cost of heat is \$170.

Check Power: \$ 70
Heat: $3x - 40 = 3(70) - 40$ = \$170
Total cost \$240

Example **2.7d** The Clarkson Soccer League has set a budget of \$3840 for soccer balls. High quality game balls cost \$36 each, while lower quality practice balls cost \$20 each. If 160 balls are to be purchased, how many balls of each type can be bought to use up exactly the budgeted amount?

Solution

When, as in this case, the items referred to in the problem are not directly related, the variable may represent either one.

Let the number of game balls be represented by x; then the number of practice balls is $(160 - x)$.

Since the prices of the two types of balls differ, the total value of each type of ball must now be represented in terms of x.

The value of x game balls is $\$36x$;
the value of $(160 - x)$ practice balls is $\$20(160 - x)$;
the total value is $\$[36x + 20(160 - x)]$.
Since the total budgeted value is given as \$3840,

$$\begin{aligned} 36x + 20(160 - x) &= 3840 \\ 36x + 3200 - 20x &= 3840 \\ 16x &= 640 \\ x &= 40 \end{aligned}$$

The number of game balls is 40 and the number of practice balls is 120.

Check Number—40 + 120 = 160

Value—game balls: 36(40)	=	\$1440
practice balls: 20(120)	=	\$2400
Total value		\$3840

***Example* 2.7e** Last year, a repair shop used 1200 small bushings. The shop paid $33\frac{1}{3}$ cents per bushing for the first shipment and $37\frac{1}{2}$ cents per bushing for the second shipment. If the total cost was \$430, how many bushings did the second shipment contain?

Solution

Let the number of bushings in the second shipment be x; then the number of bushings in the first shipment was $1200 - x$. The cost of the second shipment was $\$0.37\frac{1}{2}x$ or $\$\frac{3}{8}x$, and the cost of the first shipment was $\$0.33\frac{1}{3}(1200 - x)$ or $\$\frac{1}{3}(1200 - x)$. The total cost is $\$[\frac{3}{8}x + \frac{1}{3}(1200 - x)]$. Since the total cost is \$430,

$$\begin{aligned} \frac{3}{8}x + \frac{1}{3}(1200 - x) &= 430 \\ 24\left(\frac{3}{8}x\right) + 24\left(\frac{1}{3}\right)(1200 - x) &= 24(430) \\ 3(3x) + 8(1200 - x) &= 10\,320 \\ 9x + 9600 - 8x &= 10\,320 \\ x &= 720 \end{aligned}$$

The second shipment consisted of 720 bushings.

Check Total number of bushings: $720 + 480 = 1200$

$$\text{Total value: } 720\left(\frac{3}{8}\right) + 480\left(\frac{1}{3}\right)$$
$$= 90(3) + 160(1)$$
$$= 270 + 160$$
$$= \$430$$

Exercise 2.7

A. For each of the following problems, set up an equation in one unknown and solve.

1. Eaton's sold a sweater for \$49.49. The selling price included a markup of $\frac{3}{4}$ of the cost to the department store. What was the cost?

2. S&A Electronics sold a stereo set during a sale for \$576. Determine the regular selling price of the set if the price of the set had been reduced by $\frac{1}{3}$ of the original regular selling price.

3. This month's commodity index decreased by $\frac{1}{12}$ of last month's index to 176. What was last month's index?

4. After an increase of $\frac{1}{8}$ of his current hourly wage, Jean-Luc will receive a new hourly wage of \$10.35. How much is his hourly wage before the increase?

5. Nancy's sales last week were \$140 less than three times Vera's sales. What were Nancy's sales if together their sales amounted to \$940?

6. A metal pipe 90 cm long is cut into two pieces so that the longer piece is 15 cm longer than twice the length of the shorter piece. What is the length of the longer piece?

7. Ken and Martina agreed to form a partnership. The partnership agreement requires that Martina invest \$2500 more than two-thirds of what Ken is to invest. If the partnership's capital is to be \$55 000, how much should Martina invest?

8. A furniture company has been producing 2320 chairs a day working two shifts. The second shift has produced 60 chairs fewer than four-thirds of the number of chairs produced by the first shift. Determine the number of chairs produced by the second shift.

9. An inventory of two types of floodlights showed a total of sixty lights valued at \$2580. If Type A cost \$40 each while Type B cost \$50 each, how many Type B floodlights were in inventory?

10. A machine requires four hours to make a unit of Product A and three hours to make a unit of Product B. Last month the machine operated for 200 hours producing a total of 60 units. How many units of Product A were produced?

11. Bruce has saved \$8.80 in nickels, dimes, and quarters. If he has four nickels fewer than three times the number of dimes and one quarter more than $\frac{3}{4}$ the number of dimes, how many coins of each type does Bruce have?

12. The local amateur football club spent \$1475 on tickets to a professional football game. If the club bought ten more eight-dollar tickets than three times the number of twelve-dollar tickets and three fewer fifteen-dollar tickets than $\frac{4}{5}$ the number of twelve-dollar tickets, how many of each type of ticket did the club buy?

Review exercise

1. Simplify.
   - **(a)** $3x - 4y - 3y - 5x$
   - **(b)** $2x - 0.03x$
   - **(c)** $(5a - 4) - (3 - a)$
   - **(d)** $-(2x - 3y) - (-4x + y) + (y - x)$
   - **(e)** $(5a^2 - 2b - c) - (3c + 2b - 4a^2)$
   - **(f)** $-(2x - 3) - (x^2 - 5x + 2)$
2. Simplify.
   - **(a)** $3(-5a)$
   - **(b)** $-7m(-4x)$
   - **(c)** $14m \div (-2m)$
   - **(d)** $(-15a^2b) \div (5a)$
   - **(e)** $-6(-3x)(2y)$
   - **(f)** $4(-3a)(b)(-2c)$
   - **(g)** $-4(3x - 5y - 1)$
   - **(h)** $x(1 - 2x - x^2)$
   - **(i)** $(24x - 16) \div (-4)$
   - **(j)** $(21a^2 - 12a) \div 3a$
   - **(k)** $4(2a - 5) - 3(3 - 6a)$
   - **(l)** $2a(x - a) - a(3x + 2) - 3a(-5x - 4)$
   - **(m)** $(m - 1)(2m - 5)$
   - **(n)** $(3a - 2)(a^2 - 2a - 3)$
   - **(o)** $3(2x - 4)(x - 1) - 4(x - 3)(5x + 2)$
   - **(p)** $-2a(3m - 1)(m - 4) - 5a(2m + 3)(2m - 3)$
3. Evaluate each of the following for the values given.
   - **(a)** $3xy - 4x - 5y$ for $x = -2, y = 5$
   - **(b)** $-5(2a - 3b) - 2(a + 5b)$ for $a = -\frac{1}{4}, b = \frac{2}{3}$
   - **(c)** $\frac{2NC}{P(n + 1)}$ for $N = 12, C = 432, P = 1800, n = 35$
   - **(d)** $\frac{365I}{RP}$ for $I = 600, R = 0.15, P = 7300$
   - **(e)** $A(1 - dt)$ for $A = 720, d = 0.135, t = \frac{280}{360}$
   - **(f)** $\frac{S}{1+RT}$ for $S = 2755, R = 0.17, T = \frac{219}{365}$

4. Simplify.

(a) $(-3)^5$

(b) $\left(\frac{2}{3}\right)^4$

(c) $(-5)^0$

(d) $(-3)^{-1}$

(e) $\left(\frac{2}{5}\right)^{-4}$

(f) $(1.01)^0$

(g) $(-3)^5(-3)^4$

(h) $4^7 \div 4^2$

(i) $[(-3)^2]^5$

(j) $(m^3)^4$

(k) $\left(\frac{2}{3}\right)^3\left(\frac{2}{3}\right)^7\left(\frac{2}{3}\right)^{-6}$

(l) $\left(-\frac{5}{4}\right)^5 \div \left(-\frac{5}{4}\right)^3$

(m) $(1.03^{50})(1.03^{100})$

(n) $(1 + i)^{180} \div (1 + i)^{100}$

(o) $[(1.05)^{30}]^5$

(p) $(-2xy)^4$

(q) $\left(\frac{a^2b}{3}\right)^{-4}$

(r) $(1 + i)^{-n}$

5. Use an electronic calculator to compute each of the following.

(a) $\sqrt{0.9216}$

(b) $\sqrt[6]{1.075}$

(c) $14.974458^{\frac{1}{40}}$

(d) $1.08^{-\frac{5}{12}}$

(e) $\ln 3$

(f) $\ln 0.05$

(g) $140\ 000.00 = 5500.00(1.1146213)\left(\frac{1.1146213^n - 1}{0.1146213}\right)$

(h) $21\ 500.00 = 375.00(1.0099016^{-9})\left(\frac{1 - 1.0099016^{-n}}{0.0099016}\right)$

6. Solve each of the following equations.

(a) $9x = -63$

(b) $0.05x = 44$

(c) $-\frac{1}{7}x = 3$

(d) $\frac{5}{6}x = -15$

(e) $x - 8 = -5$

(f) $x + 9 = -2$

(g) $x + 0.02x = 255$

(h) $x - 0.1x = 36$

(i) $4x - 3 = 9x + 22$

(j) $9x - 6 - 3x = 15 + 4x - 7$

(k) $x - \frac{1}{3}x = 26$

(l) $x + \frac{3}{8}x = 77$

7. Solve each of the following equations and check your answers.

(a) $-9(3x - 8) - 8(9 - 7x) = 5 + 4(9x + 11)$

(b) $21x - 4 - 7(5x - 6) = 8x - 4(5x - 7)$

(c) $\frac{5}{7}x + \frac{1}{2} = \frac{5}{14} + \frac{2}{3}x$

(d) $\frac{4x}{3} + 2 = \frac{9}{8} - \frac{x}{6}$

(e) $\frac{7}{5}(6x - 7) - \frac{3}{8}(7x + 15) = 25$

(f) $\frac{5}{9}(7 - 6x) - \frac{3}{4}(3 - 15x) = \frac{1}{12}(3x - 5) - \frac{1}{2}$

(g) $\frac{5}{6}(4x - 3) - \frac{2}{5}(3x + 4) = 5x - \frac{16}{15}(1 - 3x)$

8. For each of the following problems, set up an equation and solve.

   (a) A company laid off one-sixth of its workforce because of falling sales. If the number of employees after the layoff is 690, how many employees were laid off?

   (b) The current average property value is two-sevenths more than last year's average value. What was last year's average property value if the current average is $81 450?

   (c) The total amount paid for a banquet, including sales tax of one-twentieth of the price quoted for the banquet, was $2457.00. How much of the amount paid was sales tax?

   (d) A piece of property with a commercial building is acquired by H & A Investments for $184 000. If the land is valued at $2000 less than one-third the value of the building, how much of the amount paid should be assigned to land?

   (e) The total average monthly cost of heat, power, and water for Sheridan Service for last year was $2010. If this year's average is expected to increase by one-tenth over last year's average, and heat is $22 more than three-quarters the cost of power while water is $11 less than one-third the cost of power, how much should be budgeted on the average for each month for each item?

   (f) Monarch Swimming Pools has a promotional budget of $87 500. The budget is to be allocated to direct selling, TV advertising, and newspaper advertising according to a formula which requires that the amount spent on TV advertising be $1000 more than three times the amount spent on newspaper advertising, and that the amount spent on direct selling be three-fourths of the total spent on TV advertising and newspaper advertising combined. How much of the budget should be allocated to direct selling?

   (g) A product requires processing on three machines. Processing time on Machine A is three minutes less than four-fifths of the number of minutes on Machine B and processing time on Machine C is five-sixths of the time needed on Machines A and B together. How many minutes processing time is required on Machine C if the total processing time on all three machines is 77 minutes?

   (h) Sport Alive sold 72 pairs of ski poles. Superlight poles sell at $30 per pair while ordinary poles sell at $16 per pair. If total sales value was $1530, how many pairs of each type were sold?

   (i) A cash box contains $74.00 made up of quarters, half-dollars, and one-dollar coins. How many quarters are in the box if the number of half-dollar coins is one more than three-fifths of the number of one-dollar coins, and the number of quarters is four times the number of one-dollar coins and half-dollar coins together?

(j) Demers Manufacturing plans to allocate direct distribution costs to three product lines based on sales value for an accounting period. Product A sells for \$20 per unit, Product B for \$15 per unit, and Product C for \$10 per unit. For last month, the number of units of Product A was five-eighths the number of units of Product B and the number of units of Product C was 16 less than three times the number of units of Product B. How much of the total direct distribution cost of \$6280 is to be allocated to each product line?

Self-test

1. Simplify.

(a) $4 - 3x - 6 - 5x$ **(b)** $(5x - 4) - (7x + 5)$

(c) $-2(3a - 4) - 5(2a + 3)$ **(d)** $-6(x - 2)(x + 1)$

2. Evaluate each of the following for the values given.

(a) $2x^2 - 5xy - 4y^2$ for $x = -3, y = +5$

(b) $3(7a - 4b) - 4(5a + 3b)$ for $a = \frac{2}{3}, b = -\frac{3}{4}$

(c) $\frac{2NC}{P(n + 1)}$ for N = 12, C = 400, P = 2000, $n = 24$

(d) $\frac{I}{Pr}$ for I = 324, P = 5400, $r = 0.15$

(e) $S(1 - dt)$ for S = 1606, $d = 0.125$, $t = \frac{240}{365}$

(f) $\frac{S}{1 + rt}$ for S = 1566, $r = 0.10$, $t = \frac{292}{365}$

3. Simplify.

(a) $(-2)^3$ **(b)** $\left(\frac{-2}{3}\right)^2$

(c) $(4)^0$ **(d)** $(3)^2(3)^5$

(e) $\left(\frac{4}{3}\right)^{-2}$ **(f)** $(-x^3)^5$

4. Use an electronic calculator to compute each of the following.

(a) $\sqrt[10]{1.35}$ **(b)** $\frac{1 - 1.03^{-40}}{0.03}$

(c) ln 1.025 **(d)** ln 0.05

5. Solve each of the following equations.

(a) $\frac{1}{81} = \left(\frac{1}{3}\right)^{n-2}$ **(b)** $\frac{5}{2} = 40\left(\frac{1}{2}\right)^{n-1}$

6. Solve each of the following equations.

(a) $-\frac{2}{3}x = 24$ **(b)** $x - 0.06x = 8.46$

(c) $0.2x - 4 = 6 - 0.3x$

(d) $(3 - 5x) - (8x - 1) = 43$

(e) $4(8x - 2) - 5(3x + 5) = 18$

(f) $x + \frac{3}{10}x + \frac{1}{2} + x + \frac{3}{5}x + 1 = 103$

(g) $x + \frac{4}{5}x - 3 + \frac{5}{6}\left(x + \frac{4}{5}x - 3\right) = 77$

(h) $\frac{2}{3}\left(3x - 1\right) - \frac{3}{4}\left(5x - 3\right) = \frac{9}{8}x - \frac{5}{6}\left(7x - 9\right)$

7. For each of the following problems, set up an equation and solve.
   - **(a)** After reducing the regular selling price by $\frac{1}{5}$, Star Electronics sold a TV set for \$192. What was the regular selling price?
   - **(b)** The weaving department of a factory occupies 400 square metres more than 2 times the floor space occupied by the shipping department. The total floor space is 6700 square metres. Determine the floor space occupied by the weaving department.
   - **(c)** A machine requires 3 hours to make a unit of Product A and 5 hours to make a unit of Product B. The machine operated for 395 hours producing a total of 95 units. How many units of Product B were produced?
   - **(d)** You invested a sum of money in a bank certificate yielding an annual return of $\frac{1}{12}$ of the sum invested. A second sum of money invested in a credit union certificate yields an annual return of $\frac{1}{9}$ of the sum invested. The credit union investment is \$500 more than $\frac{2}{3}$ of the bank investment and the total annual return is \$1000. What is the sum of money you invested in the credit union certificate?

CASE STUDY

The Rainmaster Corporation developed a new type of water-saving sprinkler system after market research found a demand for this innovative and environmentally-friendly device. Implementing production and selling requires algebraic analysis.

1. The planning department has estimated that the setup of a new production line will require $\frac{1}{4}$ of the present floor space for parts production, $\frac{1}{5}$ for assembly, and $\frac{1}{10}$ for packaging. Existing product lines will have the remaining 900 square metres of floor space.
   - **(a)** Formulate and solve the equation to allocate the available floor space.
   - **(b)** Calculate the floor space needed for each department.
2. The marketing department has projected an increase in demand after one year. Output will have to triple. The planning department projects that the increased production will require $\frac{1}{3}$ of the floor space for parts production, $\frac{1}{4}$ for assembly, and $\frac{3}{10}$ for packaging. The existing production lines will need to be enlarged to 1050 square metres.
   - **(a)** Formulate and solve the new equation for the projected allocation of floor space.

(b) Calculate the additional floor space needed to meet increased demand.

(c) Calculate the projected floor space for each department.

3. Producing this device takes three machine operations. The three machines, A, B, and C, have hourly costs of \$8.50, \$9.00, and \$10.25 respectively. The production line can be configured in two ways.

(a) Method 1: Machine A to machine B to machine C

For one unit, the time on machine A is 1.5 minutes less than on machine B. The time on machine C is 2 minutes less than half the time on machine B. Total time is 9.5 minutes. Calculate the total cost per unit.

(b) Method 2: Machine C to machine B to machine A

For one unit, the time on machine C is 1 minute more than half the time on B. The time on machine A is 3 minutes less than on machine B. Total time is 9.5 minutes. Calculate the total cost per unit.

4. The two methods take the same total time but have different unit costs. Explain why there is a difference in unit costs.

5. The manufacturer must sell the device at a price that reflects costs and profit.

(a) Calculate the selling price to the retailer. Use the lower cost from question 3 and allow a markup of $\frac{1}{2}$ on the selling price, a promotion cost of $\frac{1}{8}$ on the selling price, and a shipping cost of $\frac{1}{10}$ on the selling price.

(b) Calculate the different costs included in the selling price.

6. The retailer marks up its cost by 60% of the retail price to obtain the retail selling price. Formulate the equation and calculate the retail selling price.

7. The retailer plans to make a gross profit of \$1200 on sales of this new device. The promotional strategy is to put the first 50 units on sale at \$7.00 each and then to sell the remainder at the regular selling price. Formulate the equation and calculate how many units have to be sold at the regular price to produce a \$1200 profit.

Summary of formulae (laws) used

Formula 2.1A

$a^m \times a^n = a^{m+n}$ — The rule for multiplying two powers having the same base

Formula 2.1B

$a^m \times a^n \times a^p = a^{m+n+p}$ — The rule for multiplying three or more powers having the same base

Formula 2.2

$a^m \div a^n = a^{m-n}$ — The rule for dividing two powers having the same base

Formula 2.3
$(a^m)^n = a^{mn}$ The rule for raising a power to a power

Formula 2.4
$(ab)^m = a^m b^m$ The rule for taking the power of a product

Formula 2.5
$\left(\frac{a}{b}\right)^m = \frac{a^m}{b^m}$ The rule for taking the power of a quotient

Formula 2.6
$a^{-m} = \frac{1}{a^m}$ The definition of a negative exponent

Formula 2.7
$\left(\frac{y}{x}\right)^{-m} = \left(\frac{x}{y}\right)^m$ The rule for a fraction with a negative exponent

Formula 2.8
$a^{\frac{1}{n}} = \sqrt[n]{a}$ The definition of a fractional exponent with numerator 1

Formula 2.9
$a^{-\frac{1}{n}} = \frac{1}{\sqrt[n]{a}}$ The definition of a fractional exponent with numerator -1

Formula 2.10
$a^{\frac{m}{n}} = \sqrt[n]{a^m}$ The definition of a positive fractional exponent

Formula 2.11
$a^{-\frac{m}{n}} = \frac{1}{\sqrt[n]{a^m}}$ The definition of a negative fractional exponent

Formula 2.12
$\ln(ab) = \ln a + \ln b$ The relationship used to find the logarithm of a product

Formula 2.13
$\ln\left(\frac{a}{b}\right) = \ln a - \ln b$ The relationship used to find the logarithm of a quotient

Formula 2.14
$\ln(a^k) = k(\ln a)$ The relationship used to find the logarithm of a power

Glossary of terms used

Algebraic expression a combination of numbers, variables representing numbers, and symbols indicating an algebraic operation
Base one of the equal factors in a power
Collecting like terms adding like terms
Combining like terms see *Collecting like terms*

Common logarithms logarithms with base 10; represented by the notation $\log x$
Equation a statement of equality between two algebraic expressions
Equivalent equations equations that have the same root
Exponent the number of equal factors in a power
Factor one of the numbers that, when multiplied with the other number or numbers, yields a given product
First degree equation an equation in which the variable (or variables) appear with power '1' only
Index the power of the root indicated with the radical symbol
Least or lowest common denominator the smallest number into which a set of denominators divides without remainders
Like terms terms having the same literal coefficient
Linear equation see *First degree equation*
Literal coefficient the part of a term formed with letter symbols
Logarithm the exponent to which a base must be raised to produce a given number
Members of an equation the two sides of an equation; the left member is the left side; the right member is the right side
Monomial an algebraic expression consisting of one term
Natural logarithms logarithms with base e; represented by the notation $\ln x$
Numerical coefficient the part of a term formed with numerals
Polynomial an algebraic expression consisting of more than one term
Power a mathematical operation indicating the multiplication of a number of equal factors
Power of a root the exponent indicating the number of equal factors
Radical the indicated root when using the radical symbol for finding a root
Radicand the number under the radical symbol
Root of an equation the solution (replacement value) that, when substituted for the variable, makes the two sides equal
Root of a product one of the equal factors in the product

3 *Ratio, proportion, and percent*

Introduction

Business information is often based on a comparison of related quantities stated in the form of a ratio. When two or more ratios are equivalent, a proportion equating the ratios can be set up. Allocation problems generally involve ratios, and many of the physical, economic, and financial relationships affecting businesses may be stated in the form of ratios or proportions.

The fractional form of a ratio is frequently replaced by the percent form because relative magnitudes are more easily understood as percents. Skill in manipulating percents, finding percentages, computing rates percent, and dealing with problems of increase and decrease is fundamental to solving many business problems.

Objectives

Upon completing this chapter, you will be able to

1. set up ratios, manipulate ratios, and use ratios to solve allocation problems;
2. set up proportions, solve proportions, and use proportions to solve problems involving the equivalence of two ratios;
3. change percents to common fractions and to decimals, and change fractions and decimals to percents;
4. find percentages, compute rates percent, and find the base for a rate percent, and then apply these skills to solve business problems;
5. solve problems of increase and decrease including finding the rate of increase or decrease and finding the original quantity on which the increase or decrease is based;
6. solve a variety of business problems involving percents.

3.1 *Ratios*

A. Setting up ratios

1. A **ratio** is a comparison of the *relative* values of numbers or quantities and may be written in three alternate ways:
(a) by using the word to, such as in '5 to 3';
(b) by using a colon, such as in '5 : 3';
(c) as a common fraction, such as '$\frac{5}{3}$'.

2. When comparing more than two numbers or quantities, using the colon is preferred.
To compare the quantities 5 kg, 3 kg, and 2 kg, the ratio comparing the quantities is written

5 kg : 3 kg : 2 kg

3. When using a ratio to compare quantities, the unit of measurement is usually dropped.
If three items weigh 5 kg, 3 kg, and 2 kg respectively, their weights are compared by the ratio

5 : 3 : 2

4. The numbers appearing in a ratio are called the **terms of the ratio**. If the terms are in different units, the terms need to be expressed in the same unit of measurement before the units can be dropped.
The ratio of 1 quarter to 1 dollar becomes 25 cents to 100 cents or 25 : 100; or the ratio of 3 hours to 40 minutes becomes 180 min : 40 min or 180 : 40.

5. When, as is frequently done, rates are expressed as ratios, ratios drop the units of measurement, even though the terms of the ratio represent different things.
100 km/h becomes 100 : 1;
50 m in 5 seconds becomes 50 : 5;
$1.49 for 2 items becomes 1.49 : 2.

6. Any statement containing a comparison of two or more numbers or quantities can be used to set up a ratio.

Example **3.1a**

(i) In a company, the work of 40 employees is supervised by five managers.
The ratio of employees to managers is 40 : 5.
(ii) Variable cost is $4000 for a sales volume of $24 000.
The ratio of variable cost to sales volume is 4000 : 24 000.
(iii) The cost of a product is made up of $30 of material, $12 of direct labour, and $27 of overhead.
The elements of cost are in the ratio 30 : 12 : 27.

B. Reducing ratios to lowest terms

When ratios are used to express a comparison, they are usually reduced to *lowest* terms. Since ratios may be expressed as fractions, ratios may be manipulated according to the rules for working with fractions. Thus, the procedure used to reduce ratios to lowest terms is the same as to reduce fractions to lowest terms. However, when a ratio is expressed by an improper fraction that reduces to a whole number, the denominator '1' must be written to indicate that two quantities are being compared.

Example **3.1b** Reduce each of the following ratios to lowest terms.

(i) 80 : 35 (ii) 48 : 30 : 18

(iii) 225 : 45 (iv) 81 : 54 : 27

Solution

(i) Since each term of the ratio 80 : 35 contains a common factor 5, each term can be reduced.

$$80 : 35 = (16 \times 5) : (7 \times 5) = 16 : 7$$

or $\frac{80}{35} = \frac{16 \times 5}{7 \times 5} = \frac{16}{7}$

(ii) The terms of the ratio 48 : 30 : 18 contain a common factor 6.

$$48 : 30 : 18 = (8 \times 6) : (5 \times 6) : (3 \times 6) = 8 : 5 : 3$$

(iii) $225 : 45 = (45 \times 5) : (45 \times 1) = 5 : 1$

or $\frac{225}{45} = \frac{5}{1}$

(iv) $81 : 54 : 27 = (3 \times 27) : (2 \times 27) : (1 \times 27) = 3 : 2 : 1$

C. Equivalent ratios in higher terms

Equivalent ratios in higher terms may be obtained by *multiplying* each term of a ratio by the same number. Higher-term ratios are used to eliminate decimals from the terms of a ratio.

Example **3.1c** State each of the following ratios in higher terms so as to eliminate the decimals from the terms of the ratios.

(i) 2.5 : 3 (ii) 1.25 : 3.75 : 7.5

(iii) $\frac{1.8}{2.7}$ (iv) $\frac{19.25}{2.75}$

Solution

(i) 2.5 : 3 = 25 : 30 ← multiply each term by 10 to eliminate the decimal

= 5 : 6 ← reduce to lowest terms

(ii) $1.25 : 3.75 : 7.5$
$= 125 : 375 : 750 \leftarrow$ multiply each term by 100 to eliminate the decimals
$= (1 \times 125) : (3 \times 125) : (6 \times 125)$
$= 1 : 3 : 6$

(iii) $\frac{1.8}{2.7} = \frac{18}{27} = \frac{2}{3}$

(iv) $\frac{19.25}{2.75} = \frac{1925}{275} = \frac{7 \times 275}{1 \times 275} = \frac{7}{1}$

D. *Allocation according to a ratio*

Allocation problems require dividing a whole into a number of parts according to a ratio. The number of parts into which the whole is to be divided is the sum of the terms of the ratio.

Example **3.1d** Allocate \$480 in the ratio 5 : 3.

Solution

The division of \$480 in the ratio 5 : 3 may be achieved by dividing the amount of \$480 into (5 + 3) or 8 parts.

The value of each part = 480 ÷ 8 = 60.

The first term of the ratio consists of 5 of the 8 parts; that is,

the first term = 5 × 60 = 300 and the second term = 3 × 60 = 180.

\$480 is to be divided into \$300 and \$180.

Alternatively

\$480 in the ratio 5 : 3 may be divided by using fractions.

5 of 8 $\longrightarrow \frac{5}{8} \times 480 = 300$

3 of 8 $\longrightarrow \frac{3}{8} \times 480 = 180$

Example **3.1e** If net income of \$72 000 is to be divided among three business partners in the ratio 4 : 3 : 2, how much should each partner receive?

Solution

Divide the net income into 4 + 3 + 2 = 9 parts;
each part has a value of 72 000 ÷ 9 = \$8000.

Partner 1 receives 4 of the 9 parts $\longrightarrow$ 4 × 8000 = \$32 000
Partner 2 receives 3 of the 9 parts $\longrightarrow$ 3 × 8000 = \$24 000
Partner 3 receives 2 of the 9 parts $\longrightarrow$ 2 × 8000 = \$16 000

TOTAL \$72 000

Alternatively

Partner 1 receives $\frac{4}{9}$ of 72 000 $= \frac{4}{9} \times 72\,000 = 4 \times 8000 =$ \$32 000

Partner 2 receives $\frac{3}{9}$ of 72 000 $= \frac{3}{9} \times 72\,000 = 3 \times 8000 =$ \$24 000

Partner 3 receives $\frac{2}{9}$ of 72 000 $= \frac{2}{9} \times 72\,000 = 2 \times 8000 =$ \$16 000

TOTAL \$72 000

Example **3.1f** A business suffered a fire loss of \$224 640. It was covered by an insurance policy which stated that any claim was to be paid by three insurance companies in the ratio $\frac{1}{3} : \frac{3}{8} : \frac{5}{12}$. What is the amount that each of the three companies will pay?

Solution

When an amount is to be allocated in a ratio whose terms are fractions, the terms need to be converted into equivalent fractions with the same denominators. The numerators of these fractions may then be used as the ratio by which the amount will be allocated.

STEP 1 Convert the fractions into equivalent fractions with the same denominators.

$\frac{1}{3} : \frac{3}{8} : \frac{5}{12}$ ⟵ lowest common denominator = 24

$= \frac{8}{24} : \frac{9}{24} : \frac{10}{24}$ ⟵ equivalent fractions with the same denominators

STEP 2 Allocate according to the ratio formed by the numerators.

The numerators form the ratio 8 : 9 : 10;
the number of parts is 8 + 9 + 10 = 27;
the value of each part is 224 640 ÷ 27 = 8320

First company's share of claim = 8320 × 8 = \$ 66 560
Second company's share of claim = 8320 × 9 = \$ 74 880
Third company's share of claim = 8320 × 10 = \$ 83 200
TOTAL \$224 640

Exercise 3.1

A. Simplify each of the following ratios.

1. Reduce to lowest terms.

(a) 12 to 32 **(b)** 84 to 56

(c) 15 to 24 to 39 **(d)** 21 to 42 to 91

2. Set up a ratio for each of the following and reduce to lowest terms.
   (a) 12 dimes to 5 quarters
   (b) 15 hours to 3 days
   (c) 6 seconds for 50 metres
   (d) \$72 per dozen
   (e) \$40 per day for 12 employees for 14 days
   (f) 2 percent per month for 24 months for \$5000

3. Use equivalent ratios in higher terms to eliminate decimals and fractions from the following ratios.
   (a) 1.25 to 4
   (b) 2.4 to 8.4
   (c) 0.6 to 2.1 to 3.3
   (d) 5.75 to 3.50 to 1.25
   (e) $\frac{1}{2}$ to $\frac{2}{5}$
   (f) $\frac{5}{3}$ to $\frac{7}{5}$
   (g) $\frac{3}{8}$ to $\frac{2}{3}$ to $\frac{3}{4}$
   (h) $\frac{2}{5}$ to $\frac{4}{7}$ to $\frac{5}{14}$
   (i) $2\frac{1}{5}$ to $4\frac{1}{8}$
   (j) $5\frac{1}{4}$ to $5\frac{5}{6}$

B. Set up a ratio for each of the following and reduce the ratio to lowest terms.

1. Deli Delight budgets food costs to account for 40 percent and beverage costs to account for 35 percent of total costs. What is the ratio of food costs to beverage costs?

2. At Bargain Upholstery, direct selling expense amounted to \$2500 while sales volume was \$87 500 for last month. What is the ratio of direct selling expense to sales volume?

3. A company employs 6 supervisors for 9 office employees and 36 production workers. What is the ratio of supervisors to office employees to production workers?

4. The cost of a unit is made up of \$4.25 direct material cost, \$2.75 direct labour cost, and \$3.25 overhead. What is the ratio that exists between the three elements of cost?

C. Solve each of the following allocation problems.

1. A dividend of \$3060 is to be distributed among three shareholders in the ratio of shares held. If the three shareholders have nine shares, two shares, and one share respectively, how much does each receive?

2. The cost of operating the Maintenance Department is to be allocated to four production departments based on the floor space each occupies. Department A occupies 1000 m^2; Department B, 600 m^2; Department C, 800 m^2; and Department D, 400 m^2. If the July cost was \$21 000, how much of the cost of operating the Maintenance Department should each production department absorb?

3. Insurance cost is to be distributed among manufacturing, selling, and administration in the ratio $\frac{5}{8}$ to $\frac{1}{3}$ to $\frac{1}{6}$. If the total insurance cost was \$9450, how should it be distributed?

4. Executive salaries are charged to three operating divisions on the basis of capital investment in the three divisions. If the investment in the Northern Division is \$10.8 million, \$8.4 million in the Eastern Division, and \$14.4 million in the Western Division, how should executive salaries of \$588 000 be allocated to the three divisions?

3.2 *Proportions*

A. *Solving proportions*

When two ratios are equal, they form a **proportion**.

$$\left.\begin{array}{r} 2:3=4:6 \\ x:5=7:35 \\ \frac{2}{3}=\frac{8}{x} \\ \frac{a}{b}=\frac{c}{d} \end{array}\right\} \longleftarrow \text{are proportions}$$

Note that each proportion consists of *four terms*. These terms form an equation whose sides are common fractions.

If one of the four terms is unknown, the proportions form a linear equation in one variable. The equation can be solved by using the operations discussed in Chapter 2.

***Example* 3.2a** Solve the proportion $2:5 = 8:x$.

Solution

$2:5 = 8:x$ ⟵ original form of proportion

$\frac{2}{5} = \frac{8}{x}$ ⟵ change the proportion into fractional form

$5x\left(\frac{2}{5}\right) = 5x\left(\frac{8}{x}\right)$ ⟵ multiply by the lowest common denominator $= 5x$

$2x = 40$

$x = 20$

Check $\text{LS} = \frac{2}{5}$, $\text{RS} = \frac{8}{20} = \frac{2}{5}$

Note: The two operations usually applied to solve proportions are multiplication and division. These operations permit the use of a simplified technique called **cross-multiplication** which involves

(a) the multiplication of the numerator of the ratio on the left side with the denominator of the ratio on the right side of the proportion, and

(b) the multiplication of the numerator of the ratio on the right side with the denominator of the ratio on the left side.

When cross-multiplication is used to solve Example 3.2, the value of x is obtained as follows:

$$\frac{2}{5} \times \frac{8}{x}$$

$$x(2) = 5(8) \longleftarrow \text{cross multiply}$$

$$2x = 40$$

$$x = 20$$

***Example* 3.2b** Solve each of the following proportions.

(i) $x : 5 = 7 : 35 \longleftarrow$ original proportion

$$\frac{x}{5} = \frac{7}{35} \longleftarrow \text{in fractional form}$$

$$35(x) = 5(7) \longleftarrow \text{cross multiply}$$

$$35x = 35$$

$$x = 1$$

(ii) $2\frac{1}{2} : x = 5\frac{1}{2} : 38\frac{1}{2}$

$$2.5 : x = 5.5 : 38.5$$

$$\frac{2.5}{x} = \frac{5.5}{38.5}$$

$$38.5(2.5) = x(5.5)$$

$$96.25 = 5.5x$$

$$x = \frac{96.25}{5.5}$$

$$x = 17.5$$

$$x = 17\frac{1}{2}$$

(iii) $\frac{5}{6} : \frac{14}{3} = x : \frac{21}{10}$

$$\frac{\frac{5}{6}}{\frac{14}{3}} = \frac{\frac{x}{1}}{\frac{21}{10}} \longleftarrow \text{set up in fractional form}$$

$$\left(\frac{5}{6}\right)\left(\frac{21}{10}\right) = \left(\frac{x}{1}\right)\left(\frac{14}{3}\right) \longleftarrow \text{cross multiply}$$

$$\frac{105}{60} = \frac{14x}{3}$$
$$(14x)(60) = (105)(3)$$
$$840x = 315$$
$$x = 0.375$$

B. Problems involving proportions

Many problems contain information that permits two ratios to be set up. These ratios are in proportion, but one term of one ratio is unknown. In such cases, a letter symbol for the unknown term is used to complete the proportion statement.

To assure that the proportion is set up correctly, use the following procedure.

STEP 1 Use a complete sentence to *introduce* the *letter* symbol that you will use to represent the missing term.

STEP 2 Set up the *known ratio* on the *left* side of the proportion. Be sure to retain the units or a description of the quantities in the ratio.

STEP 3 Set up the ratio using the *letter symbol* on the *right* side of the proportion. Make certain that the unit or description of the numerator in the ratio on the right side corresponds to the unit or description of the numerator in the ratio on the left side.

Example 3.2c Solve each of the following problems involving a proportion.

(i) If five kilograms of sugar cost \$9.20, what is the cost of two kilograms of sugar?

Solution

STEP 1 Introduce the variable.
Let the cost of two kilograms of sugar be \$$x$.

STEP 2 Set up the known ratio retaining the units.
5 kg : \$9.20

STEP 3 Set up the ratio involving the variable.
2 kg : \$$x$

Hence, $$\frac{5\text{ kg}}{\$9.20} = \frac{2\text{ kg}}{\$x}$$ ⟵ make certain the units in the numerators correspond

$$\frac{5}{9.20} = \frac{2}{x}$$
$$x(5) = 9.20(2)$$
$$x = \frac{18.40}{5}$$
$$x = 3.68$$

Two kilograms of sugar cost \$3.68.

(ii) If your car can travel 385 km on 35 L of gasoline, how far can it travel on 24 L?

Solution

Let the distance travelled on 24 L be n km;
then the known ratio is 385 km : 35 L;
the second ratio is n km : 24 L.

$$\frac{385 \text{ km}}{35 \text{ L}} = \frac{n \text{ km}}{24 \text{ L}}$$

$$\frac{385}{35} = \frac{n}{24}$$

$$n = \frac{385 \times 24}{35}$$

$$n = 264$$

The car can travel 264 km on 24 L.

(iii) Past experience shows that a process requires \$17.50 worth of material for every \$12.00 spent on labour. How much should be budgeted for material if the budget for labour is \$17 760?

Solution

Let the material budget be \$$k$.

The known ratio is $\frac{\$17.50 \text{ material}}{\$12.00 \text{ labour}}$;

the second ratio is $\frac{\$k \text{ material}}{\$17\ 760 \text{ labour}}$.

$$\frac{\$17.50 \text{ material}}{\$12.00 \text{ labour}} = \frac{\$k \text{ material}}{\$17\ 760 \text{ labour}}$$

$$\frac{17.50}{12.00} = \frac{k}{17\ 760}$$

$$k = \frac{17.50 \times 17\ 760}{12.00}$$

$$k = 25\ 900$$

The material budget should be \$25 900.

***Example* 3.2d** Two contractors agreed to share revenue from a job in the ratio 2 : 3. Contractor A, who received the smaller amount, made a profit of \$480 on the job. If contractor A's profit compared to revenue is in the ratio 3 : 8, determine

(i) contractor A's revenue;

(ii) the total revenue of the job.

Solution

(i) Let $\$x$ represent contractor A's revenue.

$$\text{Then } \frac{\text{A's profit}}{\text{A's revenue}} = \frac{3}{8} \longleftarrow \text{known ratio}$$

$$\text{and } \frac{\text{A's profit}}{\text{A's revenue}} = \frac{\$480}{\$x} \longleftarrow \text{second ratio}$$

$$\frac{3}{8} = \frac{480}{x}$$

$$3x = 480 \times 8$$

$$x = \frac{480 \times 8}{3}$$

$$x = 160 \times 8$$

$$x = 1280$$

Contractor A's revenue from the job is \$1280.

(ii) Let $\$y$ represent contractor B's revenue.

$$\text{Then } \frac{\text{A's revenue}}{\text{B's revenue}} = \frac{2}{3} \longleftarrow \text{known ratio}$$

$$\text{and } \frac{\text{A's revenue}}{\text{B's revenue}} = \frac{\$1280}{\$y} \longleftarrow \text{second ratio}$$

$$\frac{2}{3} = \frac{1280}{y}$$

$$2y = 1280 \times 3$$

$$y = \frac{1280 \times 3}{2}$$

$$y = 1920$$

$$x + y = 1280 + 1920 = 3200$$

Total revenue on the job is \$3200.

Alternatively

Let total revenue be $\$z$.

$$\text{Then } \frac{\text{A's revenue}}{\text{Total revenue}} = \frac{2}{5} = \frac{\$1280}{\$z}$$

$$\frac{2}{5} = \frac{1280}{z}$$

$$2z = 1280 \times 5$$

$$z = 3200$$

Exercise 3.2

A. Find the unknown term in the following proportions.

1. $3 : n = 15 : 20$
2. $n : 7 = 24 : 42$
3. $3 : 8 = 21 : x$
4. $7 : 5 = x : 45$
5. $1.32 : 1.11 = 8.8 : k$
6. $2.17 : 1.61 = k : 4.6$
7. $m : 3.4 = 2.04 : 2.89$
8. $3.15 : m = 1.4 : 1.8$
9. $t : \frac{3}{4} = \frac{7}{8} : \frac{15}{16}$
10. $\frac{3}{4} : t = \frac{5}{8} : \frac{4}{9}$
11. $\frac{9}{8} : \frac{3}{5} = t : \frac{8}{15}$
12. $\frac{16}{7} : \frac{4}{9} = \frac{15}{14} : t$

B. Use proportions to solve each of the following problems.

1. Le Point Bookbindery pays a dividend of $1.25 per share every three months. How many months would it take to earn dividends amounting to $8.75 per share?
2. The community of Oakcrest sets a property tax rate of $28 per $1000 assessed valuation. What is the assessment if a tax of $854 is paid on a property?
3. A car requires nine litres of gasoline for 72 km. At the same rate of gasoline consumption, how far can the car travel if the gas tank holds 75 litres?
4. A manufacturing process requires $85 supervision cost for every 64 labour hours. At the same rate, how much supervision cost should be budgeted for 16 000 labour hours?
5. Suhami Chadhuri has a two-fifths interest in a partnership. She sold five-sixths of her interest for $3000.
   (a) What was the total amount of Ms. Chadhuri's interest before selling?
   (b) What is the value of the partnership?
6. Five-eighths of Jesse Black's inventory was destroyed by fire. He sold the remaining part, which was slightly damaged, for one-third of its value and received $1300.
   (a) What was the value of the destroyed part of the inventory?
   (b) What was the value of the inventory before the fire?
7. Last year, net profits of Herd Inc. were two-sevenths of revenue. If the company declared a dividend of $12 800 and five-ninths of the net profit was retained in the company, what was last year's revenue?
8. Material cost of a fan belt is five-eighths of total cost and labour cost is one-third of material cost. If labour cost is $15, what is the total cost of the article?

3.3 *Percent*

A. *The meaning of percent*

The easiest method of comparing quantities is to use ratios in which the *second* term is the number 100, that is, fractions with denominator 100. The preferred form of writing such ratios is the **percent** form.

PERCENT means HUNDREDTHS	⟶	% means $\overline{100}$

When dealing with percents, *four* different forms are interchangeable.

(i) the *percent* form
(ii) a *ratio* with second term 100
(iii) a *common fraction* with denominator 100
(iv) a *decimal* fraction

For example, 'seven percent' may be written

(i) in percent form	7%
(ii) in ratio form	7 : 100
(iii) as a common fraction	$\frac{7}{100}$
(iv) as a decimal	0.07

Conversely, any fraction involving "hundredths" may be written in the same four forms:

(i) as a decimal	0.13
(ii) as a common fraction	$\frac{13}{100}$
(iii) in ratio form	13 : 100
(iv) in percent form	13%

B. *Changing percents to common fractions*

When computing with percents, use the corresponding common fraction or decimal fraction. To convert a percent into a common fraction, replace the symbol % by the symbol $\frac{}{100}$. Then reduce the resulting fraction to lowest terms.

Example 3.3a

(i) $24\% = \frac{24}{100}$ ⟵ replace % by $\frac{}{100}$

$= \frac{6}{25}$ ⟵ reduce to lowest terms

(ii) $175\% = \frac{175}{100} = \frac{7 \times 25}{4 \times 25} = \frac{7}{4}$

(iii) $6.25\% = \frac{6.25}{100}$

$= \frac{625}{10\,000}$ ⟵ multiply by 100 to change the numerator to a whole number

$= \frac{125}{2000} = \frac{25}{400} = \frac{5}{80}$ ⟵ reduce gradually or in one step

$= \frac{1}{16}$

(iv) $0.8\% = \frac{0.8}{100} = \frac{8}{1000} = \frac{1}{125}$

(v) $0.025\% = \frac{0.025}{100} = \frac{25}{100\,000} = \frac{1}{4000}$

(vi) $\frac{1}{4}\% = \frac{\frac{1}{4}}{\frac{100}{1}}$ ⟵ replace % by $\frac{\quad}{\frac{100}{1}}$

$= \frac{1}{4} \times \frac{1}{100}$ ⟵ invert and multiply

$= \frac{1}{400}$

(vii) $\frac{3}{8}\% = \frac{\frac{3}{8}}{\frac{100}{1}} = \frac{3}{8} \times \frac{1}{100} = \frac{3}{800}$

(viii) $33\frac{1}{3}\% = \frac{33\frac{1}{3}}{100}$ ⟵ replace % by $\frac{\quad}{100}$

$= \frac{\frac{100}{3}}{\frac{100}{1}}$ ⟵ convert the mixed number $33\frac{1}{3}$ into a common fraction

$= \frac{100}{3} \times \frac{1}{100}$

$= \frac{1}{3}$

(ix) $216\frac{2}{3}\% = \frac{216\frac{2}{3}}{100} = \frac{\frac{650}{3}}{\frac{100}{1}} = \frac{\overset{13}{\cancel{650}}}{3} \times \frac{1}{\underset{2}{\cancel{100}}} = \frac{13}{6}$

Alternatively

$$216\frac{2}{3}\% = 200\% + 16\frac{2}{3}\%$$ ⟵ separate the multiple of 100% (that is, 200%) from the reminder

$$= 2 + \frac{\frac{50}{3}}{\frac{100}{1}}$$

$$= 2 + \frac{50}{3} \times \frac{1}{100}$$

$$= 2 + \frac{1}{6}$$

$$= \frac{13}{6}$$

C. Changing percents to decimals

Replacing the symbol % by $\frac{}{100}$ indicates a division by 100. Since division by 100 is performed by moving the decimal point *two places to the left*, changing a percent to a decimal is easy to do. Simply drop the symbol % and move the decimal point two places to the left.

Example 3.3b

(i) 52% = 0.52 ⟵ drop the percent symbol and move the decimal point two places to the left

(ii) 175% = 1.75

(iii) 6% = 0.06

(iv) 0.75% = 0.0075

(v) $\frac{1}{4}\% = 0.25\%$ ⟵ first change the fraction to a decimal

$= 0.0025$ ⟵ drop the % symbol and move the decimal point two place to the left

(vi) $\frac{3}{8}\% = 0.375\%$

$= 0.00375$

(vii) $\frac{2}{3}\% = 0.66\frac{2}{3}\%$ ⟵ change the fraction to a mixed decimal with at least two decimal positions

$= 0.0066\frac{2}{3}$ ⟵ drop the percent symbol and move the decimal two places to the left

(viii) $\frac{5}{8}\% = 0.625\%$

$= 0.00625$

D. *Changing decimals to percents*

Changing decimals to percents is the inverse operation of changing percents into decimals. It is accomplished by multiplying the decimal by 100%. Since multiplication by 100 is performed by moving the decimal point *two places to the right*, a decimal is easily changed to a percent. Move the decimal point two places to the right and add the % symbol.

Example 3.3c

(i) $0.36 = 0.36(100\%)$
$= 36\%$ ⟵ move the decimal point two places to the right and add the % symbol

(ii) $1.65 = 165\%$

(iii) $0.075 = 7.5\%$

(iv) $0.4 = 40\%$

(v) $0.001 = 0.1\%$

(vi) $2 = 200\%$

(vii) $0.0005 = 0.05\%$

(viii) $0.33\frac{1}{3} = 33\frac{1}{3}\%$

(ix) $1.16\frac{2}{3} = 116\frac{2}{3}\%$

(x) $1\frac{5}{6} = 1.83\frac{1}{3} = 183\frac{1}{3}\%$

E. *Changing fractions to percents*

When changing a fraction to a percent, it is best to convert the fraction to a decimal and then to change the decimal to a percent.

Example 3.3d

(i) $\frac{1}{4} = 0.25 \longleftarrow$ convert the fraction to a decimal
$= 25\% \longleftarrow$ convert the decimal to a percent

(ii) $\frac{7}{8} = 0.875 = 87.5\%$

(iii) $\frac{9}{5} = 1.8 = 180\%$

(iv) $\frac{5}{6} = 0.83\frac{1}{3} = 83\frac{1}{3}\%$

(v) $\frac{5}{9} = 0.55\frac{5}{9} = 55\frac{5}{9}\%$

(vi) $1\frac{2}{3} = 1.66\frac{2}{3} = 166\frac{2}{3}\%$

Exercise 3.3

A. Change each of the following percents into a decimal.

1. 64%
2. 300%
3. 2.5%
4. 0.1%
5. 0.5%
6. 85%
7. 250%
8. 4.8%
9. 450%
10. 7.5%
11. 0.9%
12. 95%
13. 6.25%
14. 0.4%
15. 99%
16. 225%
17. 0.05%
18. $8\frac{1}{4}\%$
19. $\frac{1}{2}\%$
20. $112\frac{1}{2}\%$
21. $9\frac{3}{8}\%$
22. 0.75%
23. $162\frac{1}{2}\%$
24. $\frac{2}{5}\%$
25. $\frac{1}{4}\%$
26. $187\frac{1}{2}\%$
27. $1\frac{3}{4}\%$
28. 0.025%
29. $137\frac{1}{2}\%$
30. $\frac{5}{8}\%$
31. 0.875%
32. $2\frac{1}{4}\%$
33. $33\frac{1}{3}\%$
34. $166\frac{2}{3}\%$
35. $16\frac{2}{3}\%$
36. $116\frac{2}{3}\%$
37. $183\frac{1}{3}\%$
38. $83\frac{1}{3}\%$
39. $133\frac{1}{3}\%$
40. $66\frac{2}{3}\%$

B. Change each of the following percents into a common fraction in lowest terms.

1. 25%	2. $62\frac{1}{2}\%$	3. 175%	4. 5%
5. $37\frac{1}{2}\%$	6. 75%	7. 4%	8. 225%
9. 8%	10. 125%	11. 40%	12. $87\frac{1}{2}\%$
13. 250%	14. 2%	15. $12\frac{1}{2}\%$	16. 60%
17. 2.25%	18. 0.5%	19. $\frac{1}{8}\%$	20. $33\frac{1}{3}\%$
21. $\frac{3}{4}\%$	22. $66\frac{2}{3}\%$	23. 6.25%	24. 0.25%
25. $16\frac{2}{3}\%$	26. 7.5%	27. 0.75%	28. $\frac{7}{8}\%$
29. 0.1%	30. $\frac{3}{5}\%$	31. $83\frac{1}{3}\%$	32. 2.5%
33. $133\frac{1}{3}\%$	34. $183\frac{1}{3}\%$	35. $166\frac{2}{3}\%$	36. $116\frac{2}{3}\%$

C. Express each of the following as a percent.

1. 3.5	2. 0.075	3. 0.005	4. 0.375
5. 0.025	6. 2	7. 0.125	8. 0.001
9. 0.225	10. 0.008	11. 1.45	12. 0.0225
13. 0.0025	14. 0.995	15. 0.09	16. 3
17. $\frac{3}{4}$	18. $\frac{3}{25}$	19. $\frac{5}{3}$	20. $\frac{7}{200}$
21. $\frac{9}{200}$	22. $\frac{5}{8}$	23. $\frac{3}{400}$	24. $\frac{5}{6}$
25. $\frac{9}{800}$	26. $\frac{7}{6}$	27. $\frac{3}{8}$	28. $\frac{11}{40}$
29. $\frac{4}{3}$	30. $\frac{9}{400}$	31. $\frac{13}{20}$	32. $\frac{4}{5}$

3.4 *The basic percentage problem*

A. *Computing percentages*

To find percentages, multiply a number by a percent.

$$50\% \text{ of } 60 = 0.50 \times 60 = 30$$

Note: 50% is called the *rate*;
60 is called the *base* or *original number*;
30 is called the *percentage* or *new number*.

PERCENTAGE = RATE × BASE	← *Formula 3.1*

or

NEW NUMBER = RATE × ORIGINAL NUMBER

To determine a percentage of a given number, change the percent to a decimal fraction or a common fraction and then multiply by the given number.

Example **3.4a**

(i) $80\% \text{ of } 400 = 0.80 \times 400$ ← convert the percent into a decimal and multiply
$= 320$

(ii) $5\% \text{ of } 1200 = 0.05 \times 1200 = 60$

(iii) $240\% \text{ of } 15 = 2.40 \times 15 = 36$

(iv) $1.8\% \text{ of } \$600 = 0.018 \times 600 = \$10.80$

(v) $33\frac{1}{3}\% \text{ of } \$45.60 = \frac{1}{3} \times 45.60 = \$15.20$

(vi) $0.25\% \text{ of } \$8000 = 0.0025 \times 8000 = \$20$

(vii) $\frac{3}{8}\% \text{ of } \$1800 = 0.375\% \text{ of } \$1800 = 0.00375 \times 1800 = \$6.75$

B. *Computation with commonly used percents*

Many of the more commonly used percents can be converted into fractions. These are easy to use when computing manually. The most important such percents and their fractional equivalents are listed in Table 3.1.

TABLE 3.1 ***Commonly used percents and their fractional equivalents***

(i)	*(ii)*	*(iii)*	*(iv)*	*(v)*
$25\% = \frac{1}{4}$	$16\frac{2}{3}\% = \frac{1}{6}$	$12\frac{1}{2}\% = \frac{1}{8}$	$20\% = \frac{1}{5}$	$8\frac{1}{3}\% = \frac{1}{12}$
$50\% = \frac{1}{2}$	$33\frac{1}{3}\% = \frac{1}{3}$	$37\frac{1}{2}\% = \frac{3}{8}$	$40\% = \frac{2}{5}$	$6\frac{2}{3}\% = \frac{1}{15}$
$75\% = \frac{3}{4}$	$66\frac{2}{3}\% = \frac{2}{3}$	$62\frac{1}{2}\% = \frac{5}{8}$	$60\% = \frac{3}{5}$	$6\frac{1}{4}\% = \frac{1}{16}$
	$83\frac{1}{3}\% = \frac{5}{6}$	$87\frac{1}{2}\% = \frac{7}{8}$	$80\% = \frac{4}{5}$	

Example 3.4b

(i) 25% of $32 = \frac{1}{4} \times 32 = 8$

(ii) $33\frac{1}{3}\%$ of $150 = \frac{1}{3} \times 150 = 50$

(iii) $87\frac{1}{2}\%$ of $96 = \frac{7}{8} \times 96 = 7 \times 12 = 84$

(iv) $83\frac{1}{3}\%$ of $48 = \frac{5}{6} \times 48 = 5 \times 8 = 40$

(v) $116\frac{2}{3}\%$ of $240 = \left(100\% + 16\frac{2}{3}\%\right)$ of 240

$$= \left(1 + \frac{1}{6}\right)(240)$$
$$= \frac{7}{6} \times 240$$
$$= 7 \times 40$$
$$= 280$$

(vi) 275% of $64 = \left(2 + \frac{3}{4}\right)(64)$

$$= \frac{11}{4} \times 64$$
$$= 11 \times 16$$
$$= 176$$

C. Using the 1% method

Percentages can be computed by determining 1% of the given number and then figuring the value of the given percent. While this method can be used to compute any percentage, it is particularly useful when dealing with *small* percents.

***Example* 3.4c** Use the 1% method to determine each of the following percentages.

(i) 3% of \$1800

Solution 1% of \$1800 = \$18
3% of \$1800 = 3 × 18 = \$54

(ii) $\frac{1}{2}$% of \$960

Solution 1% of \$960 = \$9.60
$\frac{1}{2}$% of \$960 = $\frac{1}{2} \times 9.60$ = \$4.80

(iii) $\frac{5}{8}$% of \$4440

Solution 1% of \$4440 = \$44.40
$\frac{1}{8}$% of \$4440 = $\frac{1}{8} \times 44.40$ = \$5.55
$\frac{5}{8}$% of \$4440 = 5 × 5.55 = \$27.75

(iv) $2\frac{1}{4}$% of \$36 500

Solution

1% of \$36 500	= \$365.00	
2% of \$36 500	= 2 × 365.00 =	\$730.00
$\frac{1}{4}$% of \$36 500	= $\frac{1}{4}$ × 365.00 =	91.25
$2\frac{1}{4}$% of 36 500	⟶	\$821.25

D. Finding a rate percent

Finding a rate means *comparing* two numbers. This comparison involves a **ratio** which is usually written in the form of a common fraction. When the common fraction is converted to a percent, a rate percent results.

When setting up the ratio, the base (or original number) is always the denominator of the fraction, and the percentage (or new number) is always the numerator.

$$\text{RATE} = \frac{\text{PERCENTAGE}}{\text{BASE}} \text{ or } \frac{\text{NEW NUMBER}}{\text{ORIGINAL NUMBER}}$$ ⟵ ***Formula 3.2***

The problem statement indicating that a rate percent is to be found is usually of the form

"What percent of x is y?" or
"y is what percent of x?"

This means that y is to be compared to x and requires the setting up of the ratio $y : x$ or the fraction $\frac{y}{x}$. x is the base (or original number) while y is the percentage (or new number).

Example **3.4d** Answer each of the following questions.

(i) What percent of 15 is 6?

Solution Rate $= \frac{6}{15}$ ← 6: percentage (or new number); 15: base (or original number)

$= 0.40$

$= 40\%$

(ii) 90 is what percent of 72?

Solution Rate $= \frac{90}{72}$ ← 72: original number

$= 1.25$

$= 125\%$

(iii) \$9.90 is what percent of \$550?

Solution Rate $= \frac{9.90}{550} = 0.018 = 1.8\%$

(iv) What percent of \$112.50 is \$292.50?

Solution Rate $= \frac{292.50}{112.50} = 2.60 = 260\%$

E. *Finding the base*

A great number of business problems involve the relationship from Formula 3.1,

PERCENTAGE = BASE × RATE (or NEW NUMBER = RATE × ORIGINAL NUMBER)

Since three variables are involved, three different problems may be solved using this relationship:

(a) finding the percentage (see Sections A, B, and C)

(b) finding the rate percent (see Section D)

(c) finding the base

Of the three, the problem of finding the rate is the most easily recognized. However, confusion often arises in deciding whether the percentage or the base needs to be found. In such cases it is useful to represent the unknown value by a variable and set up an equation.

Example **3.4e** Solve each of the following problems by setting up an equation.

(i) What number is 25% of 84?

Solution

Introduce a variable for the unknown value and write the statement in equation form.

What number is 25% of 84

⇓ ⇓ ⇓ ⇓

$x = 25\%$ of 84

$x = \frac{1}{4} \times 84$ ⟵ change the percent to a fraction or a decimal

$x = 21$

The number is 21.

(ii) 60% of what number is 42?

Solution 60% of what number is 42

⇓ ⇓ ⇓ ⇓

60% of $x = 42$

$0.6x = 42$

$x = \frac{42}{0.6}$

$x = 70$

The number is 70.

(iii) How much is $16\frac{2}{3}\%$ of \$144?

Solution $x = 16\frac{2}{3}\%$ of 144

$x = \frac{1}{6} \times 144$

$x = 24$

The amount is \$24.

(iv) \$160 is 250% of what amount?

Solution

$$160 = 250\% \text{ of } x$$
$$160 = 2.5x$$
$$x = \frac{160}{2.5}$$
$$x = 64$$

The amount is \$64.

F. Applications

Example 3.4f Solve each of the following problems.

(i) Variable cost on monthly sales of \$48 600 amounted to \$30 375. What is the variable cost rate based on sales volume?

Solution

$$\text{Rate} = \frac{\text{Variable Cost}}{\text{Sales Volume}} \longleftarrow \text{base for the comparison}$$
$$= \frac{30\ 375}{48\ 600}$$
$$= 0.625$$
$$= 62.5\%$$

The variable cost is 62.5% of sales volume.

(ii) What is the annual dividend on a preferred share paying 11.5% on a par value of \$20?

Solution

Let the annual dividend be \$$x$.
Since the annual dividend is 11.5% of \$20,

$$x = 11.5\% \text{ of } 20$$
$$x = 0.115 \times 20$$
$$x = 2.30$$

The annual dividend is \$2.30.

(iii) What was the amount of October sales if November sales of \$14 352 were 115% of October sales?

Solution

Let October sales be represented by \$$x$.
Since November sales equal 115% of October sales,

$$14\,352 = 115\% \text{ of } x$$
$$14\,352 = 1.15x$$
$$x = \frac{14\,352}{1.15}$$
$$x = 12\,480$$

October sales amounted to \$12 480.

(iv) The 7% goods and services tax charged on the regular selling price of a typewriter amounted to \$93.80. What was the total cost of the typewriter?

Solution

Let the regular selling price be \$$x$.
Since the sales tax is 7% of the regular selling price,

$$93.80 = 7\% \text{ of } x$$
$$93.80 = 0.07x$$
$$x = \frac{93.80}{0.07}$$
$$x = 1340$$

The regular selling price is	\$1340.00
Add 7% of \$1340	93.80
TOTAL COST	\$1433.80

Exercise 3.4

A. Compute each of the following.

1. 40% of 90

2. 0.1% of 950

3. 250% of 120

4. 7% of 800

5. 3% of 600

6. 15% of 240

7. 0.5% of 1200

8. 300% of 80

9. 0.02% of 2500

10. $\frac{1}{2}$% of 500

11. $\frac{1}{4}$% of 800

12. 0.05% of 9000

13. 0.075% of 10 000

14. $\frac{7}{8}$% of 3600

15. 2.5% of 700

16. 0.025% of 40 000

B. Use fractional equivalents to compute each of the following.

1. $33\frac{1}{3}\%$ of \$48
2. $137\frac{1}{2}\%$ of \$400
3. $162\frac{1}{2}\%$ of \$1200
4. $66\frac{2}{3}\%$ of \$72
5. $37\frac{1}{2}\%$ of \$24
6. 175% of \$1600
7. 125% of \$160
8. $12\frac{1}{2}\%$ of \$168
9. $83\frac{1}{3}\%$ of \$720
10. $166\frac{2}{3}\%$ of \$90
11. $116\frac{2}{3}\%$ of \$42
12. $16\frac{2}{3}\%$ of \$54
13. 75% of \$180
14. $183\frac{1}{3}\%$ of \$24
15. $133\frac{1}{3}\%$ of \$45
16. 25% of \$440

C. Use the 1% method to compute each of the following.

1. $\frac{1}{2}\%$ of \$3120
2. $\frac{3}{4}\%$ of \$2140
3. $\frac{3}{8}\%$ of \$432
4. $\frac{4}{5}\%$ of \$1120
5. $1\frac{1}{3}\%$ of \$3630
6. $1\frac{1}{2}\%$ of \$782
7. $2\frac{3}{8}\%$ of \$944
8. $2\frac{3}{4}\%$ of \$1632

D. Solve each of the following equations.

1. $x + 40\%$ of $x = 28$
2. $x - 20\%$ of $x = 240$
3. $x - 5\%$ of $x = 418$
4. $x + 7\%$ of $x = 214$
5. $x + 16\frac{2}{3}\%$ of $x = 42$
6. $x - 33\frac{1}{3}\%$ of $x = 54$
7. $x + 150\%$ of $x = 75$
8. $x + 200\%$ of $x = 36$

E. Find the rate percent for each of the following.

1. original amount 60; new amount 36
2. original amount 72; new amount 54
3. base \$800; percentage \$920

4. base \$140; percentage \$490
5. new amount \$6; original amount \$120
6. new amount \$11; original amount \$440
7. percentage \$132; base \$22
8. percentage \$30; base \$45
9. new amount \$150; base \$90
10. percentage \$39; original amount \$18

F. Answer each of the following questions.

1. \$60 is 30% of what amount?
2. \$36 is what percent of \$15?
3. What is 0.1% of \$3600?
4. 150% of what amount is \$270?
5. $\frac{1}{2}$% of \$612 is what amount?
6. 250% of what amount is \$300?
7. 80 is 40% of what amount?
8. \$120 is what percent of \$60?
9. What is $\frac{1}{8}$% of \$880?
10. \$180 is what percent of \$450?
11. \$600 is 250% of what amount?
12. 25% of what amount is \$28?
13. What percent of \$70 is \$350?
14. \$90 is 30% of what amount?
15. 350% of what amount is \$1050?
16. What is $\frac{1}{5}$% of \$1200?

G. Answer each of the following questions.

1. The price of a carpet was reduced by 40%. If the original price was \$70, what was the amount by which the price was reduced?

2. Labour content in an article is $37\frac{1}{2}\%$ of total cost. How much is the labour cost if the total cost is \$72?
3. If waste is normally 6% of the material used in a production process, how much of \$25 000 worth of material will be wasted?
4. If total deductions on a yearly salary of \$18 600 amounted to $16\frac{2}{3}\%$, how much was deducted?
5. If the actual sales of \$40 500 for last month were 90% of the budgeted sales, how much was the sales budget for the month?
6. The Canada Pension Plan premium deducted from an employee's wages was \$5.94. If the premium rate is 2.2% of gross wages, how much were the employee's gross wages?
7. A town's current population is 54 000. If this is 120% of the population five years ago, what was the town's population then?
8. A property was sold for 300% of what the vendors originally paid. If the vendors sold the property for \$180 000, how much did they originally pay for the property?

3.5 *Problems involving increase or decrease*

A. *Percent change*

Problems involving a *change* (an increase or a decrease) are identifiable by such phrases as

"is 20% *more than*," "is 40% *less than*,"
"is *increased by* 150%," "is *decreased by* 30%."

The amount of change is to be added for an increase to or subtracted for a decrease from the *original number* (*base*) and is usually stated as a percent of the original number.

The existing relationship may be stated as

$$\text{ORIGINAL NUMBER} \begin{array}{c} + \text{ INCREASE} \\ - \text{ DECREASE} \end{array} = \text{NEW NUMBER} \quad \longleftarrow \textit{Formula 3.3}$$

where the change (the increase or decrease) is understood to be a *percent of the original number.*

Example **3.5a** Answer each of the following questions.

(i) 36 increased by 25% is what number?

Solution

The original number is 36; ⟵ in such problems the change is a percent of the original number
the change (increase) is 25% of 36. ⟵
Since the original number is known,
let x represent the new number.

$$36 + 25\% \text{ of } 36 = x$$
$$36 + \frac{1}{4} \times 36 = x$$
$$36 + 9 = x$$
$$x = 45$$

The number is 45.

(ii) What number is 40% less than 75?

Solution

The change (decrease) is 40% of 75.
The original number is 75.
Let x represent the new number.

$$75 - 40\% \text{ of } 75 = x$$
$$75 - 0.40 \times 75 = x$$
$$75 - 30 = x$$
$$x = 45$$

The number is 45.

(iii) How much is \$160 increased by 250%?

Solution

The increase is 250% of \$160 and
the original number is \$160.
Let the new amount be \$$x$.

$$160 + 250\% \text{ of } 160 = x$$
$$160 + 2.50 \times 160 = x$$
$$160 + 400 = x$$
$$x = 560$$

The amount is \$560.

B. Finding the rate of increase or decrease

This type of problem is indicated by such phrases as

(a) "20 is what percent *more than* 15?", or

(b) "What percent *less than* 96 is 72?"

In (a), the increase, which is the difference between 15, the original number, and 20, the number after the increase, is to be compared to the original number, 15.

$$\text{The rate of increase} = \tfrac{5}{15} = \tfrac{1}{3} = 33\tfrac{1}{3}\%$$

In (b), the decrease, which is the difference between 96, the number before the decrease (the original number), and 72, the number after the decrease, is to be expressed as a percent of the original number.

$$\text{The rate of decrease} = \tfrac{24}{96} = \tfrac{1}{4} = 25\%$$

In more generalized form, the problem statement is:

$$\text{``}y \text{ is what percent} \begin{Bmatrix}\text{more}\\ \text{less}\end{Bmatrix} \text{than } x\text{?''}$$

This means the difference between x, the number before the change (the original number), and y, the number after the change, is to be expressed as a percent of the original number.

$$\boxed{\text{RATE OF CHANGE} = \frac{\text{AMOUNT OF CHANGE}}{\text{ORIGINAL NUMBER}}} \longleftarrow \textit{Formula 3.4}$$

***Example* 3.5b** Answer each of the following questions.

(i) \$425 is what percent more than \$125?

Solution

The amount before the change (the original number) is \$125.
The change (increase) = 425 − 125 = \$300.

$$\begin{aligned}\text{The rate of increase} &= \frac{\text{amount of increase}}{\text{original amount}}\\ &= \frac{300}{125} = 2.40 = 240\%\end{aligned}$$

(ii) What percent less than \$210 is \$175?

Solution

The amount before the decrease is \$210.
The decrease is $210 - 175 = \$35$.

$$\text{The rate of decrease} = \frac{35}{210} = \frac{1}{6} = 0.16\frac{2}{3} = 16\frac{2}{3}\%$$

C. *Finding the original amount*

If the quantity *after* the change has taken place is known, the quantity *before* the change (the original quantity) may be found by using the relationship stated in Formula 3.3.

Example **3.5c** Answer each of the following questions.

(i) 88 is 60% more than what number?

Solution
88 is the number after the increase;
the number before the increase is unknown.
Let the original number be x;
then the increase is 60% of x.

$$x + 60\% \text{ of } x = 88 \longleftarrow \text{using Formula 3.3}$$
$$x + 0.6x = 88$$
$$1.6x = 88$$
$$x = \frac{88}{1.6}$$
$$x = 55$$

The original number is 55.

(ii) 75 is 40% less than what number?

Solution

75 is the number after the decrease.
Let the original number be x;
then the decrease is 40% of x.

$$x - 40\% \text{ of } x = 75$$
$$x - 0.4x = 75$$
$$0.6x = 75$$
$$x = \frac{75}{0.6}$$
$$x = 125$$

The original number is 125.

(iii) What sum of money increased by 175% amounts to \$143?

Solution

\$143 is the amount after the increase.
Let the original sum of money be \$$x$;
then the increase is 175% of x.

$$x + 175\% \text{ of } x = 143$$
$$x + 1.75x = 143$$
$$2.75x = 143$$
$$x = \frac{143}{2.75}$$
$$x = 52$$

The original amount is \$52.

(iv) What sum of money when diminished by $33\frac{1}{3}\%$ is \$48?

Solution

\$48 is the amount after the decrease.
Let the original sum of money be \$$x$;
then the decrease is $33\frac{1}{3}\%$ of x.

$$x - 33\frac{1}{3}\% \text{ of } x = 48$$
$$x - \frac{1}{3}x = 48 \text{ or } x - 0.3333333x = 48$$
$$\frac{2}{3}x = 48 \text{ or } 0.6666667x = 48$$
$$x = \frac{48 \times 3}{2} \text{ or } x = \frac{48}{0.6666667}$$
$$x = 72$$

The original sum of money is \$72.

Exercise 3.5

A. Answer each of the following questions.

1. What is 120 increased by 40%?
2. What is 900 decreased by 20%?
3. How much is \$1200 decreased by 5%?
4. How much is \$24 increased by 200%?
5. What number is $83\frac{1}{3}\%$ more than 48?
6. What amount is $16\frac{2}{3}\%$ less than \$66?

B. Find the rate of change for each of the following.

1. What percent more than 30 is 45?
2. What percent less than \$90 is \$72?
3. The amount of \$240 is what percent more than \$80?
4. The amount of \$110 is what percent less than \$165?
5. What percent less than \$300 is \$294?
6. The amount of \$2025 is what percent more than \$2000?

C. Answer each of the following questions.

1. The number 24 is 25% less than what number?
2. The number 605 is $37\frac{1}{2}$% more than what number?
3. What amount increased by 150% will equal \$325?
4. What sum of money decreased by $16\frac{2}{3}$% will equal \$800?
5. After deducting 5% from a sum of money, the remainder is \$4.18. What was the original sum of money?
6. After an increase of 7%, the new amount was \$749. What was the original amount?

3.6 *Applications*

A. *Summary of useful relationships*

Problems involving percents abound in the field of business. The terminology used varies depending on the situation. However, most problems can be solved by means of the two basic relationships.

$$\boxed{\text{RATE} \times \text{ORIGINAL AMOUNT} = \text{NEW AMOUNT}} \longleftarrow \textit{Formula 3.1}$$

and

$$\boxed{\text{ORIGINAL AMOUNT} \begin{array}{c} + \text{ INCREASE} \\ - \text{ DECREASE} \end{array} = \text{NEW AMOUNT}} \longleftarrow \textit{Formula 3.3}$$

or, in the case of finding a rate percent, by means of the formulae

$$\boxed{\text{RATE} = \frac{\text{NEW AMOUNT}}{\text{ORIGINAL AMOUNT}}} \longleftarrow \textit{Formula 3.2}$$

and

$$\text{RATE OF CHANGE} = \frac{\text{AMOUNT OF CHANGE}}{\text{ORIGINAL AMOUNT}} \quad \longleftarrow \textit{Formula 3.4}$$

B. Problems involving the computation of a rate percent

Example **3.6a** Solve each of the following problems.

(i) Material content in a lighting fixture is $40. If the total cost of the fixture is $48, what percent of cost is the material cost?

Solution $$\frac{\text{MATERIAL COST}}{\text{TOTAL COST}} = \frac{40}{48} = \frac{5}{6} = 83\frac{1}{3}\%$$

(ii) A cash discount of $3.60 was allowed on an invoice of $120.00. What was the rate of discount?

Solution The rate of discount $= \dfrac{\text{AMOUNT OF DISCOUNT}}{\text{INVOICE AMOUNT}}$

$$= \frac{3.60}{120.00} = \frac{360}{12\,000} = \frac{3}{100} = 3\%$$

(iii) What percent increase did Nirel Walker receive if her bi-weekly salary rose from $800 to $920?

Solution

Salary before the increase (original salary) is $800;
the raise is 920 − 800 = $120.

$$\text{The rate of increase} = \frac{\text{AMOUNT OF INCREASE}}{\text{ORIGINAL SALARY}}$$

$$= \frac{120}{800} = 0.15 = 15\%$$

(iv) Expenditures for a government program were reduced from $75 000 to $60 000. What percent change does this represent?

Solution

Expenditure before the change is $75 000;
the change (decrease) = 75 000 − 60 000 = $15 000.

$$\text{The rate of change} = \frac{\text{AMOUNT OF CHANGE}}{\text{ORIGINAL AMOUNT}}$$

$$= \frac{15\,000}{75\,000} = 0.20 = 20\%$$

Expenditures were reduced by 20%.

C. Problems involving the basic percentage relationship

Example **3.6b** Solve each of the following problems.

(i) An electronic calculator marked \$39.95 in a bookstore is subject to 7% GST (goods and services tax) and 8% PST (provincial sales tax). What will it cost you to buy the calculator?

Solution

The cash price = marked price + GST + PST
= 39.95 + 7% of 39.95 + 8% of 39.95
= 39.95 + 0.07(39.95) + 0.08(39.95)
= 39.95 + 2.80 + 3.20
= 45.95

The calculator will cost you \$45.95.

(ii) Sales for this year are budgeted at $112\frac{1}{2}\%$ of last year's sales of \$360 000. What is the sales budget for this year?

Solution

This year's sales = $112\frac{1}{2}\%$ of 360 000
= 1.125 × 360 000
= 405 000

Budgeted sales for the year are \$405 000.

(iii) A commission of \$300 was paid to a broker's agent for the sale of a bond. If the commission was $\frac{3}{4}\%$ of the sales value of the bond, how much was the bond sold for?

Solution

The commission paid = $\frac{3}{4}\%$ of the bond sale

$$300 = \frac{3}{4}\% \text{ of } x$$

$$300 = 0.75\% \text{ of } x$$

$$300 = 0.0075x$$

$$x = 40\,000$$

The bond was sold for \$40 000.

(iv) Based on past experience, Simcoe District Credit Union estimates uncollectible loans at $1\frac{1}{4}\%$ of the total loan balances outstanding. If, at the end of March, the loans account shows a balance of \$3 248 000, how much should the credit union have in reserve for uncollectible loans at the end of March?

Solution

The provision for uncollectible loans $= 1\frac{1}{4}\%$ of 3 248 000

1% of 3 248 000 ⟶	$32 480
$\frac{1}{4}$ of 1% of 3 248 000 ⟶	8 120
$1\frac{1}{4}\%$ of 3 248 000 ⟶	$40 600

The credit union should have a reserve of $40 600 for uncollectible loans by the end of March.

(v) The consumer price index in July of this year was 225 or 180% of the index ten years ago. What was the index ten years ago?

Solution

This year's index = 180% of the index ten years ago

$$225 = 180\% \text{ of } x$$

$$225 = 1.80x$$

$$x = \frac{225}{1.8}$$

$$x = 125$$

The index ten years ago was 125.

D. Problems of increase or decrease

Example **3.6c** Solve each of the following problems.

(i) Daily car loadings for August were 5% more than for July. If August car loadings were 76 020, what were the July car loadings?

Solution

Because July is earlier than August, its car loadings are the original number and are not known. Let them be represented by x.

$$x + 5\% \text{ of } x = 76\,020$$

$$x + 0.05x = 76\,020$$

$$1.05x = 76\,020$$

$$x = \frac{76\,020}{1.05}$$

$$x = 72\,400$$

Car loadings in July numbered 72 400.

(ii) The trading price of shares of Northern Gold Mines dropped 40% to $7.20. Determine the trading price before the drop.

Solution

The trading price before the drop is the original value and is not known. Let it be \$$x$.

$$x - 40\% \text{ of } x = 7.20$$
$$x - 0.4x = 7.20$$
$$0.6x = 7.20$$
$$x = \frac{7.20}{0.6}$$
$$x = 12.00$$

The trading price before the drop was \$12.00.

(iii) Dorian Guy sold his house for \$149 500. If he sold the house for $187\frac{1}{2}\%$ more than what he paid for it, how much did he gain?

Solution

The base for the percent gain is the original amount paid for the house. Since this amount is not known, let it be \$$x$.

ORIGINAL AMOUNT PAID + GAIN = SELLING PRICE

$$x + 187\tfrac{1}{2}\% \text{ of } x = 149\ 500$$
$$x + 1.875x = 149\ 500$$
$$2.875x = 149\ 500$$
$$x = \frac{149\ 500}{2.875}$$
$$x = 52\ 000$$

The amount originally paid was \$52 000.
Gain = 149 500 − 52 000 = \$97 500.

(iv) The amount paid for an article, including 7% goods and services tax, was \$100.58. How much was the marked price of the article?

Solution

The unknown marked price, represented by \$$x$, is the base for the sales tax.

MARKED PRICE + GST = AMOUNT PAID

$$x + 7\% \text{ of } x = 100.58$$
$$x + 0.07x = 100.58$$
$$1.07x = 100.58$$
$$x = \frac{100.58}{1.07}$$
$$x = 94.00$$

The market price of the article was \$94.00.

(v) After taking off a discount of 5%, a retailer settled an invoice by paying \$532.00. How much was the amount of the discount?

Solution

The unknown amount of the invoice, represented by $\$x$, is the base for the discount.

$$\text{AMOUNT OF INVOICE} - \text{DISCOUNT} = \text{AMOUNT PAID}$$

$$x - 5\% \text{ of } x = 532$$

$$x - 0.05x = 532$$

$$0.95x = 532$$

$$x = 560$$

$$\text{Discount} = 5\% \text{ of } 560 = 0.05 \times 560 = \$28.00.$$

Exercise 3.6

A. Solve each of the following problems.

1. Of Purolator's 1200 employees, $2\frac{1}{4}\%$ did not report to work last Friday. How many employees were absent?

2. A storekeeper bought merchandise for \$1575. If she sells the merchandise at $33\frac{1}{3}\%$ above cost, how much gross profit does she make?

3. A clerk whose salary was \$280 per week was given a raise of \$35 per week. What percent increase did the clerk receive?

4. Your hydro bill for March is \$174.40. If you pay after the due date, a late payment penalty of \$8.72 is added. What is the percent penalty?

5. A sale representative receives a commission of $16\frac{2}{3}\%$ on all sales. How much must his weekly sales be so that he will make a commission of \$720 per week?

6. HRH Collection Agency retains a collection fee of 25% of any amounts collected. How much did the agency collect on a bad debt if the agency forwarded \$2490 to a client?

7. A commercial building is insured under a fire policy that has a face value of 80% of the building's appraised value. The annual insurance premium is $\frac{3}{8}\%$ on the face value of the policy and the premium for one year amounts to \$675.

   (a) What is the face value of the policy?

   (b) What is the appraised value of the building?

8. A residential property is assessed for tax purposes at 40% of its market value. The residential property tax rate is $3\frac{1}{3}\%$ of the assessed value and the tax is \$1200.

   (a) What is the assessed value of the property?

   (b) What is the market value of the property?

B. Solve each of the following problems.

1. A merchant bought an article for $7.92. How much did the article sell for if he sold it at an increase of $83\frac{1}{3}\%$?
2. A retail outlet is offered a discount of $2\frac{1}{2}\%$ for payment in cash of an invoice of $840. If it accepted the offer, how much was the cash payment?
3. A ski shop reduced its selling price on a pair of skis by $33\frac{1}{3}\%$. If the regular selling price was $225, what was the reduced price?
4. From March 1984 to March 1994, the price of gasoline increased 110%. If the price in 1984 was 33.0 cents per litre, what was the price per litre in 1994?
5. The 7% goods and services tax on a pair of shoes amounted to $5.18. What was the total cost of the shoes?
6. Ms. Daisy pays $37\frac{1}{2}\%$ of her monthly gross salary as rent on a townhouse. If the monthly rent is $600, what is her monthly salary?
7. The annual interest on a bond is $12\frac{1}{2}\%$ of its face value and amounts to $625. What is the face value of the bond?
8. A brokerage house charges a fee of $2\frac{1}{4}\%$. If its fee on a stock purchase was $432, what was the amount of the purchase?
9. Profit last quarter decreased from $6540 in the previous quarter to $1090. What was the percent decrease in profit?
10. A wage earner's hourly rate of pay was increased from $9.60 to $10.32. What was the percent raise?
11. A property bought for $42 000 is now appraised at $178 500. What is the percent gain in the value of the property?
12. The Bank of Montreal reduced its annual lending rate from 10% to 9.75%. What is the percent reduction in the lending rate?
13. After a reduction of $33\frac{1}{3}\%$ of the marked price, a fan was sold for $64.46. What was the marked price?
14. A special purpose index has increased 125% during the last ten years. If the index is now 279, what was the index ten years ago?
15. After a cash discount of 5%, an invoice was settled by a payment of $646. What was the invoice amount?
16. Sales in May increased $16\frac{2}{3}\%$ over April sales. If May sales amounted to $24 535, what were April sales?
17. The working capital at the end of the third quarter was 75% higher than at the end of the second quarter. What was the amount of working capital at the end of the second quarter if the working capital at the end of the third quarter was $78 400?

18. After real estate fees of 8% had been deducted from the proceeds of a property sale, the vendor of the property received \$88 090. What was the amount of the realtor's fee?

19. Employee compensation expense for August consisting of the gross pay plus 4% vacation pay based on gross pay was \$23 400. How much was the amount of vacation pay expense?

20. A car was sold for \$9452.80 including 7% GST and 5% PST. How much was the sales tax on the car?

Review exercise

1. Set up ratios to compare each of the following sets of quantities. Reduce each ratio to its lowest terms.

(a) twenty-five dimes and three dollars

(b) five hours to 50 min

(c) \$6.75 for thirty litres of gasoline

(d) \$21 for three-and-a-half hours

(e) 1440 words for 120 lines for 6 pages

(f) 90 kg for 24 ha (hectares) for 18 weeks

2. Solve each of the following proportions.

(a) $5 : n = 35 : 21$ **(b)** $10 : 6 = 30 : x$

(c) $1.15 : 0.85 = k : 1.19$ **(d)** $3.60 : m = 10.8 : 8.10$

(e) $\frac{5}{7} : \frac{15}{14} = \frac{6}{5} : t$ **(f)** $y : \frac{9}{8} = \frac{5}{4} : \frac{45}{64}$

3. Change each of the following percents into a decimal.

(a) 185% **(b)** 7.5% **(c)** 0.4% **(d)** 0.025%

(e) $1\frac{1}{4}\%$ **(f)** $\frac{3}{4}\%$ **(g)** $162\frac{1}{2}\%$ **(h)** $11\frac{3}{4}\%$

(i) $8\frac{1}{3}\%$ **(j)** $83\frac{1}{3}\%$ **(k)** $266\frac{2}{3}\%$ **(l)** $10\frac{3}{8}\%$

4. Change each of the following percents into a common fraction in lowest terms.

(a) 50% **(b)** $37\frac{1}{2}\%$ **(c)** $16\frac{2}{3}\%$ **(d)** $166\frac{2}{3}\%$

(e) $\frac{1}{2}\%$ **(f)** 7.5% **(g)** 0.75% **(h)** $\frac{5}{8}\%$

5. Express each of the following as a percent.

(a) 2.25 **(b)** 0.02 **(c)** 0.009 **(d)** 0.1275

(e) $\frac{5}{4}$ **(f)** $\frac{11}{8}$ **(g)** $\frac{5}{200}$ **(h)** $\frac{7}{25}$

6. Compute each of the following

   (a) 150% of 140 **(b)** 3% of 240

   (c) $9\frac{3}{4}$% of 2000 **(d)** 0.9% of 400

7. Use fractional equivalents to compute each of the following.

   (a) $66\frac{2}{3}$% of \$168 **(b)** $37\frac{1}{2}$% of \$2480

   (c) 125% of \$924 **(d)** $183\frac{1}{3}$% of \$720

8. Use the 1% method to determine each of the following.

   (a) $\frac{1}{4}$% of \$2664 **(b)** $\frac{5}{8}$% of \$1328

   (c) $1\frac{2}{3}$% of \$5400 **(d)** $2\frac{1}{5}$% of \$1260

9. Answer each of the following questions.

   (a) What is the rate percent if the base is 88 and the percentage is 55?

   (b) 63 is what percent of 36?

   (c) What is $\frac{3}{4}$% of \$64.00?

   (d) 450% of \$5.00 is what amount?

   (e) \$245 is $87\frac{1}{2}$% of what amount?

   (f) $2\frac{1}{4}$% of what amount is \$9.90?

   (g) What percent of \$62.50 is \$1.25?

   (h) \$30 is what percent of \$6?

   (i) $166\frac{2}{3}$% of what amount is \$220?

   (j) \$1.35 is $\frac{1}{3}$% of what amount?

10. Answer each of the following questions.

    (a) How much is \$8 increased by 125%?

    (b) What amount is $2\frac{1}{4}$% less than \$2000?

    (c) What percent less than \$120 is \$100?

    (d) \$975 is what percent more than \$150?

    (e) \$98 is 75% more than what amount?

    (f) After a reduction of 15%, the amount paid for a CD player was \$289. What was the price before the reduction?

    (g) What sum of money increased by 250% will amount to \$490?

11. D, E, and F own a business jointly and share profits and losses in the same proportion as their investments. How much of a profit of \$4500 will each receive if their investments are \$4000, \$6000, and \$5000 respectively?

12. Departments A, B, and C occupy floor space of 80 m², 140 m², and 160 m² respectively. If the total rental cost for the floor space is $11 400 per month, how much of the rental cost should each department pay?

13. Four beneficiaries are to divide an estate of $189 000 in the ratio $\frac{1}{3} : \frac{1}{4} : \frac{3}{8} : \frac{1}{24}$. How much should each receive?

14. Three insurance companies have insured a building in the ratio $\frac{1}{2}$ to $\frac{1}{3}$ to $\frac{2}{5}$. How much of a fire loss of $185 000 should each company pay?

15. A hot water tank with a capacity of 220 L can be heated in twenty minutes. At the same rate, how many minutes will it take to heat a tank containing 176 L?

16. If the variable cost amounts to $130 000 when sales are $250 000, what will variable cost be when sales are $350 000?

17. Gross profit for April was two-fifths of net sales, and net income was two-sevenths of gross profit. Net income was $4200.

    (a) What was the gross profit for April?

    (b) What were net sales for April?

18. In a college, $\frac{4}{9}$ of all employees are faculty and the ratio of the faculty to support staff is 5 : 4. How many people does the college employ if the support staff numbers 192?

19. In the last municipal election, $62\frac{1}{2}\%$ of the population of 94 800 was eligible to vote. Of those eligible, $33\frac{1}{3}\%$ voted.

    (a) What was the number of eligible voters?

    (b) How many voted?

20. An investment portfolio of $150 000 consists of the following: $37\frac{1}{2}\%$ in bonds, $56\frac{1}{4}\%$ in common stock, and the remainder in preferred shares. How much money is invested in each type of investment security?

21. A sales representative's orders for May were $16\frac{2}{3}\%$ less than her April orders which amounted to $51 120.

    (a) How much were the sales rep's orders in May?

    (b) By what amount did her orders decrease?

22. The value of a property has increased $233\frac{1}{3}\%$ since it was bought by the present owner. The cost of the property was $120 000.

    (a) How much is the current appraised value?

    (b) How much would the owner gain by selling at the appraised value?

23. The direct material cost of manufacturing a product is $103.95, direct labour cost is $46.20, and overhead is $57.75.

    (a) What is the percent content of each element of cost in the product?

    (b) What is the overhead percent rate based on direct labour?

24. Inspection of a production run of 2400 items showed that 180 items did not meet specifications. Of the 180 that did not pass inspection, 150 could be reworked. The remainder had to be scrapped.

    (a) What percent of the production run did not pass inspection?

    (b) What percent of the items that did not meet specifications had to be scrapped?

25. The price of a stock a week ago was \$56.25 per share. Today the price per share is \$51.75.

    (a) What is the percent change in price?

    (b) What is the new price as a percent of the old price?

26. A wage earner's hourly rate of pay increased from \$6.30 to \$16.80 during the last decade.

    (a) What has been the percent change in the hourly rate of pay?

    (b) What is the current rate of pay as a percent of the rate a decade ago?

27. A firm's bad debts of \$7875 were $2\frac{1}{4}\%$ of sales. What were the firm's sales?

28. A ski shop lists ski boots at 240% of cost. If the ski shop prices the DX2 Model at \$396.00, what was the cost of the ski boot to the dealer?

29. A property owner listed his property for 160% more than he paid for it. The owner eventually accepted an offer $12\frac{1}{2}\%$ below his asking price and sold the property for \$191 100. How much did the owner pay for the property?

30. A marina listed a yacht at $33\frac{1}{3}\%$ above cost. At the end of the season, the list price was reduced by 22.5% and the yacht was sold for \$15 500. What was the cost of the yacht to the marina?

31. A & E Holdings' profit and loss statement showed a net income of $9\frac{3}{4}\%$ or \$29 250. Twenty percent of net income was paid in corporation tax and 75% of the net income after tax was paid out as dividend to Alice and Emile who hold shares in the ratio 5 to 3.

    (a) What was the revenue of A & E Holdings?

    (b) How much was the after-tax income?

    (c) How much was paid out in dividend?

    (d) What percent of net income did Alice receive as dividend?

32. A farm was offered for sale at 350% above cost. The farm was finally sold for \$330 000 at $8\frac{1}{3}\%$ below the asking price.

    (a) What was the original cost of the farm to the owner?

    (b) How much gain did the owner realize?

    (c) What percent of the original cost does this gain represent?

Self-test

1. Compute each of the following.
   (a) 125% of \$280
   (b) $\frac{3}{8}$% of \$20 280
   (c) $83\frac{1}{3}$% of \$174
   (d) $1\frac{1}{4}$% of \$1056
2. Solve each of the following proportions.
   (a) $65 : 39 = x : 12$
   (b) $\frac{7}{6} : \frac{35}{12} = \frac{6}{5} : x$
3. Change each of the following percents into a decimal.
   (a) 175%
   (b) $\frac{3}{8}$%
4. Change each of the following percents into a common fraction in lowest terms.
   (a) $2\frac{1}{2}$%
   (b) $116\frac{2}{3}$%
5. Express each of the following as a percent.
   (a) 1.125
   (b) $\frac{9}{400}$
6. The results of a market survey indicate that 24 respondents prefer Brand X, 36 prefer Brand Y, and 20 had no preference. What percent of the sample preferred Brand Y?
7. Departments, A, B, and C occupy floor space of 40, 80 and 300 m² respectively. If the total rental for the space is \$25 200 per month, how much rent should Department B pay?
8. Past experience shows that the clientele of a restaurant spends \$9.60 on beverages for every \$12.00 spent on food. If it is expected that food sales will amount to \$12 500 for a month, how much should be budgeted for beverage sales?
9. After a reduction of $16\frac{2}{3}$% of the marked price, a pair of boots sold for \$60.00. What was the marked price?
10. A bonus is to be divided among four employees in the ratio $\frac{1}{2} : \frac{1}{3} : \frac{1}{5} : \frac{1}{6}$. What is each employee's share of a bonus of \$40 500?

11. Alanna Fawcett's hourly rate of pay was increased from $11.00 to $12.54. What was the percent raise?
12. A bicycle was sold for $282.50. The selling price included 7% GST and 6% PST. Find the amount of GST on the bike.
13. A microwave oven originally advertised at $220.00 is reduced to $209.00 during a sale. By what percent was the price reduced?
14. A special consumer index has increased 100% during the last 10 years. If the index is now 360, what was it 10 years ago?
15. Mr. Braid owned $\frac{3}{8}$ of a store. He sold $\frac{2}{3}$ of his interest in the store for $18 000. What was the value of the store?

Summary of formulae used

Formula 3.1

$$\text{PERCENTAGE} = \text{RATE} \times \text{BASE}$$

or

$$\text{NEW NUMBER} = \text{RATE} \times \text{ORIGINAL NUMBER}$$

The basic percentage relationship

Formula 3.2

$$\text{RATE} = \frac{\text{PERCENTAGE}}{\text{BASE}} \text{ or } \frac{\text{NEW NUMBER}}{\text{ORIGINAL NUMBER}}$$

Formula for finding the rate percent when comparing a number (the percentage) to another number (the base or original number)

Formula 3.3

$$\text{ORIGINAL NUMBER} \begin{matrix} + \text{ INCREASE} \\ - \text{ DECREASE} \end{matrix} = \text{NEW NUMBER}$$

The relationship to use with problems of increase or decrease (problems of change)

Formula 3.4

$$\text{RATE OF CHANGE} = \frac{\text{AMOUNT OF CHANGE}}{\text{ORIGINAL NUMBER}}$$

Formula for finding the rate of change (rate of increase or decrease)

Glossary of terms used

Cross-multiplication a short cut for solving proportions

Equivalent ratios in higher terms ratios obtained by multiplying each term of a ratio by the same number

Percent a way of writing a ratio whose second term is 100; a common fraction whose denominator is 100

Proportion a statement of equality between two ratios

Ratio a comparison by division of the relative values of numbers or quantities

Terms of a ratio the numbers appearing in a ratio

4 *Linear systems*

Introduction

In many types of problems, the relationship between two or more variables can be represented by setting up linear equations or linear inequalities. Graphic as well as algebraic techniques are available to solve such problems.

Objectives

Upon completing this chapter, you will be able to

1. graph linear equations in two variables in a set of rectangular coordinates;
2. graph linear inequalities in two variables in a set of rectangular coordinates;
3. graph linear systems consisting of two or three linear relations in two variables;
4. solve linear systems consisting of two simultaneous equations in two variables using the method of elimination by addition or subtraction;
5. solve linear systems consisting of three simultaneous equations in three variables using the method of elimination by addition or subtraction;
6. solve problems by setting up systems of linear equations in two or three variables.

4.1 *Graphing linear equations*

A. Graphing in a system of rectangular coordinates

A system of rectangular coordinates, as shown in Figure 4.1 below, consists of two straight lines that intersect at right angles in a plane. The *horizontal* line is called the **X axis** while the *vertical* line is called the **Y axis**. The point of intersection of the two axes is called the **origin**.

FIGURE 4.1 ***Rectangular coordinates***

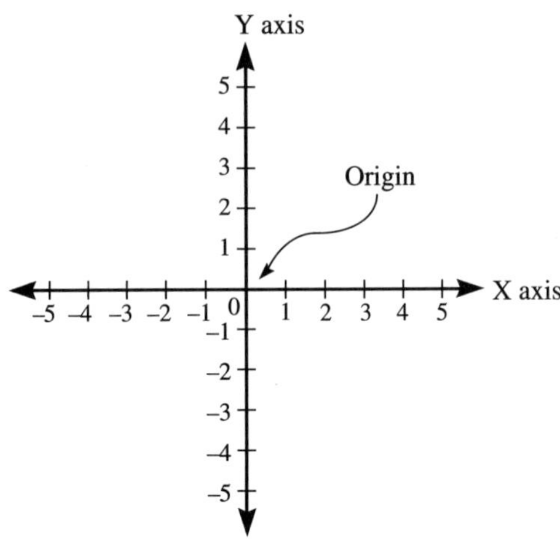

The two axes are used as number lines. By agreement, on the X axis the numbers are positive to the right of the origin and negative to the left. On the Y axis the numbers are positive above the origin and negative below the origin.

The position of any point relative to the pair of axes is defined by an *ordered pair* of numbers (x,y) such that the first number (the x value or **X coordinate**) always represents the directed distance of the point from the Y axis. The second number (the y value or **Y coordinate**) always represents the directed distance of the point from the X axis.

The origin is identified by the ordered pair (0,0); that is, the coordinates of the origin are (0,0) since the distance of the point from either axis is zero.

As shown in Figure 4.2 below, the point marked A is identified by the coordinates (4,3). That is, the directed distance of the point is four units to the right of the Y axis (its x value or X coordinate is +4), and the directed distance of the point is three units above the X axis (its Y coordinate is +3). Note that the point may be found by counting four units to the right along the X axis and then moving three units up parallel to the Y axis.

FIGURE 4.2 ***Locating a point***

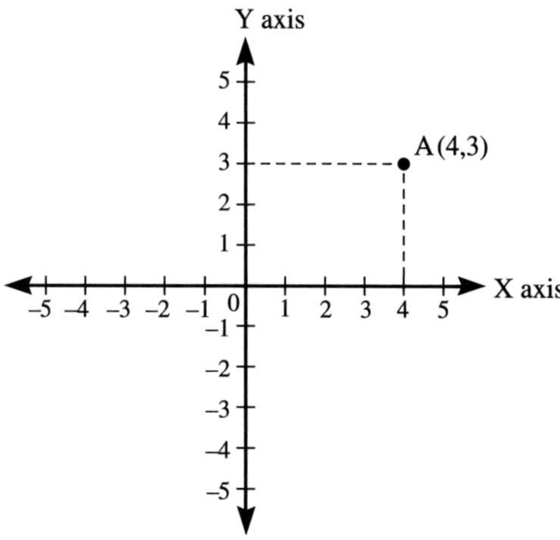

Example 4.1a Determine the coordinates of the points A, B, C, D, E, F, G, and H as marked in the following diagram.

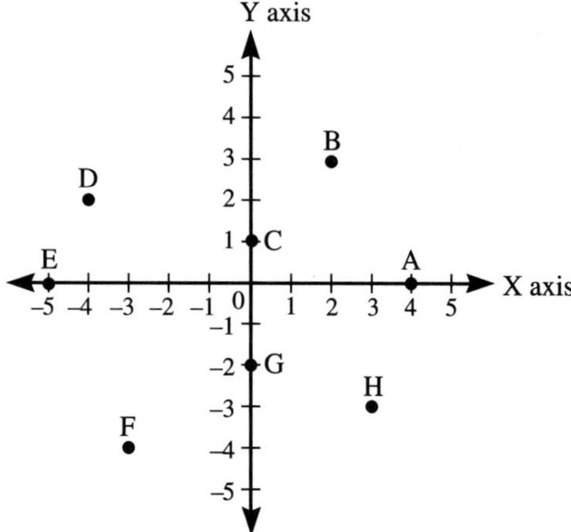

Solution

POINT	COORDINATES	
A	(4, 0) ⟵	4 units to the right of the origin ($x = 4$) on the X axis ($y = 0$)
B	(2, 3) ⟵	2 units to the right ($x = 2$) and 3 units up ($y = 3$)
C	(0, 1) ⟵	on the Y axis ($x = 0$) 1 unit up ($y = 1$)
D	(−4, 2) ⟵	4 units to the left ($x = -4$) and 2 units up ($y = 2$)
E	(−5, 0) ⟵	5 units to the left ($x = -5$) on the X axis ($y = 0$)
F	(−3, −4) ⟵	3 units to the left ($x = -3$) and 4 units down ($y = -4$)
G	(0, −2) ⟵	on the Y axis ($x = 0$) 2 units down ($y = -2$)
H	(3, −3) ⟵	3 units to the right ($x = 3$) and 3 units down ($y = -3$)

To draw the graphs of linear relations, you must plot two or more points in a set of rectangular axes. To *plot* Point (x,y), count the number of units represented by x along the X axis (to the right if x is positive, to the left if x is negative) and then count the number of units represented by y up or down (up if y is positive, down if y is negative).

Example **4.1b** Plot the following points in a set of rectangular axes.

(i) A(−3, 4) (ii) B(2, −4)

(iii) C(−4, −4) (iv) D(3, 3)

(v) E(−3, 0) (vi) F(0, −2)

Solution

(i) To plot Point A, count 3 units to the left (x is negative) and 4 units up (y is positive).

(ii) To plot Point B, count 2 units to the right (x is positive) and 4 units down (y is negative).

(iii) To plot Point C, count 4 units to the left and 4 units down.

(iv) To plot Point D, count 3 units to the right and 3 units up.

(v) To plot Point E, count 3 units to the left and mark the point on the X axis since $y = 0$.

(vi) To plot Point F, count 2 units down and mark the point on the Y axis since $x = 0$.

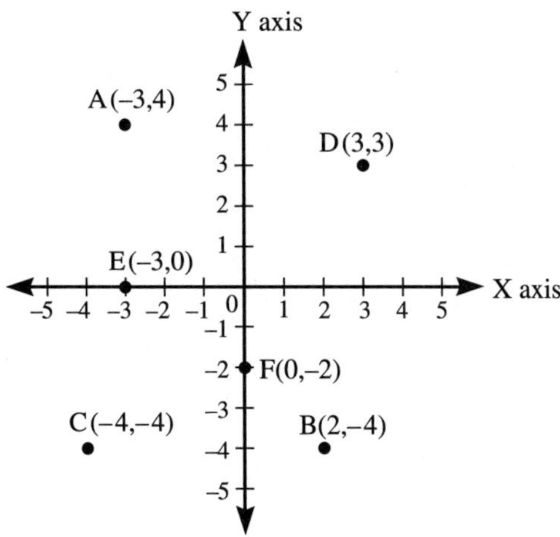

B. Constructing a table of values

To graph linear equations, plot a set of points whose coordinates *satisfy* the equation and then join the points.

A suitable set of points may be obtained by constructing a table of values. Substitute arbitrarily chosen values of x or y in the equation and compute the value of the second variable. The chosen value and the corresponding computed value form an ordered pair (x,y). A listing of such ordered pairs forms a table of values.

Example 4.1c Construct a table of values for

(i) $x = 2y$ for integral values of y from $y = +3$ to $y = -3$;

(ii) $y = 2x - 3$ for integral values of x from $x = -2$ to $x = +4$.

Solution

(i) To obtain the desired ordered pairs, substitute assumed values of y into the equation $x = 2y$.

$$y = +3 \longrightarrow x = 2(3) = 6$$
$$y = +2 \longrightarrow x = 2(2) = 4$$
$$y = +1 \longrightarrow x = 2(1) = 2$$
$$y = 0 \longrightarrow x = 2(0) = 0$$
$$y = -1 \longrightarrow x = 2(-1) = -2$$
$$y = -2 \longrightarrow x = 2(-2) = -4$$
$$y = -3 \longrightarrow x = 2(-3) = -6$$

Listing the obtained ordered pairs gives the followign table of values.

x	6	4	2	0	−2	−4	−6	⟵ corresponding computed x values
y	3	2	1	0	−1	−2	−3	⟵ chosen y values

(ii) To obtain the desired ordered pairs, substitute assumed values of x into the equation $y = 2x - 3$.

$$x = -2 \longrightarrow y = 2(-2) - 3 = -4 - 3 = -7$$
$$x = -1 \longrightarrow y = 2(-1) - 3 = -2 - 3 = -5$$
$$x = 0 \longrightarrow y = 2(0) - 3 = 0 - 3 = -3$$
$$x = 1 \longrightarrow y = 2(1) - 3 = 2 - 3 = -1$$
$$x = 2 \longrightarrow y = 2(2) - 3 = 4 - 3 = +1$$
$$x = 3 \longrightarrow y = 2(3) - 3 = 6 - 3 = +3$$
$$x = 4 \longrightarrow y = 2(4) - 3 = 8 - 3 = +5$$

Table of values

x	−2	−1	0	1	2	3	4	⟵ chosen x values
y	−7	−5	−3	−1	1	3	5	⟵ corresponding computed y values

Guidelines for constructing a table of values

1. Values may be chosen arbitrarily for either x or y.
2. The values chosen are usually integers.
3. Integers that yield an integer for the computed value are preferred.

Example **4.1d** Construct a table of values for the equation $3x - 2y = -3$. It should consist of five ordered pairs (x,y) such that x and y are integers.

Solution

(i) $y = 0$

$$3x - 2(0) = -3$$
$$3x = -3$$
$$x = -1$$

(ii) $x = 1$

$$3(1) - 2y = -3$$
$$-2y = -6$$
$$y = 3$$

(iii) $y = -3$

$$3x - 2(-3) = -3$$
$$3x = -9$$
$$x = -3$$

(iv) $x = 3$

$$3(3) - 2y = -3$$
$$-2y = -12$$
$$y = 6$$

(v) $x = -5$

$$-15 - 2y = -3$$
$$-2y = 12$$
$$y = -6$$

Table of values

x	-5	-3	-1	1	3
y	-6	-3	0	3	6

C. *Graphing linear equations*

To graph a linear equation, you need a minimum of two points. A third point is useful for checking purposes. To graph linear equations,

(1) *construct* a table of values consisting of at least two (preferably three) ordered pairs (x,y);
(2) *plot* the points in a system of rectangular axes;
(3) *join* the points by a straight line.

Example 4.1e Graph each of the following equations.

(i) $x + y = 4$

(ii) $x - y = 5$

(iii) $4x + 3y = 12$

(iv) $2x - 3y = -6$

(v) $x = y$

(vi) $y = -2x$

Solution

(i) equation: $x + y = 4$

Table of values

x	0	4	2
y	4	0	2

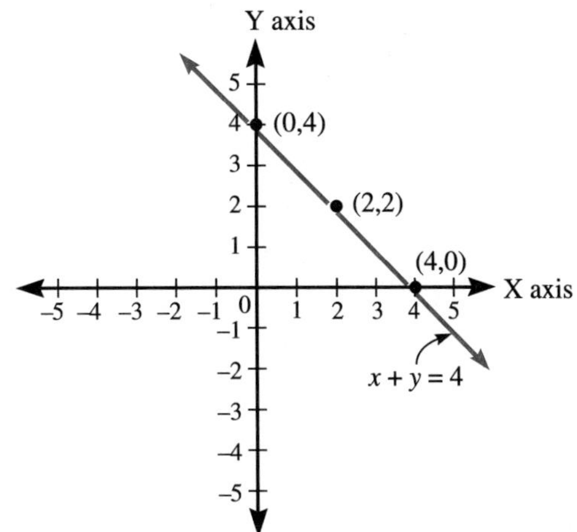

(ii) equation: $x - y = 5$

Table of values

x	0	5	3
y	−5	0	−2

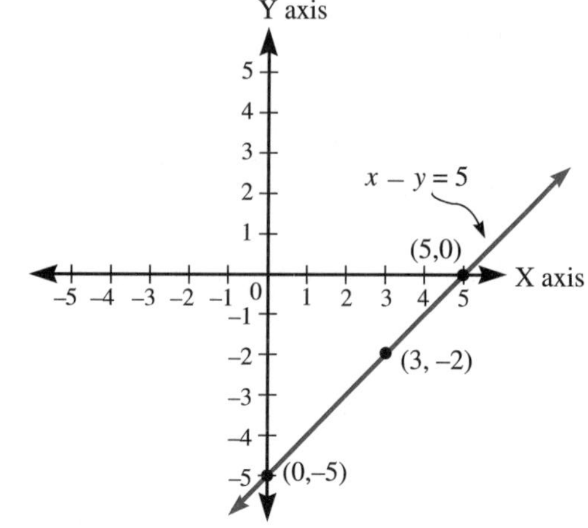

(iii) equation: $4x + 3y = 12$

Table of values

x	0	3	6
y	4	0	−4

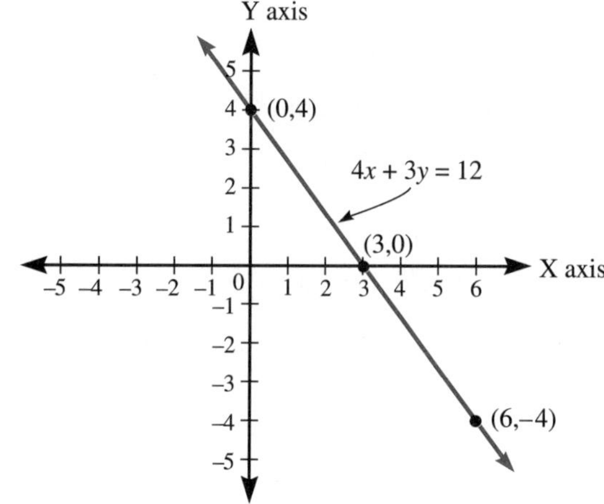

(iv) equation: $2x - 3y = -6$

Table of values

x	0	−3	3
y	2	0	4

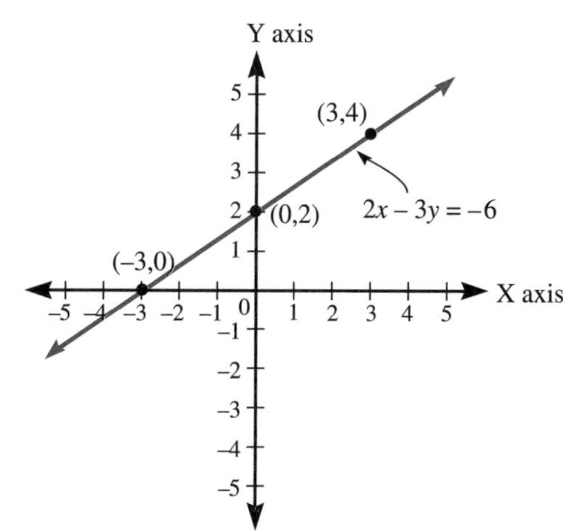

(v) equation: $x = y$

Table of values

x	0	3	-3
y	0	3	-3

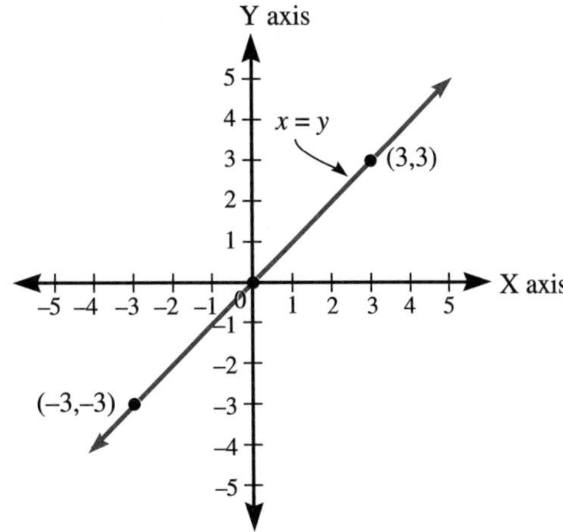

(vi) equation: $y = -2x$

Table of values

x	0	2	-2
y	0	-4	4

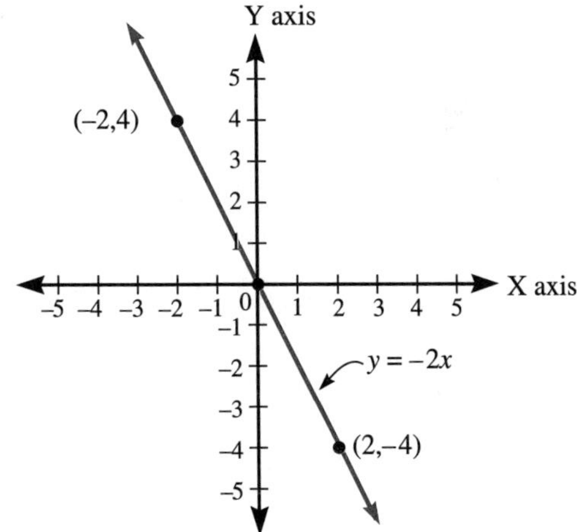

D. *Special cases—lines parallel to the axes*

(a) *Lines Parallel to the X axis*

Lines parallel to the X axis are formed by sets of points that all have the *same* y coordinates. Such lines are defined by the equation $y = k$ where k is any real number.

Example **4.1f** Graph the lines represented by

(i) $y = 3$ (ii) $y = -3$

Solution

(i) The line represented by $y = 3$ is a line parallel to the X axis and three units above it.

(ii) The line represented by $y = -3$ is a line parallel to the X axis and three units below it.

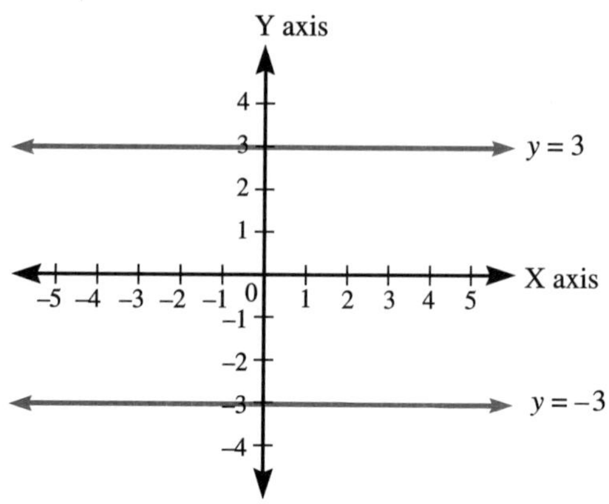

(b) *Lines Parallel to the Y axis*
Lines parallel to the Y axis are formed by sets of points that all have the *same x* coordinates. Such lines are defined by the equation $x = k$ where k is any real number.

Example 4.1g Graph the lines represented by

(i) $x = 3$ (ii) $x = -3$

Solution

(i) The line represented by $x = 3$ is a line parallel to the Y axis and three units to the right of it.

(ii) The line represented by $x = -3$ is a line parallel to the Y axis and three units to the left of it.

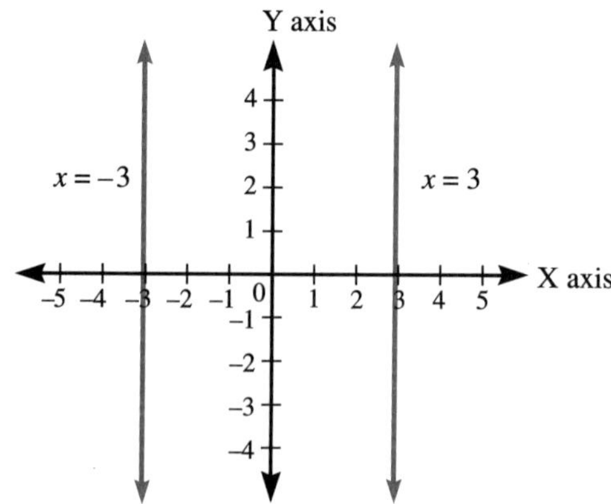

(c) *The Axes*

X axis The y coordinates of the set of points forming the X axis are zero. Thus the equation $y = 0$ represents the X axis.

Y axis The x coordinates of the set of points forming the Y axis are zero. Thus the equation $x = 0$ represents the Y axis.

Exercise 4.1

A. Do each of the following.

1. Write the coordinates of the points A, B, C, D, E, F, G, and H marked in the diagram below.

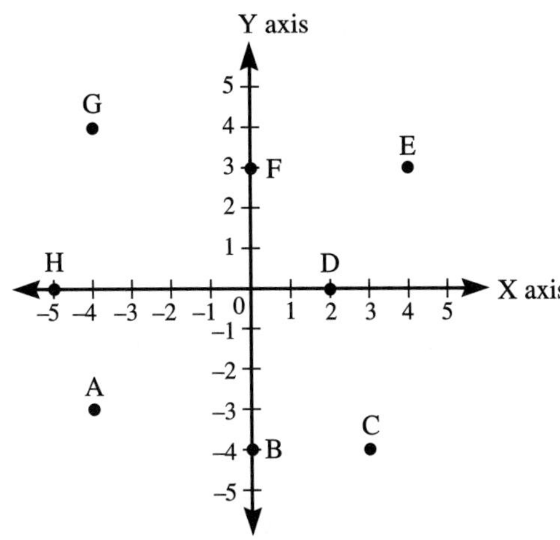

2. Plot the given sets of points in a system of rectangular axes.
   (a) A(−4,−5), B(3,−2), C(−3,5), D(0−4), E(4,1), F(−2,0)
   (b) K(4,−2), L(−3,2), M(0,4), N(−2,−4), P(0,−5), Q(−3,0)

3. Construct a table of values for each of the following equations as shown.
   (a) $x = y - 2$ for integral values of y from -3 to $+5$
   (b) $y = 2x - 1$ for integral values of x from $+3$ to -2
   (c) $y = 2x$ for integral values of x from $+3$ to -3
   (d) $x = -y$ for integral values of y from $+5$ to -5

B. Graph each of the following equations.

1. $x - y = 3$
2. $x + 2y = 4$
3. $y = -x$
4. $x = 2y$
5. $3x - 4y = 12$
6. $2x + 3y = 6$
7. $y = -4$
8. $x = 5$

4.2 Graphing inequalities

A. Basic concepts and method

A straight line drawn in a plane divides the plane into two regions:

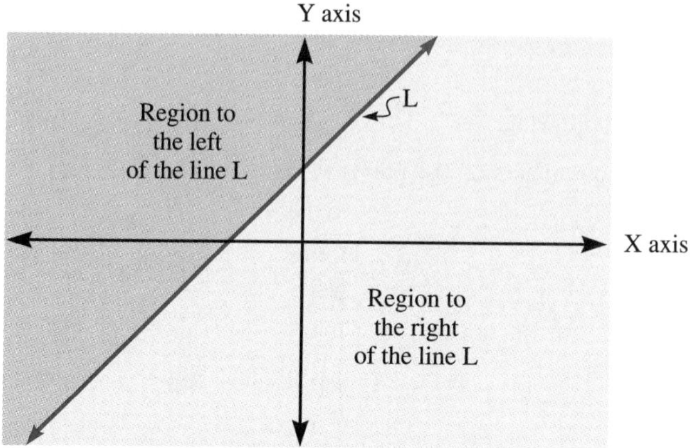

(a) the region to the left of the line drawn in the plane;

(b) the region to the right of the line drawn in the plane.

When a system of axes is introduced into the plane, each region consists of a set of points that may be represented by ordered pairs (x, y). Relative to the dividing line, the two sets of ordered pairs (x, y) that represent the points in the regions are defined by the two **inequalities** associated with the equation of the dividing line.

For the equation $x = 5$, the associated inequalities are $x < 5$ (x is less than 5) and $x > 5$ (x is greater than 5). For the equation $y = -3$, the associated inequalities are $y < -3$ and $y > -3$. For the equation $2x + 3y = 6$, the associated inequalities are $2x + 3y < 6$ and $2x + 3y > 6$.

Graphing an inequality means identifying the region that consists of the set of points whose coordinates satisfy the given inequality. To identify this region, use the following method.

1. *Draw* the graph of the equation associated with the inequality.
2. *Test* an arbitrarily selected point that is not a point on the line by substituting its coordinates in the inequality. The preferred point for testing is (0,0). If (0,0) is not available because the line passes through the origin, try the points (0,1) or (1,0).
3. **(a)** If substituting the coordinates of the selected point in the inequality yields a mathematical statement that is true, the selected point is a point in the region defined by the inequality. Thus, the region is identified as the area containing the selected point.

   (b) If substituting the coordinates of the selected point in the inequality yields a mathematical statement that is false, the selected point is not a point in the region defined by the inequality. Thus, the region defined by the inequality is the area that does not contain the point tested.

B. *Graphing inequalities of the form* ax + by > c *and* ax + by < c

Example **4.2a** Graph each of the following inequalities.

(i) $x - y > -3$ (ii) $3x + 2y < -8$

Solution

(i) The equation associated with the inequality $x - y > -3$ is $x - y = -3$.

Table of values

x	0	−3	2
y	3	0	5

Note: To show that the coordinates of the points on the line $x - y = -3$ do not satisfy the inequality, the graph of the equation is drawn as a broken line.

Since the line does not pass through the origin, the point (0,0) may be used for testing.

Substituting $x = 0$ and $y = 0$ in the inequality $x - y > -3$ yields the statement
$$0 - 0 > -3$$
$$0 > -3$$

Since the statement $0 > -3$ is true, the point (0,0) is a point in the region. The region defined by the inequality $x - y > -3$ is the area to the right of the line as shown in the diagram below.

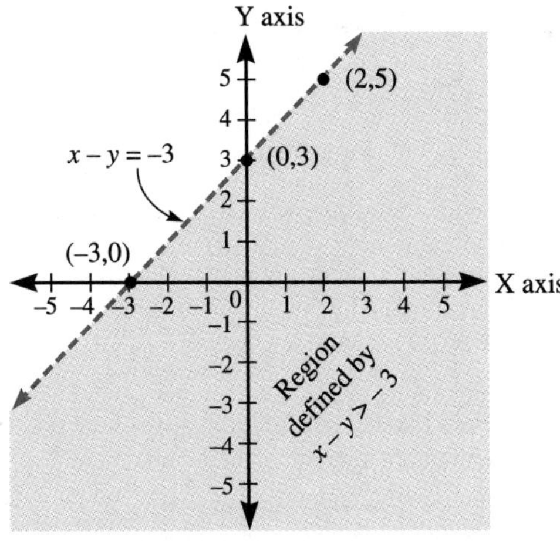

(ii) The equation associated with the inequality $3x + 2y < -8$ is $3x + 2y = -8$.

Table of values

x	0	−2	−4
y	−4	−1	2

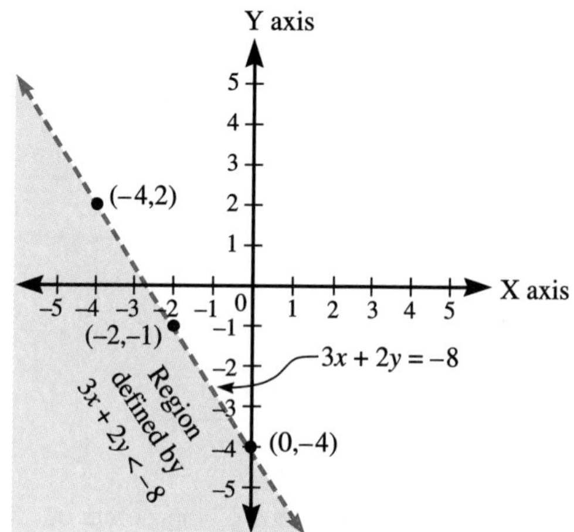

Testing the point (0,0)

$$3(0) + 2(0) < -8$$
$$0 + 0 < -8$$
$$0 < -8$$

Since the statement $0 < -8$ is false, the point (0,0) is not a point in the region defined by $3x + 2y < -8$. The region defined by the inequality is the area to the left of the line as shown.

C. *Graphing inequalities of the form* ax > by *or* ax < by

Example 4.2b Graph each of the following inequalities.

(i) $y \leqslant -x$ (ii) $3x < 2y$

Solution

(i) The equation associated with the inequality $y \leqslant -x$ is $y = -x$.

Table of values

x	0	3	−3
y	0	−3	3

Note: The inequality includes $y = -x$. Because the points on the line meet the condition stated, the graph of the equation is drawn as a full line.

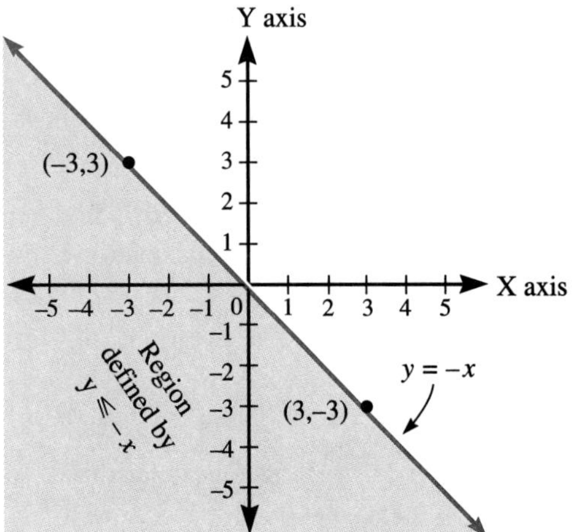

Since the line passes through the origin, the point (0,0) cannot be used for testing. Instead, we test (1,0).

Substituting $x = 1$, $y = 0$ in the inequality $y < -x$ yields the statement

$$0 < -1$$

Since the statement $0 < -1$ is false, the point (1,0) is not a point in the region defined by $y \leqslant -x$. The region defined by the inequality is the area to the left of the line *including* the line.

(ii) The equation associated with the inequality $3x < 2y$ is $3x = 2y$.

Table of values

x	0	2	-2
y	0	3	-3

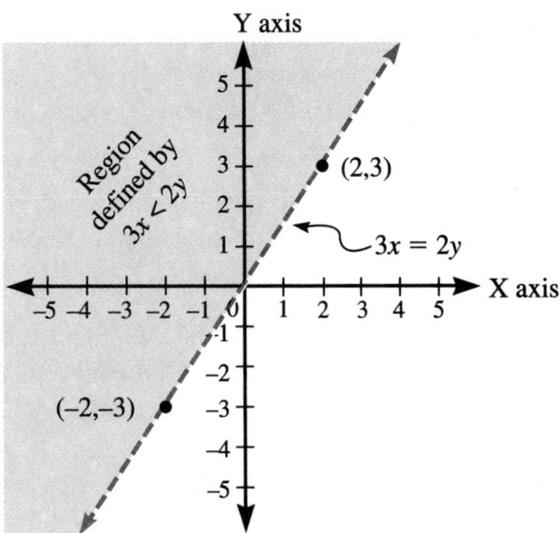

Since (0,0) is on the line, test (0,1).
Substituting $x = 0$, $y = 1$ in the inequality $3x < 2y$ yields the statement

$$0 < 2$$

Since the statement $0 < 2$ is true, the point (0,1) is a point in the region defined by $3x < 2y$. The region defined by the inequality is the area to the left of the line as shown.

D. *Graphing inequalities involving lines parallel to the axes*

Example 4.2c Graph each of the following inequalities.

(i) $x < 3$ (ii) $y \geqslant -3$

Solution

(i) The equation associated with the inequality $x < 3$ is $x = 3$. The graph of $x = 3$ is a line parallel to the Y axis three units to the right.

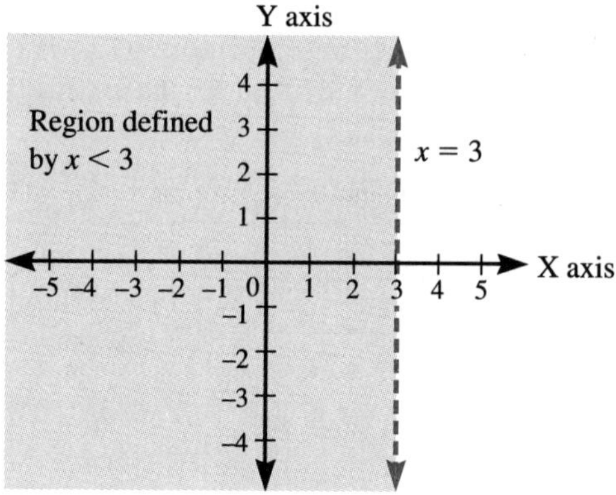

Test (0,0). Substituting $x = 0$ in the inequality $x < 3$ yields the statement

$$0 < 3$$

Since the statement $0 < 3$ is true, (0,0) is a point in the region defined by the inequality $x < 3$. The region defined by the inequality is the region to the left of the line as shown.

(ii) The equation associated with the inequality $y \geqslant -3$ is $y = -3$. The graph of $y = -3$ is a line parallel to the X axis three units below it.

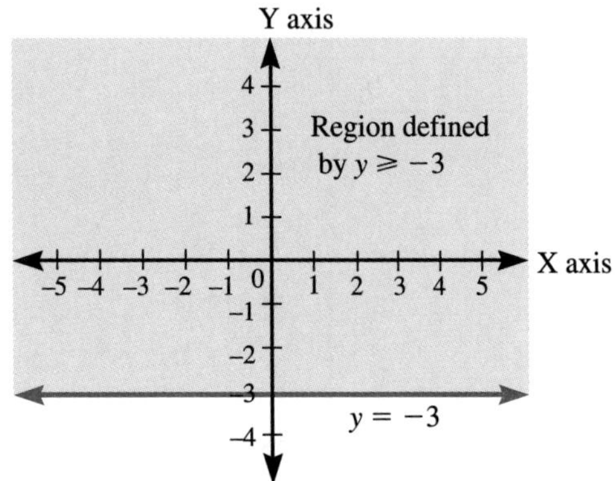

Test (0,0). Substituting $y = 0$ in the inequality $y > -3$ yields the statement

$$0 > -3$$

Since the statement $0 > -3$ is true, (0,0) is a point in the region defined by $y \geqslant -3$. The region defined by the inequality is the area above the line as shown.

Exercise 4.2

A. Graph each of the following inequalities.

1. $x + y > 4$
2. $x - y < -2$
3. $x - 2y \leqslant 4$
4. $3x - 2y \geqslant -10$
5. $2x < -3y$
6. $4y \geqslant 3x$
7. $x \geqslant -2$
8. $y < 5$

4.3 *Graphing linear systems*

A. Graphing systems of equations in two unknowns

Systems that consist of two linear equations in two variables may be solved by drawing the graph of each equation. The graph of the system (or solution) is the point where the two lines representing the equations intersect.

Example **4.3a** Graph the linear system $x + y = 5$ and $x - y = 3$.

Solution

Table of values for $x + y = 5$

x	0	5	2
y	5	0	3

Table of values for $x - y = 3$

x	0	3	2
y	-3	0	-1

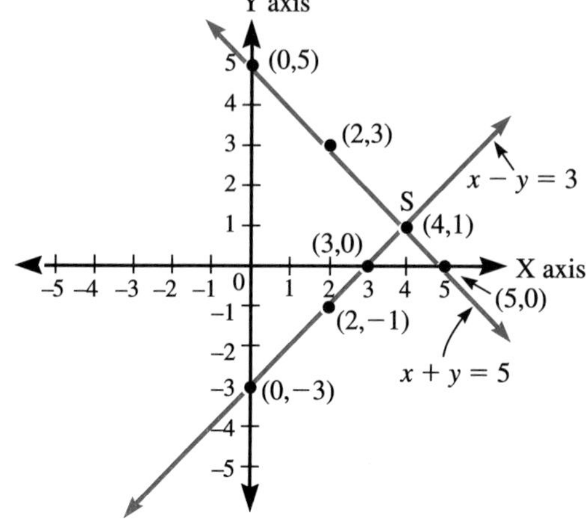

The graph of the system is S, the point of intersection of the two lines, whose coordinates apparently are (4,1). The coordinates (4,1) satisfy the equation of either line and are called the *solution* of the system.

Example 4.3b Graph the system $x = -2y$ and $y = 3$.

Solution

Table of values for $x = -2y$

x	0	-4	4
y	0	2	-2

The graph of $y = 3$ is a line parallel to the X axis three units above it.

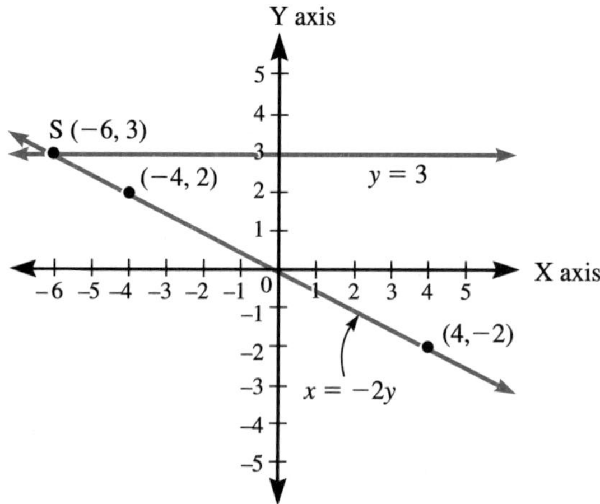

The graph of the system is S, the point of intersection of the two lines. The coordinates of S are apparently $(-6,3)$ and represent the solution of the system.

Example 4.3c Graph the triangle formed by $3x + 4y = 12$, $3x + 2y = 0$, and $x = 2$.

Solution

Table of values for $3x + 4y = 12$

x	0	4	-4
y	3	0	6

Table of values for $3x + 2y = 0$

x	0	2	-2
y	0	-3	3

As shown in the diagram, the triangle ABC is formed by the intersection of pairs of lines representing the three equations.

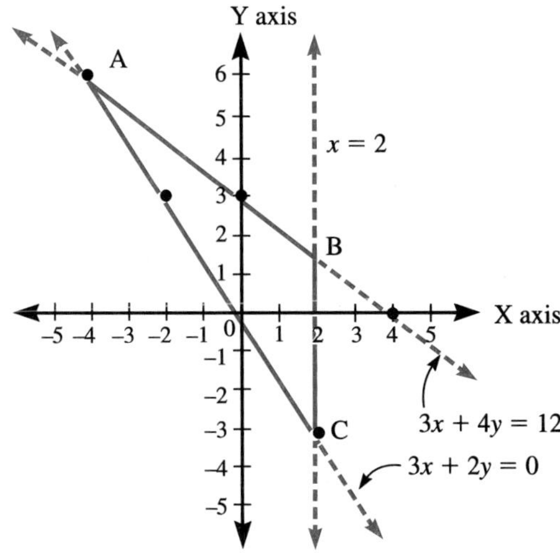

B. *Graphing systems of linear inequalities*

Systems consisting of two or more linear inequalities in two variables can be drawn by graphing each of the inequalities in the system. The graph of the system is the region *common* to all inequalities.

Example 4.3d Graph the region defined by $x > -2$ and $y > x - 3$.

Solution

The equation associated with the inequality $x > -2$ is $x = -2$. The graph of $x = -2$ is a line parallel to the Y axis and two units to the left of it. The substitution of 0 for x yields the true statement $0 > -2$. The point (0,0) is a point in the region defined by $x > -2$. The region defined by the inequality is the area to the right of the line.

The equation associated with the inequality $y > x - 3$ is $y = x - 3$. The graph of $y = x - 3$ is a line passing through the points (3,0) and (0,−3). The substitution of $x = 0$ and $y = 0$ yields the statement $0 > 0 - 3$, or $0 > -3$. Since this statement is true, the point (0,0) is a point in the region defined by the inequality $y > x - 3$. The region defined by the inequality is the area to the left of the line $y = x - 3$.

The region defined by the two inequalities is the area formed by the intersection of the two regions. The common region is shown in the diagram.

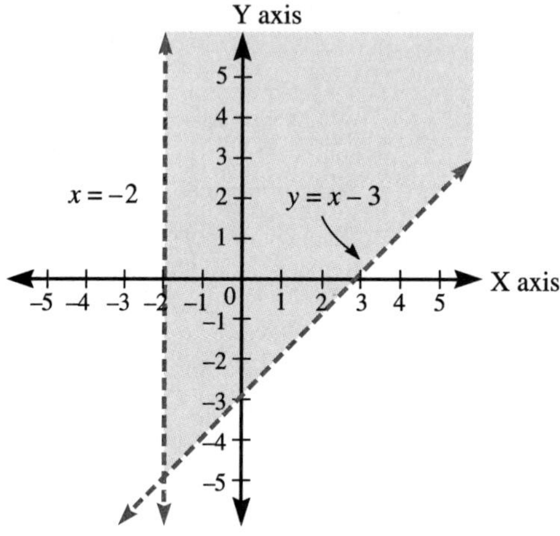

Example 4.3e Graph the region defined by $y \geqslant 0$, $4x + 5y \leqslant 20$, and $4x - 3y \geqslant -12$.

Solution

The equation associated with the inequality $y \geqslant 0$ is $y = 0$. The graph of $y = 0$ is the X axis. The region defined by the inequality $y \geqslant 0$ is the area above the X axis and includes the points forming the X axis.

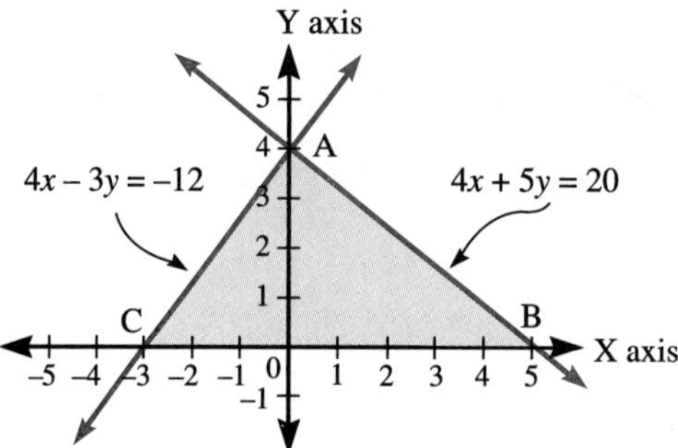

The equation associated with the inequality $4x + 5y \leqslant 20$ is $4x + 5y = 20$. The graph of the equation is the line passing through the points A(0,4) and B(5,0). The true statement $0 < 20$ shows that the origin is a point in the region defined by the inequality. The region defined by $4x + 5y \leqslant 20$ is the area to the left of the line and includes the line itself.

The equation associated with the inequality $4x - 3y \leqslant -12$ is $4x - 3y = -12$. The graph of this equation is the line passing through the points A(0,4) and C(−3,0). The true statement $0 > -12$ shows that the origin is a point in the region defined by the inequality. The region defined by $4x - 3y \geqslant -12$ is the area to the right of the line, including the line itself.

The region defined by the three inequalities is the area formed by the intersection of the three regions. It is the triangle ABC shown in the diagram.

Exercise 4.3

A. Solve each of the following linear systems graphically.

1. $x + y = 4$ and $x - y = -4$
2. $x - y = 3$ and $x + y = 5$
3. $x = 2y - 1$ and $y = 4 - 3x$
4. $2x + 3y = 10$ and $3x - 4y = -2$
5. $3x - 4y = 18$ and $2y = -3x$
6. $4x = -5y$ and $2x + y = 6$
7. $5x - 2y = 20$ and $y = 5$
8. $3y = -5x$ and $x = -3$

B. Graph the triangle formed by the following sets of equations.

1. $x = y$, $x = 4$, and $y = 0$
2. $y = -2x$, $y = 4$, and $x = 2$
3. $3x + 4y = 12$, $x = 0$, and $y = 0$
4. $x + y = -5$, $x - y = -5$, and $x = -2$

C. Graph the region defined by each of the following linear systems.

1. $y < 3$ and $x + y > 2$
2. $x - 2y < 4$ and $x > -3$
3. $3x - y \leqslant 6$ and $x + 2y > 8$
4. $5x > -3y$ and $2x - 5y \geqslant 10$
5. $2y - 3x \leqslant 9$, $x \leqslant 3$, and $y \geqslant 0$
6. $2x + y \leqslant 6$, $x \geqslant 0$, and $y \geqslant 0$
7. $y \geqslant -3x$, $y \leqslant 3$, and $2x - y \leqslant 6$
8. $2x \leqslant y$, $x \geqslant -3y$, and $x - 2y \geqslant -6$

4.4 *Algebraic solution of systems of linear equations in two variables*

A. Basic concept

Any linear system that consists of two equations in two variables can be solved graphically, as illustrated in Section 4.3. However, more efficient techniques are available. One of these techniques is based on eliminating one of the two variables from the system by addition or subtraction. This method is explained and illustrated in this text.

Solving a system of two equations requires finding a pair of values for the two variables that satisfies each of the two equations. The value of one of the two variables can be determined by first reducing the system of equations to one equation in one variable and solving this equation. The value of the variable obtained is then substituted into one of the original equations to find the value of the second variable.

B. Solving a system of two linear equations by addition or subtraction

If the coefficients of one variable are the *same* in both equations, the system can be reduced to one equation by addition or subtraction as follows.

(a) If the coefficients are numerically equal but opposite in sign, addition will eliminate the variable.

(b) If the coefficients are numerically equal and have the same sign, subtraction can eliminate the variable. Alternatively, one equation can be multiplied by -1; addition can then be used.

Example 4.4a Solve each of the following systems of equations.

(i) $x + y = 1$
$x - y = 7$

(ii) $5x + 4y = 7$
$3x - 4y = 17$

(iii) $2x + 3y = -2$
$2x - 5y = -34$

(iv) $x - 3y = 2$
$4x - 3y = -10$

Solution

(i) $x + y = 1$ ⟵ equation ①

$x - y = 7$ ⟵ equation ②

$2x = 8$ ⟵ add ① and ② to eliminate y

Note: The coefficient of y in ① is 1;
the coefficient of y in ② is -1.

Since the coefficients are the same but opposite in sign, adding the two equations will eliminate the term in y.

$x = 4$

$4 + y = 1$ ⟵ substitute the value of x in ①

$y = -3$

$\boxed{x = 4, y = -3}$ ⟵ solution

Check

in ① LS = $4 + (-3) = 4 - 3 = 1$
RS = 1
in ② LS = $4 - (-3) = 4 + 3 = 7$
RS = 7

(ii)

$$
\begin{array}{rll}
5x + 4y &= 7 & \longleftarrow \text{equation ①} \\
3x - 4y &= 17 & \longleftarrow \text{equation ②} \\
\hline
8x \quad &= 24 & \longleftarrow \text{add ① and ② to eliminate } y \\
x &= 3 & \\
5(3) + 4y &= 7 & \longleftarrow \text{substitute 3 for } x \text{ in ①} \\
15 + 4y &= 7 & \\
4y &= -8 & \\
y &= -2 &
\end{array}
$$

$\boxed{x = 3, y = -2}$

Check

in ① LS = $5(3) + 4(-2) = 15 - 8 = 7$
RS = 7
in ② LS = $3(3) - 4(-2) = 9 + 8 = 17$
RS = 17

(iii)

$$
\begin{array}{rll}
2x + 3y &= -2 & \longleftarrow \text{equation ①} \\
2x - 5y &= -34 & \longleftarrow \text{equation ②} \\
\hline
8y &= 32 & \longleftarrow \text{subtract ② from ① to eliminate } x \\
y &= 4 & \\
2x + 3(4) &= -2 & \longleftarrow \text{substitute 4 for } y \text{ in ①} \\
2x + 12 &= -2 & \\
2x &= -14 & \\
x &= -7 &
\end{array}
$$

$\boxed{x = -7, y = 4}$

Check

in ① LS = $2(-7) + 3(4) = -14 + 12 = -2$
RS = -2
in ② LS = $2(-7) - 5(4) = -14 - 20 = -34$
RS = -34

(iv)
$$\begin{aligned} x - 3y &= 2 &&\longleftarrow ① \\ 4x - 3y &= -10 &&\longleftarrow ② \end{aligned}$$

$$\begin{aligned} -4x + 3y &= 10 &&\longleftarrow ② \text{ multiplied by } -1 \text{ to set up addition} \\ x - 3y &= 2 &&\longleftarrow ① \\ \hline -3x &= 12 &&\longleftarrow \text{add} \\ x &= -4 \\ -4 - 3y &= 2 &&\longleftarrow \text{substitute } -4 \text{ for } x \text{ in } ① \\ -3y &= 6 \\ y &= -2 \end{aligned}$$

$$\boxed{x = -4, y = -2}$$

Check

in ① LS $= -4 - 3(-2) = -4 + 6 = 2 =$ RS
in ② LS $= 4(-4) - 3(-2) = -16 + 6 = -10 =$ RS

C. *Solving a system of two linear equations when the coefficients are not numerically equal*

Sometimes numerical equality of one pair of coefficients must be *created* before addition or subtraction can be used to eliminate a variable. This equality is usually achieved by multiplying one or both equations by a number or numbers that make the coefficients of the variable to be eliminated numerically equal.

Example **4.4b** Solve each of the following systems of equations.

(i) $x - 3y = -12$
$3x + y = -6$

(ii) $x + 4y = 18$
$2x + 5y = 24$

(iii) $3x - 4y = 8$
$4x + 5y = 21$

(iv) $6x - 5y + 70 = 0$
$4x = 3y - 44$

Solution

(i)
$$\begin{aligned} x - 3y &= -12 &&\longleftarrow ① \\ 3x + y &= -6 &&\longleftarrow ② \end{aligned}$$

To eliminate the term in y, multiply equation ② by 3.

$$\begin{aligned} 9x + 3y &= -18 &&\longleftarrow ② \text{ multiplied by } 3 \\ x - 3y &= -12 &&\longleftarrow ① \\ \hline 10x &= -30 &&\longleftarrow \text{add} \\ x &= -3 \end{aligned}$$

$$-3 - 3y = -12 \longleftarrow \text{substitute } -3 \text{ for } x \text{ in ①}$$
$$-3y = -9$$
$$y = 3$$

$$\boxed{x = -3,\ y = 3}$$

(ii)
$$x + 4y = 18 \longleftarrow ①$$
$$2x + 5y = 24 \longleftarrow ②$$

To eliminate the term in x, multiply ① by 2.

$$2x + 8y = 36 \longleftarrow ① \text{ multiplied by 2}$$
$$-2x - 5y = -24 \longleftarrow ② \text{ multiplied by } -1 \text{ to set up addition}$$
$$3y = 12 \longleftarrow \text{add}$$
$$y = 4$$
$$x + 4(4) = 18 \longleftarrow \text{substitute 4 for } y \text{ in ①}$$
$$x + 16 = 18$$
$$x = 2$$

$$\boxed{x = 2,\ y = 4}$$

(iii)
$$3x - 4y = 8 \longleftarrow ①$$
$$4x + 5y = 21 \longleftarrow ②$$

To eliminate the term in y, multiply ① by 5 and ② by 4.

$$15x - 20y = 40 \longleftarrow ① \text{ multiplied by 5}$$
$$16x + 20y = 84 \longleftarrow ② \text{ multiplied by 4}$$
$$31x = 124 \longleftarrow \text{add}$$
$$x = 4$$
$$4(4) + 5y = 21 \longleftarrow \text{substitute 4 for } x \text{ in ②}$$
$$16 + 5y = 21$$
$$5y = 5$$
$$y = 1$$

$$\boxed{x = 4,\ y = 1}$$

(iv)
$$6x - 5y + 70 = 0 \longleftarrow ①$$
$$4x = 3y - 44 \longleftarrow ②$$

Rearrange the two equations in the same order.

$$6x - 5y = -70 \longleftarrow ①$$
$$4x - 3y = -44 \longleftarrow ②$$

To eliminate the term in y, multiply ① by 3 and ② by -5.

$$
\begin{array}{rll}
18x - 15y = -210 & \longleftarrow & ① \text{ multiplied by } 3 \\
-20x + 15y = 220 & \longleftarrow & ② \text{ multiplied by } -5 \\
\hline
-2x \quad = 10 & \longleftarrow & \text{add} \\
x = -5 & & \\
6(-5) - 5y = -70 & \longleftarrow & \text{substitute } -5 \text{ for } x \text{ in } ① \\
-30 - 5y = -70 & & \\
-5y = -40 & & \\
y = 8 & &
\end{array}
$$

$$\boxed{x = -5, y = 8}$$

D. *Solving linear systems in two variables involving fractions*

When one or both equations contain decimal fractions or common fractions, it is best to eliminate the fractions by multiplying; then solve the system as shown in the previous examples.

Example 4.4c Solve each of the following systems of equations.

(i) $1.5x + 0.8y = 1.2$
$0.7x + 1.2y = -4.4$

(ii) $\frac{5x}{6} + \frac{3y}{8} = -1$
$\frac{2x}{3} - \frac{3y}{4} = -5$

Solution

(i)
$$
\begin{array}{rll}
1.5x + 0.8y = 1.2 & \longleftarrow & ① \\
0.7x + 1.2y = -4.4 & \longleftarrow & ②
\end{array}
$$

To eliminate the decimals, multiply each equation by 10.

$$
\begin{array}{rll}
15x + 8y = 12 & \longleftarrow & ③ \\
7x + 12y = -44 & \longleftarrow & ④
\end{array}
$$

To eliminate the term in y, multiply ③ by 3 and ④ by 2.

$$
\begin{array}{rll}
45x + 24y = 36 & \longleftarrow & ③ \text{ multiplied by } 3 \\
14x + 24y = -88 & \longleftarrow & ④ \text{ multiplied by } 2 \\
\hline
31x \quad = 124 & \longleftarrow & \text{subtract} \\
x = 4 & & \\
15(4) + 8y = 12 & \longleftarrow & \text{substitute } 4 \text{ for } x \text{ in } ③ \\
60 + 8y = 12 & & \\
8y = -48 & & \\
y = -6 & &
\end{array}
$$

$$\boxed{x = 4, y = -6}$$

(ii) $\frac{5x}{6} + \frac{3y}{8} = -1 \longleftarrow ①$

$\frac{2x}{3} - \frac{3y}{4} = -5 \longleftarrow ②$

To eliminate the fractions, multiply ① by 24 and ② by 12.

$$\frac{24(5x)}{6} + \frac{24(3y)}{8} = 24(-1) \longleftarrow \text{① multiplied by 24}$$
$$4(5x) + 3(3y) = -24$$
$$20x + 9y = -24 \longleftarrow ③$$
$$\frac{12(2x)}{3} - \frac{12(3y)}{4} = 12(-5) \longleftarrow \text{② multiplied by 12}$$
$$4(2x) - 3(3y) = -60$$
$$8x - 9y = -60 \longleftarrow ④$$

To eliminate the term in y, add ③ and ④.

$$20x + 9y = -24 \longleftarrow ③$$
$$8x - 9y = -60 \longleftarrow ④$$
$$28x = -84$$
$$x = -3$$
$$20(-3) + 9y = -24 \longleftarrow \text{substitute } -3 \text{ for } x \text{ in ③}$$
$$-60 + 9y = -24$$
$$9y = 36$$
$$y = 4$$

$x = -3, y = 4$

Exercise 4.4

A. Solve each of the following systems of equations and check your solutions.

1. $x + y = -9$
   $x - y = -7$
2. $x + 5y = 0$
   $x + 2y = 6$
3. $5x + 2y = 74$
   $7x - 2y = 46$
4. $2x + 9y = -13$
   $2x - 3y = 23$
5. $y = 3x + 12$
   $x = -y$
6. $3x = 10 - 2y$
   $5y = 3x - 38$

B. Solve each of the following systems of equations and check your solutions.

1. $4x + y = -13$
   $x - 5y = -19$
2. $6x + 3y = 24$
   $2x + 9y = -8$
3. $7x - 5y = -22$
   $4x + 3y = 5$
4. $8x + 9y = 129$
   $6x + 7y = 99$

5. $12y = 5x + 16$
$6x + 10y - 54 = 0$

6. $3x - 8y + 44 = 0$
$7x = 12y - 56$

C. Solve each of the following systems of equations.

1. $0.4x + 1.5y = 16.8$
$1.1x - 0.9y = 6.0$

2. $6.5x + 3.5y = 128$
$2.5x + 4.5y = 106$

3. $2.4x + 1.6y = 7.60$
$3.8x + 0.6y = 7.20$

4. $2.25x + 0.75y = 2.25$
$1.25x + 1.75y = 2.05$

5. $\frac{3x}{4} - \frac{2y}{3} = \frac{-13}{6}$
$\frac{4x}{5} + \frac{3y}{4} = \frac{123}{10}$

6. $\frac{9x}{5} + \frac{5y}{4} = \frac{47}{10}$
$\frac{2x}{9} + \frac{3y}{8} = \frac{5}{36}$

7. $\frac{x}{3} + \frac{2y}{5} = \frac{7}{15}$
$\frac{3x}{2} - \frac{7y}{3} = -1$

8. $\frac{x}{4} + \frac{3y}{7} = \frac{-2}{21}$
$\frac{2x}{3} + \frac{3y}{2} = \frac{-7}{36}$

4.5 *Systems of linear equations in three variables*

A. *Solving by the method of elimination*

Systems that consist of three linear equations in three variables can be solved by a process of elimination similar to the one used in Section 4.4.

The first step in the process involves reducing the system of three equations in three variables to a system of two equations in two variables. The same variable must be eliminated from two sets of equations to produce two equations in two variables. While any of the three variables may be eliminated, base the decision to eliminate a particular variable on ease of elimination.

The second step involves solving the new system by the method used in Section 4.4. Once the value of one variable has been obtained, the values of the second and third variables are obtained by successive substitution.

B. *Worked examples*

Example 4.5a Solve the system $x + y + z = 0$, $2x + 3y - z = -6$, and $5x - 3y + 2z = 21$.

Solution

$$x + y + z = 0 \longleftarrow ①$$
$$2x + 3y - z = -6 \longleftarrow ②$$
$$5x - 3y + 2z = 21 \longleftarrow ③$$

STEP 1 Eliminate z from the system and set up two equations in x and y.

(i) Eliminate z from ① and ② by adding.

$$\begin{array}{l} x + y + z = 0 \\ \underline{2x + 3y - z = -6} \\ 3x + 4y \quad = -6 \longleftarrow ④ \end{array}$$

(ii) Eliminate z from ② and ③.

$$\begin{array}{l} 2x + 3y - z = -6 \\ \underline{5x - 3y + 2z = 21} \end{array}$$

To eliminate z, multiply ② by 2 and add.

$$\begin{array}{ll} 4x + 6y - 2z = -12 & \longleftarrow ② \text{ multiplied by 2} \\ \underline{5x - 3y + 2z = 21} & \\ 9x + 3y \quad = 9 & \longleftarrow ⑤ \end{array}$$

STEP 2 Now solve the new system consisting of ④ and ⑤.

$$\begin{array}{ll} 3x + 4y = -6 & \longleftarrow ④ \\ \underline{9x + 3y = 9} & \longleftarrow ⑤ \end{array}$$

To eliminate the term in x, multiply ④ by 3.

$$\begin{array}{ll} 9x + 12y = -18 & \longleftarrow ④ \text{ multiplied by 3} \\ \underline{9x + 3y = 9} & \\ 9y = -27 & \longleftarrow \text{subtract} \\ y = -3 & \end{array}$$

STEP 3 Substitute -3 for y in an equation that has two variables.

$$\begin{array}{ll} 3x + 4(-3) = -6 & \longleftarrow \text{substitute in ④} \\ 3x - 12 = -6 & \\ 3x = 6 & \\ x = 2 & \end{array}$$

STEP 4 Substitute 2 for x and -3 for y in an equation that has three variables.

$$\begin{array}{ll} 2 + (-3) + z = 0 & \longleftarrow \text{substitute in ①} \\ -1 + z = 0 & \\ z = 1 & \end{array}$$

$$\boxed{x = 2, y = -3, z = 1}$$

Check

in ① LS $= 2 - 3 + 1 = 0$ RS $= 0$

in ② LS $= 2(2) + 3(-3) - 1$
$= 4 - 9 - 1$
$= -6$ RS $= -6$

in ③ LS $= 5(2) - 3(-3) + 2(1)$
$= 10 + 9 + 2$
$= 21$ RS $= 21$

Example **4.5b** Solve the system $3a + 4b - 2c = -28$, $5a - 3c = -19$, and $2a - 3b + c = 11$.

Solution

$$\begin{aligned} 3a + 4b - 2c &= -28 \longleftarrow ① \\ 5a \qquad - 3c &= -19 \longleftarrow ② \\ 2a - 3b + c &= 11 \longleftarrow ③ \end{aligned}$$

Since ② has the two variables a and c, eliminate the variable b from the system to set up a second equation in a and c. This can be done by multiplying ① by 3 and ③ by 4.

$$\begin{aligned} 9a + 12b - 6c &= -84 \longleftarrow ① \text{ multiplied by 3} \\ 8a - 12b + 4c &= 44 \longleftarrow ③ \text{ multiplied by 4} \\ \hline 17a \qquad - 2c &= -40 \longleftarrow ④ \end{aligned}$$

Now solve the system in two variables consisting of ② and ④.

$$\begin{aligned} 5a - 3c &= -19 \longleftarrow ② \\ 17a - 2c &= -40 \longleftarrow ④ \end{aligned}$$

To eliminate the term in c, multiply ② by 2 and ④ by -3.

$$\begin{aligned} 10a - 6c &= -38 \longleftarrow ② \text{ multiplied by 2} \\ -51a + 6c &= 120 \longleftarrow ④ \text{ multiplied by } -3 \\ \hline -41a \qquad &= 82 \\ a &= -2 \end{aligned}$$

Now substitute $a = -2$ in ② (one of the two equations in two variables).

$$\begin{aligned} 5(-2) - 3c &= -19 \\ -10 - 3c &= -19 \\ -3c &= -9 \\ c &= 3 \end{aligned}$$

Now substitute $a = -2$, $c = 3$ in ③ (one of the equations in three variables).

$$\begin{aligned} 2(-2) - 3b + 3 &= 11 \\ -4 - 3b + 3 &= 11 \\ -3b &= 12 \\ b &= -4 \end{aligned}$$

$$\boxed{a = -2,\ b = -4,\ c = 3}$$

Check

in ① $\begin{aligned} \text{LS} &= 3(-2) + 4(-4) - 2(3) \\ &= -6 - 16 - 6 \\ &= -28 \\ \text{RS} &= -28 \end{aligned}$

in ② $\begin{aligned} \text{LS} &= 5(-2) - 3(3) \\ &= -10 - 9 \\ &= -19 \\ \text{RS} &= -19 \end{aligned}$

in ③ $\begin{aligned} \text{LS} &= 2(-2) - 3(-4) + 3 \\ &= -4 + 12 + 3 \\ &= 11 \\ \text{RS} &= 11 \end{aligned}$

Example 4.5c Solve the system $3m + 2n = 4$, $5m - 4k = 0$, and $3n + 5k = 13$.

Solution

$$\begin{aligned} 3m + 2n \phantom{{}+5k} &= 4 \quad \longleftarrow ① \\ 5m \phantom{{}+2n} - 4k &= 0 \quad \longleftarrow ② \\ 3n + 5k &= 13 \quad \longleftarrow ③ \end{aligned}$$

To set up a system of two equations in m and n, use ① and eliminate the term in k from ② and ③.

$$\begin{aligned} 25m \phantom{{}+12n} - 20k &= 0 \quad \longleftarrow ② \text{ multiplied by } 5 \\ + 12n + 20k &= 52 \quad \longleftarrow ③ \text{ multiplied by } 4 \\ \hline 25m + 12n \phantom{{}+20k} &= 52 \quad \longleftarrow ④ \end{aligned}$$

Now solve the system consisting of ① and ④.

$$\begin{aligned} 3m + 2n &= 4 \quad \longleftarrow ① \\ 25m + 12n &= 52 \quad \longleftarrow ④ \end{aligned}$$

To eliminate the term in n, multiply ① by -6.

$$\begin{aligned} -18m - 12n &= -24 \longleftarrow \text{① multiplied by } -6 \\ 25m + 12n &= 52 \\ \hline 7m \qquad &= 28 \\ m &= 4 \end{aligned}$$

Substitute $m = 4$ in ①.

$$\begin{aligned} 3(4) + 2n &= 4 \\ 12 + 2n &= 4 \\ 2n &= -8 \\ n &= -4 \end{aligned}$$

Substitute $m = 4$ in ②.

$$\begin{aligned} 5(4) - 4k &= 0 \\ -4k &= -20 \\ k &= 5 \end{aligned}$$

$$\boxed{m = 4,\ n = -4,\ k = 5}$$

Check

in ① LS $= 3(4) + 2(-4) = 12 - 8 = 4$ RS $= 4$
in ② LS $= 5(4) - 4(5) = 20 - 20 = 0$ RS $= 0$
in ③ LS $= 3(-4) + 5(5) = -12 + 25 = 13$ RS $= 13$

Exercise 4.5

A. Solve each of the following systems of equations and check your solutions.

1. $x + 2y - z = 0$
$3x - 2y + 2z = -17$
$5x + 3y - 4z = -25$

2. $4x - 3y + 2z = 43$
$3x + 2y - 5z = -13$
$6x - 5y + 3z = 66$

3. $7a + 3b + 5c = 181$
$4a + 5b = 100$
$8a + 2b + 3c = 149$

4. $5a + 9b + 8c = 389$
$12a + 7b = 220$
$6b + 9c = 321$

5. $9m + 8n = 12$
$12n + 9k = 18$
$7m + 12k = 20$

6. $5p + 9q = 6$
$9p + 6r = 9$
$5q + 10r = 5$

4.6 *Problem solving*

A. Problems leading to one equation in two variables

In many problems, the relationship between two or more variables can be represented by setting up linear equations. To find the solution to such problems, there must be as many equations as there are variables.

In the case of problems involving two variables, two equations are needed to obtain a solution. If only one equation can be set up, you can represent the relationship between the two variables graphically.

***Example* 4.6a** A manufacturer processes two types of products through the Finishing Department. Each unit of Product A needs 20 time units in Finishing while each unit of Product B needs 30 time units. Per day, 1200 time units are available. Set up an equation which describes the relationship between the number of units of each product that can be processed daily in Finishing. Graph the relationship.

Solution

Let the number of units of Product A that can be processed daily be represented by x, and let the number of units of Product B be represented by y. Then the number of time units required per day for Product A is $20x$ and the number of time units for Product B is $30y$. The total number of time units per day needed by both products is $20x + 30y$. Since 1200 time units are available,

$$20x + 30y = 1200$$

Graphic representation

Table of values

x	60	0	30
y	0	40	20

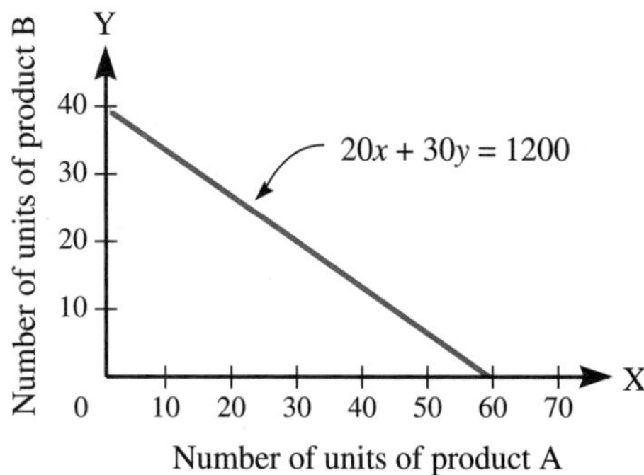

Example **4.6b** The Olympic Swim Club rents pool facilities from the city at \$2000 per month. Coaching fees and other expenses amount to \$40 per swimmer per month. Set up an equation that describes the relationship between the number of swimmers and the total monthly cost of operating the swim club. Graph the relationship.

Solution

Let the number of swimmers be represented by x, and let the total monthly cost be represented by \$$y$. Then the monthly coaching fees and expenses are \$$40x$ and total monthly costs amount to \$$(2000 + 40x)$.

$$y = 2000 + 40x$$

Graphic representation

Table of values

x	0	50	100
y	2000	4000	6000

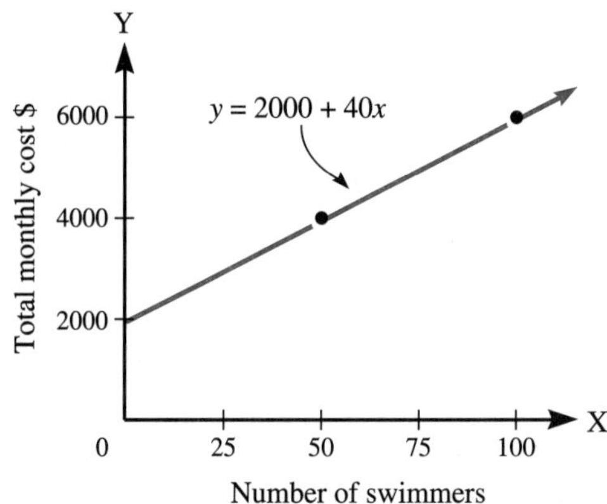

B. *Problems leading to systems of equations*

The problems in Chapter 2 were solved by using one variable, expressing all the information in terms of that variable, and setting up one equation. To solve many problems, using more than one variable and setting up a system of equations is necessary.

Example **4.6c** The sum of two numbers is 64 and their difference is 10. Find the two numbers.

Solution

Let the greater number be x and the smaller number be y. Their sum is $x + y$ and their difference is $x - y$.

$$\begin{array}{rl} x + y = 64 & \longleftarrow ① \\ x - y = 10 & \longleftarrow ② \\ \hline 2x \quad = 74 & \\ x = 37 & \\ & \\ 37 + y = 64 & \\ y = 27 & \end{array}$$

The larger number is 37 and the smaller number is 27.

Check Sum, $37 + 27 = 64$
Difference, $37 - 27 = 10$

Example **4.6d** Sheridan Service paid $240 for heat and power during January. If heat was $40 less than three times the cost of power, how much was the cost of heat for January? (See Chapter 2, Example 2.7c)

Solution

Let the cost of heat be $\$x$, and the cost of power be $\$y$. The cost of heat and power together is $\$(x + y)$.

$$x + y = 240 \qquad \longleftarrow ①$$

Heat is represented by $\$(3y - 40)$.

$$\begin{array}{rll} x = 3y - 40 & \longleftarrow & ② \\ x - 3y = -40 & \longleftarrow & ② \\ x + \;\; y = 240 & \longleftarrow & ① \\ \hline -4y = -280 & \longleftarrow & \text{subtract} \\ y = 70 & & \\ & & \\ x + 70 = 240 & \longleftarrow & \text{substitute in } ① \\ x = 170 & & \end{array}$$

The cost of heat for January was $170.

Example **4.6e** The Clarkson Soccer League has set a budget of $3840 for soccer balls. High quality game balls cost $36 each while lower quality practice balls cost $20 each. If 160 balls are to be purchased, how many balls of each type can be bought to exactly use up the budgeted amount? (See Chapter 2, Example 2.7d.)

Solution

Let the number of game balls be x;
let the number of practice balls be y;
then the total number of balls is $x + y$.

$$x + y = 160 \quad \longleftarrow \text{①}$$

The value of the x game balls is \$36x;
the value of the y practice balls is \$20y;
the total value of the balls is \$(36x + 20y).

$$\begin{array}{rcll} 36x + 20y &=& 3840 & \longleftarrow \text{②} \\ -20x - 20y &=& -3200 & \longleftarrow \text{① multiplied by } -20 \\ \hline 16x &=& 640 & \longleftarrow \text{add} \\ x &=& 40 & \\ 40 + y &=& 160 & \longleftarrow \text{substitute in ①} \\ y &=& 120 & \end{array}$$

40 game balls and 120 practice balls can be bought.

***Example* 4.6f** The Dutch Nook sells two brands of coffee — one for \$7.90 per kilogram, the other for \$9.40 per kilogram. If the store owner mixes twenty kilograms and intends to sell the mixture for \$8.50 per kilogram, how many kilograms of each brand should she use to make the same revenue as if the two brands were sold unmixed?

Solution

Let the number of kilograms of coffee sold for \$7.90 be x;
let the number of kilograms of coffee sold for \$9.40 be y;
then the number of kilograms of coffee in the mixture is $x + y$.

$$x + y = 20 \quad \longleftarrow \text{① weight relationship}$$

The value of coffee in the mixture selling for \$7.90 is \$7.90x;
the value of coffee in the mixture selling for \$9.40 is \$9.40y;
the total value of the mixture is \$(7.90x + 9.40y). Since each kilogram of mixture is to be sold at \$8.50, the value is \$8.50(20), or \$170.

$$7.90x + 9.40y = 170.00 \quad \longleftarrow \text{② value relationship}$$

$$\begin{array}{rcll} 79x + 94y &=& 1700 & \longleftarrow \text{② multiplied by 10} \\ 79x + 79y &=& 1580 & \longleftarrow \text{① multiplied by 79} \\ \hline 15y &=& 120 & \longleftarrow \text{subtract} \\ y &=& 8 & \\ x + 8 &=& 20 & \longleftarrow \text{substitute in ①} \\ x &=& 12 & \end{array}$$

The store owner should mix 12 kg of coffee selling for \$7.90 per kilogram with 8 kg of coffee selling for \$9.40 per kilogram.

Check Weight: $12 + 8 = 20$ kg
Value: $12 \times 7.90 + 8 \times 9.40 = 94.80 + 75.20 = \$170.00$

Example **4.6g** The material cost of a product is \$4 less than twice the cost of the direct labour, and the overhead is $\frac{5}{6}$ of direct labour cost. If the total cost of the product is \$157, determine the amount of each of the three elements of cost. (See Chapter 2, Example 2.7b.)

Solution

Let the cost of material be represented by $\$x$;
let the cost of direct labour be represented by $\$y$;
let the cost of overhead be represented by $\$z$;
then the total cost is $x + y + z$.

$$x + y + z = 157 \longleftarrow ①$$

Also, \$4 less than twice the cost of direct labour is $2y - 4$.

$$x = 2y - 4 \longleftarrow ②$$

$\frac{5}{6}$ of direct labour cost is $\left(\frac{5}{6}\right)y$.

$$z = \frac{5y}{6} \longleftarrow ③$$

You can now solve this system of equations by using the process of elimination shown in Section 4.5. In this case, you can solve the system more directly by replacing x and z in ①.

$$(2y - 4) + y + \left(\frac{5y}{6}\right) = 157$$
$$12y - 24 + 6y + 5y = 942$$
$$23y = 966$$
$$y = 42$$

$$x = 2(42) - 4 \longleftarrow \text{substitute in ②}$$
$$x = 80$$
$$z = \frac{5(42)}{6} \longleftarrow \text{substitute in ③}$$
$$z = 35$$

Material cost is \$80, labour cost is \$42, and overhead is \$35.

Example **4.6h** A sum of money amounting to \$12 consists of nickels, dimes, and quarters. If there are 95 coins in total and if the ratio of the number of nickels to the number of dimes is 8 to 5, how many of each type of coin make up the total?

Solution

Let the number of nickels be x;
let the number of dimes be y;
let the number of quarters be z;
then the total number of coins is $x + y + z$.

$$x + y + z = 95 \longleftarrow ①$$

The value of the x nickels is \$0.05x;
the value of the y dimes is \$0.10y;
the value of the z quarters is \$0.25z;
the total value of the coins is \$$(0.05x + 0.10y + 0.25z)$.

$$0.05x + 0.10y + 0.25z = 12 \longleftarrow ②$$

The ratio of nickels to dimes is $x : y$ or $\frac{x}{y}$.

$$x : y = 8 : 5 \text{ or } \frac{x}{y} = \frac{8}{5} \longleftarrow ③$$

To eliminate the fraction from ②, multiply by 20.

$$x + 2y + 5z = 240 \longleftarrow ④$$

For a suitable order, cross multiply the terms in ③ and rearrange them.

$$\begin{aligned} 5x &= 8y \longleftarrow \text{cross multiplying in ③} \\ 5x - 8y &= 0 \longleftarrow ⑤ \end{aligned}$$

Now solve the system of equations numbered ①, ④, and ⑤.

$$\begin{aligned} x + y + z &= 95 \longleftarrow ① \\ x + 2y + 5z &= 240 \longleftarrow ④ \\ 5x - 8y \quad &= 0 \longleftarrow ⑤ \end{aligned}$$

To eliminate the term in z from the system, multiply ① by 5 and subtract ④.

$$\begin{aligned} 5x + 5y + 5z &= 475 \\ x + 2y + 5z &= 240 \\ \hline 4x + 3y \quad &= 235 \longleftarrow ⑥ \end{aligned}$$

Now solve the system in two variables.

$$\begin{aligned} 5x - 8y &= 0 \longleftarrow ⑤ \\ 4x + 3y &= 235 \longleftarrow ⑥ \end{aligned}$$

To eliminate the term in y from the system, multiply ⑤ by 3 and ⑥ by 8.

$$\begin{aligned} 15x - 24y &= 0 \\ 32x + 24y &= 1880 \\ \hline 47x \quad &= 1880 \\ x &= 40 \end{aligned}$$

Substitute $x = 40$ in ⑤.

$$\begin{aligned} 5(40) - 8y &= 0 \\ -8y &= -200 \\ y &= 25 \end{aligned}$$

Substitute $x = 40$, $y = 25$ in ①.

$$\begin{aligned} 40 + 25 + z &= 95 \\ z &= 30 \end{aligned}$$

The sum of money consists of 40 nickels, 25 dimes, and 30 quarters.

Check Number of coins: $40 + 25 + 30 = 95$
Value: $40 \times 0.05 + 25 \times 0.10 + 30 \times 0.25 = \$12.00$
Ratio of nickels to dimes: $40 : 25 = 8 : 5$

Exercise 4.6

A. Set up an equation that describes the relationship between the two variables in each of the following. Graph that relationship.

1. A manufacturer makes two types of products. Profit on Product A is \$30 per unit while profit on Product B is \$40 per unit. Budgeted monthly profit is \$6000.

2. Smith Company manufactures two products. Product 1 requires three hours of machine time per unit while Product 2 requires four hours of machine time per unit. There are 120 hours of machine time available per week.

3. U-Save-Bucks tax consulting service rents space at \$200 per week and pays the accounting personnel \$4 per completed tax return.

4. George Bell is offered a position as a sales representative. The job pays a salary of \$500 per month plus a commission of 10% on all sales.

B. Set up a system of simultaneous equations to solve each of the following problems.

1. The sum of two numbers is 24. If twice the larger number is three more than three times the smaller number, what are the two numbers?

2. The difference between seven times the first number and four times the second number is 12. The sum of three-fourths of the first number and two-thirds of the second number is 21. Find the two numbers.

3. Loblaws sells two brands of sauerkraut. Brand X sells for \$2.25 per jar while the No-Name brand sells for \$1.75 per jar. If 140 jars were sold for a total of \$290, how many jars of each brand were sold?

4. Nancy's sales last week were \$140 less than three times Andrea's sales. Together they sold \$940. Determine how much each clerk sold last week.

5. Kaya and Fred agree to form a partnership. The partnership agreement requires that Fred invest \$2500 more than two-thirds of what Kaya is to invest. If the total investment in the partnership is to be \$55 000, how much should each partner invest?

6. A Brush with Wood has been producing 2320 chairs a day working two shifts. The second shift has produced 60 chairs fewer than four-thirds of the number of chairs produced by the first shift. Determine the number of chairs each shift has produced.

7. An inventory of two types of floodlights showed a total of sixty lights valued at \$2580. If Type A cost \$40 each while Type B cost \$50 each, how many of each type of floodlight were in inventory?

8. A machine requires four hours to make a unit of Product A and three hours to make a unit of Product B. Last month the machine operated for 200 hours producing a total of 60 units. How many units of each type of product did it produce?

9. Marysia has saved \$8.80 in nickels, dimes, and quarters. If she has four nickels fewer than three times the number of dimes and one quarter more than three-fourths the number of dimes, how many coins of each type does Marysia have?

10. The local amateur football club spent \$1475 on tickets to a professional football game. If the club bought ten more eight-dollar tickets than three times the number of twelve-dollar tickets, and three fewer fifteen-dollar tickets than four-fifths the number of twelve-dollar tickets, how many tickets of each type did the club buy?

Review exercise

1. Graph each of the following.

   (a) $2x - y = 6$ **(b)** $3x + 4y = 0$

   (c) $5x + 2y = 10$ **(d)** $y = -3$

   (e) $3x + 5y < 15$ **(f)** $5x - 4y > 0$

   (g) $x > -2$ **(h)** $4x + 3y < -12$

2. Graphically solve each of the following.

   (a) $3x + y = 6$ and $x - y = 2$

   (b) $x + 4y = -8$ and $3x + 4y = 0$

   (c) $5x = 3y$ and $y = -5$

   (d) $2x + 6y = 8$ and $x = -2$

3. Graph the regions defined by each of the following systems of inequalities.

   (a) $y < 3x - 2$ and $y < 3$

   (b) $y > -2x$ and $x < 4$

   (c) $x \geqslant -2$, $y \geqslant 0$, and $3x + 4y \leqslant 12$

   (d) $x \geqslant 0$, $y \geqslant -2$, and $5x + 3y \leqslant 15$

4. Solve each of the following systems of equations.

(a) $3x + 2y = -1$
$5x + 3y = -2$

(b) $4x - 5y = 25$
$3x + 2y = 13$

(c) $y = -10x$
$3y = 29 - x$

(d) $2y = 3x + 17$
$3x = 11 - 5y$

(e) $2x - 3y = 13$
$3x - 2y = 12$

(f) $2x = 3y - 11$
$y = 13 + 3x$

(g) $2a - 3b - 4c = 6$
$2a - b - c = 8$
$a + b - c = 0$

(h) $a + b + c = -4$
$3a - 5b = 0$
$8a + 4c = 0$

(i) $4a - 3b - 2c = 9$
$2a + 3b - 3c = -13$
$a - 2b + 4c = 15$

(j) $3a - 2b + 4c = 4$
$a + 3b - 3c = -8$
$2a + b - c = -6$

(k) $5m + 3n + 2k = 74$
$3m + 7n = 74$
$4m + 5k = 74$

(l) $\frac{3}{4}m + \frac{5}{8}n = \frac{3}{4}$
$\frac{6}{5}m + \frac{1}{3}k = \frac{21}{20}$
$\frac{5}{6}n + \frac{2}{3}k = \frac{5}{6}$

5. Write an equation describing the relationship between the two variables in each of the following problems and graph the relationship.

(a) Sun 'N' Ski Travel pays for radio advertising at the fixed rate of $1000 per week plus $75 per announcement during the week.

(b) The Bi-Products Company markets two products. Each unit of Product A requires five units of labour while each unit of Product B requires two units of labour. Two hundred units of labour are available per time period.

6. Set up a system of equations to solve each of the following problems.

(a) Find two numbers such that the sum of six times the first number and five times the second number is 93 and the difference between three-quarters of the first number and two-thirds of the second number is zero.

(b) The college theatre collected $1300 from the sale of 450 tickets. If the tickets were sold for $2.50 and $3.50 respectively, how many tickets were sold at each price?

(c) A jacket and two pairs of pants together cost $175. The jacket is valued at three times the price of one pair of pants. What is the value of the jacket?

(d) Three cases of White Bordeaux and five cases of Red Bordeaux together cost $438. Each case of Red Bordeaux costs $6 less than twice the cost of a case of White Bordeaux. Determine the cost of a case of each type.

(e) A product requires processing on three machines. Processing time on Machine A is three minutes less than four-fifths of the number of minutes on Machine B, and processing time on Machine C is five-sixths of the time needed on Machines A and B together. How many minutes processing time is required on each machine if the total processing time on all three machines is 77 minutes?

(f) Last year, the total average monthly cost of heat, power, and water for Sheridan Service was \$2010. This year's average is expected to increase by one-tenth over last year's average, and heat is expected to be \$22 more than three-fourths the cost of power while water is expected to be \$11 less than one-third the cost of power. How much should be budgeted on average for each month for each item?

(g) Widgits Unlimited has a promotional budget of \$87 500. The budget is to be allocated to direct selling, TV advertising, and newspaper advertising according to a formula. This formula requires that the amount spent on TV advertising be \$1000 more than three times the amount spent on newspaper advertising and that the amount spent on direct selling be three-fourths of the total spent on TV advertising and newspaper advertising combined. How should the budget be allocated?

(h) A cash box contains \$74 made up of quarters, half-dollars, and one-dollar coins. How many coins of each type does the box contain if the number of half-dollar coins is one more than three-fifths of the number of one-dollar coins and the number of quarters is four times the number of one-dollar and half-dollar coins together?

Self-test

1. Graphically solve each of the following systems of equations.

   (a) $x + y = -2$ and $x - y = 4$

   (b) $3x = -2y$ and $x = 2$

2. Graph the region defined by each of the following systems of inequalities.

   (a) $x < 3 - x$ and $y < 3$

   (b) $y \geqslant 0$, $y \geqslant -2$, and $3x + 2y \leqslant 12$

3. Solve each of the following systems of equations.

   (a) $6x + 5y = 9$
   $4x - 3y = 25$

   (b) $12 - 7x = 4y$
   $6 - 2y = 3x$

   (c) $5a - b + 4c = 5$
   $2a + 3b + 5c = 2$
   $7a - 2b + 6c = 5$

   (d) $6a + b - 2c = 0$
   $4b - c = -13$
   $5a + 3c = 25$

4. Erica Lottsbriner invests \$12 000 so that part earns interest at 8% per annum and part at 12% per annum. If the total annual interest on the investment is \$1120, how much has Erica invested at each rate?

5. Jack and Jill divide a profit of \$12 700. If Jack is to receive \$2200 more than two-fifths of Jill's share, how much will Jill receive?

6. Direct distribution costs are to be allocated to three products based on sales value for an accounting period. Product A sells for \$20 per unit, Product B for \$15 per unit, and Product C for \$10 per unit. Last month, the number of units of Product A was five-eighths the number of units of Product B, and the number of units of Product C was 16 less than three times the number of units of Product B. How much of the total direct distribution cost of \$6280 is to be allocated to each product?

CASE STUDY

In most businesses, various products are produced with limited production facilities. The factors of consumer demand and profitability of the products force companies to choose amongst production options. The Sterling Metal Company operates one facility that can produce three consumer goods—items A, B, and C. Limited production resources allow the production of only two items at a time. The production data for the options are as follows:

To produce items A and B

- capacity is 1200 units per hour
- total cost per unit for A is \$5.00
- total cost per unit for B is \$4.00
- total cost budget is \$5500

To produce items B and C

- capacity is 1400 units per hour
- total cost per unit for B is \$4.00
- total cost per unit for C is \$2.50
- total cost budget is \$4400

To produce items A and C

- capacity is 1350 units per hour
- total cost per unit for A is \$5.00
- total cost per unit for C is \$2.50
- total cost budget is \$5050

1. Calculate the number of each item that could be produced under each of the three production options.
2. Determine the percentage markup on each item if items A, B, and C are sold to the retailer for \$9.00, \$7.50, and \$4.75 respectively.
3. Which combination will generate the highest gross profit for Sterling Metal?
4. Why does the combination you named in question 3 generate the highest gross profit?

5. Accurately graph the production of items A and B.
   - **(a)** From the graph, estimate how many units of A can be produced if 1000 units of B are produced.
   - **(b)** Calculate the gross profit of this combination.
   - **(c)** Why is this combination not efficient?
   - **(d)** From the graph, estimate how many units of A can be produced if 200 units of B are produced.
   - **(e)** Calculate the gross profit of this combination.
   - **(f)** Why is the combination in part (d) impossible?
   - **(g)** Plot the coordinates of your answer to question 3 on the graph. What two conditions does this point meet?
6. The company would like to expand to allow all three lines to operate at once. Some preliminary studies of the limited labour resources indicate that three configurations for production are possible. These are
   (i) 5 units of A, 4 of B, and 1 of C in 17 minutes;
   (ii) 4 units of A, 6 of B, and 3 of C in 20 minutes;
   (iii) 3 units of A, 2 of B, and 6 of C in 15 minutes.
   Calculate the production time for each item.
7. If labour costs for items A, B, and C are \$29.70, \$25.60, and \$21.60 per hour respectively, calculate the per-hour labour cost for each item.
8. Increases in labour and material costs will raise the total cost of items A and B by 10% each. The capacity, cost budget, and selling price must remain the same as before.
   - **(a)** Calculate how many units of A and B can now be produced.
   - **(b)** What percent of profit is lost due to the 10% increase in costs?

Glossary of terms used

Inequality a mathematical statement involving relationships between variables described as "greater than" or "less than"

Origin the point of intersection of the two axes in a system of rectangular coordinates

X axis the horizontal reference line in a system of rectangular coordinates

X coordinate the first number in the ordered pair of numbers. It describes the position of a point relative to the axes or the directed distance of a point from the vertical axis (Y axis).

Y axis the vertical reference line in a system of rectangular coordinates

Y coordinate the second number in the ordered pair of numbers. It describes the position of a point relative to the axes or the directed distance of a point from the horizontal axis (X axis).

PART TWO

Mathematics of business and management

5 Business applications—Depreciation and break-even analysis

Introduction

Depreciation is an accounting concept. It allows the cost of depreciable assets such as buildings, machinery, and equipment to be allocated to accounting periods to properly measure net income and evaluate assets. As no single method of allocation is suitable for all depreciable assets under all circumstances, various methods of depreciation have been developed.

The main concern for owners and management in operating a business is profitability. To achieve or maintain a desired level of profitability, managers must make decisions that affect product mix, total revenue, and total cost.

A valuable tool in evaluating the potential effects of decisions on profitability is cost-volume-profit analysis. The most popular approach to cost-volume-profit analysis is called **break-even analysis**.

The Appendix contains a more extensive consideration of cost-profit-volume analysis as well as an introduction to linear programming, which is a useful mathematical tool in making decisions regarding profit mix.

Objectives

Upon completing this chapter, you will be able to

1. compute the depreciation and the book value for an asset in each year of its life and construct depreciation schedules using averaging methods (straight-line, units of product, service hours), sum-of-the-years-digits method, and declining balance methods (simple, complex, constant percentage);
2. construct detailed break-even charts and compute break-even values.

5.1 *Depreciation*

A. Basic concepts and methods

The useful life of physical assets such as plant, machinery, and equipment that are used to produce goods and services is limited due to physical deterioration, wear and tear, decay, and obsolescence. As a result, such assets lose their value over a period of time. From an accounting point of view, this loss in value, **depreciation**, is treated as an *expense* of operating a business.

To make provision for this expense, various systematic methods to record the expiration of the usefulness of such assets have been developed. Recording depreciation is a process of allocating the original cost of assets to the accounting periods that benefit from the use of the assets.

Whatever *method of depreciation* is used, certain aspects are common to all.

1. The **original cost** of the asset including all necessary and reasonable expenditures to ready the asset for its intended purpose.
2. The **residual value (scrap value, salvage value, trade-in value**) at the time the asset has lost its usefulness.
3. The **wearing value**, or the total amount of depreciation over the useful life of the asset; that is, the difference between the original cost and the residual value of the asset.
4. The **useful life** of the asset (usually stated in years).
5. The **accumulated depreciation**—the total depreciation allocated at any point in the life of the asset to expired accounting periods.
6. The **book value** or net value of the asset at any point in the life of the asset; that is, the difference between the original cost and the accumulated depreciation.
7. **Depreciation schedules** showing the details of allocating the cost of the asset to the various accounting periods.

No single method of allocating the wearing value is suitable for all depreciable assets. Instead, the various assumptions about how the loss in value should be allocated to accounting periods have led to the development of a variety of methods of depreciation.

Of the methods available, the following are described in this chapter:

(a) *Allocation on the basis of averages*
1. Straight Line
2. Service Hours
3. Units of Product

(b) *Allocation based on a diminishing charge per year*

1. Sum-of-the-years-digits
2. Declining balance:
   (i) Simple declining balance
   (ii) Complex declining balance
   (iii) Constant percentage

B. Methods of allocating depreciation based on an average

Methods of depreciation in this category are based on the assumption that the loss in value (depreciation) is the same for each unit of useful life of the asset, such as time period, service hour, or unit of product.

1. *The straight-line method of depreciation*

This method is the simplest. It is based on the assumption that the loss in value is the same for equal time periods (usually years). The depreciation per time period is found by dividing the total wearing value by the number of time periods in the life of the asset. Since the wearing value is the difference between the original cost and the residual value, the yearly depreciation is

$$\text{YEARLY DEPRECIATION} = \frac{\text{ORIGINAL COST} - \text{RESIDUAL VALUE}}{n} \quad \longleftarrow \textit{Formula } 5.1$$

where n = the numbers of years in the life of the asset

Example 5.1a A machine costing \$20 000.00 has a salvage value of \$3200.00 after five years. Use the straight-line method to

(i) compute the yearly depreciation expense;
(ii) determine the depreciation expense in Year 4;
(iii) construct a depreciation schedule.

Solution

(i) The original cost = 20 000.00;
the residual value = 3200.00;
the wearing value is 20 000.00 − 3200.00 = 16 800.00;
the life of the asset (in years) = 5.

$$\text{Yearly depreciation expense is } \frac{16\,800.00}{5} = \$3360.00.$$

(ii) The depreciation expense in Year 4 = \$3360.00.

(iii) ***Depreciation schedule (straight-line method)***

End of year	*Annual depreciation expense*	*Accumulated depreciation*	*Book value*
0			20 000.00
1	3 360.00	3 360.00	16 640.00
2	3 360.00	6 720.00	13 280.00
3	3 360.00	10 080.00	9 920.00
4	3 360.00	13 440.00	6 560.00
5	3 360.00	16 800.00	3 200.00
TOTAL	16 800.00		

Explanations of the schedule

(1) The annual depreciation expense is the same for each year and totals the wearing value of $16 800.00.
(2) The accumulated depreciation is a running total of the annual depreciation. After five years, it equals the wearing value.
(3) The book value diminishes each year by the annual depreciation expense. After five years, it must equal the salvage value of $3200.00.

2. *The service-hours method of depreciation*

The underlying assumption for this method is similar to that for the straight-line method. However this method is based on the number of useful service hours in the life of the asset.

$$\text{DEPRECIATION PER SERVICE HOUR} = \frac{\text{ORIGINAL COST} - \text{RESIDUAL VALUE}}{n}$$

where n = the number of service hours in the life of the asset

← ***Formula* 5.2**

The depreciation expense for a time period (such as a year) is found by multiplying the number of service hours in the time period by the depreciation per service hour.

***Example* 5.1b** Assuming that the useful life of the machine in Example 5.1a is 9600 hours, use the service-hours method to

(i) determine the depreciation expense per service hour;
(ii) determine the depreciation expense in Year 4 if the number of service hours in Year 4 is 1880;
(iii) construct a depreciation schedule if the service hours per year for the five years are respectively 2000, 1960, 1840, 1880, and 1920.

Solution

(i) The original cost = 20 000.00;
the residual value = 3200.00;
the wearing value is 20 000.00 − 3200.00 = 16 800.00;
the life of the asset (in number of service hours) = 9600.

The depreciation per service hour is $\frac{16\,800.00}{9600}$ = \$1.75.

(ii) Depreciation in Year 4 is 1.75(1880) = \$3290.00.

(iii) ***Depreciation schedule (service-hours method)***

End of year	*Annual depreciation expense*	*Accumulated depreciation*	*Book value*
0			20 000.00
1	1.75(2000) = 3 500.00	3 500.00	16 500.00
2	1.75(1960) = 3 430.00	6 930.00	13 070.00
3	1.75(1840) = 3 220.00	10 150.00	9 850.00
4	1.75(1880) = 3 290.00	13 440.00	6 560.00
5	1.75(1920) = 3 360.00	16 800.00	3 200.00
TOTAL	16 800.00		

3. *The units-of-product method*

This method is based on the assumption that the loss in value is the same per unit of product.

$$\text{DEPRECIATION PER UNIT OF PRODUCT} = \frac{\text{ORIGINAL COST} - \text{RESIDUAL VALUE}}{n}$$ ← ***Formula* 5.3**

where n = the number of product units in the life of the asset

The depreciation expense for a time period (such as a year) is found by multiplying the number of product units in the time period by the depreciation per unit.

Example 5.1c Assuming that the machine in Example 5.1a can make 240 000 units of product during its useful life, use the units-of-product method to

(i) determine the depreciation expense per unit of product;

(ii) determine the depreciation in Year 4 if the number of units of product in Year 4 is 46 400;

(iii) construct a depreciation schedule if the number of units of product during each of the five years is respectively 50 800, 49 200, 46 700, 46 400, and 46 900.

Solution

(i) The original cost = 20 000.00;
the residual value = 3200.00;
the wearing value is 20 000.00 − 3200.00 = 16 800.00;
the life of the asset (in number of units of product) = 240 000.
The depreciation per unit of product is $\frac{16\ 800.00}{240\ 000} = \$0.07$.

(ii) The depreciation in Year 4 is 0.07(46 400) = $3248.00.

(iii) ***Depreciation schedule (units-of-product method)***

End of year	*Annual depreciation expense*	*Accumulated depreciation*	*Book value*
0			20 000.00
1	0.07(50 800) = 3 556.00	3 556.00	16 444.00
2	0.07(49 200) = 3 444.00	7 000.00	13 000.00
3	0.07(46 700) = 3 269.00	10 269.00	9 731.00
4	0.07(46 400) = 3 248.00	13 517.00	6 483.00
5	0.07(46 900) = 3 283.00	16 800.00	3 200.00
TOTAL	16 800.00		

C. *Methods of allocating depreciation as a diminishing charge per year*

Methods of depreciation in this category are based on the assumption that the loss in value is highest in the first year and then diminishes yearly during the useful life of an asset.

1. *The sum-of-the-years-digits method*

This method assumes that the loss in value diminishes by a constant amount from year to year. First, the number of parts into which the wearing value is to be divided must be determined. This number is the sum of the digits corresponding to the years in the life of the asset in sequential order starting with 1. Proportional parts of the total depreciation expense are then assigned to each year in reverse order of the digits.

Example **5.1d** Assume that the machine in Example 5.1a is depreciated by the sum-of-the-years-digits method.

(i) Determine the depreciation for each year.

(ii) Construct a depreciation schedule.

Solution

(i) The original cost = 20 000.00;
the residual value = 3200.00;
the wearing value is 20 000.00 − 3200.00 = 16 800.00;
the life of the asset (in years) = 5.

The yearly depreciation is determined by following the steps outlined below.

Year in life of asset	*Digit identifying year*	*Proportional part of wearing value assigned to year*	*Yearly depreciation expense*
One	1	5	5(1120.00) = 5600.00
Two	2	4	4(1120.00) = 4480.00
Three	3	3	3(1120.00) = 3360.00
Four	4	2	2(1120.00) = 2240.00
Five	5	1	1(1120.00) = 1120.00
Sum of the digits		15	
Value of each of the 15 parts is $\frac{16\,800.00}{15} = 1120.00$			

STEP 1 Identify each year in the life of the asset by a digit in sequential order starting with 1, i.e., 1, 2, 3, 4, 5.

STEP 2 Assign to each year proportional parts of the total wearing value in *reverse* order of the digits identifying the years, i.e., 5, 4, 3, 2, 1.

STEP 3 Determine the sum of the years-digits: 1 + 2 + 3 + 4 + 5 = 15. Since the sum of the years-digits is always the sum of an arithmetic progression formed by the first n whole numbers, it can be more conveniently determined by using the formula

$$S_n = \frac{n(n+1)}{2}$$

$$S_5 = \frac{5(5+1)}{2} = 15$$

STEP 4 Compute the value of each of the 15 parts of the wearing value.

$$\frac{16\,800.00}{15} = \$1120.00$$

STEP 5 Determine the yearly depreciation by multiplying the value of one part (\$1120.00) by the number of parts assigned to each year.

An algebraic approach can replace the arithmetic approach shown above.

$nk + (n - 1)k + (n - 2)k + \dots + 3k + 2k + k = \text{Wearing Value}$

n = the digit identifying the last year in the life of the asset

k = the value of one of the $n\frac{(n+1)}{2}$ proportional parts

$$k[n + (n - 1) + (n - 2) + \dots + 3 + 2 + 1] = \text{Wearing Value}$$

$$k\left[\frac{n(n+1)}{2}\right] = \text{Wearing Value}$$

$$k = \frac{\text{WEARING VALUE}}{\frac{n(n+1)}{2}}$$ ← ***Formula* 5.4**

In this example, $5k + 4k + 3k + 2k + k = 16\,800.00$

or, directly by formula, $k = \frac{16\,800.00}{\frac{5(5+1)}{2}} = \frac{16\,800.00}{15} = \$1120.00$

(ii) ***Depreciation schedule (sum-of-the-years-digits method)***

End of year	*Parts*	*Annual depreciation expense*	*Accumulated depreciation*	*Book value*
0				20 000.00
1	5	5 600.00	5 600.00	14 400.00
2	4	4 480.00	10 080.00	9 920.00
3	3	3 360.00	13 440.00	6 560.00
4	2	2 240.00	15 680.00	4 320.00
5	1	1 120.00	16 800.00	3 200.00
TOTAL	15	16 800.00		

2. *Declining-balance methods*

In these methods, the depreciation for a particular year is based on the book value at the end of the previous year and is calculated over the years at a constant rate. Three variations are used.

(a) The simple declining-balance method

(b) The complex declining-balance method

(c) The constant-percentage method

All three methods work in basically the same way and differ only in how the rate of depreciation, d, is determined.

(a) The simple declining-balance method

When this variation of the declining balance methods is used, the rate of depreciation is determined by

$$d = 2 \times \frac{1}{n}$$

where n = the number of years in the life of the asset ⟵ *Formula* 5.5

No consideration is given to the residual value until the final year in the life of the asset or until the book value drops below the residual value.

Example 5.1e Assume that the machine in Example 5.1a is depreciated by the simple declining-balance method.

(i) Determine the rate of depreciation.

(ii) Compute the depreciation for Year 4.

(iii) Construct a depreciation schedule.

Solution

(i) The rate of depreciation is $2\left(\frac{1}{5}\right) = \frac{2}{5} = 40\%$

(ii)

Original book value	20 000.00
Depreciation in Year 1: 40% of 20 000.00	8 000.00
Book Value End of Year 1	12 000.00
Depreciation in Year 2: 40% of 12 000.00	4 800.00
Book Value End of Year 2	7 200.00
Depreciation in Year 3: 40% of 7200.00	2 880.00
Book Value End of Year 3	4 320.00

Ordinarily, the depreciation for Year 4 would be computed as 40% of 4320.00 = 1728.00. However, when \$1728.00 is subtracted from \$4320.00, the result is smaller than the residual value of \$3200.00. When this happens, the depreciation is the difference between the previous book value and the residual value; that is, the depreciation for Year 4 is 4320.00 − 3200.00 = \$1120.00.

(iii) ***Depreciation schedule (simple declining-balance method)***

End of year	*Annual depreciation expense*		*Accumulated depreciation*	*Book value*
0				20 000.00
1	0.40(20 000.00) =	8 000.00	8 000.00	12 000.00
2	0.40(12 000.00) =	4 800.00	12 800.00	7 200.00
3	0.40(7200.00) =	2 880.00	15 680.00	4 320.00
4	4320.00 − 3200.00 =	1 120.00	16 800.00	3 200.00
5	3200.00 − 3200.00 =	0.00	16 800.00	3 200.00
TOTAL		16 800.00		

Alternative Approach to part (ii)
In part (ii), the successive book values were obtained by subtracting the amount of depreciation for each year. Alternatively, the book value can be determined by multiplying the value at the beginning of the year by net factor 1 − 0.40 = 0.60.

Book value at the end of Year 1 = 20 000.00(0.60) = 12 000.00;
Book value at the end of Year 2 = 12 000.00(0.60) = 7 200.00;
Book value at the end of Year 3 = 7 200.00(0.60) = 4 320.00.

This approach permits the book value to be determined directly at any time by multiplying the original book value by the product of the net factors. For the book value at the end of Year 3, the product of the net factors = (0.60)(0.60)(0.60).

The book value at the end of Year 3

$$
\begin{aligned}
&= 20\ 000.00(0.60)(0.60)(0.60) \\
&= 20\ 000.00(0.60)^3 \\
&= 20\ 000.00(0.216) \\
&= \$4320.00
\end{aligned}
$$

***Example* 5.1f** Equipment costing \$36 000.00 with a scrap value of \$4300.00 is depreciated over twenty years by the simple declining-balance method. Determine the depreciation in Year 8.

Solution

The original cost = 36 000.00;

the rate of depreciation = $2\left(\frac{1}{20}\right) = \frac{1}{10} = 0.10 = 10\%$;

the net factor = 1 − 0.10 = 0.90.

Since the depreciation in Year 8 is 10% of the previous book value, we need to determine the book value after seven years. During each of the first seven years, depreciation of 10% has been taken from the successive book values starting with the original book value.

Using the net factor approach, the book value after seven years

$= 36\ 000.00(0.90)(0.90)(0.90)(0.90)(0.90)(0.90)(0.90)$
$= 36\ 000.00(0.90)^7$
$= 36\ 000.00(0.4782969)$
$= \$17\ 218.69$

The depreciation in Year 8 is $0.10(17\ 218.69) = \$1721.87$.

(b) The complex declining-balance method

While the simple declining-balance method ignores any residual value in establishing the rate of depreciation, the complex variation takes the residual value into account by using the following formula to determine the rate of depreciation.

$$d = 1 - \sqrt[n]{\frac{\text{RESIDUAL VALUE}}{\text{ORIGINAL COST}}} \quad \longleftarrow \textit{Formula } 5.6$$

where n = the number of years in the life of the asset

Development of Formula 5.6

Let the original cost be represented by C; let the residual value after n years be represented by T_n; let the book value after n years be represented by B_n; let the number of years in the life of the asset be represented by n; and let the rate of depreciation that will reduce the original cost to the residual value in n years be represented by d.

Then the book value after

one year	$B_1 = C - Cd = C(1 - d)$
two years	$B_2 = B_1 - B_1d = B_1(1 - d) = C(1 - d)(1 - d) = C(1 - d)^2$
three years	$B_3 = B_2 - B_2d = B_2(1 - d) = C(1 - d)^2(1 - d) = C(1 - d)^3$
four years	$B_4 = C(1 - d)^4$
five years	$B_5 = C(1 - d)^5$
n years	$B_n = C(1 - d)^n$

However, after n years $B_n = T_n$:

$$T_n = C(1 - d)^n$$

$$\frac{T_n}{C} = (1 - d)^n \longleftarrow \text{divide both sides by C}$$

$$\sqrt[n]{\frac{T_n}{C}} = 1 - d \longleftarrow \text{take the } n\text{th root}$$

$$d = 1 - \sqrt[n]{\frac{T_n}{C}} = 1 - \sqrt[n]{\frac{\text{Residual value}}{\text{Original cost}}}$$

Example 5.1g Assuming that the machine in Example 5.1a is depreciated by the complex declining-balance method,

(i) determine the rate of depreciation;

(ii) compute the depreciation in Year 4;

(iii) construct a depreciation schedule.

Solution

(i) The original cost = 20 000.00;
the residual value = 3200.00;
the life of the asset (in years) = 5.

$$d = 1 - \sqrt[5]{\frac{3200.00}{20\,000.00}} = 1 - \sqrt[5]{0.16} = 1 - 0.6931448 = 0.3068552$$

The rate of depreciation d = 30.68552%.

(ii) The book value after three years
= 20 000.00(1 − 0.3068552)^3
= 20 000.00(0.6931448)^3
= 20 000.00(0.3330213)
= \$6660.43
The depreciation in Year 4 is 6660.43(0.3068552) = \$2043.79.

(iii) ***Depreciation schedule (complex declining-balance method)***

End of year	*Annual depreciation expense*	*Accumulated depreciation*	*Book value*
0			20 000.00
1	6 137.10	6 137.10	13 862.90
2	4 253.90	10 391.00	9 609.00
3	2 948.57	13 339.57	6 660.43
4	2 043.79	15 383.36	4 616.64
5	1 416.64	16 800.00	3 200.00
TOTAL	16 800.00		

(c) The constant percentage method

This variation of the declining-balance methods is based on an arbitrarily established yearly rate of depreciation. It is the method commonly used for income tax purposes when computing capital cost allowance.

Under the regulations of the Income Tax Act, a capital cost allowance may be claimed for depreciable business assets according to their classification at a maximum rate established for each classification.

The most common classes are

Class 3 Buildings—maximum rate 3%;
Class 8 Machinery and Equipment—maximum rate 20%;
Class 10 Cars, trucks, vans, tractors, contractor's equipment—maximum rate 30%.

***Example* 5.1h** Assuming that the machine in Example 5.1a falls into Class 8, develop a capital cost allowance schedule for the five years at the maximum allowable rate.

Solution

The original cost = 20 000.00;
the residual value = 3200.00;
the life of the asset (in years) = 5;
the maximum allowable rate = 20%.

Capital cost allowance schedule

End of year	*Annual capital cost allowance*	*Accumulated capital cost allowance*	*Book value*
0			20 000.00
1	4 000.00	4 000.00	16 000.00
2	3 200.00	7 200.00	12 800.00
3	2 560.00	9 760.00	10 240.00
4	2 048.00	11 808.00	8 192.00
5	1 638.40	13 446.40	6 553.60
TOTAL	13 446.40		

Note: The depreciated value of the machine after five years is well above its estimated residual value at that time. The tax implications are beyond the scope of this text and are not considered here.

D. *Finding the book value and yearly depreciation without a depreciation schedule*

The book value after a given number of years or the depreciation in any particular year can be determined without constructing a depreciation schedule using any of the methods illustrated.

Example 5.1i Equipment costing \$35 720.00 has an estimated trade-in value of \$1400.00 after fifteen years. Find (a) the book value after nine years and (b) the depreciation charge in Year 10 using

(i) the straight-line method;

(ii) the sum-of-the-years-digits method;

(iii) the simple declining-balance method;

(iv) the complex declining-balance method.

Solution

The original cost = 35 720.00;
the residual value = 1400.00;
the wearing value is 35 720.00 − 1400.00 = 34 320.00;
$n = 15$.

(i) *Straight-Line Method*

The yearly depreciation is $\frac{34\ 320.00}{15} = \$2288.00$.

The accumulated depreciation after nine years is 2288.00(9) = \$20 592.00.

(a) The book value after nine years is 35 720.00 − 20 592.00 = \$15 128.00.

(b) The depreciation in Year 10 (as in any year) = \$2288.00.

(ii) *Sum-of-the-Years-Digits Method*

The number of parts into which the wearing value is to be divided is $\frac{(15)(16)}{2} = 120$.

The value of each part is $\frac{34\ 320}{120} = \$286.00$.

The sum of the number of parts assigned to the first nine years

$= 15 + 14 + 13 + 12 + 11 + 10 + 9 + 8 + 7$

$= 120 -$ sum of the parts in the remaining six years

$= 120 - \frac{6(7)}{2} = 120 - 21 = 99$

The accumulated depreciation for the first nine years = 99(286.00)
= \$28 314.00

(a) The book value after nine years is 35 720.00 − 28 314.00 = \$7406.00

(b) Since Year 10 is the first of the remaining six years, six parts are assigned; the depreciation in Year 10 is 6(286.00) = \$1716.00.

(iii) *Simple Declining-Balance Method*

The rate of depreciation is $2\left(\frac{1}{15}\right) = 0.1333333 = 13.33333\%$.

(a) The book value after nine years
$= 35\ 720.00(1 - 0.1333333)^9$ ⟵ see Example 5.1e
$= 35\ 720.00(0.8666667)^9$
$= 35\ 720.00(0.2758475)$
$= \$9853.27$

(b) The depreciation in Year 10 is $9853.27(0.1333333) = \$1313.77$.

(iv) *Complex Declining-Balance Method*

$$\text{Rate} = 1 - \sqrt[15]{\frac{1400.00}{35\ 720.00}} = 1 - 0.8057762 = 0.1942238 = 19.42238\%$$

(a) The book value after nine years
$= 35\ 720.00(1 - 0.1942238)^9$
$= 35\ 720.00(0.8057762)^9$
$= 35\ 720.00(0.1431957)$
$= \$5114.95$

(b) The depreciation in Year 10 is $5114.95(0.1942238) = \$993.45$.

E. *Computer application—Depreciation schedules*

Many of the problems dealt with in this text can be solved by computers. Refer to the programs included in the Solutions Manual. The programs are written in BASIC for use on an IBM PC or IBM compatibles.

A computer solution for the construction of depreciation schedules by either the straight-line method or the sum-of-the-years-digit method is provided by Program 6 (see the Solutions Manual).

Exercise 5.1

A. For each of the following, construct a depreciation schedule using the indicated methods of depreciation.

1. Equipment with an original book value of $40 000 is estimated to have a scrap value of $5000 after ten years. The number of service hours for each of the first four years will be 2025, for each of the next three years 1990, and for each of the last three years 1775. For each of the first four years, the number of units of product

is expected to be 10 750, for each of the next three years 9800, and for each of the last three years 9200. For income tax purposes, the equipment is grouped into Class 8. Construct a depreciation schedule using

(a) the straight-line method;

(b) the service-hours method;

(c) the units-of-product method;

(d) the sum-of-the-years-digit method;

(e) the simple declining-balance method;

(f) the complex declining-balance method;

(g) the constant percentage method.

2. A combine costing $32 000 has a trade-in value of $5000 after eight years. Construct a depreciation schedule using

(a) the straight-line method;

(b) the sum-of-the-years-digits method;

(c) the simple declining-balance method;

(d) the complex declining-balance method.

B. Answer the following questions.

1. A building costing $560 000 is estimated to have a life of 40 years and a salvage value of $68 000. Compute the book value after 15 years and the depreciation charge in Year 16 for

(a) the straight-line method;

(b) the sum-of-the-years-digits method;

(c) the simple declining-balance method;

(d) the complex declining-balance method.

2. Heavy machinery costing $150 000 with a scrap value of $13 500 is estimated to have a life of 25 years. Compute the book value after 10 years and the depreciation charge in Year 11 for

(a) the straight-line method;

(b) the sum-of-the-years-digits method;

(c) the simple declining-balance method;

(d) the complex declining-balance method.

5.2 *Break-even analysis*

A. Cost-volume-profit relationships

A primary function of accounting is the collection of cost and revenue data. This data is then used to examine the existing relationships between cost behaviour and revenue behaviour.

Any analysis, whether graphic or algebraic, makes certain assumptions about the behaviour of costs and revenue. In its simplest form, cost-volume-profit analysis makes the following assumptions.

1. Revenue per unit of output is constant. Total revenue varies directly with volume.
2. Costs can be classified as either fixed or variable.
3. **Fixed costs** remain constant over the time period considered for all levels of output. Examples of costs in this category are depreciation, rent, property taxes, and supervision and management salaries. Since fixed costs are constant in total, they vary per unit of output. They decrease per unit of output as volume increases and increase per unit of output as volume decreases.
4. **Variable costs** are constant per unit of output regardless of volume. They fluctuate in total amount as volume fluctuates. Examples of costs in this category are direct material costs, direct labour costs, and sales commissions.

The above assumptions present a simplified view of the real world. Fixed costs are not constant across all levels of output; instead they tend to change in a step-like manner. Per unit variable costs are not always constant; they are often influenced by economies of scale. Costs cannot be rigidly classified into fixed costs and variable costs. Rather, many costs are semi-variable; that is, they contain a fixed component as well as a variable component. However, for purposes of an uncomplicated introductory analysis, these assumptions serve a useful purpose.

Using these simplified assumptions, the behaviour of revenue and the behaviour of costs may be represented graphically by straight-line diagrams as shown in Figures 5.1 and 5.2.

FIGURE 5.1 ***Revenue behaviour***

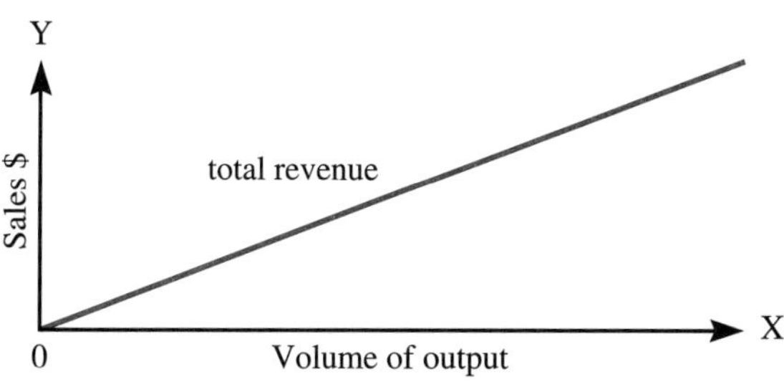

FIGURE 5.2 ***Cost behaviour***

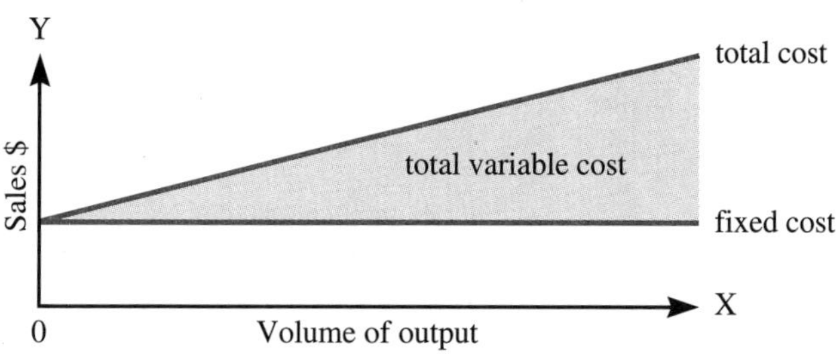

B. Break-even chart

The break-even approach to cost-volume-profit analysis focuses on profitability. It is specifically concerned with identifying the level of output at which the business neither makes a profit nor sustains a loss, that is, the level of output at which

$$\text{NET INCOME} = 0$$

The level of output at which NI = 0 is called the **break-even point** and is obtained from the relationship

$$\text{TOTAL REVENUE} = \text{TOTAL COST}$$

In addition, the following relationships are useful.

$$\text{TOTAL REVENUE} = \text{VOLUME} \times \text{UNIT REVENUE}$$

$$\text{TOTAL VARIABLE COST} = \text{VOLUME} \times \text{VARIABLE COST PER UNIT}$$

$$\text{TOTAL COST} = \text{FIXED COST} + \text{TOTAL VARIABLE COST}$$

The relationship between revenue and costs at different levels of output may be portrayed graphically by showing revenue behaviour (Figure 5.1) and cost behaviour (Figure 5.2) on the same graph. The resulting graph shows the break-even point and is known as a **break-even chart** (see Figure 5.3).

FIGURE 5.3 *Break-even chart*

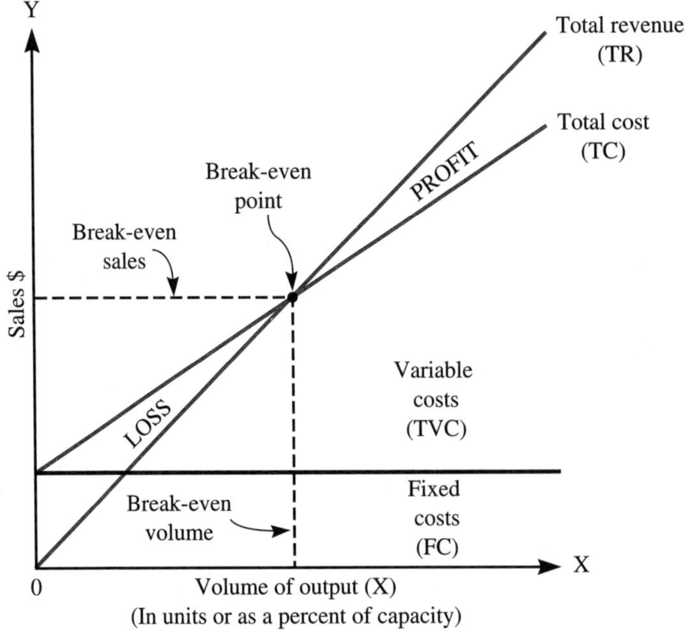

Notes on the charts

1. The horizontal axis represents volume of output either as a number of units or as a percent of capacity. The vertical axis represents dollar values (sales revenue). The origin is at zero—zero volume and zero dollars.
2. The total revenue line is drawn by plotting two or more total revenue points (one of which is always the origin) and joining them.
3. The fixed cost line is drawn parallel to the horizontal axis from the point on the vertical axis that represents total fixed cost dollars.
4. The total cost line is drawn by plotting two or more total cost points (one of which is always the point at which the fixed cost line starts on the vertical axis) and joining them.
5. The point at which the total revenue line and the total cost line intersect is the break-even point.
6. The point of intersection on the horizontal axis of the perpendicular drawn from the break-even point to the horizontal axis indicates the break-even volume in units or as a percent of capacity.
7. The point of intersection on the vertical axis of the perpendicular drawn from the break-even point to the vertical axis indicates the break-even volume in dollars ($ Sales).
8. The area between the horizontal axis and the fixed cost line represents the fixed cost in dollars.
9. The area between the fixed cost line and the total cost line represents the total variable cost in dollars for all levels of operations.
10. The area between the total revenue line and the total cost line to the left of the break-even point represents the loss area, that is, where total revenue is less than total cost.
11. The area between the total cost line and the total revenue line to the right of the break-even point represents the profit area, that is, where total revenue is greater than total cost.

The graphic approach of a break-even chart is complemented by an algebraic approach that uses the relationship Total Revenue = Total Cost.

Both approaches are illustrated in the examples that follow. Two distinct situations may be encountered depending on the accounting data that is available. In the first situation, illustrated in Section C, the accounting information is in units. In the second situation, illustrated in Section D, the accounting information is in total dollars.

C. Break-even analysis—Case 1

The available accounting data is in units.

***Example* 5.2a** Market research for a new product indicates that the product can be sold at $50.00 per unit. Cost analysis provides the following information.

Fixed cost per period = \$8640.00
Variable cost per unit = \$30.00
Production capacity per period = 900 units

Perform a break-even analysis. Provide

(i) an algebraic statement of
 (a) the total revenue,
 (b) the total cost;

(ii) a detailed break-even chart;

(iii) computation of the break-even point
 (a) in units,
 (b) as a percent of capacity,
 (c) in dollars.

Solution

(i) Let the volume in units be X.

(a) Total revenue, TR = Volume × Unit revenue
= (X)(50.00)
= 50.00X
Total revenue, TR = 50X.

(b) Total variable cost = Volume × Variable cost per unit
= (X)(30.00)
= 30.00X
Total cost, TC = Fixed cost + Total variable cost
= 8640.00 + 30.00X
Total cost, TC = 8640 + 30X.

(ii) *Break-Even Chart*

You can draw the break-even chart by graphing the revenue function, TR = 50X, and the cost function, TC = 8640 + 30X.

Since capacity is 900 units, the horizontal scale needs to allow for X values up to 900. The vertical scale must allow for maximum sales dollars of (900)(50) = 45 000.

Graphing the revenue function, TR = 50X

To graph the revenue function, assume at least two values of X and compute the corresponding value of TR.

For X = 0, TR = (50)(0) = 0 ⟶ Graph point (0,0)
For X = 900, TR = (50)(900) = 45 000 ⟶ Graph point (900,45 000)

While any value of X may be used, the two values selected are the preferred values. They represent the two extreme values (minimum and maximum volume) for the example.

Graphing the cost function, TC = 8640 + 30X

Assume two values of X and compute the corresponding value of TC.

For X = 0, TC = 8640 + 30(0) = 8640 ⟶ Graph point (0,8640)
For X = 900, TC = 8640 + 30(900)
= 8640 + 27 000 = 35 640 ⟶ Graph point (900,35 640)

FIGURE 5.4 ***Break-even chart for example 5.2a***

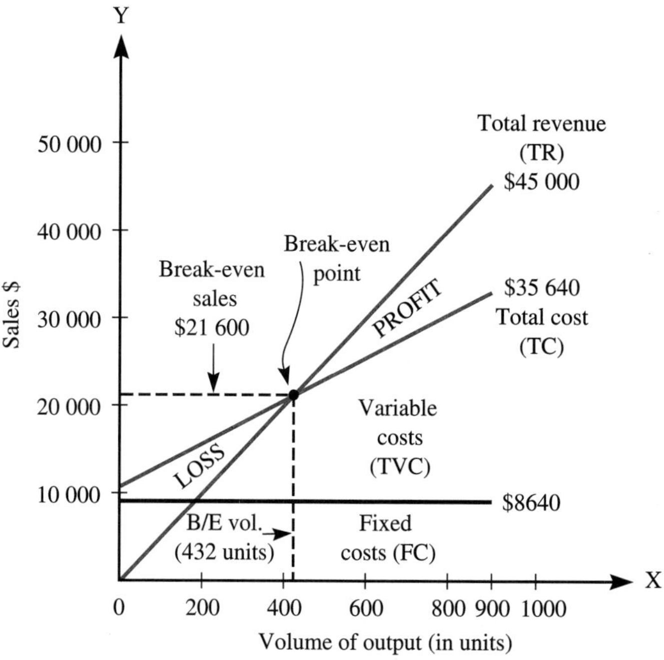

(iii) To determine the break-even point, use the break-even relationship.

Total Revenue, TR = Total Cost, TC

$$50X = 8640 + 30X$$
$$20X = 8640$$
$$X = 432$$

(a) The break-even volume in units is 432.

(b) As a percent of capacity, the break-even volume is $\frac{432}{900} = 0.48 = 48\%$.

(c) The break-even volume in dollars = (432)(50) = \$21 600.

D. *Break-even analysis—Case 2*

The available accounting data is in total dollars.

***Example* 5.2b** The following information is available about the operations of the King Corp. for the current year.

Sales		\$40 000
Fixed costs	\$12 600	
Variable costs	16 000	
Total cost		28 600
Net income		\$11 400

Capacity is a sales volume of \$60 000.

Perform a break-even analysis. Provide

(i) an algebraic statement of
 (a) the revenue function,
 (b) the cost function;

(ii) a detailed break-even chart;

(iii) computation of the break-even point
 (a) in sales dollars,
 (b) as a percent of capacity.

Solution

(i) When the data is in terms of dollars rather than units, express the functions in terms of sales volume.

Let X represent the sales volume in dollars.

(a) The revenue function is Total Revenue, TR = X.

(b) Since variable costs are directly related to sales volume, they can be expressed as a percent of sales volume.

In this example, total variable costs are \$16 000 for a sales volume of \$40 000.

$$\frac{\text{Total Variable Cost}}{\text{Total Revenue}} = \frac{16\ 000}{40\ 000} = 0.40 = 40\%$$

$$\text{Total Variable Cost} = 40\% \text{ of Total Revenue} = 0.40\ \text{TR}$$

$$\text{The cost function is TC} = 12\ 600 + 0.40\ \text{TR}$$

$$\text{or TC} = 12\ 600 + 0.40\text{X}$$

(ii) When the accounting data is in terms of total dollars, the horizontal axis represents output in terms of percent of sales capacity. Subdivide the horizontal scale to allow percent sales levels up to 100%. The vertical scale must allow for the maximum sales level of \$60 000.

Graphing the Revenue Function, TR = X

To graph the revenue function, assume at least two sales volume levels expressed as a percent of capacity.

For X = 0, TR = 0 ⟶ Graph point (0,0)
For X = 60 000, TR = 60 000 ⟶ Graph point (60 000, 60 000)

The line joining the two points represents the revenue function.

Graphing the Cost Function, TC = 12 600 + 0.40X

Assume two sales volume levels and compute TC.

For X = 0, TC = 12 600 + 0.40(0)
= 12 600 ⟶ Graph point (0,12 600)
For X = 60 000, TC = 12 600 + 0.40(60 000)
= 12 600 + 24 000
= 36 600 ⟶ Graph point (60 000,36 600)

FIGURE 5.5 ***Break-even chart for example 5.2b***

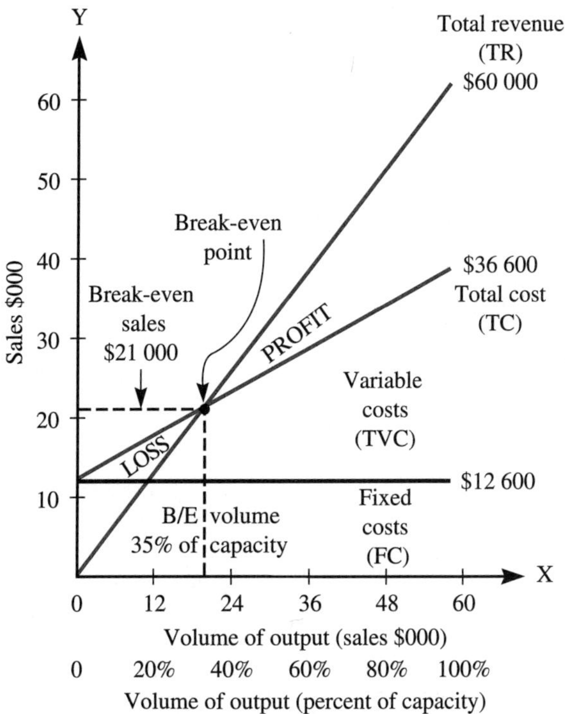

(iii) The break-even point is given by

$$X = 12\,600 + 0.40X$$
$$0.60\,X = 12\,600$$
$$X = 21\,000$$

(a) The break-even volume in dollars is \$21 000.

(b) The break-even point is $\frac{21\,000}{60\,000} = 35\%$ of sales capacity.

E. Finding the break-even point by using unit contribution

As an alternative to using the break-even relationship, Total Revenue = Total Cost, we can use the concept of contribution margin per unit to determine break-even volume:

$$\text{CONTRIBUTION MARGIN PER UNIT} = \text{SELLING PRICE PER UNIT} - \text{VARIABLE COST PER UNIT}$$

$$\text{BREAK-EVEN VOLUME} = \frac{\text{FIXED COST}}{\text{UNIT CONTRIBUTION MARGIN}}$$

Example **5.2c** Use contribution margin per unit to determine the break-even volume for Example 5.2a.

Solution

Fixed cost = \$8640.00;
Selling price per unit = \$50.00;
Variable cost per unit = \$30.00.
Contribution margin per unit = 50.00 − 30.00 = \$20.00

$$\text{Break-even volume} = \frac{\text{Fixed cost}}{\text{Contribution margin}} = \frac{8640.00}{20.00} = 432$$

Break-even volume is 432 units.

Example **5.2d** Use contribution margin per unit to determine the break-even volume for Example 5.2b.

Solution

Fixed cost = \$12 600.00;
When the sales volume is given in total dollars, the selling price per unit = \$1.00;
Variable cost per unit = 40% of \$1.00 = \$0.40.
Contribution margin = 1.00 − 0.40 = \$0.60.

$$\text{Break-even volume} = \frac{12\,600.00}{0.60} = 21\,000.00.$$

Break-even volume is a sales volume of \$21 000.

F. Computer application—Break-even analysis

Program 1—Break-even analysis—provides a numerical computer solution for Case 1 illustrated in this text.

Exercise 5.2

A. For each of the following, perform a break-even analysis showing

(a) an algebraic statement of
  (i) the revenue function,
  (ii) the cost function;

(b) a detailed break-even chart;

(c) computation of the break-even point
  (i) in units (if applicable),
  (ii) as a percent of capacity,
  (iii) in sales dollars.

1. Engineering estimates show that the variable cost of manufacturing a new product will be \$35 per unit. Based on market research, the selling price of the product is to be \$120 per unit and variable selling expense is expected to be \$15 per unit. The fixed costs applicable to the new product are estimated to be \$2800 per period and capacity per period is 100 units.

2. A firm manufactures a product that sells for \$12.00 per unit. Variable cost per unit is \$8.00 and fixed cost per period is \$1200. Capacity per period is 1000 units.

3. The following data pertains to the operating budget of Matt Mfg.

Sales			\$720 000
	Fixed cost	\$220 000	
	Total variable cost	324 000	544 000
Net income			\$176 000

Capacity is a sales volume of \$800 000 per period.

4. Harrow Seed and Fertilizer has compiled the following estimates for operations.

Sales			\$120 000
	Fixed cost	\$43 200	
	Variable costs	48 000	91 200
Net income			\$28 800

Capacity is a sales volume of \$150 000.

Review exercise

1. A machine costing $12 000 has a trade-in value of $2460 after eight years. Construct a depreciation schedule using
   (a) the sum-of-the-years-digit method;
   (b) the simple declining-balance method;
   (c) the complex declining-balance method.
2. Equipment with an original cost of $32 000 has an estimated life of 25 years and a scrap value of $480. Compute the book value after 20 years and the depreciation charge in Year 21 using
   (a) the straight-line method;
   (b) the sum-of-the-years-digit method;
   (c) the simple declining-balance method;
   (d) the complex declining-balance method.
3. A machine with an original cost of $9160 has a trade-in value of $2230 after six years. Construct a depreciation schedule using the sum-of-the-years-digits method.
4. A building has an original cost of $80 000, a life of 25 years, and a salvage value of $8500. Find the book value of the building after fifteen years using the simple declining-balance method.
5. A turbine costing $75 000 has a life of twenty years and a scrap value of $3500. Determine the depreciation in Year 12 using the complex declining-balance method.
6. The lighting division of Universal Electric Company plans to introduce a new street light based on the following accounting information.

   Fixed costs per period are $3136; variable cost per unit is $157; selling price per unit is $185; and capacity per period is 320 units.

   (a) Draw a detailed break-even chart.
   (b) Compute the break-even point
   (i) in units; (ii) as a percent of capacity;
   (iii) in dollars.
   (c) Determine the break-even point as a percent of capacity
   (i) if fixed costs are reduced to $2688;
   (ii) if fixed costs increase to $4588 and variable costs are reduced to 80% of the selling price;
   (iii) if the selling price is reduced to $171.
7. The following information is available from the accounting records of Eva Corporation.

   Fixed costs per period are $4800. Sales volume for the last period was $19 360 and variable costs were $13 552. Capacity per period is a sales volume of $32 000.

(a) Draw a detailed break-even chart.

(b) Compute the break-even point

(i) in dollars; (ii) as a percent of capacity.

(c) Determine the break-even point

(i) if fixed costs are decreased by \$600;
(ii) if fixed costs are increased to \$5670 and variable costs are changed to 55% of sales.

8. The operating budget of the Bea Company contains the following information.

Sales at 80% of capacity		\$400 000
Fixed costs	\$105 000	
Variable costs	260 000	365 000
Net income		\$35 000

(a) Draw a detailed break-even chart.

(b) Compute the break-even point

(i) as a percent of capacity; (ii) in dollars.

(c) Determine the break-even point in dollars if fixed costs are reduced by \$11 200 while variable costs are changed to 72% of sales.

9. A manufacturer of major appliances provides the following information about the operations of the refrigeration division.

Fixed costs per period are \$26 880; variable costs per unit are \$360; selling price per unit is \$640; and capacity is 150 units.

(a) Compute the break-even point

(i) in units; (ii) as a percent of capacity; (iii) in dollars.

(b) Determine the break-even point in dollars if fixed costs are increased to \$32 200.

(c) Determine the break-even point as a percent of capacity if fixed costs are reduced to \$23 808 while variable costs are increased to 60% of sales.

Self-test

1. An asset costing \$85 000 has an expected salvage value of \$5000 after sixteen years. Compute the book value of the asset after ten years using the straight-line method.

2. Equipment costing \$25 000 has an estimated disposal value of \$1600 after twelve years. What is the book value of the asset after seven years by the sum-of-the-years-digits method?

3. A vault has been installed at a cost of \$45 000 and is expected to have a residual value of \$2500 after twenty years. Determine the depreciation charge in Year 15 using the complex declining-balance method.

4. The Superior Records Company sells albums for $10 each. Manufacturing cost is $2.60 per album; marketing costs are $2.40 per album; and royalty payments are 20% of the selling price. The fixed cost of preparing the albums is $18 000. Capacity is 15 000 albums.

   (a) Draw a detailed break-even chart.

   (b) Compute the break-even point

   (i) in units; (ii) in dollars; (iii) as a percent of capacity.

   (c) Determine the break-even point in units if fixed costs are increased by $1600 while manufacturing cost is reduced $0.50 per album.

   (d) Determine the break-even point in units if the selling price is increased by 10% while fixed costs are increased by $2900.

5. The management of Lambda Corporation has received the following forecast for the next year.

Sales revenue		$600 000
Fixed costs	$275 000	
Variable costs	270 000	545 000
Net income		$ 55 000

   Capacity is a sales volume of $800 000.

   (a) Compute the break-even point

   (i) in dollars; (ii) as a percent of capacity.

   (b) Determine the break-even volume in dollars if fixed costs are increased by $40 000 while variable costs are held to 40% of sales.

Summary of formulae used

Formula 5.1

$$\text{YEARLY DEPRECIATION} = \frac{\text{ORIGINAL COST} - \text{RESIDUAL VALUE}}{n}$$

where n = the number of years in the life of the asset

Formula for finding the yearly depreciation when using the straight-line method

Formula 5.2

$$\text{DEPRECIATION PER SERVICE HOUR} = \frac{\text{ORIGINAL COST} - \text{RESIDUAL VALUE}}{n}$$

where n = the number of service hours in the life of the asset

Formula for finding the depreciation per service hour when using the service-hours method

Formula 5.3

$$\text{DEPRECIATION PER UNIT OF PRODUCT} = \frac{\text{ORIGINAL COST} - \text{RESIDUAL VALUE}}{n}$$

where n = the number of product units in the life of the asset

Formula for finding the depreciation per unit of product when using the unit-of-product method

Formula 5.4

$$k = \frac{\text{WEARING VALUE}}{\frac{n(n+1)}{2}}$$

where Wearing Value = Original Cost − Residual Value

Formula for finding the value of one part (constant of proportion) when using the sum-of-the-years-digits method

Formula 5.5

$$d = 2 \times \frac{1}{n}$$

where n = the number of years in the life of the asset

Formula for finding the rate of depreciation when using the simple declining-balance method

Formula 5.6

$$d = 1 - \sqrt[n]{\frac{\text{RESIDUAL VALUE}}{\text{ORIGINAL COST}}}$$

Formula for finding the rate of depreciation when using the complex declining-balance method

Glossary of terms used

Accumulated depreciation the total depreciation allocated to the accounting periods at any point in the life of an asset

Book value the net value of an asset at any point in its life; the difference between the original cost and the accumulated depreciation

Break-even analysis a method of determining the level of output at which a business neither makes a profit nor sustains a loss

Break-even chart a graphic representation of cost-volume-profit relationships used to identify the break-even point

Break-even point the level of output at which net income is zero

Cost function an algebraic expression stating the relationship between cost and volume

Depreciation loss in value of an asset due to physical deterioration, wear and tear, or decay and obsolescence

Depreciation schedule chart showing how the loss in value is allocated to the various accounting periods

Fixed costs costs that remain constant for the time period for all levels of output considered

Methods of depreciation systematic ways of allocating depreciation to accounting periods

Original cost the necessary and reasonable costs incurred in readying an asset for its intended purpose

Residual value the value of an asset when it has lost its usefulness or is disposed

Revenue function an algebraic expression representing the behaviour of revenue

Salvage value see *Residual value*

Scrap value see *Residual value*

Trade-in value see *Residual value*

Variable costs costs that are constant per unit of output regardless of volume; they fluctuate in total amount as volume fluctuates.

Wearing value the total depreciation over the life of an asset; the difference between original cost and residual value

6 *Commercial discount, markup, and markdown*

Introduction

The merchandising chain is made up of retailers, wholesalers, distributors, and manufacturers. Merchandise is usually bought and sold among the members of the chain on credit terms. The prices quoted to other members often involve trade discounts, and payments may be subject to cash discounts.

In every situation, the vendor must allow for a margin that will permit the business to cover its cost price and its overhead and provide a reasonable profit. Occasionally, competitive action or economic conditions necessitate selling merchandise for less than the regular selling price.

This chapter deals with the various aspects of discount, markup, and markdown.

Objectives

Upon completing this chapter, you will be able to

1. solve problems involving trade discounts, including discount series and equivalent single rates of discount;
2. deal with the three most commonly used methods of cash discount;
3. solve problems involving margin based on either cost or selling price;
4. solve pricing problems involving markup, markdown, and discounts.

6.1 *Trade discount*

A. Basic concepts and computations

A **trade discount** is a reduction of a catalogue or list price and is usually stated as a percent of the catalogue or list price.

Trade discounts are used by manufacturers, wholesalers, and distributors as pricing tools for a number of reasons. The most important reasons are

(a) to facilitate the establishment of price differentials for different groups of customers;

(b) to facilitate the communication of changes in prices;

(c) to reduce the cost of making changes in prices.

When computing trade discounts, keep in mind that the rate of discount is based on the list price.

AMOUNT OF DISCOUNT = RATE OF DISCOUNT × LIST PRICE	←——*Formula* **6.1**

The amount of discount is then subtracted from the list price. The remainder is the net selling price (or simply the net price) for the vendor. For the buyer, this remainder represents the **net cost**.

NET PRICE OR NET COST = LIST PRICE − AMOUNT OF TRADE DISCOUNT	←——*Formula* **6.2**

Example **6.1a** An item listed at \$80.00 is subject to a trade discount of 25%.

Compute (i) the amount of discount;

(ii) the net price or net cost.

Solution

(i) Amount of discount = Rate of discount × List price
= (0.25)(80.00) = \$20.00

(ii) Net price or Net cost = List price − Trade discount
= 80.00 − 20.00 = \$60.00

B. *The net factor approach to computing the net price or net cost*

Instead of computing the amount of discount and then deducting this amount from the list price, the net price or net cost can be found by using the more efficient net factor approach developed in the following illustration.

Referring back to Example 6.1a, the solution can be restated as follows.

List price	\$80.00
Less trade discount 25% of 80.00	20.00
Net price or Net cost	\$60.00

Since the discount is given as a percent of the list price, the three dollar values may be stated as percents of list price.

List price	\$80.00 ——→	100% of List price
Less trade discount	\$20.00 ——→	25% of List price
Net price or Net cost	\$60.00 ——→	75% of List price

Note: The "75%," called the **Net Cost Factor** or **Net Factor** (in abbreviated form, '**NCF**') is obtained by deducting the 25% discount from 100%.

NET COST FACTOR (NCF) = 100% − % DISCOUNT	⟵ *Formula* 6.3A

The resulting relationship between net price or net cost and list price may be stated generally.

NET PRICE OR NET COST = NET COST FACTOR (NCF) × LIST PRICE	⟵ *Formula* 6.4A

The two relationships represented by Formulae 6.3A and 6.4A can be restated in algebraic terms:

Convert the % discount into its decimal equivalent represented by d and express 100% by its decimal equivalent 1.

NET COST FACTOR $= 1 - d$	⟵ ***Formula* 6.3B**

Let the list price be represented by L and let the net price or net cost be represented by N.

$N = (1 - d)L$ or $N = L(1 - d)$	⟵ ***Formula* 6.4B**

Example **6.1b** Find the net price for

(i) list price \$36.00 less 15%;

(ii) list price \$125.64 less 37.5%;

(iii) list price \$86.85 less $33\frac{1}{3}\%$;

(iv) list price \$49.98 less $16\frac{2}{3}\%$.

Solution

(i) Net price = Net cost factor × List price ⟵ using Formula 6.4A
= (100% − 15%)(36.00) ⟵ using Formula 6.3A
= (85%)(36.00) ⟵ subtract
= (0.85)(36.00) ⟵ convert the percent into a decimal
= \$30.60

(ii) Net price = $(1 - d)$L ⟵ using Formula 6.4B
= (1 − 0.375)(125.64) ⟵ 37.5% = 0.375
= (0.625)(125.64)
= \$78.53

(iii) Net price $= (100\% - 33\frac{1}{3}\%)(86.85)$ ← using Formula 6.3A

$= (66\frac{2}{3}\%)(86.85)$

$= (0.6666667)(86.85)$ ← use a sufficient number of decimals

$= \$57.90$

(iv) Net price $= (1 - 0.16\frac{2}{3})(49.98)$ ← using Formula 6.4B

$= (0.83\frac{1}{3})(49.98)$

$= (0.8333333)(49.98)$ ← use a sufficient number of decimals

$= \$41.65$

C. Discount series

If a list price is subject to two or more discounts, these discounts are called a **discount series**. When computing the net price or net cost, the discounts making up the discount series are applied to the list price successively. The net price resulting from the first discount becomes the list price for the second discount; the net price resulting from the second discount becomes the list price for the third discount; and so on. In fact, finding the net price when a list price is subject to a discount series consists of solving as many discount problems as there are discounts in the discount series.

Example **6.1c** An item listed at $150.00 is subject to the discount series 20%, 10%, 5%. Determine the net price.

Solution

List price	$150.00	← Problem 1
Less first discount 20% of 150.00	30.00	
Net price after first discount	$120.00	← Problem 2
Less second discount 10% of 120.00	12.00	
Net price after second discount	$108.00	← Problem 3
Less third discount 5% of 108.00	5.40	
Net price	$102.60	

Because the solution to Example 6.1c consists of three problems involving a simple discount, the net cost factor approach can be used to solve it or any problem involving a series of discounts.

Problem 1 Net price after the first discount

$= \text{NCF for 20\% discount} \times \text{Original list price}$

$= (1 - 0.20)(150.00)$

$= (0.80)(150.00)$

$= \$120.00$

Problem 2 Net price after the second discount
$= \text{NCF for 10\% discount} \times \text{Net price after the first discount}$
$= (1 - 0.10)(120.00)$
$= (0.90)(120.00)$
$= (0.90)(0.80)(150.00)$
$= \$108.00$

Problem 3 Net price after the third discount
$= \text{NCF for 5\% discount} \times \text{Net price after the second discount}$
$= (1 - 0.05)(108.00)$
$= (0.95)(108.00)$
$= (0.95)(0.90)(0.80)(150.00)$
$= \$102.60$

The final net price of \$102.60 is obtained from
$(0.95)(0.90)(0.80)(150.00)$
$= (0.80)(0.90)(0.95)(150.00)$ ←——the order of the factors may be rearranged
$= \text{NCF for 20\%} \times \text{NCF for 10\%} \times \text{NCF for 5\%} \times \text{Original list price}$
= Product of the NCF's for the discounts in the discount series × Original list price
= Net cost factor for the discount series × Original list price

This result may be generalized to find the net price or net cost for a list price subject to a discount series.

NCF FOR THE DISCOUNT SERIES = NCF FOR THE FIRST DISCOUNT × NCF FOR THE SECOND DISCOUNT × . . . × NCF FOR THE LAST DISCOUNT

←——***Formula* 6.5A**

NET PRICE OR NET COST = NCF FOR THE DISCOUNT SERIES × LIST PRICE

←——***Formula* 6.6A**

The two relationships represented by Formulae 6.5A and 6.6A can be restated in algebraic terms.

Let the net price or net cost be represented by N,
the original list price by L,
the first rate of discount by d_1,
the second rate of discount by d_2,
the third rate of discount by d_3, and
the last rate of discount by d_n.

Then Formula 6.5A can be shown as

NCF FOR A DISCOUNT SERIES $= (1 - d_1)(1 - d_2)(1 - d_3)\ldots(1 - d_n)$

←——***Formula* 6.5B**

and Formula 6.6A can be shown as

NET PRICE OR NET COST $= (1 - d_1)(1 - d_2)(1 - d_3)\ldots(1 - d_n)\text{L}$

←——***Formula* 6.6B**

Example **6.1d** Determine the net cost for

(i) an office desk listed at \$440.00 less 25%, 15%, 2%;

(ii) a power drill listed at \$180.00 less 30%, 12.5%, 5%, 5%;

(iii) a home computer listed at \$1260.00 less $33\frac{1}{3}$%, $16\frac{2}{3}$%, 2.5%;

(iv) an electronic chessboard at \$1225.00 less $66\frac{2}{3}$%, $8\frac{1}{3}$%.

Solution

(i) Net cost = NCF for the discount series × list price ⟵ using Formula 6.6A

$$= (1 - 0.25)(1 - 0.15)(1 - 0.02)(440.00)$$
$$= (0.75)(0.85)(0.98)(440.00)$$
$$= \$274.89$$

(ii) Net cost = $L(1 - d_1)(1 - d_2)(1 - d_3)(1 - d_4)$ ⟵ using Formula 6.6B

$$= 180.00(1 - 0.30)(1 - 0.125)(1 - 0.05)(1 - 0.05)$$
$$= 180.00(0.70)(0.875)(0.95)(0.95)$$
$$= \$99.50$$

(iii) Net cost $= 1260.00(1 - 0.33\frac{1}{3})(1 - 0.16\frac{2}{3})(1 - 0.025)$

$$= 1260.00(0.66\tfrac{2}{3})(0.83\tfrac{1}{3})(0.975)$$
$$= 1260.00(0.6666667)(0.8333333)(0.975)$$
$$= \$682.50$$

(iv) Net cost $= (1 - 0.66\frac{2}{3})(1 - 0.08\frac{1}{3})(1225.00)$

$$= (0.33\tfrac{1}{3})(0.91\tfrac{2}{3})(1225.00)$$
$$= (0.3333333)(0.9166667)(1225.00)$$
$$= \$374.31$$

D. *Computing rates of discount*

Since the rate of trade discount is based on a list price, computing a rate of discount involves comparing the amount of discount to the list price.

$$\text{RATE OF TRADE DISCOUNT} = \frac{\text{AMOUNT OF DISCOUNT}}{\text{LIST PRICE}}$$ ⟵ ***Formula* 6.7**

Example **6.1e** Find the rate of discount for

(i) skis listed at \$280.00 less a discount of \$67.20;

(ii) ski gloves listed at \$36.80 whose net price is \$23.92;

(iii) ski sweaters whose net cost is \$55.68 after a discount of \$40.32.

Solution

(i) $\text{Rate of discount} = \dfrac{\text{Amount of discount}}{\text{List price}} = \dfrac{67.20}{280.00} = 0.24 = 24\%$

(ii) Amount of discount = List price − Net price = 36.80 − 23.92 = \$12.88

$\text{Rate of discount} = \dfrac{\text{Amount of discount}}{\text{List price}} = \dfrac{12.88}{36.80} = 0.35 = 35\%$

(iii) Since Amount of discount = List price − Net cost,
List price = Net cost + Amount of discount = 55.68 + 40.32 = \$96.00

$\text{Rate of discount} = \dfrac{\text{Amount of discount}}{\text{List price}} = \dfrac{40.32}{96.00} = 0.42 = 42\%$

Example **6.1f** A manufacturer sells skidoos to dealers at a list price of \$2100.00 less 40%, 10%, 5%. Determine

(i) the amount of discount;

(ii) the single rate of discount.

Solution

(i) Net price = NCF × List price
= (1 − 0.40)(1 − 0.10)(1 − 0.05)(2100.00)
= (0.60)(0.90)(0.95)(2100.00)
= \$1077.30

Amount of discount = List price − Net price
= 2100.00 − 1077.30 = \$1022.70

(ii) $\text{Rate of discount} = \dfrac{\text{Amount of discount}}{\text{List price}} = \dfrac{1022.70}{2100.00} = 0.487 = 48.7\%$

Note: Taking off a single discount of 48.7% has the *same* effect as using the discount series 40%, 10%, 5%. That is, the single discount of 48.7% is equivalent to the discount series 40%, 10%, 5%. The sum of the discounts in the series, 40% + 10% + 5% or 55%, is *not* equivalent to the single discount.

E. Single equivalent rates of discount

For every discount series, a single equivalent rate of discount exists. You can find this equivalent rate by choosing a suitable list price and computing first the amount of discount and then the rate of discount.

Example **6.1g** Find the single equivalent rate of discount for the discount series 30%, 8%, 2%.

Solution

Assume a list price of \$1000.00.

Net price = NCF for the series × List price
= (0.70)(0.92)(0.98)(1000.00)
= (0.63112)(1000.00)
= \$631.12

Amount of discount = 1000.00 − 631.12 = \$368.88

Single equivalent rate of discount = $\frac{368.88}{1000.00}$ = 0.36888 = 36.888%

Note: The net cost factor for the series = (0.70)(0.92)(0.98) = 0.63112, and 1 − 0.63112 = 0.36888. Therefore, you can find the single equivalent rate of discount by subtracting the net cost factor for the series from 1.

SINGLE EQUIVALENT RATE OF DISCOUNT FOR A DISCOUNT SERIES = 1 − NCF FOR THE DISCOUNT SERIES $= 1 - [(1 - d_1)(1 - d_2)(1 - d_3)\ldots(1 - d_n)]$	⟵ ***Formula* 6.8**

Example **6.1h** Determine the single equivalent rate of discount for each of the following discount series.

(i) 25%, 20%, 10% (ii) 30%, 12.5%, 2.5% (iii) $33\frac{1}{3}$%, 15%, 5%, 5%

Solution

(i) Single equivalent rate of discount
= 1 − (1 − 0.25)(1 − 0.20)(1 − 0.10) ⟵ using Formula 6.8
= 1 − (0.75)(0.80)(0.90)
= 1 − 0.540000
= 0.46
= 46%

(ii) Single equivalent rate of discount
= 1 − (1 − 0.30)(1 − 0.125)(1 − 0.025)
= 1 − (0.70)(0.875)(0.975)
= 1 − 0.5971875
= 0.4028125
= 40.28125%

(iii) Single equivalent rate of discount
$= 1 - (1 - 0.33\frac{1}{3})(1 - 0.15)(1 - 0.05)(1 - 0.05)$
$= 1 - (0.66\frac{2}{3})(0.85)(0.95)(0.95)$
= 1 − 0.5114167
= 0.4885833
= 48.85833%

Note: When computing or using single equivalent rates of discount, use a sufficient number of decimals to ensure an acceptable degree of accuracy.

Example **6.1i** Determine the amount of discount for each of the following list prices subject to the discount series 40%, 12.5%, $8\frac{1}{3}\%$, 2%.

(i) \$625.00 (ii) \$786.20 (iii) \$1293.44

Solution

Single equivalent rate of discount

$= 1 - (1 - 0.40)(1 - 0.125)(1 - 0.08\frac{1}{3})(1 - 0.02)$

$= 1 - (0.60)(0.875)(0.91\frac{2}{3})(0.98)$

$= 1 - 0.4716250$

$= 0.528375$

$= 52.8375\%$

(i) Amount of discount = Rate of discount × List price
= (0.528375)(625.00)
= \$330.23

(ii) Amount of discount = (0.528375)(786.20)
= \$415.41

(iii) Amount of discount = (0.528375)(1293.44)
= \$683.42

F. Additional problems

Example **6.1j** The local Home Hardware store has listed a power saw for \$136.00 less 30%. A catalogue store in a nearby shopping mall lists the same model for \$126.00 less 20%, 15%. What additional discount must Home Hardware give to meet the catalogue store price?

Solution

Home Hardware net price = 136.00(0.70)	\$95.20
Catalogue store price = 126.00(0.80)(0.85)	85.68
Additional discount needed	\$ 9.52

$$\text{Additional rate of discount needed} = \frac{9.52}{95.20} = 0.10 = 10\%$$

Example **6.1k** A manufacturer can cover its cost and make a reasonable profit if it sells an article for \$63.70. At what price should the article be listed so that a discount of 30% can be allowed?

Solution

Let the list price be represented by \$L.
The net cost factor is 0.70 and the net price is \$63.70.

$$63.70 = 0.70\text{ L} \longleftarrow \text{using Formula 6.4}$$

$$\text{L} = \frac{63.70}{0.70} = \$91.00$$

The article should be listed at \$91.00.

Example **6.11** Redden Distributors bought a shipment of personal computers for \$477.36 each. What were the computers listed at if the list price was subject to discounts of 15%, 10%, 4%?

Solution

Let the list price be \$L.
The net cost factor is (0.85)(0.90)(0.96) ⟵ using Formula 6.5A
The net price is \$477.36.

$$477.36 = (0.85)(0.90)(0.96)\text{L}$$

$$\text{L} = \frac{477.36}{(0.85)(0.90)(0.96)} = \$650.00$$

The computers were listed at \$650.00.

Exercise 6.1

A. For each of the following questions, find the missing value or values as indicated.

	Rate of discount	*List price*	*Net price*	*Single equivalent rate of discount*
1.	45%	\$24.60	?	Not applicable
2.	$16\frac{2}{3}$%	\$184.98	?	Not applicable
3.	37.5%	?	\$84.35	Not applicable
4.	22%	?	\$121.29	Not applicable
5.	?	\$76.95	\$51.30	Not applicable
6.	?	\$724.80	\$616.08	Not applicable
7.	25%, 10%	\$44.80	?	?
8.	$33\frac{1}{3}$%, 5%	\$126.90	?	?
9.	40%, 12.5%, 2%	\$268.00	?	?
10.	20%, $16\frac{2}{3}$%, 3%	\$72.78	?	?
11.	35%, $33\frac{1}{3}$%, 10%	?	\$617.50	?
12.	20%, 20%, 10%	?	\$53.28	?

B. Answer each of the following questions.

1. A patio chair is listed for \$240.00 less 30%, 20%, 5%.

(a) What is the net price?

(b) How much is the amount of discount allowed?

(c) What is the exact single rate of discount that was allowed?

2. A power saw is listed for \$174.00 less $16\frac{2}{3}\%$, 10%, 8%.

(a) What is the net price?

(b) How much is the amount of discount allowed?

(c) What is the exact single rate of discount that was allowed?

3. A motorcycle listed for \$975.00 is sold for \$820.00. What is the rate of discount that was allowed?

4. A washer-dryer combination listed at \$1136.00 has a net price of \$760.00. What is the rate of discount?

5. Compute the equivalent single rate of discount for each of the following discount series.

(a) 30%, 12.5% **(b)** $33\frac{1}{3}\%$, 20%, 3%

6. Determine the equivalent single rate of discount for each of the following series of discounts.

(a) $16\frac{2}{3}\%$, 7.5% **(b)** 25%, $8\frac{1}{3}\%$, 2%

7. A $16\frac{2}{3}\%$ discount allowed on a T-shirt amounted to \$14.82. What was the net price?

8. A store advertises a discount of \$44.24 on winter boots. If the discount is 35%, for how much were the boots sold?

9. A distributor lists an item for \$85.00 less 20%. To improve lagging sales, the price of the item is to be reduced to \$57.80. What additional rate of discount should be offered?

10. Crosstown Jewellers sell digital watches for \$340.00 less 25%. Their competitors across the street offer the same type of watch for \$360.00 less 30%, 15%. What additional rate of discount must Crosstown offer to meet the competitors' price?

11. The net purchase price of a freezer after a discount of $16\frac{2}{3}\%$ is \$355.00. What is the list price?

12. The net price of an article is \$63.31. What is the list price if a discount of 35% was allowed?

13. Arrow Manufacturing offers discounts of 25%, 12.5%, 4% on a line of products. For how much should an item be listed if it is to be sold for $113.40?

14. What is the list (suggested retail) price of an article that is subject to discounts of $33\frac{1}{3}$%, 10%, 2% if the net price is $564.48?

6.2 *Cash discount*

A. Basic concepts

Goods among manufacturers, wholesalers, distributors, and retailers are usually sold on credit rather than for cash. To encourage prompt payment, many businesses offer a reduction in the amount of the invoice. The reduction, called a **cash discount**, is a sales discount for the seller and a purchase discount for the buyer.

Sales discounts are offered in a variety of ways. The three most commonly used methods are

1. **ordinary dating;**
2. **end-of-the-month (or proximo) dating;**
3. **receipt-of-goods dating.**

The invoice's terms of payment specify the method and size of cash discount. Regardless of the method used, all **payment terms** have two things in common.

1. The cash discount is stated as a *percent* of the net amount (face value) of the invoice.
2. The time period during which the cash discount applies is stipulated.

If payment is not made during the stipulated discount period, the net amount of the invoice is to be paid by the *due date*. This date is either stipulated by the terms of payment or implied by the prevailing business practice. If payment is not made by the due date, the account is overdue and might be subject to late payment charges.

In dealing with cash discounts, the major new problem is how to interpret the terms of payment. Otherwise, the mathematics of working with cash discounts is similar to that used in working out trade discounts.

B. Ordinary dating

The most frequently used method of offering a cash discount is ordinary dating and the most commonly used payment terms are *2/10, n/30* (read *two ten, net thirty*).

This payment term means that if payment is made *within* ten days of the date of the invoice, a discount of 2% may be deducted from the net amount. Otherwise, payment of the net amount of the invoice is due within thirty days.

FIGURE 6.1 ***Interpretation of payment terms***

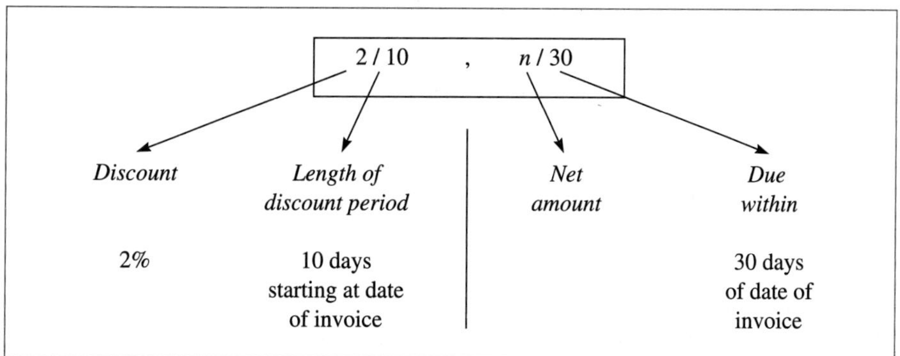

Example **6.2a** Determine the payment needed to settle an invoice of $950.00 dated September 22, terms 2/10, n/30, if the invoice is paid

(i) on October 10; (ii) on October 1.

Solution

The terms of the invoice state that a 2% discount may be deducted from the invoice amount of $950.00 if the invoice is paid within ten days of the invoice date of September 22.

Ten days after September 22 is October 2. The discount period ends October 2.

(i) Payment on October 10 is beyond the last day for taking the discount. The discount cannot be taken. The full amount of the invoice of $950.00 must be paid.

(ii) October 1 is within the discount period; the 2% discount can be taken.

Amount paid = Net amount − 2% of the net amount
= 950.00 − 0.02(950.00)
= 950.00 − 19.00
= $931.00

Alternatively, using the net cost factor approach,

Amount paid = NCF for a 2% discount × Net amount
= 0.98(950.00)
= $931.00

Example **6.2b** An invoice of $2185.65 dated May 31, terms 3/15, n/60, is paid on June 15. What is the size of the payment?

Solution

The discount period ends June 15.
Since payment is made on June 15 (the last day for taking the discount), the 3% discount is allowed.

Amount paid = 0.97(2185.65) = \$2120.08

Example **6.2c** An invoice for \$752.84 dated March 25, terms 5/10, 2/30, n/60, is paid on April 20. What is the amount paid?

Solution

The payment terms state that

(i) a 5% discount may be taken within ten days of the invoice date (April 4); or

(ii) a 2% discount may be taken within 30 days of the invoice date (after April 4 but no later than April 24); or

(iii) the net amount is due within 60 days of the invoice date if advantage is not taken of the cash discounts offered.

The 5% cash discount is *not* allowed; payment on April 20 is after the end of the discount period for the 5% discount. However, the 2% discount *is* allowed since payment on April 20 is within the 30 day period for the 2% discount.

Amount paid = 0.98(752.84) = \$737.78

Example **6.2d** Three invoices with terms 5/10, 3/20, n/60 are paid on November 15. The invoices are for \$645.00 dated September 30, \$706.00 dated October 26, and \$586.00 dated November 7. What is the total amount paid?

Solution

Invoice dated	*End of discount period*		*Discount allowed*	*Amount paid*	
	For 5%	*For 3%*			
Sept. 30	Oct. 10	Oct. 20	None		\$645.00
Oct. 26	Nov. 5	Nov. 15	3%	0.97(706.00)	684.82
Nov. 7	Nov. 17	Nov. 27	5%	0.95(586.00)	556.70
				Amount paid	\$1886.52

C. End-of-the-month or proximo dating

End-of-the-month dating is shown in the terms of payment by the abbreviation E.O.M. (*end of month*), such as in 2/10, E.O.M. The abbreviation E.O.M. means that the discount may be taken within the stipulated number of days following the end of the month shown in the invoice date. The abbreviation has the effect of shifting the invoice date to the last day of the month. The abbreviation "prox." (meaning "in the following month") has a similar effect.

In either case, the final date for paying the net amount of the invoice is usually not shown but it is commonly understood to be *twenty* days after the last day for taking the discount.

Example 6.2e An invoice for \$1233.95 dated July 16, terms 2/10 E.O.M., is paid on August 10. What is the amount paid?

Solution

The abbreviation E.O.M. means that the invoice is to be treated as if the invoice date were July 31. Therefore, the last day for taking the discount is August 10.

$$\text{Amount paid} = 0.98(1233.95) = \$1209.27$$

D. *Receipt-of-goods dating*

When the abbreviation R.O.G. (*receipt of goods*) appears in the terms of payment, as in 2/10, *n*/30 R.O.G., the last day for taking the discount is the stipulated number of days after the date the merchandise is received rather than the invoice date. This method of offering a cash discount is used when the transportation of the goods takes a long time, as in the case of long-distance overland shipments by rail or truck, or shipments by boat.

Example 6.2f Hansa Import Distributors has received an invoice of \$8465.00 dated May 10, terms 3/10, n/30 R.O.G., for a shipment of cuckoo clocks that arrived on July 15. What is the last day for taking the cash discount and how much is to be paid if the discount is taken?

Solution

The last day for taking the discount is ten days after receipt of the shipment, that is, July 25.

$$\text{Amount paid} = 0.97(8465.00) = \$8211.05$$

E. *Partial payments and additional problems*

The problem of a cash discount for a **partial payment** arises when a business pays *part* of an invoice within the discount period. In such cases, the purchaser is entitled to the cash discount on the partial amount paid.

Example 6.2g Sheridan Service has received an invoice of \$2780.00 dated August 18, terms 2/10 E.O.M. What payment must be made on September 10 to reduce the debt

(i) by \$1000.00? (ii) to \$1000.00?

Solution

Since the terms of payment involve end-of-month dating, the last day for taking the cash discount is September 10. The discount of 2% may be taken off the partial payment.

(i) Reducing the debt by \$1000.00 requires paying \$1000.00 less the discount.

$$\text{Amount paid} = 1000.00(0.98) = \$980.00$$

(ii) Reducing the debt to \$1000.00 requires paying (\$2780.00 − 1000.00), that is, \$1780.00 less the discount.

$$\text{Amount paid} = 1780.00(0.98) = \$1744.40$$

Example **6.2h** A cheque for \$1480.22 was received on June 24 in full payment of an invoice dated June 14, terms 3/10, n/30. What was the net amount of the invoice?

Solution

Since the payment was made by the last day of the discount period, the purchaser was entitled to the 3% cash discount. The payment of \$1480.22 is the amount left *after* taking 3% off the net invoice amount.

Let the net invoice amount be $\$x$.

$$\begin{aligned} \text{Amount paid} &= \text{NCF} \times \text{Net amount of invoice} \\ 1480.22 &= 0.97x \\ x &= \frac{1480.22}{0.97} = \$1526.00 \end{aligned}$$

The net amount of the invoice was \$1526.00.

Example **6.2i** Applewood Supplies received a payment of \$807.50 from Sheridan Service on October 10 on an invoice of \$2231.75 dated September 15, terms 5/10 prox.

(i) For how much should Applewood credit Sheridan Service's account for the payment?

(ii) How much does Sheridan Service still owe on the invoice?

Solution

Since the payment terms involve proximo dating, the payment is within the discount period. Sheridan Service is entitled to the 5% discount on the partial payment. The amount of \$807.50 represents a partial payment reduced by 5%.

Let the credit allowed be $\$x$.

$$\begin{aligned} \text{Amount paid} &= \text{NCF} \times \text{Credit allowed} \\ 807.50 &= 0.95x \\ x &= \frac{807.50}{0.95} = \$850.00 \end{aligned}$$

(i) Applewood should credit the account of Sheridan Service with \$850.00.

(ii) Sheridan Service still owes (\$2231.75 − 850.00) = \$1381.75.

Exercise 6.2

A. Determine the amount paid to settle each of the following invoices on the date indicated.

	Invoice amount	*Payment terms*	*Date of invoice*	*Date goods received*	*Date paid*
1.	\$640.00	2/10, *n*/30	Aug 10	Aug 11	Sept 9
2.	\$1520.00	3/15, *n*/60	Sept 24	Sept 27	Oct 8
3.	\$783.95	3/10, 1/20, *n*/60	May 18	May 20	June 5
4.	\$1486.25	5/10, 2/30, *n*/60	June 28	June 30	July 8
5.	\$1160.00	2/10 E.O.M.	Mar 22	Mar 29	April 10
6.	\$920.00	3/15 E.O.M.	Oct 20	Oct 30	Nov 12
7.	\$4675.00	2/10 R.O.G.	April 15	May 28	June 5
8.	\$2899.65	4/20 R.O.G.	July 17	Sept 21	Oct 10

B. Determine the missing values for each of the following. Assume that a partial payment was made on each of the invoices by the last day for taking the cash discount.

	Amount of invoice	*Payment terms*	*Amount of credit for payment*	*Net payment received*	*Invoice balance due*
1.	\$1450.00	3/10, *n*/30	\$600.00	?	?
2.	\$3126.54	2/10 E.O.M.	\$2000.00	?	?
3.	\$964.50	5/20 R.O.G.	?	?	\$400.00
4.	\$1789.95	4/15, *n*/60	?	?	\$789.95
5.	\$1620.00	3/20 E.O.M.	?	\$785.70	?
6.	\$2338.36	2/10 R.O.G.	?	\$1311.59	?

C. Answer the following questions.

1. Santucci Appliances received an invoice dated August 12 with terms 3/10 E.O.M. for the items listed below:

5 G.E. refrigerators at \$980.00 each less 25%, 5%;

4 Inglis dishwashers at \$696.00 each less $16\frac{2}{3}$%, 12.5%, 4%.

(a) What is the last day for taking the cash discount?

(b) What is the amount due if the invoice is paid on the last day for taking the discount?

(c) What is the amount of the cash discount if a partial payment is made such that a balance of \$2000.00 remains outstanding on the invoice?

2. Import Exclusives Ltd. received an invoice dated May 20 from Dansk Specialities of Copenhagen with terms 5/20 R.O.G. for

   100 teak trays at $34.30 each;
   25 teak icebuckets at $63.60 each;
   40 teak salad bowls at $54.50 each.

   All items are subject to trade discounts of $33\frac{1}{3}\%$, $7\frac{1}{2}\%$, 5%.

   (a) If the shipment was received on June 28, what is the last day of the discount period?

   (b) What is the amount due if the invoice is paid in full on July 15?

   (c) If a partial payment only is made on the last day of the discount period, what amount is due to reduce the outstanding balance to $2500.00?

3. What amount must be remitted if invoices dated July 25 for $929.00, August 10 for $763.00, and August 29 for $864.00, all with terms 3/15 E.O.M., are paid together on September 12?

4. The following invoices, all with terms 5/10, 2/30, *n*/60, were paid together on May 15. Invoice No. 234 dated March 30 is for $394.45; invoice No. 356 dated April 15 is for $595.50; and invoice No. 788 dated May 10 is for $865.20. What amount was remitted?

5. An invoice for $5275.00 dated November 12, terms 4/10 E.O.M., was received on November 14. What payment must be made on December 10 to reduce the debt to $3000.00?

6. What amount will reduce the amount due on an invoice of $1940.00 by $740.00 if the terms of the invoice are 5/10, *n*/30 and the payment was made during the discount period?

7. Sheridan Service received an invoice dated September 25 from Wolfedale Automotive. The invoice amount was $2540.95, and the payment terms were 3/10, 1/20, *n*/30. Sheridan Service made a payment on October 5 to reduce the balance due by $1200.00, made a second payment on October 15 to reduce the balance to $600.00, and paid the remaining balance on October 30.

   (a) How much did Sheridan Service pay on October 5?

   (b) How much did it pay on October 15?

   (c) What was the amount of the final payment on October 30?

8. The Ski Shop received an invoice for $9600.00 dated August 11, terms 5/10, 2/30, *n*/90, for a shipment of skis. The Ski Shop made two partial payments.

(a) How much was paid on August 20 to reduce the unpaid balance to \$7000.00?

(b) How much was paid on September 10 to reduce the outstanding balance by \$3000.00?

(c) What is the remaining balance on September 10?

9. Jelinek Sports received a cheque for \$1867.25 in partial payment of an invoice owed by the Ski Shop. The invoice was for \$5325.00 with terms 3/20 E.O.M. dated September 15, and the cheque was received on October 18.

(a) With how much should Jelinek Sports credit the account of the Ski Shop?

(b) How much does the Ski Shop still owe Jelinek?

10. Darrigo Grape received an invoice for \$13 780 dated September 28, terms 5/20 R.O.G., from Nappa Vineyards for a carload of grape juice received October 20. Darrigo made a partial payment of \$5966.00 on November 8.

(a) By how much did Darrigo reduce the amount due on the invoice?

(b) How much does Darrigo still owe?

6.3 *Markup*

A. Basic concepts and calculations

The primary purpose of operating a business is to generate profits. Businesses engaged in merchandising generate profits through their buying and selling activities. The amount of profit depends on many factors, one of which is the pricing of goods. The selling price must cover

(i) the cost of buying the goods;

(ii) the operating expenses (or overhead) of the business;

(iii) the profit required by the owner to stay in business.

SELLING PRICE = COST OF BUYING + EXPENSES + PROFIT

$$S = C + E + P$$ ←——*Formula* 6.9A

Example **6.3a** Sheridan Service buys a certain type of battery for \$84.00 each. Operating expenses of the business are 25% of cost and the owner requires a profit of 10% of cost. For how much should Sheridan sell the batteries?

Solution

Selling Price = Cost of buying + Expenses + Profit
= 84.00 + 25% of 84.00 + 10% of 84.00
= 84.00 + 0.25(84.00) + 0.10(84.00)
= 84.00 + 21.00 + 8.40
= \$113.40

Sheridan should sell the batteries for \$113.40 to cover the cost of buying, the operating expenses, and the required profit.

Note: In example 6.3a, the selling price is \$113.40 while the cost is \$84.00. The difference between selling price and cost = 113.40 − 84.00 = \$29.40. This difference covers operating expenses of \$21.00 and a profit of \$8.40 and is known as **margin, markup**, or **gross profit**.

MARKUP = EXPENSES + PROFIT

$$M = E + P$$ ← *Formula* **6.10**

Using this relationship between markup, expenses, and profit, the relationship stated in Formula 6.9 becomes

SELLING PRICE = COST OF BUYING + MARKUP

$$S = C + M$$ ← *Formula* **6.9B**

The following diagram illustrates the relationships established in Formulae 6.9A, 6.9B, and 6.10.

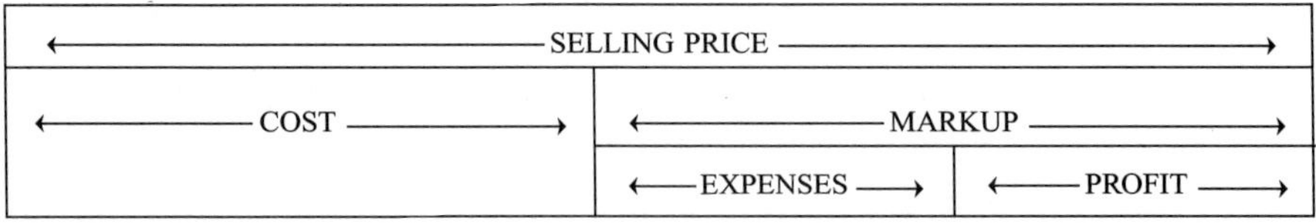

***Example* 6.3b** Friden Business Machines bought two types of electronic calculators for resale. Model A cost \$42.00 and sells for \$56.50. Model B cost \$78.00 and sells for \$95.00. Business overhead is 24% of cost. For each model, determine

(i) the markup or gross profit;

(ii) the operating expenses (or overhead);

(iii) the profit.

Solution

	Model A	*Model B*
(i)	$C + M = S$ $42.00 + M = 56.50$ $M = 56.50 - 42.00$ $M = \$14.50$ The markup on Model A is \$14.50.	$C + M = S$ ⟵ using Formula 6.9B $78.00 + M = 95.00$ $M = 95.00 - 78.00$ $M = \$17.00$ The markup on Model B is \$17.00.
(ii)	Expenses (or overhead) = 24% of 42.00 = 0.24(42.00) = \$10.08 Overhead for Model A is \$10.08.	Expenses (or overhead) = 24% of 78.00 = 0.24(78.00) = \$18.72 Overhead for Model B is \$18.72.
(iii)	$E + P = M$ $10.08 + P = 14.50$ $P = 14.50 - 10.08$ $P = \$4.42$ Profit on Model A is \$4.42.	$E + P = M$ ⟵ using Formula 6.10 $18.72 + P = 17.00$ $P = 17.00 - 18.72$ $P = -\$1.72$ Profit on Model B is −\$1.72, that is, a loss of \$1.72.

***Example* 6.3c** A ski shop bought 100 pairs of skis for \$105.00 per pair and sold 60 pairs for the regular selling price of \$295.00 per pair. The remaining skis were sold during a clearance sale for \$180.00 per pair. Overhead is 40% of the regular selling price. Determine

(i) the markup, the overhead, and the profit per pair of skis sold at the regular selling price;

(ii) the markup, the overhead, and the profit per pair of skis sold during the clearance sale;

(iii) the total profit realized.

Solution

(i) *At regular selling price*

Markup

$$C + M = S$$
$$105.00 + M = 295.00$$
$$M = \$190.00$$

Overhead

E = 40% of Regular selling price
= 0.40(295.00)
= $118.00

Profit

$$E + P = M$$
$$118.00 + P = 190.00$$
$$P = \$72.00$$

(ii) *At clearance price*

Markup

$$C + M = S$$
$$105.00 + M = 180.00$$
$$M = \$75.00$$

Overhead

E = 40% of Regular selling price
= 0.40(295.00)
= $118.00

Profit

$$E + P = M$$
$$118.00 + P = 75.00$$
$$P = -\$43.00$$

(iii)

Profit from sale of 60 pairs at regular selling price	= 60(72.00)	$4320.00
Profit from sale of 40 pairs during clearance sale	= 40(−43.00)	−1720.00
	Total profit	$2600.00

B. *Rate of markup*

A markup may be stated in one of two ways:

1. as a percent of cost;
2. as a percent of selling price.

Since the two methods produce different results, using both creates some difficulties in dealing with markups. Great care must be taken to note whether the markup is based on the cost or on the selling price.

Finding the rate of markup, as in finding any rate, involves comparing two numbers. One is used as the base while the second number is expressed as a fraction (percent) of the base.

$$\text{RATE OF MARKUP BASED ON COST} = \frac{\text{MARKUP}}{\text{COST}} = \frac{M}{C}$$ ←——***Formula* 6.11**

$$\text{RATE OF MARKUP BASED ON SELLING PRICE} = \frac{\text{MARKUP}}{\text{SELLING PRICE}} = \frac{M}{S}$$ ←——***Formula* 6.12**

***Example* 6.3d** Compute (a) the missing value (cost, selling price, markup), (b) the rate of markup based on cost, and (c) the rate of markup based on selling price for each of the following.

(i) cost, \$60.00; selling price, \$75.00
(ii) cost, \$48.00; markup, \$16.00
(iii) selling price, \$88.00; markup, \$33.00
(iv) cost, \$8.00; markup, \$8.00
(v) selling price, \$24.00; markup, \$18.00

Solution

	(a) *Missing value*	*(b)* *Rate of markup based on cost*	*(c)* *Rate of markup based on selling price*
(i)	Markup = 75.00 − 60.00 = \$15.00	$\frac{15}{60} = 0.25 = 25\%$	$\frac{15}{75} = 0.20 = 20\%$
(ii)	Selling price = 48.00 + 16.00 = \$64.00	$\frac{16}{48} = \frac{1}{3} = 33\frac{1}{3}\%$	$\frac{16}{64} = 0.25 = 25\%$
(iii)	Cost = 88.00 − 33.00 = \$55.00	$\frac{33}{55} = 0.60 = 60\%$	$\frac{33}{88} = 0.375$ $= 37.5\%$
(iv)	Selling price = 8.00 + 8.00 = \$16.00	$\frac{8}{8} = 1.00 = 100\%$	$\frac{8}{16} = 0.50 = 50\%$
(v)	Cost = 24.00 − 18.00 = 6.00	$\frac{18}{6} = 3.00 = 300\%$	$\frac{18}{24} = 0.75 = 75\%$

C. Finding the cost or selling price

When the rate of markup is given and either the cost or the selling price is known, the missing value can be found using Formula 6.9B.

COST + MARKUP = SELLING PRICE	C + M = S

When using this formula, pay special attention to the base of the markup, that is, whether it is based on cost or based on selling price.

***Example* 6.3e** What is the selling price of an article costing \$72.00 if the mark-up is

(i) 40% of cost? (ii) 40% of the selling price?

Solution

(i)
$$C + M = S \longleftarrow \text{using Formula 6.9B}$$
$$C + 40\% \text{ of } C = S \longleftarrow \text{replacing M by 40\% of C is the crucial step in the solution}$$
$$72.00 + 0.40(72.00) = S$$
$$72.00 + 28.80 = S$$
$$S = \$100.80$$

If the markup is 40% based on cost, the selling price is \$100.80.

(ii)
$$C + M = S$$
$$C + 40\% \text{ of } S = S$$
$$72.00 + 0.40\,S = S$$
$$72.00 = S - 0.40\,S$$
$$72.00 = 0.60S$$
$$S = \frac{72.00}{0.60}$$
$$S = \$120.00$$

If the markup is 40% based on selling price, the selling price is \$120.00.

Note: In problems of this type, replace M by X% of C or X% of S before using specific numbers. This approach is used in the preceding problem and in the following worked examples.

***Example* 6.3f** What is the cost of an article selling for \$65.00 if the markup is

(i) 30% of selling price? (ii) 30% of cost?

Solution

(i)
$$C + M = S$$
$$C + 30\% \text{ of } S = S \longleftarrow \text{replace M by 30\% of S}$$
$$C + 0.30(65.00) = 65.00$$
$$C + 19.50 = 65.00$$
$$C = 65.00 - 19.50$$
$$C = \$45.50$$

If the markup is 30% based on selling price, the cost is \$45.50.

(ii)
$$\begin{aligned} C + M &= S \\ C + 30\% \text{ of } C &= S \longleftarrow \text{replace M by 30\% of C} \\ C + 0.30\,C &= 65.00 \\ 1.30\,C &= 65.00 \\ C &= \frac{65.00}{1.30} \\ C &= \$50.00 \end{aligned}$$

If the markup is 30% based on cost, the cost is $50.00.

***Example* 6.3g** Find the missing value in each of the following.

	(i)	(ii)	(iii)	(iv)	(v)
Cost	$45.00	$84.00	?	?	?
Selling price	?	?	$3.24	$23.10	$42.90
Markup based on cost	$33\frac{1}{3}\%$	?	?	37.5%	50%
Markup based on selling price	?	40%	$16\frac{2}{3}\%$	?	?

Solution

(i)
$$\begin{aligned} C + M &= S \\ C + 33\tfrac{1}{3}\% \text{ of } C &= S \\ 45.00 + \tfrac{1}{3}(45.00) &= S \\ 45.00 + 15.00 &= S \\ S &= \$60.00 \end{aligned}$$

$$\text{Markup based on selling price} = \frac{15}{60} = 0.25 = 25\%$$

(ii)
$$\begin{aligned} C + M &= S \\ C + 40\% \text{ of } S &= S \\ 84.00 + 0.40\,S &= S \\ 84.00 &= 0.60\,S \\ S &= \frac{84.00}{0.60} \\ S &= \$140.00 \end{aligned}$$

$$\text{Markup based on cost} = \frac{140.00 - 84.00}{84.00} = \frac{56.00}{84.00} = 0.6666667 = 66\tfrac{2}{3}\%$$

(iii)
$$C + M = S$$
$$C + 16\tfrac{2}{3}\% \text{ of } S = S$$
$$C + (\tfrac{1}{6})(3.24) = 3.24$$
$$C + 0.54 = 3.24$$
$$C = \$2.70$$

$$\text{Markup based on cost} = \frac{3.24 - 2.70}{2.70} = \frac{0.54}{2.70} = 0.20 = 20\%$$

(iv)
$$C + M = S$$
$$C + 37.5\% \text{ of } C = S$$
$$C + 0.375\,C = 23.10$$
$$1.375\,C = 23.10$$
$$C = \frac{23.10}{1.375}$$
$$C = \$16.80$$

$$\text{Markup based on selling price} = \frac{23.10 - 16.80}{23.10} = \frac{6.30}{23.10} = 0.2727273 = 27.27\%$$

(v)
$$C + M = S$$
$$C + 50\% \text{ of } C = S$$
$$C + 0.50\,C = 42.90$$
$$1.50\,C = 42.90$$
$$C = \$28.60$$

$$\text{Markup based on selling price} = \frac{42.90 - 28.60}{42.90} = \frac{14.30}{42.90} = 0.3333333 = 33\tfrac{1}{3}\%$$

***Example* 6.3h** The Beaver Ski Shop sells ski vests for \$98.00. The markup based on cost is 75%.

(i) For how much did the Ski Shop buy the vest?

(ii) What is the rate of markup based on the selling price?

Solution

(i)
$$C + M = S$$
$$C + 75\% \text{ of } C = S$$
$$C + 0.75\,C = 98.00$$
$$1.75\,C = 98.00$$
$$C = 56.00$$

The Ski Shop paid \$56.00 for the vest.

(ii) Rate of markup based on selling price
$$= \frac{\text{markup}}{\text{selling price}}$$
$$= \frac{98.00 - 56.00}{98.00}$$
$$= \frac{42.00}{98.00} = 0.4285714 = 42.86\%$$

***Example* 6.3i** Sheridan Service bought four Michelin tires from Canadian Tire at \$343.00 and sold the tires at a markup of 30% of the selling price.

(i) For how much were the tires sold?

(ii) What is the rate of markup based on cost?

Solution

(i)

$$\begin{aligned} C + M &= S \\ C + 30\% \text{ of } S &= S \\ 343.00 + 0.30\,S &= S \\ 343.00 &= 0.70\,S \\ S &= 490.00 \end{aligned}$$

Sheridan sold the tires for \$490.00.

(ii)

$$\begin{aligned} \text{Rate of markup based on cost} &= \frac{\text{markup}}{\text{cost}} \\ &= \frac{490.00 - 343.00}{343.00} \\ &= \frac{147.00}{343.00} = 0.4285714 = 42.86\% \end{aligned}$$

***Example* 6.3j** The gross profit on each of two articles is \$25.80. If the rate of markup for Article A is 40% of cost while the rate is 40% of the selling price for Article B, determine the cost and the selling price of each.

Solution

For Article A

$$\begin{aligned} \text{Gross Profit (or Markup)} &= 40\% \text{ of Cost} \\ 25.80 &= 0.40\,C \\ C &= 64.50 \end{aligned}$$

The cost of Article A is \$64.50.
The selling price is 64.50 + 25.80 = \$90.30.

For Article B

$$\begin{aligned} \text{Gross Profit (or Markup)} &= 40\% \text{ of Selling price} \\ 25.80 &= 0.40\,S \\ S &= 64.50 \end{aligned}$$

The selling price of Article B is \$64.50.
The cost = 64.50 − 25.80 = \$38.70.

Exercise 6.3

A. For each of the following, determine

(a) the amount of markup;

(b) the amount of overhead;

(c) the profit or loss realized on the sale;

(d) the rate of markup based on cost;

(e) the rate of markup based on selling price.

	Cost	*Selling price*	*Overhead*
1.	$24.00	$30.00	16% of Cost
2.	$72.00	$96.00	15% of Selling price
3.	$52.50	$87.50	36% of Selling price
4.	$42.45	$67.92	60% of Cost
5.	$27.00	$37.50	34% of Selling price
6.	$36.00	$42.30	21% of Cost

B. For each of the following, compute the missing values as shown.

				Rate of Markup based on	
	Cost	*Selling price*	*Markup*	*Cost*	*Selling price*
1.	$25.00	$31.25	?	?	?
2.	$63.00	$84.00	?	?	?
3.	$64.00	?	$38.40	?	?
4.	?	$162.00	$27.00	?	?
5.	$54.25	?	?	40%	?
6.	?	$94.50	?	?	30%
7.	?	$66.36	?	50%	?
8.	?	$133.25	?	$66\frac{2}{3}\%$	?
9.	$31.24	?	?	?	60%
10.	$87.74	?	?	?	$33\frac{1}{3}\%$
11.	?	?	$22.26	?	$16\frac{2}{3}\%$
12.	?	?	$90.75	125%	?

C. Answer each of the following questions.

1. Windsor Hardware buys outdoor lights for $5.00 per dozen less 20%, 20%. The store's overhead is 45% of cost and the required profit is 15% of cost. For how much per dozen should the lights be sold?

2. A merchant buys an item listed at $96.00 less $33\frac{1}{3}\%$ from a distributor. Overhead is 32% of cost and profit is 27.5% of cost. For how much should the item be retailed?

3. Aldo's Shoes bought a shipment of 200 pairs of women's shoes for $42.00 per pair. The store sold 120 pairs at the regular selling price of $125.00 per pair, 60 pairs at a clearance sale at a discount of 40%, and the remaining pairs during an inventory sale at a break-even price. The store's overhead is 50% of cost.

(a) What was the price at which the shoes were sold during the clearance sale?

(b) What was the price during the inventory sale?

(c) What was the total profit realized on the shipment?

(d) What was the average rate of markup based on cost that was realized on the shipment?

4. The Pottery bought 600 pans auctioned off en bloc for $4950.00. On inspection, the pans were classified as normal quality, seconds, and substandard. The 360 normal quality pans were sold at a markup of 80% of cost, the 190 pans classified as seconds were sold at a markup of 20% of cost, and the pans classified as substandard were disposed of at a loss of 20% of their auctioned price.

(a) What was the unit price at which each of the three classifications was sold?

(b) If overhead is $33\frac{1}{3}\%$ of cost, what was the amount of profit realized on the purchase?

(c) What was the average rate of markup based on the selling price at which the pans were sold?

5. Tennis rackets are listed at $55.00 less 40%, 25%. They were sold for $54.45.

(a) What is the markup as a percent of cost?

(b) What is the markup as a percent of selling price?

6. A dealer bought personal computers for $1240.00 less 50%, 10%. They were sold for $1395.00.

(a) What was the markup as a percent of cost?

(b) What was the markup as a percent of selling price?

7. A bookstore makes a gross profit of $3.42 on a textbook. The store's markup is 15% of cost.

(a) For how much did the bookstore buy the textbook?

(b) What is the selling price of the textbook?

(c) What is the rate of markup based on the selling price?

8. An appliance store sells electric kettles at a markup of 18% of the selling price. The store's margin on a particular model is $6.57.

(a) What was the cost of the kettles to the store?

(b) For how much does the store sell the kettles?

(c) What is the percent markup based on cost?

9. The markup on an item selling for $74.55 is 40% of cost.
   (a) What is the cost of the item?
   (b) What is the rate of markup based on the selling price?
10. Sheridan Service sells oil at a markup of 40% of the selling price. If Sheridan paid $0.99 per litre of oil,
    (a) what is the selling pricc per litre?
    (b) what is the rate of markup based on cost?
11. The Ski Shop purchased ski poles for $12.80 per pair. The poles are marked up 60% of the selling price.
    (a) For how much does the Ski Shop sell a pair of ski poles?
    (b) What is the percent markup based on cost?
12. Nippon Photographic Supplies sells a Pentax camera for $444.98. The markup is 90% of cost.
    (a) How much does the store pay for the cameras?
    (b) What is the rate of markup based on selling price?

6.4 *Problems involving markup, markdown, and discount*

A. Markdown

A **markdown** is a reduction in the price of an article. Markdowns are used for a variety of purposes, such as sales promotions, meeting competitors' prices, reducing excess inventories, clearing out seasonal merchandise, and selling off discontinued items. A markdown, unlike a markup, is always stated as a percent of the price to be reduced and is computed as if it were a discount.

While markdowns are simple to calculate, the rather wide variety of terms used to identify both the price to be reduced (such as selling price, regular selling price, list price, marked price, price tag) and the reduced price (such as sale price or clearance price) introduces an element of confusion.

In general,

REDUCED PRICE = PRICE TO BE REDUCED − MARKDOWN

However, since the markdown is a percent of the price that is to be reduced, the net cost factor approach used with discounts is applicable (see Formula 6.4A).

REDUCED PRICE = NCF × PRICE TO BE REDUCED where NCF = 100% − % markdown

Example 6.4a A ski suit regularly selling for $280.00 is marked down 45% during the Beaver Ski Shop's annual clearance sale. What is the new price of the ski suit?

Solution

Sale price = Regular selling price − Markdown
= 280.00 − 45% of 280.00
= 280.00 − 0.45(280.00)
= 280.00 − 126.00
= \$154.00

Alternatively

Sale price = NCF × Regular selling price
= (100% − 45%)(280.00)
= 0.55(280.00)
= \$154.00

The ski suit sold for \$154.00.

Example **6.4b** Solomon 555 ski bindings bought for \$57.75 were marked up 45% of the selling price. When the binding was discontinued, it was marked down 40%. What was the final price of the binding?

Solution

First determine the regular selling price (marked price).

$$C + M = S$$
$$C + 45\% \text{ of } S = S$$
$$57.75 + 0.45S = S$$
$$57.75 = 0.55S$$
$$S = \$105.00$$

The marked price is \$105.00.

Sale price = Marked price − Markdown *or* (= NCF × Marked price)
= 105.00 − 40% of 105.00 (= 0.60 × 105.00)
= 105.00 − 42.00 (= \$63.00)
= \$63.00

The sale price is \$63.00.

Example **6.4c** Lund Sporting Goods sold a bicycle regularly priced at \$195.00 for \$144.30.

(i) What is the amount of markdown?

(ii) What is the rate of markdown?

Solution

(i) Markdown = Price to be reduced − Reduced price
= Regular selling price − Sale price
= 195.00 − 144.30
= \$50.70

(ii) Rate of markdown $= \dfrac{\text{Markdown}}{\text{Price to be reduced}}$

$$= \frac{50.70}{195.00} = 0.26 = 26\%$$

B. *Further problems*

The pricing relationship, Selling price = Cost + Expense + Profit (S = C + E + P), plays an important role in pricing. It describes how big a markup is needed to cover overhead and a reasonable profit, and how large a markdown can be tolerated. Use this relationship as a guide in considering the effect of markdown decisions on the operations of a business.

The cost of buying an article plus the overhead represents the total handling cost of the article.

TOTAL COST = COST OF BUYING + OVERHEAD

If an article is sold at a price that equals the **total cost**, the business makes no profit nor does it suffer a loss. This price is called the break-even point and is discussed in Chapter 5. Any business, of course, prefers to sell at least at a break-even price. If the price is insufficient to recover the total cost, the business will suffer an operating loss. If the price does not even cover the cost of buying, the business suffers an absolute loss. To determine the profit or loss, the following accounting relationship is used.

PROFIT = REVENUE − TOTAL COST

***Example* 6.4d** During its annual Midnight Madness Sale the Ski Shop sold a pair of ski boots, regularly priced at $245.00, at a discount of 40%. The boots cost $96.00 and expenses are 26% of the regular selling price.

(i) For how much were the ski boots sold?

(ii) What was their total handling cost?

(iii) What operating profit or loss was made on the sale?

Solution

(i) Sale price = 0.60(245.00) = $147.00

(ii) Total cost = Cost of buying + Expenses
= 96.00 + 0.26(245.00)
= 96.00 + 63.70
= $159.70

(iii) Profit = Revenue − Total cost
= 147.00 − 159.70
= −$12.70 (a loss)

Since the total cost was higher than the revenue received from the sale of the ski boots, the Ski Shop had an operating loss of \$12.70.

***Example* 6.4e** The Cook Nook paid \$115.24 for a set of dishes. Expenses are 18% of selling price and the required profit is 15% of selling price. During an inventory sale, the set of dishes was marked down 30%.

(i) What was the sale price?

(ii) What was the operating profit or loss?

Solution

(i) First determine the selling price.

$$\begin{aligned}
\text{Selling price} &= \text{Cost} + \text{Expenses} + \text{Profit} \\
S &= C + 18\% \text{ of } S + 15\% \text{ of } S \\
S &= C + 0.18S + 0.15S \\
S &= 115.24 + 0.33S \\
0.67S &= 115.24 \\
S &= \frac{115.24}{0.67} = \$172.00
\end{aligned}$$

$$\begin{aligned}
\text{Sale price} &= \text{Selling price} - \text{Markdown} \\
&= S - 30\% \text{ of } S \\
&= S - 0.30S \\
&= 0.70S \\
&= 0.70(172.00) \\
&= \$120.40
\end{aligned}$$

The sale price is \$120.40.

(ii)
$$\begin{aligned}
\text{Total cost} &= \text{Cost of buying} + \text{Expenses} \\
&= C + 18\% \text{ of } S \\
&= 115.24 + 0.18(172.00) \\
&= 115.24 + 30.96 \\
&= \$146.20
\end{aligned}$$

$$\begin{aligned}
\text{Profit} &= \text{Revenue} - \text{Total cost} \\
&= 120.40 - 146.20 \\
&= -\$25.80
\end{aligned}$$

The dishes were sold at an operating loss of \$25.80.

***Example* 6.4f** The Winemaker sells California concentrate for \$22.50. The store's overhead is 50% of cost and the owners require a profit of 30% of cost.

(i) For how much does The Winemaker buy the concentrate?

(ii) What is the break-even price?

(iii) What is the highest rate of markdown at which the store will still break even?

(iv) What is the highest rate of discount that can be advertised without incurring an absolute loss?

Solution

(i)
$$S = C + E + P$$
$$S = C + 50\% \text{ of } C + 30\% \text{ of } C$$
$$S = C + 0.50\,C + 0.30\,C$$
$$22.50 = 1.80\,C$$
$$C = \frac{22.50}{1.80} = \$12.50$$

The Winemaker bought the concentrate for \$12.50.

(ii) Total cost $= C + 50\% \text{ of } C$
$= 1.50C$
$= 1.50(12.50)$
$= \$18.75$

To break even, the concentrate must be sold for \$18.75.

(iii) To break even, the maximum markdown is $22.50 - 18.75 = \$3.75$.

$$\text{Rate of markdown} = \frac{3.75}{22.50} = 0.1666667 = 16\tfrac{2}{3}\%$$

The highest rate of markdown to break even is $16\frac{2}{3}\%$.

(iv) The lowest price at which the concentrate can be offered for sale without incurring an absolute loss is the cost at which the concentrate was bought, that is, \$12.50. The maximum amount of discount $= 22.50 - 12.50 = \$10.00$.

$$\text{Rate of discount} = \frac{10.00}{22.50} = 0.4444444 = 44\tfrac{4}{9}\%$$

The maximum rate of discount that can be advertised without incurring an absolute loss is $44\frac{4}{9}\%$.

Example **6.4g** Big Sound Electronics bought stereo equipment for \$960.00 less 30%, 15%. Overhead is 25% of regular selling price. Big Sound marks all merchandise at a price that allows the store to offer a discount of 20% while still making its usual profit of 15% of regular selling price. During its annual mid-summer sale, the usual discount of 20% was replaced by a markdown of 45%. What operating profit or loss was made when the equipment was sold?

Solution

Complex problems of this type are best solved by a systematic approach. Consider the given information step by step. The following computations are necessary to determine the profit.

(i) the purchase price to the store;

(ii) the regular selling price required to cover cost, expenses, and the usual profit;

(iii) the marked price from which the 20% discount is offered;

(iv) the mid-summer sale price;

(v) the total handling cost;

(vi) the operating profit or loss.

Step-by-Step Computations

(i) Cost = NCF × List price = 0.70(0.85)(960.00) = \$571.20

(ii)
$$\begin{aligned} S &= C + E + P \\ S &= C + 25\% \text{ of } S + 15\% \text{ of } S \\ S &= C + 0.25S + 0.15S \\ S &= 571.20 + 0.40S \\ 0.60S &= 571.20 \\ S &= \frac{571.20}{0.60} = \$952.00 \end{aligned}$$

The regular selling price is \$952.00.

(iii) Marked price − Discount = Regular selling price

Let the marked price be $\$x$.

$$\begin{aligned} x - 20\% \text{ of } x &= 952.00 \\ x - 0.20x &= 952.00 \\ 0.80x &= 952.00 \\ x &= \frac{952.00}{0.80} = \$1190.00 \end{aligned}$$

The marked price was \$1190.00.

(iv)
$$\begin{aligned} \text{Sale price} &= \text{Marked price} - \text{Markdown} \\ &= x - 45\% \text{ of } x \\ &= x - 0.45x \\ &= 0.55x \\ &= 0.55(1190.00) \\ &= \$654.50 \end{aligned}$$

(v)
$$\begin{aligned} \text{Total cost} &= \text{Cost of buying} + \text{Overhead} \\ &= C + 25\% \text{ of } S \\ &= 571.20 + 0.25(952.00) \\ &= 571.20 + 238.00 \\ &= \$809.20 \end{aligned}$$

(vi)
$$\begin{aligned} \text{Profit} &= \text{Revenue} - \text{Total cost} \\ &= 654.50 - 809.20 \\ &= -\$154.70 \end{aligned}$$

The equipment was sold at an operating loss of \$154.70.

***Example* 6.4h** Magder's Furniture Emporium bought a dining room suite that must be retailed for $5250.00 to cover the wholesale price, overhead of 50% of the wholesale price, and a normal profit of 25% of the wholesale price. The suite is marked so that the store can allow a 20% discount and still receive the required retail price.

When the suite remained unsold, the store owner decided to mark the suite down for an inventory clearance sale. To arrive at the rate of markdown, the owner decided that the store's profit would have to be no less than 10% of the normal profit and that part of the markdown would be covered by reducing the commission paid to the salesperson. The normal commission (which accounts for 40% of the overhead) was reduced by $33\frac{1}{3}$%.

What is the maximum rate of markdown that can be advertised instead of the usual 20%?

Solution

STEP 1 Determine the wholesale cost.

$$S = C + E + P$$
$$S = C + 50\% \text{ of } C + 25\% \text{ of } C$$
$$S = C + 0.50C + 0.25C$$
$$5250.00 = 1.75C$$
$$C = \frac{5250.00}{1.75} = \$3000.00$$

STEP 2 Determine the marked price.

Let the marked price be $\$x$.

Marked price − Discount = Selling price

$$x - 20\% \text{ of } x = S$$
$$x - 0.20x = S$$
$$0.80x = 5250.00$$
$$x = \frac{5250.00}{0.80} = \$6562.50$$

STEP 3 Determine the required profit.

Normal profit = 25% of Wholesale cost
= 0.25(3000.00)
= $750.00

Required profit = 10% of Normal profit
= 0.10(750.00)
= $75.00

STEP 4 Determine the amount of overhead to be recovered.

Normal overhead = 50% of Wholesale cost
= 0.50(3000.00)
= $1500.00

Normal commission = 40% of Normal overhead
= 0.40(1500.00)
= \$600.00

Reduction in overhead = $33\frac{1}{3}\%$ of commission

= $(\frac{1}{3})(600.00)$
= \$200.00

Overhead to be recovered = 1500.00 − 200.00 = \$1300.00

STEP 5 Determine the sale price.

Sale price = Cost + Overhead + Profit
= 3000.00 + 1300.00 + 75.00
= \$4375.00

STEP 6 Determine the amount of markdown.

Markdown = Marked price − Sale price
= 6562.50 − 4375.00
= \$2187.50

STEP 7 Determine the rate of markdown.

$$\text{Rate of markdown} = \frac{\text{Amount of markdown}}{\text{Marked price}}$$

$$= \frac{2187.50}{6562.50}$$

$$= 0.3333333$$

$$= 33\tfrac{1}{3}\%$$

Instead of the usual 20%, the store can advertise a markdown of $33\frac{1}{3}\%$.

Exercise 6.4

A. Compute the missing value. Assume that all items carry a marked price such that a discount may be allowed to obtain the selling price.

	Cost	*Markup*	*Selling price*	*Discount*	*Marked price*	*Markdown*	*Sale price*
1.	\$51.00	25% of S	?	20%	?	26%	?
2.	?	50% of C	\$105.00	25%	?	?	\$84.00
3.	\$40.00	? of C	?	$16\frac{2}{3}\%$	\$144.00	?	\$90.00
4.	\$29.16	? of S	?	10%	\$72.00	35%	?
5.	?	60% of C	\$72.80	?	?	36%	\$61.60
6.	?	$33\frac{1}{3}\%$ of C	?	16%	?	40%	\$45.00

B. Compute the missing values for each of the following.

	Regular selling price	*Markdown*	*Sale price*	*Cost*	*Overhead*	*Total cost*	*Operating profit (loss)*
1.	$85.00	40%	?	$42.00	20% of S	?	?
2.	?	$33\frac{1}{3}\%$	$42.00	$34.44	12% of S	?	?
3.	?	35%	$62.66	?	25% of S	$54.75	?
4.	$72.80	$12\frac{1}{2}\%$	?	$54.75	20% of C	?	?
5.	?	25%	$120.00	$105.00	? of S	?	($4.20)
6.	$92.40	$16\frac{2}{3}\%$	?	?	15% of C	?	$8.46

C. Answer each of the following questions.

1. A cookware set that cost a dealer $440.00 less 55%, 25% is marked up 180% of cost. For quick sale, the cookware was reduced 45%.
   (a) What is the sale price?
   (b) What rate of markup based on cost was realized?

2. A gas barbecue that cost a retailer $420.00 less $33\frac{1}{3}\%$, 20%, 5%. It carries a price tag at a markup of 60% of the regular selling price. During the end-of-season sale, the barbecue is marked down 45%.
   (a) What is the sale price?
   (b) What rate of markup based on cost will be realized?

3. Bargain City discount clothing store purchased raincoats for $36.75. The store requires a gross profit of 30% of the regular selling price. What price should be marked on the raincoats if the store wants to offer a 25% discount without reducing its gross profit?

4. The Outdoor Shop buys tents for $264.00 less 25%. The store operates on a margin of $33\frac{1}{3}\%$ of regular selling price and advertises that all merchandise is sold at a discount of 20% of the marked price. What is the marked price of the tents?

5. The Stereo Shop sold a radio regularly priced at $125.00 for $75.00. The radio was originally purchased for $120.00 less $33\frac{1}{3}\%$, 15%. The store's overhead is 12% of the regular selling price.
   (a) What was the rate of markdown at which the radio was sold?
   (b) What was the operating profit or loss?
   (c) What rate of markup based on cost was realized?
   (d) What was the rate of markup based on the sale price?

6. An automatic dishwasher cost a dealer \$620.00 less $37\frac{1}{2}\%$, 4%. It is regularly priced at \$558.00. The dealer's overhead is 15% of the regular selling price and the dishwasher was cleared out for \$432.45.
   (a) What was the rate of markdown at which the dishwasher was sold?
   (b) What is the regular markup based on selling price?
   (c) What was the operating profit or loss?
   (d) What rate of markup based on cost was realized?

7. A jewellery store paid \$36.40 for a watch. Store expenses are 24% of regular selling price and the normal net profit is 20% of regular selling price. During a Special Bargain Day Sale, the watch was sold at a discount of 30%. What operating profit or loss was realized on the sale?

8. A hardware store paid \$33.45 for a set of cookware. Overhead is 15% of the regular selling price and profit is 10% of the regular selling price. During a clearance sale, the set was sold at a markdown of 15%. What was the operating profit or loss on the sale?

9. A clothing store buys shorts for \$24.00 less 40%, $16\frac{2}{3}\%$. The shorts are marked up to cover overhead of 25% of cost and a profit of $33\frac{1}{3}\%$ of cost.
   (a) What is the regular selling price of the shorts?
   (b) What is the maximum amount of markdown to break even?
   (c) What is the rate of markdown if the shorts are sold at the break-even price?

10. Furniture City bought chairs for \$75.00 less $33\frac{1}{3}\%$, 20%, 10%. The store's overhead is 75% of cost and normal profit is 25% of cost.
    (a) What is the marked price of the chairs?
    (b) At what price can the chairs be put on sale so that the store incurs an operating loss of no more than $33\frac{1}{3}\%$ of the overhead?
    (c) What is the maximum rate of markdown at which the chairs can be offered for sale in part (b)?

11. The Bay bought stereo equipment listed at \$900.00 less 60%, $16\frac{2}{3}\%$. Expenses are 45% of the regular selling price and normal profit is 15% of the regular selling price. The equipment was marked so that the store could advertise a 37.5% discount while still maintaining its usual markup. During the annual inventory sale, the unsold equipment was marked down 55%. What operating profit or loss was realized on the equipment sold during the sale?

12. Lund's Pro Shop purchased sets of golf clubs for \$500.00 less 40%, $16\frac{2}{3}\%$. Expenses are 20% of the regular selling price and the required profit is 17.5% of the regular selling price. The sets were marked so that the shop can offer a 36% discount without affecting its margin. At the end of the season, the unsold sets were advertised at a discount of 54%. What operating profit or loss was realized on the sets sold at the reduced price?

13. Bad Boy Appliances bought microwave ovens for \$900.00 less $33\frac{1}{3}\%$, 5%. Expenses are 15% of the regular selling price and profit is 9% of the regular selling price. For competitive reasons, the store marks all merchandise so that a discount of 25% can be advertised without affecting the margin. To promote sales, the ovens were marked down 40%. What operating profit or loss did the store make on the ovens sold during the sales promotion?

14. Bluc Lake Marina sells a make of cruiser for \$16 800.00. The selling price covers overhead of 15% of cost and a normal profit of 10% of cost. The cruisers were marked so that the marina can offer a 20% discount while still maintaining its regular gross profit. At the end of the boating season, the cruiser was marked down. The marina made 25% of its usual profit and reduced the usual commission paid to the sales personnel by $33\frac{1}{3}\%$. The normal commission accounts for 50% of the normal overhead. What was the rate of markdown?

Review exercise

1. A tool box is listed for \$56.00 less 25%, 20%, 5%.
   (a) What is the net price of the tool box?
   (b) What is the amount of discount?
   (c) What is the single rate of discount that was allowed?

2. Compute the exact rate of discount allowed on a lawn mower that lists for \$168.00 and is sold for \$105.00.

3. Determine the exact single rate of discount equivalent to the discount series 35%, 12%, 5%.

4. A 40% discount allowed on an article amounts to \$1.44. What is the net price?

5. Baton Construction Supplies has been selling wheelbarrows for \$112.00 less 15%. What additional discount percent must the company offer to meet a competitor's price of \$80.92?

6. A freezer was sold during a clearance sale for \$387.50. If the freezer was sold at a discount of $16\frac{2}{3}\%$, what was the list price?

7. The net price of a snow shovel is \$20.40 after discounts of 20%, 15%. What is the list price?

8. On May 18, an invoice dated May 17 for \$4000.00 less 20%, 15%, terms 5/10 E.O.M., was received by Aldo Distributors.
   (a) What is the last day of the discount period?
   (b) What is the amount due if the invoice is paid within the discount period?

9. What amount must be remitted if the following invoices, all with terms 5/10, 2/30, *n*/60, are paid together on December 8?

Invoice No. 312 dated November 2 for $923.00
Invoice No. 429 dated November 14 for $784.00
Invoice No. 563 dated November 30 for $873.00

10. Delta Furnishings received an invoice dated May 10 for a shipment of goods received June 21. The invoice was for $8400.00 less $33\frac{1}{3}\%$, $12\frac{1}{2}\%$ with terms 3/20 R.O.G. How much must Delta pay on July 9 to reduce its debt

(a) by $2000.00? **(b)** to $2000.00?

11. The Peel Trading Company received an invoice dated September 20 for $16 000.00 less 25%, 20%, terms 5/10, 2/30, *n*/60. Peel made a payment on September 30 to reduce the debt to $5000.00 and a payment on October 20 to reduce the debt by $3000.00.

(a) What amount must Peel remit to pay the balance of the debt at the end of the credit period?

(b) What is the total amount paid by Peel?

12. Emco Ltd. received an invoice dated May 5 for $4000.00 less 15%, $7\frac{1}{2}\%$, terms 3/15 E.O.M. A cheque for $1595.65 was mailed by Emco on June 15 as part payment of the invoice.

(a) By how much did Emco reduce the amount due on the invoice?

(b) How much does Emco still owe?

13. Home Hardware buys cat litter for $6.00 less 20% per bag. The store's overhead is 45% of cost and the owner requires a profit of 20% of cost.

(a) For how much should the bags be sold?

(b) What is the amount of markup included in the selling price?

(c) What is the rate of markup based on selling price?

(d) What is the rate of markup based on cost?

(e) What is the break-even price?

(f) What operating profit or loss is made if a bag is sold for $6.00?

14. A retail store realizes a gross profit of $31.50 if it sells an article at a margin of 35% of the selling price.

(a) What is the regular selling price?

(b) What is the cost?

(c) What is the rate of markup based on cost?

(d) If overhead is 28% of cost, what is the break-even price?

(e) If the article is sold at a markdown of 24%, what is the operating profit or loss?

15. Using a margin of 35% of cost, a store priced a book at \$8.91.

    (a) What was the cost of the item?

    (b) What is the margin as a percent of selling price?

16. A bicycle helmet costing \$54.25 was marked up to realize a gross profit of 30% of the selling price.

    (a) What was the selling price?

    (b) What was the gross profit as a percent of cost?

17. A bedroom suite that cost a dealer \$1800.00 less 37.5%, 18% carries a price tag at a markup of 120% of cost. For quick sale, the bedroom suite was marked down 40%.

    (a) What was the sale price?

    (b) What rate of markup based on cost was realized?

18. Gino's purchased men's suits for \$195.00 less $33\frac{1}{3}\%$. The store operates at a normal gross profit of 35% of regular selling price. The owner marks all merchandise so that the store can offer a $16\frac{2}{3}\%$ discount. What is the marked price?

19. An appliance store sold G.E. coffee makers for \$22.95 during a promotional sale. The store bought the coffee makers for \$36.00 less 40%, 15%. Overhead is 25% of the regular selling price.

    (a) If the store's margin is 40% of selling price, what was the rate of markdown?

    (b) What operating profit or loss was made during the sale?

    (c) What rate of markup based on cost was realized?

20. Harvey and Billnot buy shirts for \$21.00 less 25%, 20%. The shirts are priced to cover expenses of 20% of selling price and a profit of 17% of selling price. For a special weekend sale, shirts were marked down 20%.

    (a) What was the operating profit or loss on the shirts sold during the weekend sale?

    (b) What rate of margin was realized based on the sale price?

21. A jewellery store paid a unit price of \$250.00 less 40%, $16\frac{2}{3}\%$, 8% for a shipment of watches. The store's overhead is 65% of cost and the normal profit is 55% of cost.

    (a) What is the regular selling price of the watches?

    (b) What is the selling price for the store to break even?

    (c) What is the rate of markdown to sell the watches at the break-even price?

22. Sight and Sound bought colour TV sets for \$1080.00 less $33\frac{1}{3}\%$, $8\frac{1}{3}\%$. Overhead is 18% of selling price and required profit is $15\frac{1}{3}\%$ of selling price. The TV sets were marked so that the store was able to advertise a discount of 25% while still maintaining its margin. To clear the inventory, the remaining TV sets were marked down $37\frac{1}{2}\%$.

    (a) What operating profit or loss is realized at the reduced price?

    (b) What is the realized rate of markup based on cost?

23. Ward Machinery lists a log splitter at \$1860.00 less $33\frac{1}{3}\%$, 15%. To meet competition, Ward wants to reduce its net price to \$922.25. What additional percent discount must Ward allow?

24. West End Appliances bought food processors for \$180.00 less 40%, $16\frac{2}{3}\%$, 10%. The store's overhead is 45% of selling price and the profit required is $21\frac{1}{4}\%$ of selling price.

(a) What is the break-even price?

(b) What is the maximum rate of markdown that the store can offer to break even?

(c) What is the realized rate of markup based on cost if the food processors are sold at the break-even price?

25. A merchant realizes a margin of \$42.00 by selling an article at a markup of 37.5% of cost.

(a) What is the regular selling price?

(b) What is the rate of markup based on selling price?

(c) If the merchant's expenses are 17.5% of the selling price, what is the break-even price?

(d) If the article is reduced for sale to \$121.66, what is the rate of markdown?

26. The Knit Shoppe bought 250 sweaters for \$3100.00; 50 sweaters were sold at a markup of 150% of cost and 120 sweaters at a markup of 75% of cost; 60 of the sweaters were sold during a clearance sale for \$15.00 each and the remaining sweaters were disposed of at 20% below cost.

(a) What was the margin realized on the purchase?

(b) What was the percent markup realized based on cost?

(c) What was the gross profit realized based on selling price?

Self-test

1. Determine the net cost of an article listed at \$590.00 less 37.5%, 12.5%, $8\frac{1}{3}\%$.

2. What rate of discount has been allowed if an item that lists for \$270.00 is sold for \$168.75?

3. Compute the single discount percent equivalent to the discount series 40%, 10%, $8\frac{1}{3}\%$ (the rate must be exact).

4. Discount Electronics lists an article for \$1020.00 less 25% and 15%. A competitor carries the same article for \$927.00 less 25%. What further discount (correct to the nearest 1/10 of 1%) must the competitor allow so that its net price is the same as the discount store's?

5. What amount must be remitted if the following invoices, all with terms 4/10, 2/30, *n*/60, are paid on May 10?

   $850.00 less 20%, 10% dated March 21

   $960.00 less 30%, $16\frac{2}{3}$% dated April 10

   $1040.00 less $33\frac{1}{3}$%, 25%, 5% dated April 30

6. An invoice for $3200.00, dated March 20, terms 3/10 E.O.M., was received March 23. What payment must be made on April 10 to reduce the debt to $1200.00?

7. On January 15, Sheridan Service received an invoice dated January 14, terms 4/10 E.O.M., for $2592.00. On February 9, Sheridan Service mailed a cheque for $1392.00 in partial payment of the invoice. By how much did Sheridan Service reduce its debt?

8. What is the selling price of an item bought for $1270.00 if the markup is 20% of the selling price?

9. The regular selling price of merchandise sold in a store includes a markup of 40% based on selling price. During a sale, an item that cost the store $180.00 was marked down 20%. For how much was the item sold?

10. The net price of an article is $727.20 after discounts of 20% and 10% have been allowed. What was the list price?

11. An item that cost the dealer $350 less 35%, 12.5% carries a price tag at a markup of 150% of cost. For quick sale, the item was reduced 30%. What was the sale price?

12. Find the cost of an item sold for $1904.00 to realize a markup of 40% based on cost.

13. An article cost $900.00 and sold for $2520.00. What was the percent markup (to the nearest $\frac{1}{100}$ of 1%) based on cost?

14. A gross profit of $90.00 is made on a sale. If the gross profit was 45% based on selling price, what was the cost?

15. An appliance shop reduces the price of an appliance for quick sale from $1560.00 to $1195.00. Compute the markdown correct to the nearest $\frac{1}{100}$ of 1%.

16. An invoice shows a net purchase price of $552.44 after discounts of $33\frac{1}{3}$%, 20%, $8\frac{1}{3}$%. What was the list price?

17. A retailer buys an appliance for resale at $1480.00 less 25%, 15%. The store marks the merchandise to cover expenses of 40% of the regular selling price and a net profit of 10% of the regular selling price. During a clearance sale, the appliance was sold at a markdown of 45%. What was the operating profit or loss?

18. Discount Electronics buys stereos for $830.00 less 37.5%, 12.5%. Expenses are 20% of normal selling price and the required profit is 15% of normal selling price. All merchandise is marked so that the store can advertise a discount of 30% while still maintaining its regular markup. During the annual clearance sale, the marked price of unsold items is marked down 50%. What operating profit or loss does the store make on items sold during the sale?

CASE STUDY

Kitchen Mate manufactures kitchen utensils. One item that has been produced for several years has a total production cost of $7.80.

1. This item is marked up 125% based on cost. Calculate the regular selling price.

2. Kitchen Mate gives the Buy Direct outlet a 30% discount and the wholesaler a 10%, 8%, 5% series discount on the regular selling price. Calculate the net cost price for the two distributors.

3. The Buy Direct outlet sells the item to the public with a 55% markup based on the regular selling price. Calculate the selling price.

4. The wholesaler adds a markup of 60% of cost and sells to an independent retailer with terms 10/10, *n*/30. Calculate the net cost to the retailer if the bill is paid within 10 days.

5. The retailer needs to have a markup of 25% based on selling price to break even. Calculate the break-even price for the retailer.

6. If the retailer has to match Buy Direct's selling price, what profit will it realize? What percent markup based on cost does this price represent?

7. The retailer decides to advertise a 30% discount on the item to match Buy Direct's price. What will be the advertised regular selling price?

8. Calculate the total percent markup on the item based on manufacturer's cost from the manufacturer to the consumer at Buy Direct's selling price.

9. To stay in business, the independent retailer has to have a markup of 40% based on the retail selling price.

(a) Calculate the retail selling price.

(b) Suggest methods an independent retailer could use to compete with Buy Direct.

Summary of formulae used

Formula 6.1

$$\text{AMOUNT OF DISCOUNT} = \text{RATE OF DISCOUNT} \times \text{LIST PRICE}$$

Finding the amount of discount when the list price is known

Formula 6.2

$$\text{NET PRICE or NET COST} = \text{LIST PRICE} - \text{AMOUNT OF TRADE DISCOUNT}$$

Finding the net amount when the amount of discount is known

Formula 6.3A

$$\text{NET COST FACTOR (NCF)} = 100\% - \%\ \text{DISCOUNT}$$

Finding the net cost factor (NCF)

Formula 6.3B

NET COST FACTOR (NCF) $= 1 - d$

where d = rate of discount in decimal form.

Restatement of Formula 6.3A in algebraic terms.

Formula 6.4A

$$\begin{array}{c}\text{NET PRICE}\\ \text{or}\\ \text{NET COST}\end{array} = \begin{array}{c}\text{NET COST}\\ \text{FACTOR (NCF)}\end{array} \times \begin{array}{c}\text{LIST}\\ \text{PRICE}\end{array}$$

Finding the net amount directly without computing the amount of discount

Formula 6.4B

$$N = (1 - d)L \quad \text{or} \quad N = L(1 - d)$$

Formula 6.5A

$$\begin{array}{c}\text{NET COST FACTOR}\\ \text{(NCF) FOR}\\ \text{THE DISCOUNT SERIES}\end{array} = \begin{array}{c}\text{NCF FOR}\\ \text{THE FIRST}\\ \text{DISCOUNT}\end{array} \times \begin{array}{c}\text{NCF FOR}\\ \text{THE SECOND}\\ \text{DISCOUNT}\end{array} \times \ldots \times \begin{array}{c}\text{NCF FOR}\\ \text{THE LAST}\\ \text{DISCOUNT}\end{array}$$

Formula 6.5B

$$\text{NCF FOR A DISCOUNT SERIES} = (1 - d_1)(1 - d_2)(1 - d_3)\ldots(1 - d_n)$$

Formula 6.6A

$$\begin{array}{c}\text{NET COST}\\ \text{or}\\ \text{NET PRICE}\end{array} = \begin{array}{c}\text{NET COST FACTOR FOR}\\ \text{THE DISCOUNT SERIES}\end{array} \times \begin{array}{c}\text{LIST}\\ \text{PRICE}\end{array}$$

Finding the net amount directly when a list price is subject to a series of discounts

Formula 6.6B

$$\begin{array}{c}\text{NET COST}\\ \text{or}\\ \text{NET PRICE}\end{array} = (1 - d_1)(1 - d_2)(1 - d_3)\ldots(1 - d_n)L$$

Formula 6.7

$$\begin{array}{c}\text{RATE OF}\\ \text{TRADE DISCOUNT}\end{array} = \frac{\text{AMOUNT OF DISCOUNT}}{\text{LIST PRICE}}$$

Finding the rate of discount

Formula 6.8

SINGLE EQUIVALENT RATE OF DISCOUNT FOR A DISCOUNT SERIES

$= 1 -$ NCF FOR THE DISCOUNT SERIES

$= 1 - [(1 - d_1)(1 - d_2)(1 - d_3)\ldots(1 - d_n)]$

Finding the single rate of discount that has the same effect as a given series of discounts

Formula 6.9A

SELLING PRICE = COST + EXPENSES + PROFIT

or

$$S = C + E + P$$

Basic relationship between selling price, cost, overhead, and profit

Formula 6.9B

SELLING PRICE = COST + MARKUP

or

$$S = C + M$$

Formula 6.10

$$\text{MARKUP} = \text{EXPENSES} + \text{PROFIT}$$

or

$$M = E + P$$

Relationship between markup, overhead, and profit

Formula 6.11

$$\frac{\text{RATE OF MARKUP}}{\text{BASED ON COST}} = \frac{\text{MARKUP}}{\text{COST}} = \frac{M}{C}$$

Finding the rate of markup as a percent of cost

Formula 6.12

$$\text{RATE OF MARKUP BASED ON SELLING PRICE} = \frac{\text{MARKUP}}{\text{SELLING PRICE}} = \frac{M}{S}$$

Finding the rate of markup as a percent of selling price

Glossary of terms used

Cash discount a reduction in the amount of an invoice
Discount series two or more discounts taken off a list price in succession
End-of-month dating payment terms based on the last day of the month in which the invoice is dated
Gross profit see *Markup*
Margin see *Markup*
Markdown a reduction in a price
Markup the difference between the cost of merchandise and the selling price
Net cost the difference between a list price and the amount of discount
Net cost factor (NCF) the difference between 100% and a percent discount—the net cost expressed as a fraction of the list price
Ordinary dating payment terms based on the date of an invoice
Payment terms a statement of the conditions under which a cash discount may be taken
Partial payment part payment of an invoice
Proximo dating see *End-of-month dating*
Receipt-of-goods dating payment terms based on the date the merchandise is received
Single equivalent rate of discount the single rate of discount that has the same effect as a specific series of discounts
Total cost the cost at which merchandise is bought plus the overhead
Trade discounts a reduction of a catalogue or list price

7 *Simple interest*

Introduction

The use of money as a means of exchange has led to the practice of lending and borrowing money. Lenders usually require compensation for their services in the form of interest. The amount of such interest is based on three factors: the amount of money borrowed, the rate of interest at which it is borrowed, and the time period for which it is borrowed.

Objectives

Upon completing this chapter, you will be able to

1. interpret the letter symbols used in the formula $I = Prt$;
2. determine the exact time in days between two dates;
3. compute the exact simple interest by means of the formula $I = Prt$;
4. find the principal, rate, or time using the formula $I = Prt$;
5. use the formula $S = P(1 + rt)$ to find the amount (or maturity value) when the principal, rate, and time are given;
6. use the formula $P = \frac{S}{1 + rt}$ to compute the principal (or present value) when the maturity value, rate, and time are given;
7. compute equivalent values for specified focal dates.

7.1 *Basic concepts and formula*

A. Formula

Interest is the rent charged for the use of money. The amount of **simple** interest is determined by the relationship

$$\text{Interest} = \text{Principal} \times \text{Rate} \times \text{Time}$$
$$I = Prt \qquad \longleftarrow \textit{Formula } 7.1$$

where I is the amount of interest earned;

P is the principal sum of money earning the interest;
r is the simple annual (yearly) rate of interest;
t is the time period in years.

B. *Matching* r *and* t

While the time may be stated in days, months, or years, the rate of interest is a yearly charge unless otherwise stated. In using the simple interest formula, it is imperative that the time t corresponds to the interest rate r. Months or days often need to be converted into years.

***Example* 7.1a** State r and t for each of the following.

(i) Rate 9%; time 3 years

Solution

The annual rate $r = 9\% = 0.09$
The time in years $t = 3$

(ii) Rate 8.5%; time 18 months

Solution

The annual rate $r = 8.5\% = 0.085$

The time in years $t = \frac{18}{12}$

Note: To convert months into years, divide by 12.

(iii) Rate $11\frac{1}{4}\%$; time 243 days

Solution

The annual rate $r = 11.25\% = 0.1125$

The time in years $t = \frac{243}{365}$

Note: To convert days into years, divide by 365.

Exercise 7.1

A. State r and t for each of the following.

1. Rate is $12\frac{1}{2}\%$; time is $1\frac{1}{4}$ years
2. Rate is $9\frac{3}{4}\%$; time is 21 months
3. Rate is 10.25%; time is 165 days
4. Rate is $15\frac{1}{2}\%$; time is 332 days

7.2 *Determining the number of days*

A. Counting exact time

When the **interest period** involves two dates, the number of days between the two dates must be determined. In counting the number of days, the traditional practice was to count the ending date but *not* the beginning date. However, the current practice, associated with the computerization of interest calculation, is to count the beginning date but *not* the ending date. While in most cases the end result is the same, there are situations in which slightly different answers result, depending on the method used. This text will use the current method of counting the beginning date.

Counting days requires knowing the order of the twelve months in the year and the number of days in each month. The number of days in each of the twelve months in order (ignoring leap years) is listed below.

1. January	31	2. February	28	3. March	31
4. April	30	5. May	31	6. June	30
7. July	31	8. August	31	9. September	30
10. October	31	11. November	30	12. December	31

Example 7.2a Find the number of days between January 30 and June 1.

Solution

The beginning date is January 30 ⟵ to be counted
The ending date is June 1 ⟵ do *not* count

Number of days			
	January	2	⟵ (31 − 29)
	February	28	
	March	31	
	April	30	
	May	31	
	June	0	
	TOTAL	122	

Example 7.2b Find the number of days between November 12, 1994, and May 5, 1995.

Solution

The beginning date is November 12 ⟵ to be counted
The ending date is May 5 ⟵ do *not* count

Number of days			
	November 1994	19	⟵ (30 − 11))
	December	31	
	January 1995	31	
	February	28	

March	31
April	30
May	4
TOTAL	174

B. *Using a table*

Exact time can also be obtained from a table listing the number of each day of the year. (See Table 7.1.) When using such a table, take care to distinguish between two cases:

(i) the beginning date and the ending date are in the *same* year;

(ii) the ending date is in the year *following* the beginning date or in a later year.

TABLE 7.1 ***The number of each day of the year***

Day of Month	*Jan.*	*Feb.*	*Mar.*	*Apr.*	*May*	*June*	*July*	*Aug.*	*Sept.*	*Oct.*	*Nov.*	*Dec.*	*Day of Month*
1	1	32	60	91	121	152	182	213	244	274	305	335	*1*
2	2	33	61	92	122	153	183	214	245	275	306	336	*2*
3	3	34	62	93	123	154	184	215	246	276	307	337	*3*
4	4	35	63	94	124	155	185	216	247	277	308	338	*4*
5	5	36	64	95	125	156	186	217	248	278	309	339	*5*
6	6	37	65	96	126	157	187	218	249	279	310	340	*6*
7	7	38	66	97	127	158	188	219	250	280	311	341	*7*
8	8	39	67	98	128	159	189	220	251	281	312	342	*8*
9	9	40	68	99	129	160	190	221	252	282	313	343	*9*
10	10	41	69	100	130	161	191	222	253	283	314	344	*10*
11	11	42	70	101	131	162	192	223	254	284	315	345	*11*
12	12	43	71	102	132	163	193	224	255	285	316	346	*12*
13	13	44	72	103	133	164	194	225	256	286	317	347	*13*
14	14	45	73	104	134	165	195	226	257	287	318	348	*14*
15	15	46	74	105	135	166	196	227	258	288	319	349	*15*
16	16	47	75	106	136	167	197	228	259	289	320	350	*16*
17	17	48	76	107	137	168	198	229	260	290	321	351	*17*
18	18	49	77	108	138	169	199	230	261	291	322	352	*18*
19	19	50	78	109	139	170	200	231	262	292	323	353	*19*
20	20	51	79	110	140	171	201	232	263	293	324	354	*20*
21	21	52	80	111	141	172	202	233	264	294	325	355	*21*
22	22	53	81	112	142	173	203	234	265	295	326	356	*22*
23	23	54	82	113	143	174	204	235	266	296	327	357	*23*
24	24	55	83	114	144	175	205	236	267	297	328	358	*24*
25	25	56	84	115	145	176	206	237	268	298	329	359	*25*
26	26	57	85	116	146	177	207	238	269	299	330	360	*26*
27	27	58	86	117	147	178	208	239	270	300	331	361	*27*
28	28	59	87	118	148	179	209	240	271	301	332	362	*28*
29	29		88	119	149	180	210	241	272	302	333	363	*29*
30	30		89	120	150	181	211	242	273	303	334	364	*30*
31	31		90		151		212	243		304		365	*31*

Note: In leap years, February 29 becomes day 60 and the numbers in the table increase by 1 for all following days.

Example **7.2c** Find the number of days between May 29 and August 3.

Solution

The beginning date is May 29 ⟶	Day 149
The ending date is August 3 ⟶	Day 215
The difference in days is (215 − 149)	66

Example **7.2d** Find the number of days between September 1, 1997, and April 1, 1998.

Solution

The beginning date is September 1, 1997 ⟶	Day 244
Number of days in 1997 is 365	
Number of days remaining in 1997 is (365 − 244)	= 121
The ending date is April 1, 1998 ⟶	Day 91
The total number of days is (121 + 91)	= 212

C. *Leap years*

Leap years are evenly divisible by 4, such as 1988, 1992, and 1996. An extra day is added to February if a year is a **leap year**. However, the first year of a century is not a leap year unless the number is *evenly* divisible by 400. This means that the year 1900 was not a leap year but the year 2000 is. It will have the extra day.

Example **7.2e** Find the number of days between December 12, 1995, and April 1, 1996,

(i) by counting; (ii) by using Table 7.1.

Solution

(i) The beginning date is December 12, 1995
The ending date is April 1, 1996

Number of days			
	December 1995	20	⟵ (31 − 11)
	January 1996	31	
	February	29	⟵ Leap year
	March	31	
	April	0	
	TOTAL	111	

(ii) The beginning date is December 12, 1995 ⟶		Day 346
The number of days in 1995 is 365		
The number of days remaining in 1995 is (365 − 346)	=	19
The ending date is April 1, 1996 ⟶		Day 92
(for a leap year, increase the table number 91 by 1 to 92)		
TOTAL		111

Exercise 7.2

A. Determine the exact time by counting days for each of the following.

1. January 18, 1995, to May 10, 1995
2. August 30, 1996, to April 1, 1997
3. November 1, 1995, to April 15, 1996
4. December 24, 1996, to February 5, 1998

B. Determine the exact time using a table. (See Table 7.1.)

1. April 1, 1996, to December 1, 1996
2. July 30, 1994, to March 30, 1995
3. April 5, 1995, to March 11, 1996
4. August 25, 1998, to May 20, 2000

7.3 *Computing the amount of interest*

If the principal, rate, and time are known, the amount of interest can be determined by the formula I = Prt.

A.

***Example* 7.3a** Compute the amount of interest for

(i) \$3600.00 at 9% p.a. (per annum) for 3 years;
(ii) \$5240.00 at 10.5% p.a. for 16 months;
(iii) \$1293.60 at 11.75% p.a. for 215 days.

Solution

(i) P = 3600.00; r = 9% = 0.09; t = 3
I = Prt = (3600.00)(0.09)(3) = \$972.00

(ii) $P = 5240.00; r = 10.5\% = 0.105; t = 16 \text{ months} = \frac{16}{12}$

$$I = Prt = (5240.00)(0.105)\left(\frac{16}{12}\right) = \$733.60$$

(iii) $P = 1293.60; r = 11.75 = 0.1175; t = 215 \text{ days} = \frac{215}{365}$

$$I = Prt = (1293.60)(0.1175)\left(\frac{215}{365}\right) = \$89.53$$

B.

Example 7.3b Find the amount of interest earned by \$785.95 invested at 9.25% from January 30, 1997, to April 21, 1997.

Solution

Number of days	January	2 ⟵(31 − 29)
	February	28
	March	31
	April	20
	TOTAL	81

$$P = 785.95; r = 9.25\% = 0.0925; t = \frac{81}{365}$$

$$I = (785.95)(0.0925)\left(\frac{81}{365}\right) = \$16.13$$

C.

Example 7.3c Compute the amount of interest on \$1240.00 earning 10.75% p.a. from September 30, 1995, to May 15, 1996.

Solution

The beginning date is September 30, 1995 ⟶	Day 273	
The number of days remaining in 1995 is (365 − 273) =	92	
The ending date is May 15, 1996 (Day 135 + 1)	136	⟵leap year
TOTAL	228	

$$P = 1240.00; r = 10.75\% = 0.1075; t = \frac{228}{365}$$

$$I = (1240.00)(0.1075)\left(\frac{228}{365}\right) = \$83.27$$

Note: 365 is used to convert the number of days into years even if the year involved is a leap year.

Exercise 7.3

A. Compute the amount of interest for each of the following.

1. \$4000.00 at $10\frac{1}{2}\%$ for $2\frac{1}{4}$ years.
2. \$645.00 at $6\frac{1}{4}\%$ for $1\frac{3}{4}$ years
3. \$1660 at 9.75% for 16 months
4. \$742.40 at 10.9% for 9 months
5. \$980.00 at 11.5% for 244 days
6. \$465.40 at 12.4% for 163 days

B. Compute the amount of interest for each of the following.

1. \$275.00 at 9.25% from November 30, 1996, to May 5, 1997
2. \$1090.60 at 7.8% from October 12, 1995, to April 24, 1996
3. \$424.23 at $12\frac{3}{4}\%$ from April 4, 1995, to November 4, 1995
4. \$724.85 at 10.4% from August 30, 1994, to March 30, 1995

7.4 *Finding the principal, rate, or time*

A. Problems derived from the simple interest formula

The simple interest formula $I = Prt$ contains the four variables I, P, r, and t. If any *three* of the four are given, the value of the unknown variable can be computed by substituting the known values in the formula or by solving for the unknown variable first and then substituting in the resulting derived formula.

The three derived formulae are

(i) to find the principal P, $$P = \frac{I}{rt}$$ ⟵ *Formula 7.2A*

(ii) to find the rate of interest r, $$r = \frac{I}{Pt}$$ ⟵ *Formula 7.2B*

(iii) to find the time period t, $$t = \frac{I}{Pr}$$ ⟵ *Formula 7.2C*

Note: **(a)** In Formula 7.2B, if the time period t is expressed *in years*, the value of r represents an *annual* rate of interest in decimal form.

(b) In Formula 7.2C, if the rate of interest r is an *annual* rate, the value of t represents *years* in decimal form.

B. Finding the principal

If the amount of interest, the rate of interest, and the time period are known, the principal can be determined.

Example **7.4a** What principal will earn interest of \$57.40 at 10.25% in 8 months?

Solution

$$\text{I} = 57.40; \quad r = 10.25\%; \quad t = \frac{8}{12}$$

(i) Using the formula I = Prt,

$$57.40 = (\text{P})(0.1025)\left(\frac{8}{12}\right) \longleftarrow \text{by substitution}$$

$$57.40 = (\text{P})(0.0683333) \longleftarrow (0.1025)\left(\frac{8}{12}\right)$$

$$\text{P} = \frac{57.40}{0.0683333} \longleftarrow \text{divide 57.40 by the coefficient of P}$$

$$= \$840.00$$

(ii) Using the derived formula $\text{P} = \frac{\text{I}}{rt}$,

$$\text{P} = \frac{57.40}{(0.1025)(\frac{8}{12})} \longleftarrow \text{by substitution}$$

$$= \frac{(57.40)(12)}{(0.1025)(8)} \longleftarrow \text{move the 12 into the numerator}$$

$$= \$840.00$$

Note:

(1) When the time is given in months, the formula may be modified to

$$\text{P} = \frac{(\text{I})(12)}{(r)(t \text{ in months})}$$

(2) When the time is given in days, the formula may be modified to

$$\text{P} = \frac{(\text{I})(365)}{(r)(t \text{ in days})}$$

Example **7.4b** Determine the sum of money that must be invested for 245 days at 9.75% to earn \$71.99.

Solution

$$\text{I} = 71.99; \quad r = 9.75\% = 0.0975; \quad t = \frac{245}{365}$$

(i) Using the formula I = Prt,

$$71.99 = (P)(0.0975)\left(\frac{245}{365}\right)$$

$$71.99 = (P)(0.0654452)$$

$$P = \frac{71.99}{0.0654452}$$

$$= \$1100.00$$

(ii) Using the derived formula $P = \frac{I}{rt}$,

$$P = \frac{71.99}{(0.0975)(\frac{245}{365})}$$

$$= \frac{(71.99)(365)}{(0.0975)(245)} \longleftarrow \text{move the 365 into the numerator}$$

$$= \$1100.00$$

C. *Finding the rate*

If the amount of interest, the principal, and the time period are known, the rate of interest can be determined.

***Example* 7.4c** Find the annual rate of interest required for \$744.00 to earn \$75.95 in 14 months.

Solution

$$I = 75.95; \quad P = 744.00; \quad t = \frac{14}{12}$$

(i) Using the formula I = Prt,

$$75.95 = (744)(r)\left(\frac{14}{12}\right)$$

$$75.95 = (868)(r)$$

$$r = \frac{75.95}{868}$$

$$= 0.0875$$

$$= 8.75\% \longleftarrow \text{convert to a percent}$$

(ii) Using the derived formula $r = \frac{I}{Pt}$,

$$r = \frac{75.95}{(744.00)(\frac{14}{12})}$$

$$= \frac{(75.95)(12)}{(744.00)(14)}$$

$$= 0.0875$$

$$= 8.75\%$$

Note:

(1) When the time is given in months, the formula may be modified to

$$r = \frac{(\text{I})(12)}{(\text{P})(t \text{ in months})}$$

(2) When the time is given in days, the formula may be modified to

$$r = \frac{(\text{I})(365)}{(\text{P})(t \text{ in days})}$$

Example **7.4d** Find the yearly rate of interest on a principal of \$1600.00 earning interest of \$59.18 in 120 days.

Solution

$$\text{I} = 59.18; \quad \text{P} = 1600.00; \quad t = \frac{120}{365}$$

(i) Using the formula I = Prt,

$$59.18 = (1600.00)(r)\left(\frac{120}{365}\right)$$

$$59.18 = (526.0274)(r)$$

$$r = \frac{59.18}{526.0274}$$

$$= 0.1125$$

$$= 11.25\%$$

(ii) Using the derived formula $r = \dfrac{\text{I}}{\text{P}rt}$,

$$r = \frac{59.18}{(1600.00)(\frac{120}{365})}$$

$$= \frac{(59.18)(365)}{(1600.00)(120)}$$

$$= 0.1125$$

$$= 11.25\%$$

D. Finding the time

If the amount of interest, the principal, and the rate of interest are known, the time period can be determined.

Example 7.4e Find the number of years required for \$745.00 to earn \$178.80 simple interest at 8% p.a.

Solution

$$I = 178.80; \quad P = 745.00; \quad r = 8\% = 0.08$$

(i) Using the formula $I = Prt$,

$$178.80 = (745.00)((0.08)(t)$$

$$178.80 = (59.60)(t)$$

$$t = \frac{178.80}{59.60}$$

$$= 3.00 \text{ (years)}$$

(ii) Using the derived formula $t = \frac{I}{Pr}$,

$$t = \frac{178.80}{(745.00)(0.08)}$$

$$= 3.00 \text{ (years)}$$

Note:

(1) The value of t in the formula $I = Prt$ will be in years. If the time period is to be stated in months or in days, it is necessary to multiply the initial value of t by 12 for months or 365 for days.

(2) If the time is to be shown in months, the derived formula may be modified to

$$t = \frac{(I)(12)}{Pr}$$

(3) If the time is to be shown in days, the derived formula may be modified to

$$t = \frac{(I)(365)}{Pr}$$

Example 7.4f Determine the number of months required for a deposit of \$1320.00 to earn \$51.70 interest at 11.75%.

Solution

$$I = 51.70; \quad P = 1320.00; \quad r = 11.75\% = 0.1175$$

(i) Using the formula I = P*rt*,

$$\begin{aligned} 51.70 &= (1320.00)(0.1175)(t) \\ 51.70 &= (155.10)(t) \\ t &= \frac{51.70}{155.10} \\ &= 0.3333333 \text{ years} \\ &= (0.3333333)(12) \text{ months} \\ &= 4 \text{ months} \end{aligned}$$

(ii) Using the derived formula $t = \frac{I}{Pr}$,

$$\begin{aligned} t &= \frac{51.70}{(1320.00)(0.1175)} \text{ years} \\ &= \frac{(51.70)(12)}{(1320.00)(0.1175)} \text{ months} \\ &= 4 \text{ months} \end{aligned}$$

***Example* 7.4g** How many days are needed for \$1500.00 to earn \$69.04 at 10.5% p.a.?

Solution

$$I = 69.04; \quad P = 1500.00; \quad r = 10.5\% = 0.105$$

(i) Using the formula I = P*rt*,

$$\begin{aligned} 69.04 &= (1500.00)(0.105)(t) \\ 69.04 &= (157.50)(t) \\ t &= \frac{69.04}{157.50} \\ &= 0.4383492 \text{ years} \\ &= (0.4383492)(365) \text{ days} \\ &= 160 \text{ days} \end{aligned}$$

(ii) Using the derived formula $t = \frac{I}{Pr}$,

$$\begin{aligned} t &= \frac{69.04}{(1500.00)(0.105)} \text{ years} \\ &= \frac{(69.04)(365)}{(1500.00)(0.105)} \text{ days} \\ &= 160 \text{ days} \end{aligned}$$

Exercise 7.4

A. Determine the missing value for each of the following.

	Interest	*Principal*	*Rate*	*Time*
1.	\$67.83	?	9.5%	7 months
2.	\$256.25	?	10.25%	250 days
3.	\$215.00	\$2400.00	?	10 months
4.	\$53.40	\$750.00	?	315 days
5.	\$136.34	\$954.00	$12\frac{1}{4}\%$	? (months)
6.	\$52.64	\$1295.80	$9\frac{3}{4}\%$	? (months)
7.	\$15.30	\$344.75	11.25%	? (days)
8.	\$68.96	\$830.30	10.75%	? (days)

B. Find the value indicated for each of the following.

1. Find the principal that will earn \$148.32 at 6.75% in 8 months.
2. Determine the deposit that must be made to earn \$39.27 in 225 days at 11%.
3. A loan of \$880.00 can be repaid in 15 months by paying the principal sum borrowed plus \$104.50 interest. What was the rate of interest charged?
4. At what rate of interest will \$1387.00 earn \$63.84 in 200 days?
5. In how many months will \$1290.00 earn \$156.68 interest at $13\frac{1}{4}\%$?
6. Determine the number of days it will take \$564.00 to earn \$22.39 at 11.5%.
7. What principal will earn \$39.96 from June 18, 1995, to December 15, 1995 at 9.25%?
8. What rate of interest is required for \$740.48 to earn \$42.49 interest from September 10, 1995, to March 4, 1996?

7.5 *The amount of a sum of money*

A. Basic concept

The **amount of a sum of money** (or **maturity value**) is the value obtained by adding the original principal and the interest due.

AMOUNT (OR MATURITY VALUE) = PRINCIPAL + INTEREST
$S = P + I$

← *Formula* 7.3

Example **7.5a** Determine the amount (maturity value), principal, or interest as indicated.

(i) The principal is \$2200.00 and the interest is \$240.00. Find the amount.

Solution

$P = 2200.00; \quad I = 240.00$

$$\begin{aligned} S &= P + I \\ &= 2200.00 + 240.00 \\ &= \$2440.00 \end{aligned}$$

(ii) The principal is \$850.00 and the amount is \$920.00. Find the interest.

Solution

$P = 850.00; \quad S = 920.00$

$$\begin{aligned} S &= P + I \\ 920.00 &= 850.00 + I \\ 920.00 - 850.00 &= I \\ I &= \$70.00 \end{aligned}$$

(iii) The amount is \$430.00 and the interest is \$40.00. Find the principal.

Solution

$S = 430.00; \quad I = 40.00$

$$\begin{aligned} S &= P + I \\ 430.00 &= P + 40.00 \\ 430.00 - 40.00 &= P \\ P &= \$390.00 \end{aligned}$$

B. *The amount formula* $S = P(1 + rt)$

The formulae $I = Prt$ and $S = P + I$ are combined to obtain the amount formula for simple interest.

$S = P + I$

$S = P + Prt$ ⟵ substitute Prt for I

$\boxed{S = P(1 + rt)}$ ⟵ take out the common factor P ⟵ *Formula* 7.4

Example **7.5b** Find the amount of \$720.00 earning 11% p.a. for 146 days.

Solution

$$P = 720.00; \quad r = 11\% = 0.11; \quad t = \frac{146}{365}$$

$$\begin{aligned} S &= P(1 + rt) \\ &= (720.00)\left[1 + (0.11)\left(\frac{146}{365}\right)\right] \\ &= (720.00)(1 + 0.044) \\ &= (720.00)(1.044) \\ &= \$751.68 \end{aligned}$$

Example 7.5c Find the maturity value of a deposit of $1250.00 invested at 9.75% p.a. from October 15, 1994, to May 1, 1995.

Solution

The time period in days = 17 + 30 + 31 + 31 + 28 + 31 + 30 + 0 = 198.

$$P = 1250.00; \quad r = 9.75\% = 0.0975; \quad t = \frac{198}{365}$$

$$\begin{aligned} S &= P(1 + rt) \\ &= (1250.00)\left[1 + (0.0975)\left(\frac{198}{365}\right)\right] \\ &= (1250.00)(1 + 0.0528904) \\ &= (1250.00)(1.0528904) \\ &= \$1316.11 \end{aligned}$$

Exercise 7.5

A. Use the amount formula to answer each of the following.

1. Find the amount of $480.00 at $12\frac{1}{2}\%$ for 220 days.
2. Find the maturity value of $732.00 invested at 9.8% from May 20, 1996, to November 23, 1996.
3. Compute the accumulated value of $820.00 over 9 months at $11\frac{3}{4}\%$.
4. What payment is required to pay off a loan of $1200.00 at 14% seven months later?

7.6 *Present value*

A. Finding the principal when the amount is known

The formula S = P(1 + *rt*) permits the calculation of the principal when the maturity value, the rate, and the time are given.

Example **7.6a** Find the principal that will amount to $1294.50 in 9 months at 10.5% per annum.

Solution

$$S = 1294.50; \quad r = 10.5\% = 0.105; \quad t = \frac{9}{12}$$

$$S = P(1 + rt) \longleftarrow \text{use the amount formula when S is known}$$

$$1294.50 = (P)\left[1 + (0.105)\left(\frac{9}{12}\right)\right]$$

$$1294.50 = (P)(1 + 0.07875)$$

$$1294.50 = (P)(1.07875)$$

$$P = \frac{1294.50}{1.07875}$$

$$P = \$1200.00$$

Example **7.6b** What sum of money must be invested on January 31, 1996, to amount to $7700.00 on August 18, 1996, at 10% p.a.?

Solution

The time period in days = 1 + 29(leap year) + 31 + 30 + 31 + 30 + 31 + 17 = 200

$$S = 7700.00; \quad r = 10\% = 0.10; \quad t = \frac{200}{365}$$

$$7700.00 = (P)\left[1 + (0.10)\left(\frac{200}{365}\right)\right] \longleftarrow \text{using Formula 7.4}$$

$$7700.00 = (P)(1 + 0.0547945)$$

$$7700.00 = (P)(1.0547945)$$

$$P = \frac{7700.00}{1.0547945}$$

$$P = \$7300.00$$

Note: (1) The total interest earned is $7700 − $7300 = $400.00.

(2) The daily amount of interest is $\frac{\$400.00}{200} = \$2.00$.

B. The present value concept and formula

When interest is paid for the use of money, the value of any sum of money subject to interest changes with time. This change is called the **time value of money**.

To illustrate the concept of time value of money, Example 7.6b is represented on the time graph shown in Figure 7.1.

FIGURE 7.1 ***Time graph for Example 7.6b***

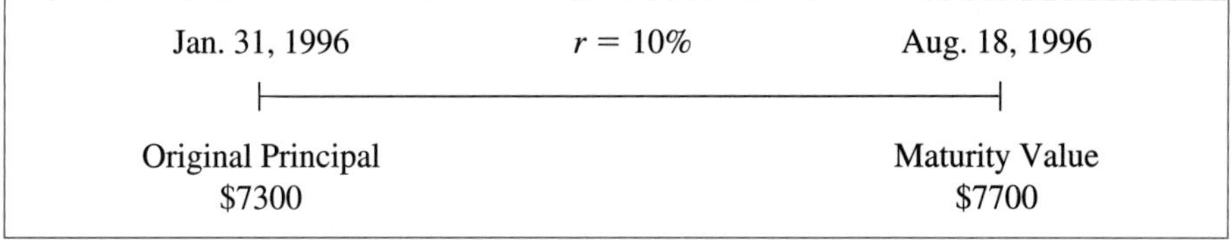

As shown, the original principal of $7300 will grow to $7700 at 10% in 200 days. The original principal earns $400 interest in 200 days; that is, the original principal of $7300 will grow by $2.00 per day. Accordingly, the value of the investment changes day by day. If the value of the investment on a particular date is considered, it is called the **present value** of the amount (or maturity value) on that date.

In this example, the original principal of $7300 is the present value of $7700 on January 31, 1996.

The present value of an amount at any given time is the principal needed to grow to that amount at a given rate of interest over a given period of time.

Since the problem of finding the present value is equivalent to finding the principal when the amount, rate, and time are given, the amount formula $S = P(1 + rt)$ applies. However, as the problem of finding the present value of an amount is one of the frequently recurring problems in financial analysis, it is useful to solve the amount formula for P to obtain the present value formula.

$$S = P(1 + rt) \longleftarrow \text{starting with the amount formula}$$

$$\frac{S}{(1 + rt)} = \frac{P(1 + rt)}{(1 + rt)} \longleftarrow \text{divide both sides by } (1 + rt)$$

$$\frac{S}{(1 + rt)} = P \longleftarrow \text{reduce the fraction } \frac{(1 + rt)}{(1 + rt)} \text{ to } 1$$

$$\boxed{P = \frac{S}{1 + rt}} \longleftarrow \text{present value formula for simple interest} \longleftarrow \textit{Formula } 7.5$$

Example 7.6c Find the present value of an investment with a maturity value of $918.00 eight months before the due date at 12% p.a.

Solution

$$S = 918.00; \quad r = 12\% = 0.12; \quad t = \frac{8}{12}$$

$$P = \frac{S}{1 + rt}$$

$$P = \frac{918.00}{1 + (0.12)(\frac{8}{12})} \longleftarrow \text{using Formula 7.5}$$

$$= \frac{918.00}{1 + 0.08}$$

$$= \frac{918.00}{1.08}$$

$$= \$850.00$$

Example **7.6d** Find the sum of money which, deposited in an account on April 1, will grow to \$674.73 by September 10 at 10.75% p.a.

Solution

The time in days = 30 + 31 + 30 + 31 + 31 + 9 = 162

$$S = 674.73; \quad r = 10.75\% = 0.1075; \quad t = \frac{162}{365}$$

$$P = \frac{674.73}{1 + (0.1075)(\frac{162}{365})}$$

$$= \frac{674.73}{1 + 0.0477123}$$

$$= \frac{674.73}{1.0477123}$$

$$= \$644.00$$

Exercise 7.6

A. Find the principal and the missing value in each of the following.

	Amount	*Interest*	*Rate*	*Time*
1.	\$305.90	?	12%	15 months
2.	\$729.30	\$117.30	?	20 months
3.	?	\$29.67	8.6%	8 months
4.	?	\$27.11	9.5%	240 days
5.	\$2195.10	\$170.10	10.5%	?
6.	\$1079.68	?	13.5%	275 days

B. Solve each of the following.

1. What principal will amount to \$1276.99 at 10.8% in 5 months?
2. What sum of money will accumulate to \$492.67 in 93 days at 14.6%?
3. Determine the present value of a debt of \$1760.00 due in four months if interest at $9\frac{3}{4}\%$ is allowed.
4. Find the present value of a debt of \$460.00 ninety days before it is due if money is worth 12%.

7.7 *Equivalent values*

A. Dated values

If a sum of money is subject to a rate of interest, it will grow over time. Thus, the value of the sum of money changes with time; this change is known as the time value of money.

For example, a sum of $1000.00 invested today at 12% p.a. simple interest has a value of $1000.00 today, $1030.00 in three months, $1060.00 in six months, and $1120.00 in one year.

The value of the original sum at any particular time is a **dated value** of that sum and the various dated values at different times are equivalent to the original sum of money.

Time	*Dated value*
Today	$1000.00
3 months from now	$1030.00
6 months from now	$1060.00
1 year from now	$1120.00

Consider the case of an obligation of $500.00 payable today. Suppose the debtor requests an extension of four months of the obligation. How much should he expect to pay in four months time if money is worth 18% p.a.?

Since the lender could invest the $500.00 at 18% p.a., the debtor should be prepared to pay the dated value. This dated value includes interest for the additional time period. It represents the amount to which the $500.00 will grow in four months and is found using Formula 7.4.

$$
\begin{aligned}
S &= P(1 + rt) \\
&= 500.00\left[1 + (0.18)\left(\frac{4}{12}\right)\right] \\
&= 500.00(1 + 0.06) \\
&= \$530.00
\end{aligned}
$$

Now consider the case of an obligation of $1090.00 due six months from now. Suppose the debtor offers to pay the debt today. How much should the payment be if money is worth 18% p.a.?

Since the lender could invest the payment at 18% p.a., the payment should be the sum of money that will grow to $1090.00 in six months at 18% p.a. By definition, this sum of money is the present value of the $1090.00. The present value represents the dated value of the $1090.00 today and is found using Formula 7.5.

$$P = \frac{S}{1 + rt}$$

$$= \frac{1090.00}{I + (0.18)(\frac{6}{12})}$$

$$= \frac{1090.00}{1 + 0.09}$$

$$= \$1000.00$$

Because of the time value of money, sums of money located at different times are *not* directly comparable. For example, imagine you are given a choice between \$2000.00 today and \$2200.00 one year from now. It does not automatically follow, from the point of view of investing money, that either the larger sum of money or the chronologically earlier sum of money is preferable.

To make a rational choice, we must allow for the rate money is worth and choose a comparison date or **focal date** to obtain the dated values of the sums of money at a specific time.

Dated values at the *same* time are directly comparable and may be obtained for simple interest by using either the amount formula, Formula 7.4, $S = P(1 + rt)$, or the present value formula, Formula 7.5, $P = \frac{S}{1 + rt}$.

B. Choosing the appropriate formula

The choice of which formula to use for finding dated values depends on the due date of the sum of money relative to the selected focal (or comparison) date.

(a) If the due date falls before the focal date, use the amount formula.

FIGURE 7.2 ***When to use the amount formula***

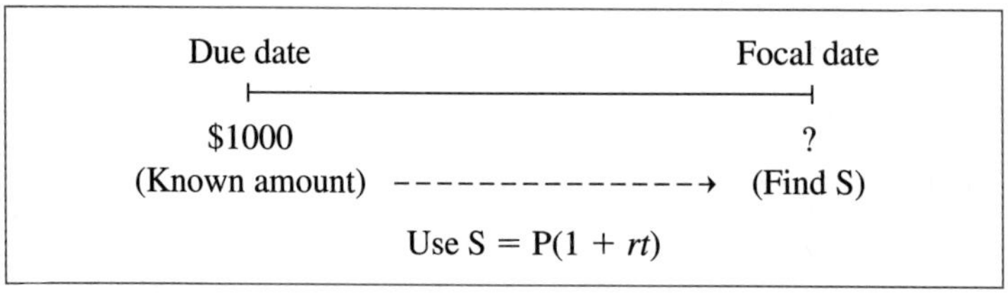

Due date — Focal date

\$1000 (Known amount) - - - - - - - - - - - - - - - → ? (Find S)

Use $S = P(1 + rt)$

Explanation of diagram: We are looking for a future value relative to the given value. This future value will be higher than the known value by the interest that accumulates on the known value from the due date to the focal date. Because this is an amount problem (note that the arrow points to the right), the amount formula $S = P(1 + rt)$ applies.

(b) If the due date falls after the focal date, use the present value formula.

FIGURE 7.3 ***When to use the present value formula***

Focal date — Due date

? — $1000

(Find P) ←- - - - - - - - - - - - - - - - (Known amount)

Use $P = \frac{S}{1 + rt}$

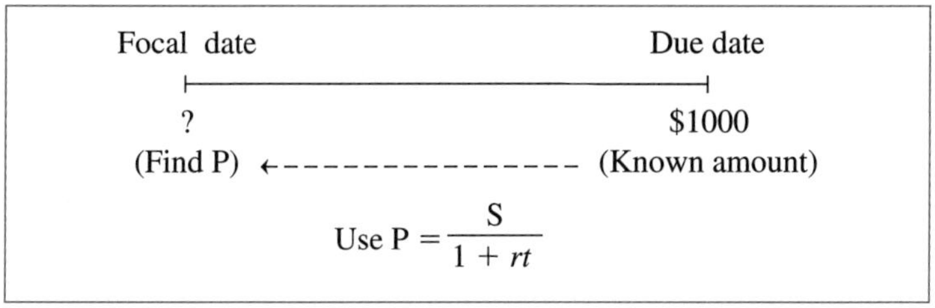

Explanation of diagram: We are looking for an earlier value relative to the given value. This earlier value will be less than the given value by the interest that would accumulate on the unknown earlier value from the focal date to the due date. We are, in fact, looking for the principal that will grow to the given value. Because this is a present value problem (note that the arrow points to the left), the present value formula $P = \frac{S}{1 + rt}$ is appropriate.

C. Finding the equivalent single payment

Example **7.7a** A debt can be paid off by payments of $920.00 one year from now and $1300.00 two years from now. Determine the single payment now that would settle the debt. Allow for simple interest at 15% p.a.

Solution

See Figure 7.4 for the graphic representation of the dated values. Refer to Figures 7.2 and 7.3 to determine which formula is appropriate.

FIGURE 7.4 ***Graphic representation of the dated values***

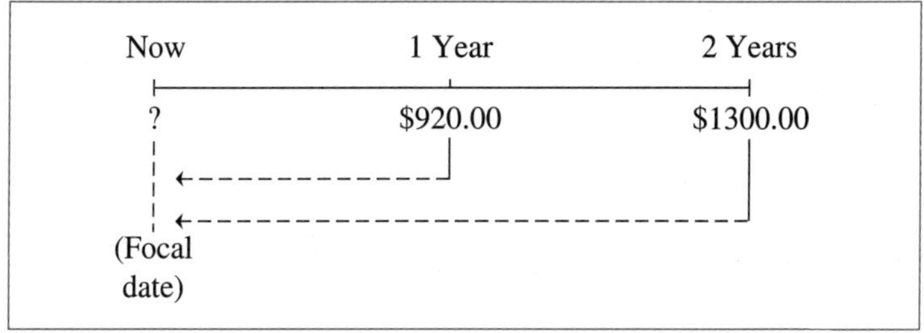

Since the focal date is *earlier* relative to the dates for the given sums of money (the arrows point to the left), the present value formula $P = \frac{S}{1 + rt}$ is appropriate.

(i) The present value of the $920.00 at the focal date

$$P = \frac{920.00}{1 + (0.15)(1)}$$
$$= \frac{920.00}{1.15}$$
$$= 800.00$$

(ii) The present value of the $1300.00 at the focal date

$$P = \frac{1300.00}{1 + (0.15)(2)} = \frac{1300.00}{1.30} = 1000.00$$

(iii) Single payment required now = 800.00 + 1000.00 = $1800.00

Example 7.7b Debt payments of $400 due today, $500 due in five months, and $618 due in one year are to be combined into a single payment to be made nine months from now with interest allowed at 12% p.a.

Solution

FIGURE 7.5 ***Graphic representation of the dated values***

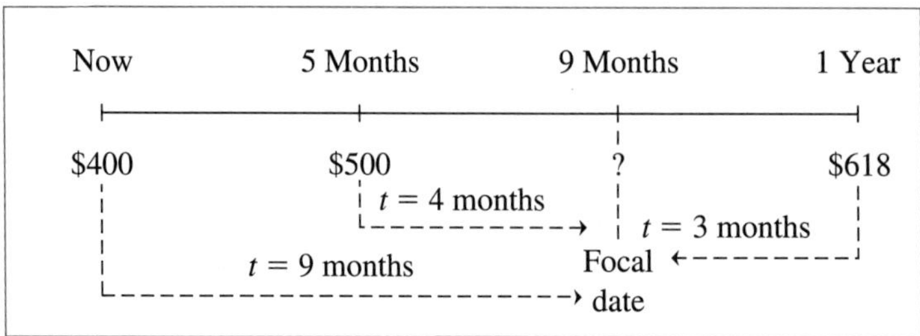

Since the focal date is in the *future* relative to the $400 now and the $500 five months from now (the arrows point to the right), the amount formula $S = P(1 + rt)$ is appropriate for these two amounts. However, since the focal date is *earlier* relative to the $618 one year from now (the arrow points to the left), the present value formula $P = \frac{S}{1 + rt}$ is appropriate for this amount.

(i) The amount of $400 at the focal date

$$P = 400.00; \quad r = 12\% = 0.12; \quad t = \frac{9}{12}$$

$$S = 400\left[1 + (0.12)\left(\frac{9}{12}\right)\right] = 400(1 + 0.09) = 400(1.09) = 436.00$$

(ii) The amount of $500 at the focal date

$$P = 500.00; \quad r = 12\% = 0.12; \quad t = \frac{4}{12}$$

$$S = 500\left[1 + (0.12)\left(\frac{4}{12}\right)\right] = 500(1 + 0.04) = 500(1.04) = 520.00$$

(iii) The present value of $618 at the focal date

$$S = 618.00; \quad r = 12\% = 0.12; \quad t = \frac{3}{12}$$

$$P = \frac{618.00}{1 + (0.12)(\frac{3}{12})} = \frac{618.00}{1 + 0.03} = \frac{618.00}{1.03} = 600.00$$

(iv) The single payment needed = 436.00 + 520.00 + 600.00 = $1556.00

D. Finding the value of two or more equivalent payments

The **equivalent values** obtained when using simple interest formulae are influenced by the choice of focal date. Although the differences in the values obtained are small, the parties to the financial transaction need to agree on this date.

Example 7.7c Debts of $400.00 due now and $700.00 due in 5 months are to be settled by a payment of $500.00 in 3 months and a final payment in 8 months. Determine the value of the final payment at 15% p.a. with a focal date 8 months from now.

Solution

Let the value of the final payment be $x.

(i) Represent the data given in a time diagram.

FIGURE 7.6 ***Graphic representation of data***

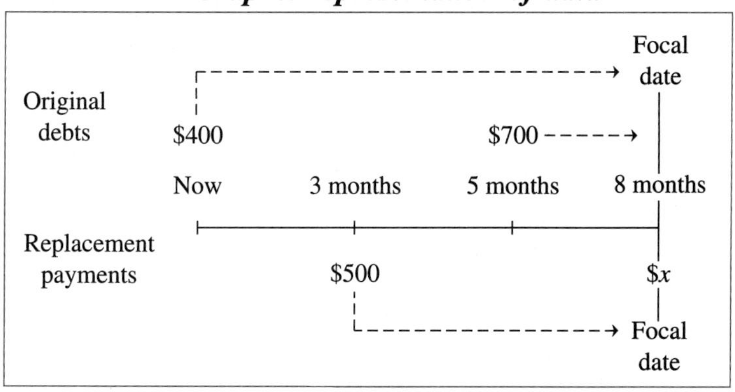

(ii) Dated value of the original debts

(a) The value at the focal date of the \$400 due 8 months before the focal date is found by using the amount formula.

$$S = 400\left[1 + (0.15)\left(\frac{8}{12}\right)\right] = 400(1 + 0.10) = 400(1.10) = \$440.00$$

(b) The value at the focal date of the \$700 due 3 months before the focal date is found by using the amount formula.

$$S = 700\left[1 + (0.15)\left(\frac{3}{12}\right)\right] = 700(1 + 0.0375) = 700(1.0375) = \$726.25$$

(iii) Dated value of the replacement payments

(a) The value at the focal date of the \$500 payment made 5 months before the focal date is found by using the amount formula.

$$S = 500\left[1 + (0.15)\left(\frac{5}{12}\right)\right] = 500(1 + 0.0625) = 500(1.0625) = \$531.25$$

(b) The value at the focal date of the final payment is \$$x$ (no adjustment for interest is necessary for a sum of money located at the focal date).

(iv) The **equation of values** at the focal date is now set up by matching the dated values of the original debts to the dated values of the replacement payments.

THE SUM OF THE DATED VALUES OF THE REPLACEMENT PAYMENTS = THE SUM OF THE DATED VALUES OF THE ORIGINAL DEBTS

$$500\left[1 + (0.15)\left(\frac{5}{12}\right)\right] + x = 400\left[1 + (0.15)\left(\frac{8}{12}\right)\right] + 700\left[1 + (0.15)\left(\frac{3}{12}\right)\right]$$

$$531.25 + x = 440.00 + 726.25$$

$$531.25 + x = 1166.25$$

$$x = 1166.25 - 531.25$$

$$x = 635.00$$

The final payment to be made in 8 months is \$635.00.

Example 7.7d Debts of \$2000 due 60 days ago and \$1800 due in 30 days are to be settled by three equal payments due now, 60 days from now, and 120 days from now. Find the size of the equal payments at 10% p.a. The agreed focal date is now.

Solution

Let the size of the equal payments be \$$x$.

(i) Graphic representation of data

FIGURE 7.7 ***Graphic representation of data***

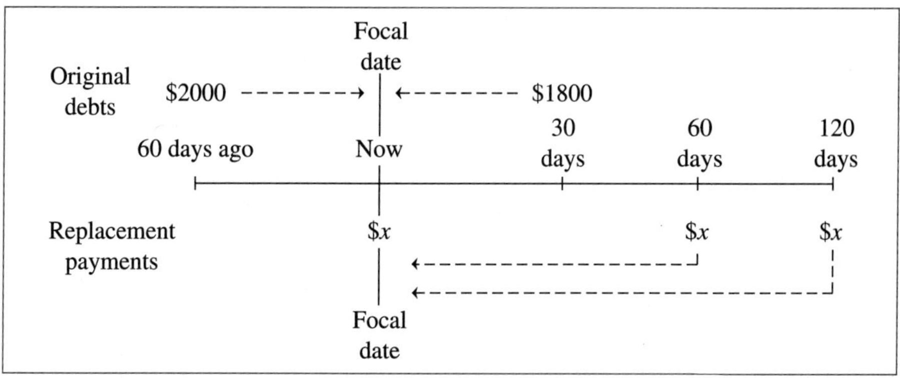

(ii) Dated value of the original debts at the focal date

(a) Because the $2000 debt is due 60 days before the focal date, the amount formula is appropriate.

$$S = 2000\left[1 + (0.10)\left(\frac{60}{365}\right)\right] = 2000(1 + 0.0164384) = \$2032.88$$

(b) Because the $1800 debt is due 30 days after the focal date, the present value formula is appropriate.

$$P = \frac{1800}{1 + (0.10)(\frac{30}{365})} = \frac{1800}{1 + 0.0082192} = \$1785.33$$

(iii) Dated value of the replacement payments at the focal date

(a) Since the first payment is to be made at the focal date, its value is $\$x$.

(b) Because the second payment is to be made 60 days after the focal date, the present value formula is appropriate.

$$P = \frac{x}{1 + (0.10)(\frac{60}{365})} = \frac{x}{1 + 0.0164384}$$

$$= \frac{1}{1.0164384}(x) = \$0.9838275x$$

(c) Because the third payment is to be made 120 days after the focal date, the present value formula is appropriate.

$$P = \frac{x}{1 + (0.10)(\frac{120}{365})} = \frac{x}{1 + 0.0328767}$$

$$= \frac{1}{1.0328767}(x) = \$0.9681698x$$

(iv) The equation of values (dated value of the replacement payments = dated value of the original debts)

$$x + 0.9838275x + 0.9681698x = 2032.88 + 1785.33$$
$$2.9519973x = 3818.21$$
$$x = \frac{3818.21}{2.9519973}$$
$$x = 1293.43$$

The size of each of the three equal payments is \$1293.43.

Example 7.7e Two debts, one of \$4000 due in three months with interest at 12% and the other of \$3000 due in eighteen months with interest at 15%, are to be discharged by making two equal payments. What is the size of the equal payments if the first is due one year from now, the second two years from now, money is worth 18%, and the chosen focal date is one year from now?

Solution

Let the size of the equal payments be \$$x$.

(i) Graphic representation of data

FIGURE 7.8 ***Graphic representation of data***

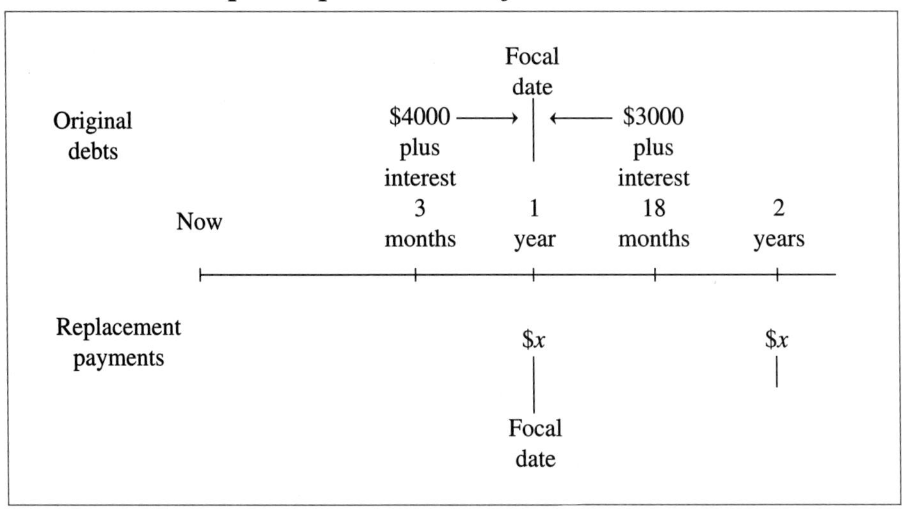

(ii) Maturity value of the original debts
Since the two original debts are interest bearing, their maturity values need to be determined first.

(a) For the \$4000 debt: $P = 4000$; $r = 12\% = 0.12$; $t = \frac{3}{12}$

Maturity value, $S = 4000\left[1 + (0.12)\left(\frac{3}{12}\right)\right] = 4000(1.03) = \$4120$

(b) For the \$3000 debt: $P = 3000$; $r = 15\% = 0.15$; $t = \frac{18}{12}$

Maturity value, $S = 3000\left[1 + (0.15)\left(\frac{18}{12}\right)\right] = 3000(1.225) = \$3675$

(iii) Dated value of the money value of the original payments at 18%

(a) Because the maturity value of \$4120 is due 9 months before the focal date, the amount formula is appropriate.

$$S = 4120\left[1 + (0.18)\left(\frac{9}{12}\right)\right] = 4120(1.135) = \$4676.20$$

(b) Because the maturity value of \$3675 is due 6 months after the focal date, the present value formula is appropriate.

$$P = \frac{3675}{1 + (0.18)(\frac{6}{12})} = \frac{3675}{1.09} = \$3371.56$$

(iv) Dated value of the replacement payments

(a) Since the first replacement payment is made at the focal date, its value is $\$x$.

(b) Because the second replacement payment is made 12 months after the focal date, the present value formula is appropriate.

$$P = \frac{x}{1 + (0.18)(\frac{12}{12})} = \frac{x}{1.18} = 0.8474576x$$

(v) The equation of values

$$x + 0.8474576x = 4676.20 + 3371.56$$

$$1.8474576x = 8047.76$$

$$x = \frac{8047.76}{1.8474576}$$

$$x = 4356.13$$

The size of the equal payments is \$4356.13.

Example 7.7f A loan of \$2000 made at 13.5% p.a. is to be repaid in four equal payments due at the end of the next four quarters respectively. Determine the size of the quarterly payments if the agreed focal date is the date of the loan.

Solution

Let the size of the equal quarterly payments be represented by $x.

(i) Graphic representation of data

FIGURE 7.9 ***Graphic representation of data***

Original debts	$2000 Now	3 months	6 months	9 months	12 months
Replacement payments	Focal date	$x	$x	$x	$x

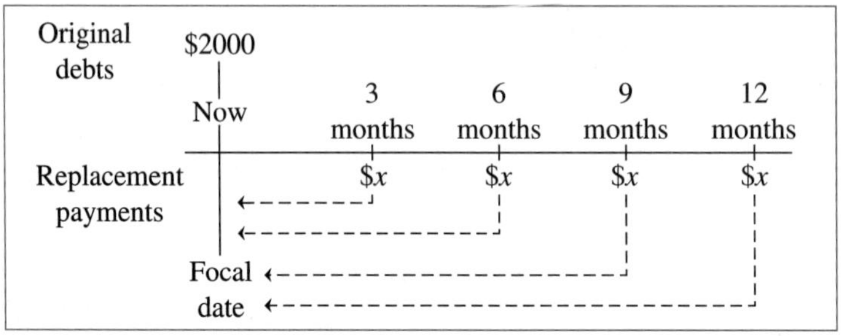

(ii) Dated value of debt at the focal date is $2000.00.

(iii) Dated value of payments at the focal date
The payments are due 3, 6, 9, and 12 months after the focal date respectively. Their values are

(a) $P_1 = \frac{x}{1 + (0.135)(\frac{3}{12})} = \frac{x}{1 + 0.03375} = \frac{1}{1.03375}(x) = 0.9673519x$

(b) $P_2 = \frac{x}{1 + (0.135)(\frac{6}{12})} = \frac{x}{1 + 0.06750} = \frac{1}{1.06750}(x) = 0.9367682x$

(c) $P_3 = \frac{x}{1 + (0.135)(\frac{9}{12})} = \frac{x}{1 + 0.10125} = \frac{1}{1.10125}(x) = 0.9080590x$

(d) $P_4 = \frac{x}{1 + (0.135)(\frac{12}{12})} = \frac{x}{1 + 0.13500} = \frac{1}{1.13500}(x) = 0.8810573x$

(iv) $0.9673519x + 0.9367682x + 0.9080590x + 0.8810573x = 2000.00$

$$3.6932364x = 2000.00$$

$$x = 541.53$$

The size of the quarterly payment is $541.53.

Exercise 7.7

A. Find the equivalent replacement payments indicated for each of the following debts.

	Original debt	*Replacement payment*	*Focal date*	*Rate*
1.	$800 due today	In full	4 months from today	11%
2.	$1200 due 3 months ago	In full	today	12%
3.	$600 due in 2 months	In full	7 months from today	7%
4.	$900 due in 8 months	In full	2 months from today	10%
5.	$500 due 4 months ago, $600 due in 2 months	In full	today	12%
6.	$800 due today and $700 due in 2 months	In full	4 months from today	9%
7.	$2000 due today	$1200 in 3 months and the balance in 6 months	today	12%
8.	$400 due 1 month ago, $600 due in 3 months	$500 today and the balance in 6 months	today	8%
9.	$1200 due today	Two equal payments due in 3 and 6 months	today	10%
10.	$1800 due 30 days ago	Three equal payments due today, in 30 days, and in 60 days	today	9%
11.	$1500 due 4 months ago. $1200 due in 8 months with 14% interest.	$700 due now and two equal payments due in 6 months and in 12 months	today	17%
12.	$2000 due in 6 months with interest at 15%. $1600 due in 2 years with interest at 13%.	three equal payments due in 6, 12, and 18 months respectively	one year from today	16%

B. Solve each of the following problems.

1. Debt payments of $600 each are due 3 months and 6 months from now respectively. If interest at 10% is allowed, what single payment is required to settle the debt today?

2. A loan payment of $1000 was due 60 days ago and another payment of $1200 is due in 30 days. What single payment 90 days from now will pay off the two obligations if interest is to be 12% and the agreed focal date is 90 days from now?

3. Loans of $400 due 3 months ago and $700 due today are to be repaid by a payment of $600 in one month and the balance in 4 months. If money is worth 6% and the agreed focal date is one month from today, what is the size of the final payment?

4. Two obligations of $800 each, due 60 days ago and 30 days ago respectively, are to be settled by two equal payments to be made today and 60 days from now respectively. If interest allowed is 15% and the agreed focal date is today, what is the size of the equal payments?

5. A loan of $4000 is to be repaid by 3 equal payments due in 4, 8, and 12 months respectively. Determine the size of the equal payments at 12% with a focal date today.

6. A loan of $1500 taken out on March 1 requires equal payments on April 30, June 20, and August 10, and a final payment of $400 on September 30. If the focal date is September 30, what is the size of the equal payments at 13%?

7. Two debt payments, the first $800 due today, the second $1000 due in nine months with interest at 13%, are to be settled by two equal payments due in three and six months respectively. Determine the size of the equal payments if money is worth 15% and the agreed focal date is today.

8. Payments of $1200 due one year ago and $1500 due with interest of 14% in nine months are to be settled by three equal payments due today, six months, and one year from now at 18%. Determine the size of the equal payments if the agreed focal date is one year from today.

Review exercise

1. Determine the exact time for
   (a) April 25 to October 14;
   (b) July 30 to February 1.

2. Compute the amount of interest for
   (a) $1975.00 at 5.5% for 215 days;
   (b) $844.65 at 13.25% from May 30 to January 4.

3. What principal will earn
   (a) $83.52 interest at 12% in 219 days?
   (b) $34.40 interest at $9\frac{3}{4}$% from October 30, 1996, to June 1, 1997?

4. Answer each of the following.
   (a) What was the rate of interest if the interest on a loan of $675 for 284 days was $39.39?

(b) How long will it take for \$2075 to earn \$124.29 interest at $8\frac{1}{4}\%$ p.a.? (State your answer in days.)

(c) If \$680 is worth \$698.70 after three months, what interest rate was charged?

(d) How many months will it take \$750 to grow to \$795 at 7.2% p.a.?

5. Solve each of the following.

   (a) What principal will have a maturity value of \$665.60 at 10% in 146 days?

   (b) What is the present value of \$6300 due in 16 months at $7\frac{3}{4}\%$?

6. What principal will earn \$61.52 at 11.75% in 156 days?

7. What sum of money will earn \$112.50 from September 1, 1997, to April 30, 1998, at 14.5%?

8. At what rate of interest must a principal of \$1435.00 be invested to earn interest of \$45.46 in 125 days?

9. At what rate of interest will \$1500.00 grow to \$1622.21 from June 1 to December 1?

10. In how many months will \$2500.00 earn \$182.29 interest at 12.5%?

11. In how many days will \$3100.00 grow to \$3195.72 at 5.75%?

12. Compute the accumulated value of \$4200.00 at 11.5% after eleven months.

13. What is the amount to which \$1550.00 will grow from June 10 to December 15 at 14%?

14. What sum of money will accumulate to \$1516.80 in eight months at 8%?

15. What principal will amount to \$3441.62 if invested at 13% from November 1, 1995, to May 31, 1996?

16. What is the present value of \$3780.00 due in nine months if interest is 12%?

17. Find the present value on June 1 of \$1785.00 due on October 15 if interest is 7.5%.

18. Debt payments of \$1750.00 and \$1600.00 are due four months and nine months from now respectively. What single payment is required to pay off the debt today if interest is 13.5%?

19. A loan payment of \$1450.00 was due 45 days ago and a payment of \$1200.00 is due in 60 days. What single payment made 30 days from now is required to settle the two payments if interest is 16% and the agreed focal date is 30 days from now?

20. Debt obligations of \$800.00 due two months ago and \$1200.00 due in one month are to be repaid by a payment of \$1000.00 today and the balance in three months. What is the size of the final payment if interest is 7.75% and the agreed focal date is one month from now?

21. An obligation of $10 000.00 is to be repaid by equal payments due in 60 days, 120 days, and 180 days respectively. What is the size of the equal payments if money is worth 13% and the agreed focal date is today?

22. Payments of $4000 each due in four, eight, and twelve months respectively are to be settled by five equal payments due today, three months from now, six months from now, nine months from now, and twelve months from now. What is the size of the equal payments if interest is 12.75% and the agreed focal date is today?

23. A loan of $5000.00 due in one year is to be repaid by three equal payments due today, six months from now, and one year from now respectively. What is the size of the equal payments if interest is 14% and the agreed focal date is today?

24. Three debts, the first for $1000 due two months ago, the second for $1200 due in 2 months, and the third for $1400 due in 4 months, are to be paid by a single payment today. How much is the single payment if money is worth 11.5% p.a. and the agreed focal date is today?

25. Debts of $700 due 3 months ago and of $1000 due today are to be paid by a payment of $800 in two months and a final payment in five months. If 9% interest is allowed and the focal date is five months from now, what is the size of the final payment?

26. A loan of $3000 is to be repaid in three equal instalments due 90, 180, and 300 days respectively after the date of the loan. If the focal date is the date of the loan and interest is 10.9% p.a., find the size of the instalments.

27. Three debts, the first for $2000 due three months ago, the second for $1500 with interest of 12% due in nine months, and the third for $1200 with interest of 15% due in eighteen months, are to be paid in three equal instalments due today, six months from now, and one year from now respectively. If money is worth 13% and the agreed focal date is today, determine the size of the equal payments.

28. A debt of $6500 is to be settled by four equal payments due today, and one year, two years, and three years from now respectively. Determine the size of the equal payments if money is worth 12% and the agreed focal day is today.

Self-test

1. Find the amount of interest earned by $1290.00 at 10.5% p.a. in 173 days.
2. In how many months will $8500.00 grow to $8818.75 at 5% p.a.?
3. What interest rate is paid if the interest on a loan of $2500.00 for 6 months is $156.25?
4. What principal will have a maturity value of $10 000.00 at 8.25% p.a. in 3 months?
5. What is the amount to which $5500.00 will grow at 8.75% p.a. in 10 months?
6. What principal will earn $67.14 interest at 6.25% p.a. for 82 days?

7. What is the present value of $5000.00 due at 17.25% p.a. in 243 days?
8. What rate of interest is paid if the interest on a loan of $2500.00 is $179.32 from November 14, 1996, to May 20, 1997?
9. How many days will it take for $8500.00 to earn $1024.13 at 12.25% p.a.?
10. What principal will earn $113.66 interest at 19.75% p.a. from February 4, 1996, to July 6, 1996?
11. What sum of money will accumulate to $7500.00 at 11.75% p.a. in 88 days?
12. Find the amount of interest on $835.00 at 7.5% p.a. from October 9, 1995, to August 4, 1996?
13. A loan of $3320.00 is to be repaid by 3 equal payments due in 92 days, 235 days, and 326 days respectively. Determine the size of the equal payments at 8.75% p.a. with a focal date today.
14. Debt payments of $1725.00 due today, $510.00 due in 75 days, and $655 due in 323 days are to be combined into a single payment to be made 115 days from now. What is that single payment if money is worth 20% p.a. and the agreed focal date is 115 days from now?
15. Debt payments of $1010.00 due 5 months ago and $1280.00 due today are to be repaid by a payment of $615.00 in 4 months and the balance in 7 months. If money is worth 17.75% p.a. and the agreed focal date is in 7 months, what is the size of the final payment?
16. A debt of $1310.00 due 5 months ago and a second debt of $1225.00 due in 3 months with interest at 12% p.a. are to be settled by two equal payments due now and 7 months from now respectively. Find the size of the equal payments at 10.25% p.a. with the agreed focal date now.

CASE STUDY

You are an employee in the real estate department of the Royal Bank. It is your responsibility to determine the financial assets and liabilities of Owen Sports, a business that has been sold. The date is November 15.

1. An invoice for $7200 from Aspen Ski dated September 22 with terms 5/10, *n*/30 has not been paid. The rate for overdue accounts is 1.5% per month from the invoice date. Calculate the amount owing to Aspen Ski.
2. The Precision Skate Company is expecting a payment of principal and interest in the amount of $8300 on January 25 to pay for Christmas stock delivered on

October 23. Precision charges simple interest of 1% per month. Calculate the present value of this debt.

3. Owen Sports holds a short-term mortgage that cannot be paid off early without a thirty-day penalty. The amount borrowed on August 4 was $9200 and the amount to be repaid on February 4 is $9500. Calculate the amount needed to discharge the mortgage today.

4. Owen Sports received $5500 of stock on October 3 from Hockey Blades. It will pay $5622, which includes a 9% simple interest charge.

   (a) When is the debt due?

   (b) Calculate the present value of the debt from the due date.

5. Owen Sports returned 20 basketball sweaters to the Uniform Company for credit. The retail price was $48.95 with a markup of 45% of cost. The Uniform Company charges a 10% restocking fee. Calculate the cash value of the credit.

6. Owen Sports has not paid the fees for a building maintenance contract. The contract is for three payments of $500 due on April 1, August 1, and December 1. Calculate the value of these payments today if the interest is 9% per annum.

7. Owen Sports rents part of its building to another business. The rent is $600 per month and due on the first of the month. Payments have not been received for September, October, and November. Calculate the value of these payments if interest is 12% per annum.

8. Calculate the net assets/liabilities of Owen Sports.

Summary of formulae used

Formula 7.1

$$I = Prt$$

Finding the amount of interest when the principal, the rate, and the time are known

Formula 7.2A

$$P = \frac{I}{rt}$$

Finding the principal directly when the amount of interest, the rate of interest, and the time are known

Formula 7.2B

$$r = \frac{I}{Pt}$$

Finding the rate of interest directly when the amount of interest, the principal, and the time are known

Formula 7.2C

$$t = \frac{I}{Pr}$$

Finding the time directly when the amount of interest, the principal, and the rate of interest are known

Formula 7.3

$S = P + I$ — Finding the amount (maturity value) when the principal and the amount of interest are known

Formula 7.4

$S = P(1 + rt)$ — Finding the amount (maturity value) at simple interest directly when the principal, rate of interest, and time are known

Formula 7.5

$P = \frac{S}{1 + rt}$ — Finding the present value at simple interest when the amount, the rate of interest, and the time are known

Glossary of terms used

Amount of a sum of money the value obtained when the amount of interest is added to the original principal

Dated value the value of a sum of money at a specific time relative to its due date and allowing for interest

Equation of values the equation obtained when matching the dated values of the original payments at an agreed focal date to the dated values of the replacement payments at the same focal date

Equivalent values the dated values of an original sum of money

Exact time the period in days between two calendar dates

Focal date a specific time chosen to compare the time value of one or more dated sums of money

Interest rent paid for the use of money

Interest period the time period for which interest is charged

Leap year a year with an extra day in February

Maturity value see *Amount of a sum of money*

Present value the principal that grows to a given amount (maturity value) over a given period of time at a given rate of interest

Simple interest interest calculated on the original principal by the formula $I = Prt$

Time value of money a concept of money value that allows for a change in the value of a sum of money over time if the sum of money is subject to a rate of interest

8 *Simple interest applications*

Introduction

Simple interest calculation is usually restricted to financial instruments subject to time periods of less than one year. The two specific usages considered in this chapter are short-term promissory notes and demand loans.

Objectives

Upon completing this chapter, you will be able to

1. recognize promissory notes and interpret correctly related terms such as maker, payee, face value, term of a note, three days of grace, due date, interest period, and maturity value;
2. determine the maturity value of interest-bearing notes by using the formula $S = P(1 + rt)$;
3. determine the present value of promissory notes;
4. discount promissory notes using simple discount;
5. compute interest and balances for demand loans;
6. develop repayment schedules for amortized loans.

8.1 *Promissory notes—Basic concepts and computations*

A. Nature of promissory notes and illustration

A **promissory note** is a written promise by one party to pay a certain sum of money, with or without interest, at a specific date to another party. (See the illustration that follows.)

FIGURE 8.1 ***Promissory note illustrated***

$650.00 MISSISSAUGA, ONTARIO OCTOBER 30, 1996

FOUR MONTHS after date I promise to pay to the order of

CREDIT VALLEY NURSERY

SIX-HUNDRED-FIFTY AND 00/100 ························ Dollars

at SHERIDAN CREDIT UNION LIMITED for value received

with interest at 10.5% per annum.

Signed D. Peel

B. Related terms explained

The following information is directly available in the promissory note (see items a, b, c, d, e, f below) or can be determined (see items g, h, i, j).

(a) The **maker** of the note is the party making the promise to pay. ⟶ (D. Peel)

(b) The **payee** of the note is the party to whom the promise is made. ⟶ (Credit Valley Nursery)

(c) The **face value** of the note is the sum of money (principal) specified. ⟶ ($650.00)

(d) The **rate of interest** is stated as a simple annual rate based on the face value. ⟶ (10.5%)

(e) The **issue date** is the date on which the note was made. ⟶ (October 30, 1996)

(f) The **term** of the note is the length of time before the note matures (becomes payable). ⟶ (four months)

(g) The **due date** or **date of maturity** is the date on which the note is to be paid. ⟶ (See Subsection C)

(h) The **interest period** is the time period from the date of issue to the legal due date. ⟶ (See Subsection C)

(i) The **amount of interest** is payable together with the face value on the legal due date. ⟶ (See Subsection C)

(j) The **maturity value** is the amount payable on the due date (face value plus interest) ⟶ (See Subsection C)

C. Computed values

Example **8.1a** For the promissory note illustrated in Figure 8.1, determine

(i) the due date; (ii) the interest period;

(iii) the amount of interest; (iv) the maturity value.

Solution

(i) *Finding the due date*

The Canadian law relating to promissory notes adds **three days of grace** to the term of the note to obtain the **legal due date** (Bills of Exchange Act, Section 42). Since calendar months vary in length, the month in which the term ends does not necessarily have a date that corresponds to the date of issue. In such cases, the last day of the month is used as the end of the term of the note. Three days of grace are added to that date to determine the legal due date.

With reference to the promissory note in Figure 8.1,

the date of issue is October 30,
the term of the note is four months
the month in which the term ends is February,
the end of the term is February 28 (since February has no day corresponding to day 30, the last day of the month is used to establish the end of the term of the note),
the legal due date (adding 3 days) is March 3.

(ii) *Determining the interest period*

If the note bears interest, the interest period covers the number of days from the date of issue of the note to the legal due date.

October 30 to March 3 ⟶ $(2 + 30 + 31 + 31 + 28 + 2) = 124$ days

(iii) *Computing the amount of interest*

The interest payable on the note is the simple interest based on the face value of the note for the interest period at the stated rate. It is found using the simple interest formula $\boxed{I = Prt}$ ⟵ *Formula* **7.1**

$$I = (650.00)(0.105)\left(\frac{124}{365}\right) = \$23.19$$

(iv) *Finding the maturity value of the note*
The maturity value of the promissory note is the total amount payable at the legal due date.

$$\text{Face Value} + \text{Interest} = 650.00 + 23.19 = \$673.19$$

Exercise 8.1

A. Determine each of the items listed from the information provided in the promissory note below.

$530.00	OAKVILLE, ONTARIO	DECEMBER 30, 1994

FIVE MONTHS after date I promise to pay

to the order of JANE WELTON

FIVE-HUNDRED-THIRTY and 00/100 .... Dollars

at SHERIDAN CENTRAL BANK for value received

with interest at 13.5% per annum.

Signed E. Salt

1. Date issued
2. Legal due date
3. Face value
4. Interest rate
5. Interest period (days)
6. Amount of interest
7. Maturity value

B. For each of the following notes, determine

(a) the legal due date;
(b) the interest period (in days);
(c) the amount of interest;
(d) the maturity value.

1. The face value of a five-month, 12 percent note dated September 30, 1995, is $840.
2. A note for $760 dated March 20, 1996, with interest at 7% per annum, is issued for 120 days.
3. A sixty-day, 10.5 percent note for $1250 is issued January 31, 1997.
4. A four-month, 13 percent note for $2000 is issued July 31, 1995.

8.2 *Maturity value of promissory notes*

A. Using the formula S = P(1 + rt)

Since the maturity value of a promissory note is the principal (face value) plus the interest accumulated to the legal due date, the amount formula for simple interest will determine the maturity value directly.

$$S = P(1 + rt) \longleftarrow \textit{Formula 7.4}$$

S = maturity value of the promissory note;
P = the face value of the note;
r = the rate of interest on the note;
t = the interest period (the number of days between the *date of issue* and the *legal due date*).

B. Worked examples

***Example* 8.2a** For the promissory note illustrated in Figure 8.1, determine the maturity value using the amount formula $S = P(1 + rt)$.

Solution

$$P = 650.00; \quad r = 0.105; \quad t = \frac{124}{365}$$

$$S = 650.00\left[1 + (0.105)\left(\frac{124}{365}\right)\right] = 650.00(1 + 0.0356712) = \$673.19$$

***Example* 8.2b** Find the maturity value of an \$800, six-month note with interest at 12.5% dated May 31.

Solution

The date of issue is May 31;
the term of the note is six months;
the term ends November 30;
the legal due date is December 3;
the interest period (May 31 to December 3) has 186 days.

$$P = 800.00; \quad r = 0.125; \quad t = \frac{186}{365}$$

$$S = 800.00\left[1 + (0.125)\left(\frac{186}{365}\right)\right] = 800.00(1 + 0.0636986) = \$850.96$$

***Example* 8.2c** Determine the maturity value of a ninety-day, $750 note dated December 15, 1995, with interest at 11%.

Solution

The date of issue is December 15, 1995;
the term is 90 days;
the term ends March 14, 1996 (from 90 days take away 16 days remaining in December, 31 days for January, 29 days for February, 1996 being a leap year, which leaves 14 days for March);
the legal due date (adding the three days of grace) is March 17;
the interest period (December 15 to March 17) has 93 days.

$$P = 750.00; \quad r = 0.11; \quad t = \frac{93}{365}$$

$$S = 750.00\left[1 + (0.11)\left(\frac{93}{365}\right)\right] = 750.00(1 + 0.0280274) = \$771.02$$

Exercise 8.2

A. Use the amount formula to compute the maturity value of each of the following promissory notes.

1. A four-month, 11.5% note for $620 is issued May 25.

2. A $350 note is issued on October 30 at 13% for 90 days.

3. A 150-day note for $820 with interest at 5% is dated June 28.

4. A seven-month, $420 note dated November 1, 1995, earns interest at 9.5%.

8.3 *Present value of promissory notes*

A. Finding the face value

The face value (or principal) of promissory notes can be obtained by solving the amount formula $S = P(1 + rt)$ for P, that is, by using the present value formula

$$\boxed{P = \frac{S}{1 + rt}} \longleftarrow \textbf{\textit{Formula}} \ \textbf{7.5}$$

P = the face value (or present value) of the note at the date of issue;
S = the maturity value;
r = the rate of interest;
t = the interest period.

***Example* 8.3a** A five-month note dated January 31, 1995, and bearing interest at 12% p.a. has a maturity value of $567.16. Find the face value of the note.

Solution

FIGURE 8.2 ***Graphic representation of data***

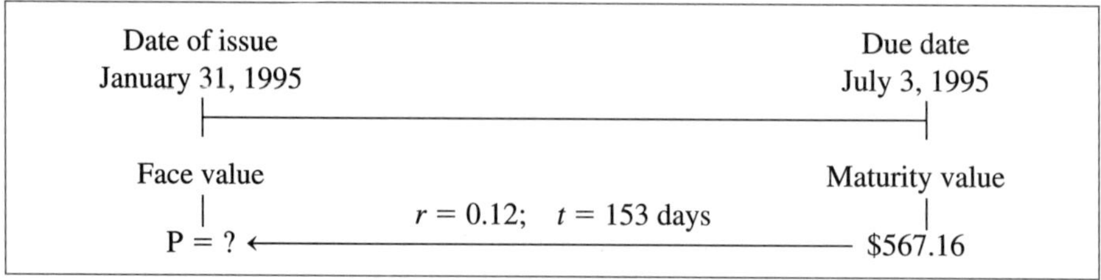

The term of the note ends June 30;
the legal due date is July 3;
the interest period (January 31 to July 3) has 153 days.

$$S = 567.16; \quad r = 0.12; \quad t = \frac{153}{365}$$

$$P = \frac{567.16}{1 + (0.12)\left(\frac{153}{365}\right)} = \frac{567.16}{1 + 0.0503014} = \$540.00$$

B. Present value of promissory notes

The **present value of a promissory note** is its value any time before the due date allowing for the rate money is worth. That is, it is the present value of the maturity value of the promissory note.

To determine the present value, we need to know the maturity value of the note. In computing the maturity value and the present value, we must consider *two* rates of interest:

(a) the rate of the interest stated on the promissory note. This is the rate needed to determine the maturity value;

(b) the rate money is worth. This rate is needed to determine the present value of the note at the date specified (the focal date).

As the two rates are likely to be *different*, take care in using them.

Example 8.3b A seven-month note for $1500 is issued on March 31 bearing interest at 9%. Find the present value of the note on the date of issue if money is worth 12%.

Solution

(i) First, determine the *maturity value* of the note. Use the date of issue as the focal date.

The term of the note ends October 31;
the legal due date is November 3;
the interest period (March 31 to November 3) has 217 days.

FIGURE 8.3 ***Graphic representation of data***

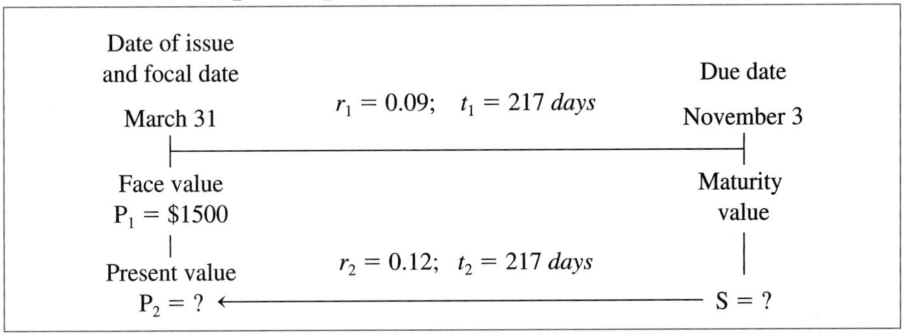

Date of issue and focal date		Due date
March 31	$r_1 = 0.09$; $t_1 = 217$ *days*	November 3
Face value $P_1 = \$1500$		Maturity value
Present value $P_2 = ?$ ←	$r_2 = 0.12$; $t_2 = 217$ *days*	$S = ?$

$$P_1 = 1500.00; \quad r_1 = 0.09; \quad t_1 = \frac{217}{365}$$

$$S = 1500\left[1 + (0.09)\left(\frac{217}{365}\right)\right] = 1500(1 + 0.0535069) = \$1580.26$$

(ii) Second, use the maturity value found in part (i) to determine the *present value* at the specified date.

The focal date (date of issue) is March 31;
the legal due date is November 3;
the interest period (March 31 to November 3) has 217 days.

$$S = 1580.26; \quad r_2 = 0.12; \quad t_2 = \frac{217}{365}$$

$$P_2 = \frac{1580.26}{1 + (0.12)(\frac{217}{365})} = \frac{1580.26}{1 + 0.0713425} = \$1475.03$$

Note: The present value at the date of issue is less than the face value of the note because the interest rate on the note (9.0%) is less than the rate money is worth (12.0%).

Example **8.3c** Find the present value on the date of issue of a non-interest-bearing \$950, three-month promissory note dated April 30 if money is worth 13.5%.

Solution

FIGURE 8.4 ***Graphic representation of data***

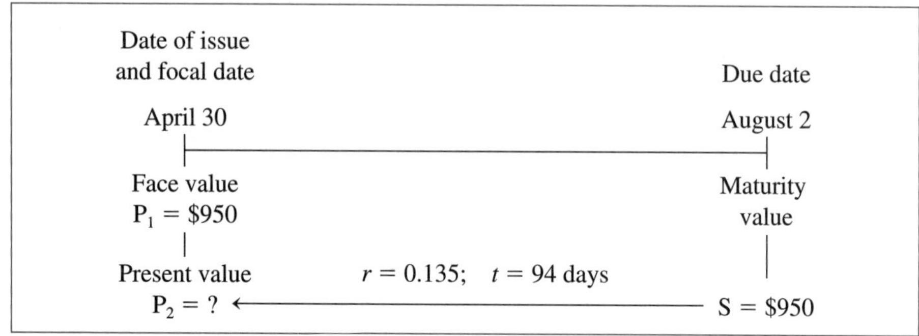

The term of the note ends July 30;
the legal due date is August 2;
the interest period (April 30 to August 2) has 94 days.

If a promissory note is *non*-interest-bearing, the maturity value of the note is the same as the face value of the note.

The maturity value of the note is the face value—\$950.00.

$$S = 950.00; \quad r = 0.135; \quad t = \frac{94}{365}$$

$$P = \frac{950.00}{1 + (0.135)\left(\frac{94}{365}\right)} = \frac{950.00}{1 + 0.0347671} = \$918.08$$

Example **8.3d** A 180-day note for \$2000 with interest at 15% is dated September 18, 1996. Find the value of the note on December 1, 1996, if money is worth 11.5%.

Solution

(i) Find the maturity value of the note.
The 180-day term ends March 17, 1997;
the legal due date is March 20, 1997;
the interest period (September 18 to March 20) has 183 days.

FIGURE 8.5 ***Graphic representation of data***

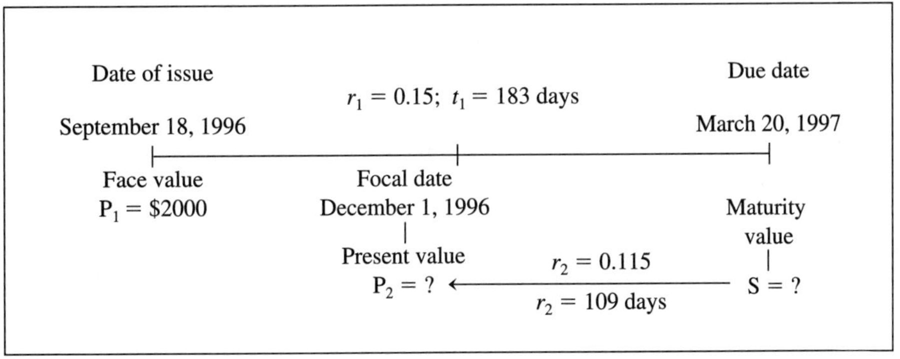

$$P_1 = 2000;\ r_1 = 0.15;\ t_1 = \frac{183}{365}$$

$$S = 2000\left[1 + (0.15)\left(\frac{183}{365}\right)\right] = 2000(1 + 0.0752055) = \$2150.41$$

(ii) Find the present value.
The focal date is December 1, 1996;
the interest period (December 1 to March 20) has 109 days.

$$S = 2150.41;\ r_2 = 0.115;\ t_2 = \frac{109}{365}$$

$$P_2 = \frac{2150.41}{1 + (0.115)\left(\frac{109}{365}\right)} = \frac{2150.41}{1 + 0.0343425} = \$2079.01$$

***Example* 8.3e** Find the value of a non-interest-bearing \$400, 120-day note dated March 2 on May 15 if money is worth 13%.

Solution

The 120-day term ends June 30;
the legal due date is July 3;
the focal date is May 15;
the interest period (May 15 to July 3) has 49 days;
the maturity value of the note is its face value, \$400.00.

FIGURE 8.6 ***Graphic representation of data***

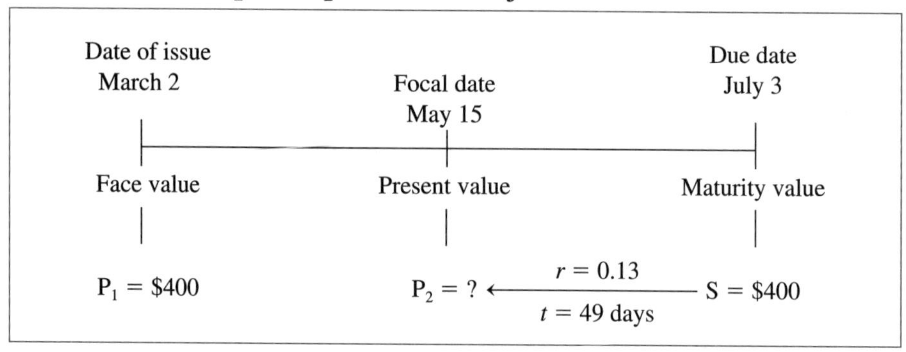

$$S = 400.00; r = 0.13; t = \frac{49}{365}$$

$$P_2 = \frac{400.00}{1 + (0.13)(\frac{49}{365})} = \frac{400.00}{1 + 0.0174521} = \$393.14$$

Exercise 8.3

A. Compute the face value of each of the following promissory notes.

1. A six-month note dated April 9 with interest at 13% has a maturity value of $485.15.
2. The maturity value of a 150-day 12.5 percent note dated March 25 is $1641.74.

B. Find the present value on the date indicated of each of the following promissory notes:

1. a non-interest-bearing note for $1200 issued August 10 for three months if money is worth 11%, on the date of issue;
2. a non-interest-bearing note for $750 issued February 2, 1996, for 180 days if money is worth 12.5%, on June 1, 1996;
3. a sixty-day, 14% note for $1600 issued October 28 if money is worth 12%, on November 30;
4. a four-month note for $930 dated April 1 with interest at 10.5% if money is worth 12%, on June 20.

8.4 *The simple discount method of discounting promissory notes*

A. *Discounting promissory notes*

Promissory notes are negotiable; that is, they can be transferred or sold by one party (the holder of the note) to another party (the buyer). The act of selling or buying a promissory note is called **discounting**.

The buyer of the note buys its maturity value. The purchase price that the buyer offers is agreed upon by the two parties to the transaction at a rate of interest satisfactory to the buyer.

The following terms are important in computing the discounted value of a note.

(a) The **rate of discount** is the rate of interest to be used in discounting.

(b) The **date of discount** is the date on which the discounting takes place.

(c) The **discount period** is the time period from the date of discount to the legal due date.

(d) The **proceeds** of the note is the amount the buyer pays.

(e) The **amount of discount** is the difference between the maturity value and the proceeds of the note.

B. Simple discount

When the simple discount method is used, the proceeds of a promissory note are the present value of the note at the date of discount. The present value formula $P = \frac{S}{(1 + rt)}$ applies:

P is the proceeds of the note;
S is the maturity value;
r is the discount rate to be used;
t is the discount period.

Using this formula means that the amount of discount is the same as the amount of simple interest based on the present value of the note on the date of discount. That is, discounting promissory notes by the simple discount method requires the same formulas and computations used in subsections 8.3B and C.

C. Discounting non-interest-bearing notes

Example **8.4a** A two-month, non-interest-bearing promissory note for $700.00 is dated June 30. Find the proceeds of the note and the amount of discount if the note is discounted on July 31 at 9%.

Solution

The maturity value is the face value of the note $700.00;
the term of the note ends August 30;
the legal due date of the note is September 2;
the discount date is July 31;
the discount period (July 31 to September 2) has 33 days.

$$S = 700.00;\ r = 0.09;\ t = \frac{33}{365}$$

$$P = \frac{700.00}{1 + (0.09)\left(\frac{33}{365}\right)} = \frac{700.00}{1 + 0.008137} = \$694.35$$

The proceeds of the note on July 31 are \$694.35.
The amount of simple discount (simple interest) is (700.00 − 694.35) = \$5.65.

Note: The buyer of the promissory note invests \$694.35 for 33 days and will make 9% p.a. simple interest. This figure can be verified by computing the amount of simple interest.

$$I = Prt = (694.35)(0.09)\left(\frac{33}{365}\right) = \$5.65$$

D. Discounting interest-bearing notes

***Example* 8.4b** A 150-day, 10% promissory note for \$1200 dated October 28, 1995, is sold January 31, 1996, to yield 13%. Determine the proceeds of the note and the amount of discount.

Solution

(i) *Diagram*
The information needed in discounting interest-bearing notes is essentially the same as used in computing the present value of such notes. See Figure 8.7.

FIGURE 8.7 ***Graphic representation of data***

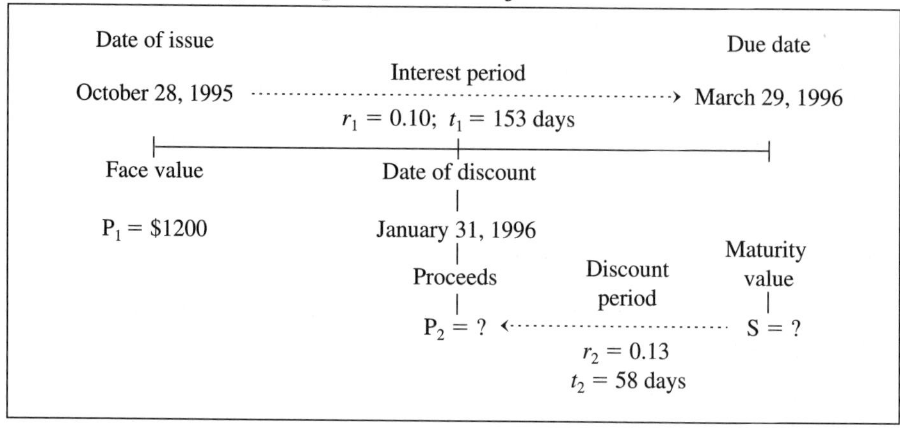

(ii) *Find the maturity value*

The 150-day term of the note ends March 26 (note that 1996 is a leap year; February has 29 days);
the legal due date is March 29;
the interest period (October 28 to March 29) has 153 days.

$$P_1 = 1200;\ r_1 = 0.10;\ t_1 = \frac{153}{365}$$

$$S = 1200\left[1 + (0.10)\left(\frac{153}{365}\right)\right] = 1200(1 + 0.0419178) = \$1250.30$$

(iii) *Find the proceeds* (present value on January 31, 1996)

The date of discount is January 31, 1996;
the discount period (January 31 to March 29) has 58 days.

$$S = 1250.30;\ r_2 = 0.13;\ t_2 = \frac{58}{365}$$

$$P_2 = \frac{1250.30}{1 + (0.13)\left(\frac{58}{365}\right)} = \frac{1250.30}{1 + 0.0206575} = \$1224.99$$

The proceeds of the note on January 31, 1996, are \$1224.99.
The amount of simple discount is 1250.30 − 1224.99 = \$25.31. This figure is the same amount as the simple interest on \$1224.99 at 13% for 58 days [found by $(1224.99)(0.13)\left(\frac{58}{365}\right)$].

Exercise 8.4

A. Find the proceeds and the amount of discount for each of the following using the simple discount method.

1. A 90-day non-interest-bearing note for \$1000 dated May 1 is discounted June 10 at 15%.

2. A five-month non-interest-bearing note for \$680 issued December 2, 1996, is discounted at 12% on February 15, 1997.

3. A three-month \$850 note with interest at 9% dated June 1 is discounted at 11.5% on July 20.

4. A 120-day note for \$1300 with interest at 13.5% issued August 12 is discounted September 30 at 8%.

8.5 *Demand loans*

A. Nature of demand loans

When borrowing on a **demand** note, the borrower receives the full face value of the note. The lender may demand payment of the loan in full or in part at any time. Conversely, the borrower may repay all of the loan or any part at any time without notice and without interest penalty. Interest, based on the unpaid balance, is usually payable monthly. The interest rate on such loans is normally not fixed for the duration of the loan but fluctuates with market conditions. Thus the total interest cost cannot be predicted with certainty. Note that the method of counting days is to count the first day but not the last.

B. Examples

Example **8.5a** Penny Rose borrowed \$1200.00 from the Royal Bank on a demand note. She agreed to repay the loan in six equal monthly instalments and also authorized the bank to collect interest monthly from her bank account at 15% p.a. calculated on the unpaid balance. What will the loan cost?

Solution

$$\text{Monthly payment of principal} = \frac{1200.00}{6} = \$200.00$$

$$\text{Monthly rate of interest} = \frac{15\%}{12} = 1.25\%$$

Month	*Loan amount owing during month*	*Interest collected for month*
1	\$1200.00 ⟵ Original	\$15.00 ⟵ (1200)(0.0125)
2	\$1000.00 ⟵ 1200 − 200	\$12.50 ⟵ (1000)(0.0125)
3	\$ 800.00 ⟵ 1000 − 200	\$10.00 ⟵ (800)(0.0125)
4	\$ 600.00 ⟵ 800 − 200	\$ 7.50 ⟵ (600)(0.0125)
5	\$ 400.00 ⟵ 600 − 200	\$ 5.00 ⟵ (400)(0.0125)
6	\$ 200.00 ⟵ 400 − 200	\$ 2.50 ⟵ (200)(0.0125)
	Total interest cost ⟶	\$52.50

Example **8.5b** On August 17, Sheridan Toy Company borrowed \$30 000.00 from Peel Credit Union on a demand note to finance its inventory. Interest on the loan, calculated on the daily balance, is charged against the borrower's current account on the 17th of each month while the loan is in force. The company makes a payment of \$5000.00 on September 24, makes a further payment of \$10 000.00 on October 20, and pays the balance on December 10. The interest on demand loans on August 17 was 12% p.a. The rate was changed to 13% effective October 1, to 14.5% effective November 1, and to 14% effective December 1. Determine the cost of financing the loan.

Solution

Payment date	*Interest period*	*Principal*	*Rate*	*Amount of interest due*	
Sept. 17	Aug. 17–Sept. 17	\$30 000.00	12.0%	\$305.75 ⟵	$(30\ 000)(0.12)\left(\frac{31}{365}\right)$
Oct. 17	Sept. 17–Sept. 24	\$30 000.00	12.0%	\$ 69.04 ⟵	$(30\ 000)(0.12)\left(\frac{7}{365}\right)$
	Sept. 24–Sept. 30*	\$25 000.00	12.0%	57.53 ⟵	$(25\ 000)(0.12)\left(\frac{7}{365}\right)$
	Oct. 1–Oct. 17	\$25 000.00	13.0%	142.47 ⟵	$(25\ 000)(0.13)\left(\frac{16}{365}\right)$
				\$269.04	
Nov. 17	Oct. 17–Oct. 20	\$25 000.00	13.0%	\$ 26.71 ⟵	$(25\ 000)(0.13)\left(\frac{3}{365}\right)$
	Oct. 20–Oct. 31*	\$15 000.00	13.0%	64.11 ⟵	$(15\ 000)(0.13)\left(\frac{12}{365}\right)$
	Nov. 1–Nov. 17	\$15 000.00	14.5%	95.34 ⟵	$(15\ 000)(0.145)\left(\frac{16}{365}\right)$
				\$186.16	
Dec. 10	Nov. 17–Nov. 30*	\$15 000.00	14.5%	\$ 83.42 ⟵	$(15\ 000)(0.145)\left(\frac{14}{365}\right)$
	Dec. 1–Dec. 10	\$15 000.00	14.0%	51.78 ⟵	$(15\ 000)(0.14)\left(\frac{9}{365}\right)$
				\$135.20	
	TOTAL COST OF FINANCING ⟶			\$896.15	

*Inclusive

C. Partial payments

Demand loans and similar debts are sometimes paid off by a series of **partial payments**. The commonly used approach to dealing with this type of loan repayment, called the **Declining Balance Method**, requires that each partial payment is applied first to the accumulated interest. Any remainder is then used to reduce the outstanding principal. Thus, interest is always calculated on the unpaid balance and the new unpaid balance is determined after each partial payment.

The following step-by-step procedure is useful in dealing with such problems.

(a) Compute the interest due to the date of the partial payment.

(b) Compare the interest due computed in part (a) with the partial payment received and do part (c) if the partial payment is greater than the interest due or do part (d) if the partial payment is less than the interest due.

(c) *Partial payment greater than interest due*

(i) Deduct the interest due from the partial payment.

(ii) Deduct the remainder in part (i) from the principal balance to obtain the new unpaid balance.

(d) *Partial payment less than interest due*
In this case, the partial payment is not large enough to cover the interest due.
(i) Deduct the partial payment from the interest due to determine the unpaid interest due at the date of the principal payment.
(ii) Keep a record of this balance and apply any future partial payments to this unpaid interest first.

***Example* 8.5c** On April 20, Bruce borrowed $4000.00 at 13% on a note requiring payment of principal and interest on demand. Bruce paid $600.00 on May 10 and $1200.00 on July 15. What payment is required on September 30 to pay the note in full?

Solution

April 20
Original loan balance ⟶ $4000.00

May 10
Deduct
First partial payment ⟶ $ 600.00
Less interest
April 20–May 10 ⟶ 28.49 ⟵ $(4000)(0.13)\left(\frac{20}{365}\right)$

571.51

Unpaid balance ⟶ $3428.49

July 15
Deduct
Second partial payment ⟶ $1200.00
Less interest
May 10–July 15 ⟶ 80.59 ⟵ $(3428.49)(0.13)\left(\frac{66}{365}\right)$

1119.41

Unpaid balance ⟶ $2309.08

Sept. 30
Add
Interest
July 15–Sept. 30 ⟶ 63.33 ⟵ $(2309.08)(0.13)\left(\frac{77}{365}\right)$

Payment required to pay the note in full ⟶ $2372.41

***Example* 8.5d** The Provincial Bank lent $20 000.00 to the owner of the Purple Pelican on April 1 for commercial improvements. The loan was secured by a demand note subject to a variable rate of interest. This rate was 12% on April 1. The rate of interest was raised to 14% effective August 1 and reduced to 13% effective

November 1. Partial payments, applied to the loan by the Declining Balance Method, were made as follows: June 10, \$1000.00; September 20, \$500.00; November 15, \$1200.00. How much interest is due to the Provincial Bank on December 31?

Solution

April 1				
Original loan balance ⟶			\$20 000.00	
June 10				
Deduct				
First partial payment ⟶		\$1000.00		
Less interest				
April 1–June 10 ⟶		460.27		⟵ $(20\,000.00)(0.12)\left(\frac{70}{365}\right)$
			539.73	
Unpaid loan balance ⟶			\$19 460.27	
Sept. 20				
Deduct				
Second partial payment ⟶		\$ 500.00		
Less interest				
June 10–Sept. 20				
June 10–July 31* ⟶	\$332.69			⟵ $(19\,460.27)(0.12)\left(\frac{52}{365}\right)$
Aug. 1–Sept. 20 ⟶	373.21	705.90		⟵ $(19\,460.27)(0.14)\left(\frac{50}{365}\right)$
Unpaid interest to Sept. 20 ⟶		\$ 205.90		
Unpaid loan balance ⟶			\$19 460.27	
Nov. 15				
Third partial payment ⟶		\$1200.00		
Less interest				
Unpaid interest to Sept. 20 ⟶	\$205.90			⟵ (see above)
Sept. 20–Oct. 31* ⟶	313.50			⟵ $(19\,460.27)(0.14)\left(\frac{42}{365}\right)$
Nov. 1–Nov. 15 ⟶	97.03			⟵ $(19\,460.27)(0.13)\left(\frac{14}{365}\right)$
		616.43		
			583.57	
Unpaid loan balance ⟶			\$18 876.70	
Dec. 31				
Interest due				
Nov. 15–Dec. 31 ⟶		309.27		⟵ $(18\,876.70)(0.13)\left(\frac{46}{365}\right)$

*Inclusive

Exercise 8.5

A. Determine the total interest cost for each of the following loans.

1. Jean-Luc borrowed $1500.00 from his bank secured by a demand note. He agreed to repay the loan in five equal monthly instalments and authorized the bank to collect the interest monthly from his bank account at 9.0% per annum calculated on the unpaid balance.

2. Jamie borrowed $900.00 from the Essex District Credit Union. The line of credit agreement provided for repayment of the loan in four equal monthly payments plus interest at 12% per annum calculated on the unpaid balance.

3. Erindale Automotive borrowed $8000.00 from the Bank of Montreal on a demand note on May 10. Interest on the loan, calculated on the daily balance, is charged to Erindale's current account on the 10th of each month. Erindale made a payment of $2000.00 on July 20, a payment of $3000.00 on October 1, and repaid the balance on December 1. The rate of interest on the loan on May 10 was 18% per annum. The rate was changed to 19.5% on August 1 and to 18.5% on October 1.

4. The Tomac Swim Club arranged short-term financing of $12 500.00 on July 20 with the Bank of Commerce and secured the loan with a demand note. The club repaid the loan by payments of $6000.00 on September 15, $3000.00 on November 10, and the balance on December 30. Interest, calculated on the daily balance and charged to the club's current account on the last day of each month, was at 15.5% per annum on July 20. The rate was changed to 14.5% effective September 1 and to 15% effective December 1.

B. Use the Declining Balance Method to answer each of the following.

1. A loan of $6000.00 made at 16% per annum on March 10 is repaid in full on November 15. A payment of $2000.00 was made on June 30 and of $2500.00 on September 5. What was the final payment?

2. D. Slipp borrowed $15 000.00 on August 12. She paid $6000.00 on November 1, $5000.00 on December 15, and the balance on February 20. The rate of interest on the loan was 10.5%. How much did she pay on February 20?

3. The Continental Bank made a loan of $20 000.00 on March 25 to Dr. Hirsch to purchase equipment for her office. The loan was secured by a demand loan subject to a variable rate of interest which was 14% on March 25. The rate of interest was raised to 15.5% effective July 1 and to 16.5% effective September 1. Dr. Hirsch made partial payments on the loan as follows: $600.00 on May 15; $800.00 on June 30; and $600.00 on October 10. The terms of the note require payment of any accrued interest on October 31. How much must Dr. Hirsch pay on October 31?

4. Dirk Ward borrowed $12 000.00 for investment purposes on May 10 on a demand note providing for a variable rate of interest and payment of any accrued interest on December 31. He paid $300.00 on June 25, $150 on September 20, and $200.00

on November 5. How much is the accrued interest on December 31 if the rate of interest was 9.5% on May 10, 8% effective August 1, and 6.5% effective November 1?

8.6 *Loan repayment schedules*

A. Purpose

In the case of loans repaid in fixed instalments (often called a **blended payment**), the constant periodic payment is first applied to pay the accumulated interest. The remainder of the payment is then used to reduce the unpaid balance of principal.

FIGURE 8.8 ***Statement of disclosure***

STATEMENT OF DISCLOSURE

(COST OF LOAN AND ANNUAL INTEREST RATE) PURSUANT TO THE CONSUMER PROTECTION ACT

Name of Credit Union *SHERIDAN* Account No. *2000*

1) Balance of existing loan (if any) $ *2000.00*

2) Add new amount loaned $ *4000.00*

3) Full amount of loan $ *6000.00*

4) Cost of Borrowing expressed in dollars and cents (Interest calculated on full amount of loan (Item 3) $ *2604.00*

5) Annual Interest Rate charged (calculated in accordance with the Consumer Protection Act) *15.0* %

6) If any charge is made to the borrower in addition to interest herein noted, it must be disclosed here. $ ______
(Description) ......
Frequency of instalments *60 MONTHS* Amount of instalments $ *143.40* First instalment due ______ 19 ___

I, the undersigned, acknowledge receipt of this statement of cost of loan and annual interest rate, prior to the advance of the credit.

DATE ______ X ......
SIGNATURE OF BORROWER

COMPLETE IN DUPLICATE
Original to Borrower

NOTE: Where more than one maker or co-maker, separate Disclosure Forms should be signed for individually.

Courtesy Peel Sheridan Dufferin Educational Credit Union Limited

While lenders are obliged to disclose to the borrower the total cost of borrowing as well as the interest rate (see Figure 8.8), a detailed statement of the cost of borrowing as well as the effect of the periodic payments on the principal may be obtained by constructing a loan repayment schedule, or an amortization schedule.

The information usually contained in such a schedule includes

(a) the payment number or payment date;

(b) the amount paid at each payment date;

(c) the interest paid by each payment;

(d) the principal repaid by each payment;

(e) the unpaid loan balance after each payment;

Figure 8.9 provides a possible design for such schedules and the same design is used in the solution to Example 8.6a.

FIGURE 8.9 ***Basic design of a loan repayment schedule***

①	②	③	④	⑤	⑥
Payment number	*Balance before payment*	*Amount paid*	*Interest paid*	*Principal repaid*	*Balance after payment*

B. *Construction of loan repayment schedules illustrated*

Example **8.6a** You borrowed \$1600.00 from Sheridan Credit Union at 15% p.a. and agreed to repay the loan in monthly instalments of \$300.00 each, such payments to cover interest due and repayment of principal. Use the design shown in Figure 8.9 to construct a complete repayment schedule including the totalling of Columns ③, ④, and ⑤ ("Amount paid," "Interest paid," and "Principal repaid").

Solution

See Figure 8.10 and the explanatory notes that follow.

FIGURE 8.10 ***Loan repayment schedule for Example 8.6a***

①	②	③	④	⑤	⑥
Payment number	*Balance before payment*	*Amount paid (1)*	*Interest paid (2)*	*Principal repaid (3)*	*Balance after payment (4)*
0					1600.00(5)
1	1600.00	300.00	20.00(6)	280.00(7)	1320.00(8)
2	1320.00	300.00	16.50(9)	283.50(10)	1036.50(11)
3	1036.50	300.00	12.96	287.04	749.46
4	749.46	300.00	9.37	290.63	458.83
5	458.83	300.00	5.74	294.26	164.57(12)
6	164.57	166.63(15)	2.06(14)	164.57(13)	– . – –
Totals (16)		1666.63(18)	66.63(19)	1600.00(17)	

Explanatory notes

(1) The Amount Paid shown in column ③ is the agreed-upon monthly payment of \$300.00.

(2) The Interest Paid shown in column ④ is at 15% per annum. This figure is converted into a periodic (monthly) rate of $\frac{15\%}{12}$ (1.25% per month) to facilitate the computation of the monthly amount of interest paid. (See notes (6) and (9).)

(3) The amount of Principal Repaid each month shown in column ⑤ is found by subtracting the Interest Paid for the month (column ④ from the Amount Paid for the month (column 3). (See notes (7) and (10).)

(4) The Balance After Payment for a month shown in column ⑥ is found by subtracting the Principal Repaid for the month (column ⑤) from the Balance Before Payment for the month (column ②) OR from the previous Balance After Payment figure (column ⑥). (See notes (8) and (11).)

(5) The original loan balance of \$1600.00 is introduced as the starting amount for the schedule and is the only amount shown in Line 0.

(6) Interest paid in Payment number 1
= 1.25% of 1600.00 = (0.0125)(1600.00) = \$20.00

(7) Principal Repaid by Payment number 1
= 300.00 − 20.00 = \$280.00

(8) Balance After Payment for Payment number 1
= 1600.00 − 280.00 = \$1320.00

(9) Interest Paid in Payment number 2
= 1.25% of 1320.00 = (0.0125)(1320.00) = \$16.50

(10) Principal Repaid by Payment number 2
= 300.00 − 16.50 = \$283.50

(11) Balance After Payment for Payment number 2
= 1320.00 − 283.50 = \$1036.50

(12) The Balance After Payment for Payment number 5 of \$164.57 is smaller than the regular monthly payment of \$300.00. The next payment need only be sufficient to pay the outstanding balance of \$164.57 plus the interest due. (See notes (13), (14), and (15).)

(13) Principal Repaid in Payment number 6 must be \$164.57 to pay off the outstanding loan balance.

(14) Interest Paid in Payment number 6 is the interest due on \$164.57 = 1.25% of 164.57 = (0.0125)(164.57) = \$2.06.

(15) Amount paid in Payment number 6
= 164.57 + 2.06 = \$166.63.

(16) The Totals of columns ③, ④, and ⑤ serve as a check of the arithmetic accuracy of the payment schedule. (See notes (17), (18), and (19).)

(17) Principal Repaid, the total column ⑤, must equal the original loan balance of \$1600.00.

(18) Amount Paid, the total of column ③, must equal the total of all the payments made (five payments of \$300.00 each plus the final payment of \$166.63).
(19) Interest paid, the total of column ④, must be the difference between the totals of columns ③ and ⑤ = 1666.63 − 1600.00 = \$66.63.

C. Computer application—Loan repayment schedule

Computers are ideally suited for the construction of repayment schedules because of the iterative nature of the mathematical processes used in developing the schedules.

Program 2—Loan payment schedule—provides a computer solution similar to Figure 8.10 (see the Solutions Manual).

Exercise 8.6

A. Use the design shown in Figure 8.9 to construct a complete repayment schedule including the totalling of the Amount Paid, Interest Paid, and Principal Repaid columns for each of the following loans.

1. Carla borrowed \$1200.00 from the Royal Bank at 16.5% per annum calculated on the monthly unpaid balance. She agreed to repay the loan in blended payments of \$180.00 per month.

2. On March 15, Julio borrowed \$900.00 from Sheridan Credit Union at 15% per annum calculated on the daily balance. He gave the Credit Union six cheques for \$135.00 dated the 15th of each of the next six months starting April 15 and a cheque dated October 15 for the remaining balance to cover payment of interest and repayment of principal.

Review exercise

1. A four-month promissory note for \$1600.00 dated June 30 bears interest at 14.5%.
   (a) What is the due date of the note?
   (b) What is the amount of interest payable at the due date?
   (c) What is the maturity value of the note?

2. Determine the maturity value of a 120-day note for \$1250.00 dated May 23 and bearing interest at 15.75%.

3. Compute the face value of a 90-day note dated September 10 bearing interest at 9.25% whose maturity value is \$767.68.

4. The maturity value of a seven-month promissory note issued July 31, 1997, is \$3275.00. What is the present value of the note on the date of issue if interest is 13.75%?

5. Compute the maturity value of a 150-day, 12% promissory note with a face value of \$5000.00 dated August 5.

6. What is the face value of a three-month promissory note dated November 30, 1995, with interest at 11.5 percent if its maturity value is \$967.84?

7. A 90-day, $800 promissory note was issued July 31 with interest at 14%. What is the present value of the note on October 20?
8. An $1850, four-month promissory note with interest at 12.5% issued June 1 is discounted on August 28 at 15.5%. Find the amount of discount and the proceeds of the note using the simple discount method.
9. Determine the present value on the date of issue of a non-interest-bearing promissory note for $1300 dated March 10 for four months if money is worth 9.5%.
10. Find the proceeds and the discount of a five-month, $700 promissory note dated September 6 with interest at 10.5% discounted on November 28 at 13.5% by the simple discount method.
11. Tryman borrowed $10 000 on March 10 on a demand note. The loan was repaid by payments of $3000 on June 20, $4000 on September 1, and the balance on November 15. Interest, calculated on the daily balance and charged to Tryman's current account on the last day of each month, was at 19% on March 10 but was changed to 20% effective June 1 and to 18% effective October 1. How much did the loan cost?
12. Quick Print Press borrowed $20 000 from the Provincial Bank on May 25 at 17.5% and secured the loan by signing a promissory note subject to a variable rate of interest. Quick Print made partial payments of $5000 on July 10 and $8000 on September 15. The rate of interest was increased to 18% effective August 1 and to 18.5% effective October 1. What payment must Quick Print make on October 31 if, under the terms of the loan agreement, any interest accrued as of October 31 is to be paid on October 31?
13. You borrowed $3000 at 18% per annum calculated on the unpaid monthly balance and agreed to repay the principal together with interest in monthly payments of $500 each. Construct a complete repayment schedule.

Self-test

1. For the following promissory note, determine the amount of interest due at maturity.

$565.00 TORONTO, ONTARIO JANUARY 10, 1996

FIVE MONTHS after date we promise to pay to the order of

WILSON LUMBER COMPANY

EXACTLY FIVE-HUNDRED-SIXTY-FIVE and 00/100 -------------- Dollars

at WILSON LUMBER COMPANY for value received

with interest at 13.25% per annum.

Due ____________ (seal) ____________

(seal) ____________

2. Find the maturity value of a $1140.00, 7.75%, 120-day, note dated February 19, 1997.
3. Determine the face value of a four-month promissory note dated May 20, 1995, with interest at 11.5% p.a. if the maturity value of the note is $1206.05.
4. Find the present value of a non-interest-bearing seven-month promissory note for $1800 dated August 7, 1997, on December 20, 1997, if money is then worth 13.75%.
5. A 180-day note dated September 14, 1996, is made at 9.25% for $1665.00. What is the present value of the note on October 18, 1996, if money is worth 15.5%?
6. The owner of Jane's Boutique borrowed $6000.00 from Halton Community Credit Union on June 5. The loan was secured by a demand note with interest calculated on the daily balance and charged to the store's account on the 5th day of each month. The loan was repaid by payments of $1500.00 on July 15, $2000.00 on October 10, and $2500.00 on December 30. The rate of interest charged by the credit union was 14.5% on June 5. The rate was changed to 15.5% effective July 1 and to 16% effective October 1. Determine the total interest cost on the loan.
7. Herb's Restaurant borrowed $24 000.00 on March 1 on a demand note providing for a variable rate of interest. While repayment of principal is open, any accrued interest is to be paid on November 30. Payments on the loan were made as follows: $600.00 on April 15, $500.00 on July 20, and $1000.00 on October 10. The rate of interest was 14% on March 1 but was changed to 15.5% effective August 1 and to 14.5% effective November 1. Using the Declining Balance Method to record the partial payments, determine the accrued interest on November 30.
8. Use the design shown in Figure 8.9 to construct a complete repayment schedule, including the totalling of the Amount Paid, Interest Paid, and Principal Repaid columns, for a loan of $4000 repaid in monthly instalments of $750.00 each including interest of 13.5% per annum calculated on the unpaid balance.

CASE STUDY

You own Jane's Interior Design Studio and have decided to expand. The bank will lend you money only if all other debts and credits are consolidated as of today. Using the following transactions, you are to prepare a financial report for the bank reporting the business's financial standing as of December 18.

1. Jane's gave a 90-day promissory note for $3200 bearing 11% interest to Colour Paint on November 7. Calculate the present value of the note if the rate is now 9.5%.

2. The Westmount Community Centre paid for renovations by issuing a 3-month note to Jane's on October 17. The face value was $4500 and interest was 8%. Calculate the note's present value if rates are now 9.5%.

3. On November 13, the Children's Medical Centre paid for decorating with a 120-day note. The face value was $3700 and interest was 7%. The bank will buy this note at 10%. Calculate the proceeds.

4. Jane's borrowed $4800 from the bank on September 18. The repayment schedule called for six equal payments of $800 applied to the loan. Interest was 9% per annum calculated monthly on the unpaid balance and due in the third and sixth months. Calculate the total amount owing to repay the loan. This month's payment has already been made.

5. Jane's took out a demand loan for $3200 at the credit union on September 1. It is subject to a monthly variable rate of interest. The rate of interest was 8% on September 1, 8.5% on October 1, 7.75% on November 1, and 7.5% on December 1. Payments were made of $400 on October 1, $600 on November 1, and $1000 on December 1. Calculate the total amount due.

6. Calculate Jane's total debt or credit.

7. Jane's requires financing of $24 000 plus or minus debt or credit for the expansion. This amount will be repaid in equal monthly instalments over two years. Interest will be paid separately at 9% per annum compounded monthly. Calculate the first monthly payment.

8. The bank will lend Jane's the money only if the total monthly payments are no more than 33% of the business's net monthly profit. Recent financial statements show that Jane's has net monthly profits of $3000. Will Jane's qualify for the loan?

9. What would Jane's net monthly profit have to be to qualify for the loan?

10. What percentage increase in net monthly profits does Jane's need to qualify for the loan?

11. If Jane's passes this required increase on to its retail prices, calculate the new selling price of a roll of wallpaper that costs $8.00 and has a markup of 65% based on cost.

12. What is the new percent markup based on cost? How does a percentage increase in selling price affect markup based on cost?

Summary of formulae used

Formula 7.1

$I = Prt$ — Finding the amount of interest on promissory notes

Formula 7.4

$S = P(1 + rt)$ — Finding the maturity value of promissory notes directly

Formula 7.5

$P = \dfrac{S}{1 + rt}$ — Finding the present value of promissory notes given the maturity value

Glossary of terms used

Amount of discount the difference between the maturity value of a promissory note and its proceeds when discounted

Blended payments the usual method of repaying a personal consumer loan by fixed periodic (monthly) payments that cover payment of interest and repayment of principal

Date of discount the date on which a promissory note is bought or sold

Date of issue the date on which a promissory note is made

Date of maturity see *Legal due date*

Declining balance method the commonly used approach to applying partial payments to demand loans whereby each partial payment is first applied to pay the interest due and then applied to the outstanding principal

Demand loan a loan for which repayment in full or in part may be required at any time

Discount see *Amount of discount*

Discounting the act of buying or selling promissory notes

Discount period the time, in days, from the date of discount to the legal due date

Due date see *Legal due date*

Face value the sum of money specified on the promissory note

Interest-bearing promissory notes notes subject to the rate of interest stated on the note

Interest period the time, in days, from the date of issue to the legal due date for promissory notes

Issue date see *Date of issue*

Legal due date the date on which the promissory note is to be paid

Loan repayment schedule a detailed statement of instalment payments, interest cost, repayment of principal, and outstanding balance of principal for an instalment plan

Maker the party making the promise to pay by signing the promissory note

Maturity value the amount (face value plus interest) that must be paid on the legal due date to honour the note

Non-interest-bearing promissory notes notes that do not require the payment of interest (the maturity value of such notes is the same as their face value)

Payee the party to whom the promise to pay is made

Present value of a promissory note the value of a promissory note at a specified date before the legal due date determined on the basis of a specified rate of interest or rate of discount or the rate money is worth

Proceeds the sum of money for which a promissory note is bought or sold at the date of discount

Promissory note a written promise to pay a specified sum of money after a specified period of time with or without interest as specified

Rate money is worth the prevailing rate of interest

Rate of discount the rate used to determine the proceeds of a promissory note

Rate of interest the simple annual rate of interest based on the face value

Simple discount the method of discounting promissory notes using the present value approach (simple interest) to determine the proceeds; the amount of discount deducted from the maturity value to find the proceeds when using the simple discount method

Term of a promissory note the time period for which the note was written (in days or months)

Three days of grace the number of days added to the term of a note in Canada to determine its legal due date

PART THREE

Mathematics of finance and investment

9 Compound interest—amount and present value

Introduction

The simple interest method discussed in Chapter 7 is usually used only for time periods of less than one year. For longer terms, the compound interest method (whereby interest is added periodically to the principal) is generally used.

As in the case of simple interest, the two basic problems centre on the determination of *Amount* and *Present Value*. This involves computing the compounding factor $(1 + i)^n$. The arithmetic difficulties associated with computing the numerical value of $(1 + i)^n$ have disappeared with the availability of electronic calculators equipped with an exponential function (universal power key and universal root key).

Objectives

Upon completing this chapter, you will be able to

1. determine the rate per compounding period i and the number of compounding periods n, set up the compounding factor $(1 + i)^n$ in exponential form, and compute the numerical value of $(1 + i)^n$;
2. use the compound amount formula $S = P(1 + i)^n$ to compute future values, including problems involving changes in rate of interest and principal;
3. use the present value formula $P = \frac{S}{(1 + i)^n}$ to compute the present value of future sums of money;
4. discount long-term promissory notes;
5. solve problems involving equations of value.

9.1 Basic concepts and computations

A. Basic procedure for computing compound interest

The term **compound interest** refers to a procedure for computing interest whereby the interest for a specified time period is added to the original principal. The resulting amount becomes the new principal for the next time period. The interest earned in earlier periods earns interest in future periods.

The compound interest method is generally used to calculate interest for long-term investments. The amount of compound interest for the first interest period is the same as the amount of simple interest, but for further interest periods the amount of compound interest becomes increasingly greater than the amount of simple interest.

The basic procedure for computing compound interest and the effect of compounding is illustrated in Table 9.1. The table also provides a comparison of compound interest and simple interest for an original principal of $10 000.00 invested at 10% per annum for six years.

TABLE 9.1 ***Compound interest versus simple interest for a principal of $10 000.00 invested at 10% per annum for 6 years***

Year		*At compound interest*		*At simple interest*	
		Interest computation	*Amount*	*Interest computation*	*Amount*
	Original Principal		10 000.00		10 000.00
1	Add Interest	(0.10)(10 000.00)	1 000.00	(0.10)(10 000.00)	1 000.00
	Amount End Year 1		11 000.00		11 000.00
2	Add Interest	(0.10)(11 000.00)	1 100.00	(0.10)(10 000.00)	1 000.00
	Amount End Year 2		12 100.00		12 000.00
3	Add Interest	(0.10)(12 100.00)	1 210.00	(0.10)(10 000.00)	1 000.00
	Amount End Year 3		13 310.00		13 000.00
4	Add Interest	(0.10)(13 310.00)	1 331.00	(0.10)(10 000.00)	1 000.00
	Amount End Year 4		14 641.00		14 000.00
5	Add Interest	(0.10)(14 641.00)	1 464.10	(0.10)(10 000.00)	1 000.00
	Amount End Year 5		16 105.10		15 000.00
6	Add Interest	(0.10)(16 105.10)	1 610.51	(0.10)(10 000.00)	1 000.00
	Amount End Year 6		17 715.61		16 000.00

The method of computation used in Table 9.1 represents the step-by-step approach used in maintaining a savings account record. It is sometimes called the *Bankbook Method* of computing compound interest. Note that the amount of interest is determined for each interest period based on the previous balance and is then added to that balance.

Note the following about the end results after six years.

	At compound interest	*At simple interest*
Amount after six years	$17 715.61	$16 000.00
Less original principal	10 000.00	10 000.00
Amount of interest	$ 7 715.61	$ 6 000.00

In this case, the compound interest exceeds the simple interest by \$1715.61. This difference represents the amount of interest earned by interest added to the principal at the end of each compounding period.

B. Computer application—accumulation of principal

The Bankbook Method of accumulating a sum of money at compound interest is an iterative process illustrated in Computer Program 3 (see Solutions Manual).

C. The amount formula for compound interest

While the Bankbook Method is useful in maintaining a savings account record, it is impractical for computational purposes. As in the case of simple interest, the **amount** or **future value** can be found by using the amount formula.

For simple interest the amount formula is $S = P(1 + rt)$, Formula 7.4.

For compound interest, the amount formula is

$$S = P(1 + i)^n \quad \longleftarrow \textit{Formula } \mathbf{9.1}$$

S = the amount or future value;
P = the original principal;
i = the periodic rate of interest;
n = the number of compounding periods.

The results of Table 9.1 could have been obtained by using the two amount formulae.

For simple interest

$$\begin{aligned} S = P(1 + rt) &= 10\,000.00[1 + (0.10)(6)] \\ &= 10\,000.00(1 + 0.60) \\ &= 10\,000.00(1.60) \\ &= \$16\,000.00 \end{aligned}$$

For compound interest

$$\begin{aligned} S = P(1 + i)^n &= 10\,000.00(1 + 0.10)^6 \\ &= 10\,000.00(1.10)^6 \\ &= 10\,000.00(1.10)(1.10)(1.10)(1.10)(1.10)(1.10) \\ &= 10\,000.00(1.771561) \\ &= \$17\,715.61 \end{aligned}$$

D. Finding i *and* n

When using the compound interest formula, determining the factor $(1 + i)^n$ is the main computational problem. The value of this factor, called the **compounding factor** or **accumulation factor**, depends on the values of i and n.

The value of i, the periodic rate of interest, is determined from the stated rate of interest to be used in compounding. The stated rate is called the **nominal rate of interest**. Since the nominal rate of interest is usually stated as an annual rate, the value of i is obtained by dividing the nominal rate by the number of **conversion periods** per year.

The commonly used conversion periods cover a number of months, usually an exact divisor of twelve, namely

(a) 12 months, called annual compounding ⟶ 1 conversion per year;

(b) 6 months, called semi-annual compounding ⟶ 2 conversions per year;

(c) 3 months, called quarterly compounding ⟶ 4 conversions per year;

(d) 1 month, called monthly compounding ⟶ 12 conversions per year.

The number of **compounding periods** n must correspond to the time interval used for i. That is, the total time period expressed in years must be multiplied by the number of possible conversion periods per year to obtain n.

Example **9.1a** Determine i and n for

(i) 9% p.a. compounded annually for 14 years;

(ii) 7% p.a. compounded semi-annually for 15 years;

(iii) 14% p.a. compounded quarterly for 12.5 years;

(iv) 18% p.a. compounded monthly for 10.75 years;

(v) 15% p.a. compounded quarterly for 30 months;

(vi) 13.5% p.a. compounded semi-annually for 42 months.

Solution

(i) $i = \frac{9\%}{1} = 9\% = 0.09 \longleftarrow$ 1 conversion period per year

$n = (14)(1) = 14$

(ii) $i = \frac{7\%}{2} = 3.5\% = 0.035 \longleftarrow$ 2 conversion periods per year

$n = (15)(2) = 30$

(iii) $i = \frac{14\%}{4} = 3.5\% = 0.035 \longleftarrow$ 4 conversion periods per year

$n = (12.5)(4) = 50$

(iv) $i = \frac{18\%}{12} = 1.5\% = 0.015 \longleftarrow$ 12 conversion periods per year

$n = (10.75)(12) = 129$

(v) $i = \frac{15\%}{4} = 3.75\% = 0.0375$

$n = \left(\frac{30}{12}\right)(4) = (2.5)(4) = 10 \longleftarrow$ divide by 12 to convert months into years

(vi) $i = \frac{13.5\%}{2} = 6.75\% = 0.0675$

$n = \left(\frac{42}{12}\right)(2) = (3.5)(2) = 7 \longleftarrow$ divide by 12 to convert months into years

E. Computing the compounding factor $(1 + i)^n$

Once you have determined the numerical values of i and n, you can obtain the exponential form of the compounding factor by substituting in the general form $(1 + i)^n$.

In Example 9.1a, the exponential form of the factor is

(i) for $i = 0.09$, $n = 14 \longrightarrow (1 + 0.09)^{14} \longrightarrow (1.09)^{14}$

(ii) for $i = 0.035$, $n = 30 \longrightarrow (1 + 0.035)^{30} \longrightarrow (1.035)^{30}$

(iii) for $i = 0.035$, $n = 50 \longrightarrow (1 + 0.035)^{50} \longrightarrow (1.035)^{50}$

(iv) for $i = 0.015$, $n = 129 \longrightarrow (1 + 0.015)^{129} \longrightarrow (1.015)^{129}$

(v) for $i = 0.0375$, $n = 10 \longrightarrow (1 + 0.0375)^{10} \longrightarrow (1.0375)^{10}$

(vi) for $i = 0.0675$, $n = 7 \longrightarrow (1 + 0.0675)^{7} \longrightarrow (1.0675)^{7}$

The numerical value of any of these factors can now be computed using electronic calculators. For calculators equipped with the exponential function feature [Y^X], the numerical value of the compounding factor can be computed directly.

STEP 1 Enter the numerical value of $(1 + i)$ in the keyboard.

STEP 2 Press the function key [Y^X].

STEP 3 Enter the numerical value of n in the keyboard.

STEP 4 Press [=].

STEP 5 Read the answer in the display.

The numerical value of the compounding factors in Example 9.1a are obtained as follows.

	(i)	*(ii)*	*(iii)*	*(iv)*	*(v)*	*(vi)*
Step 1 Enter	1.09	1.035	1.035	1.015	1.0375	1.0675
Step 2 Press	Y^X	Y^X	Y^X	Y^X	Y^X	Y^X
Step 3 Enter	14	30	50	129	10	7
Step 4 Press	=	=	=	=	=	=
Step 5 Read	3.341727	2.8067937	5.5849268	6.8252638	1.4450439	1.5797021

Note: Do not be concerned if your calculator shows a difference in the last decimal. There is no error. It reflects the precision of the calculator.

With the increasing availability of inexpensive electronic calculators, the two traditional methods of determining the compounding factor $(1 + i)^n$ are rapidly falling into disuse. The use of logarithms for this purpose has virtually disappeared and the use of tables is diminishing. Neither method is used in this text.

Exercise 9.1

A. Determine i and n for each of the following.

1. 12% compounded annually for 5 years
2. 14.4% compounded semi-annually for 8 years
3. 13.5% compounded quarterly for 9 years
4. 7% compounded monthly for 4 years
5. 15.5% compounded semi-annually for 13.5 years
6. 11.5% compounded quarterly for five and three-quarter years
7. 15% compounded monthly for 12.5 years
8. 10.75% compounded quarterly for three years, nine months
9. 12.25% compounded semi-annually for 54 months
10. 8.1% compounded monthly for 15.5 years

B. Set up and compute the compounding factor $(1 + i)^n$ for each of the questions in part A.

C. Answer each of the following questions.

1. For a sum of money invested at 14% compounded quarterly for 12 years, state
   (a) the number of compounding periods;
   (b) the periodic rate of interest;
   (c) the compounding factor in exponential form;
   (d) the numerical value of the compounding factor.

2. For each of the following periodic rates of interest, determine the nominal annual compounding rate.
   (a) $i = 2\%$; compounding is quarterly
   (b) $i = 1.5\%$; compounding is monthly
   (c) $i = 6.5\%$; compounding is semi-annual
   (d) $i = 9.75\%$; compounding is annual

9.2 *Using the compound amount formula* $S = P(1 + i)^n$

A. *Finding the compound amount (maturity value)*

***Example* 9.2a** Find the amount to which \$6000.00 will grow if invested at 10% per annum compounded quarterly for 5 years.

Solution

The original principal P = 6000.00;

the quarterly rate of interest $i = \frac{10\%}{4} = 2.5\% = 0.025$;

the number of compounding periods (quarters) $n = (5)(4) = 20$.

$$\begin{aligned} S &= P(1 + i)^n && \longleftarrow \text{using Formula 9.1} \\ &= 6000.00(1 + 0.025)^{20} && \longleftarrow \text{substituting for P, } i, n \\ &= 6000.00(1.025)^{20} && \longleftarrow \text{exponential form of factor} \\ &= 6000.00(1.6386164) && \longleftarrow \text{using a calculator} \\ &= \$9831.70 \end{aligned}$$

***Example* 9.2b** What is the amount after 78 months of \$2500 invested at 14.25% p.a. compounded semi-annually?

Solution

The original principal P = 2500.00;

the semi-annual rate of interest $i = \frac{14.25\%}{2} = 7.125\% = 0.07125$;

the number of compounding periods (each period is six months)

$n = \left(\frac{78}{12}\right)(2) = (6.5)(2) = 13.$

$$\begin{aligned} S &= P(1 + i)^n \\ &= 2500.00(1 + 0.07125)^{13} \\ &= 2500.00(1.07125)^{13} \\ &= 2500.00(2.4467007) \\ &= \$6116.75 \end{aligned}$$

***Example* 9.2c** Accumulate a deposit of \$1750.00 made into a Registered Retirement Savings Plan from March 1, 1982, to December 1, 2000, at 11.5% p.a. compounded quarterly.

Solution

The original principal P = 1750.00;

the quarterly rate of interest $i = \frac{11.5\%}{4} = 2.875\% = 0.02875$;

the time period from March 1, 1982, to December 1, 2000, contains 18 years and 9 months, or 18.75 years: $n = (18.75)(4) = 75$.

$$\begin{aligned} S &= P(1 + i)^n \\ &= 1750.00(1 + 0.02875)^{75} \\ &= 1750.00(1.02875)^{75} \\ &= 1750.00(8.3798958) \\ &= \$14\,664.82 \end{aligned}$$

B. *Using preprogrammed financial calculators*

Preprogrammed financial calculators are used to solve compounding problems by selecting the compound interest mode, entering the given values, and retrieving the answer.

Slight variations exist in the programming of the various models, particularly in distinguishing between compound interest calculations and annuity calculations. Refer to the instruction booklet for the particular model used.

The four variables used in compound interest calculations—P, S, i, n—are programmed into the calculator and are addressed by using keys as follows. Make sure that the calculator is set in the financial mode.

Key	*Press to enter or retrieve*
FV	the future value or amount S
PV	the present value or principal P
%i	the periodic (conversion) rate i
N	the number of compounding periods n

A fifth key, the periodic payment key [PMT], is not needed for compound interest calculations. However, enter zero as payment to ensure that you are using the compound interest mode.

To begin a compound interest calculation, enter a zero payment; that is, press 0 [PMT]. If new values are entered in any order for any three of the four compound interest variables, the value of the fourth variable is retrieved by pressing the compute key [CPT] followed by the key representing the unknown fourth variable. In models such as the Texas Instruments BA-II that do not have a [CPT] key, press the [2nd] key instead.

To solve Example 9.2a in which P = 6000, i = 2.5%, and n = 20, use the following procedure.

Key in	*Press*	*Display shows*		
0	PMT	0	⟵	this step ensures that the calculator performs a compound interest calculation
6000	PV	6000	⟵	this enters the present value (principal) P
2.5	%i	2.5	⟵	this enters the conversion rate i
20	N	20	⟵	this enters the number of compounding periods n
CPT	FV	9831.6986	⟵	this retrieves the wanted amount S

Note: If your calculator does not have a CPT key, press 2nd FV . This amount is $9831.70.

C. Applications involving changes in interest rate or principal

Example **9.2d** A deposit of $2000.00 earns interest at 12% p.a. compounded monthly for four years. At that time, the interest rate changes to 13% p.a. compounded quarterly. What is the value of the deposit three years after the change in the rate of interest?

Solution

The data given can be represented on a time diagram as shown in Figure 9.1.

FIGURE 9.1 ***Graphic representation of data***

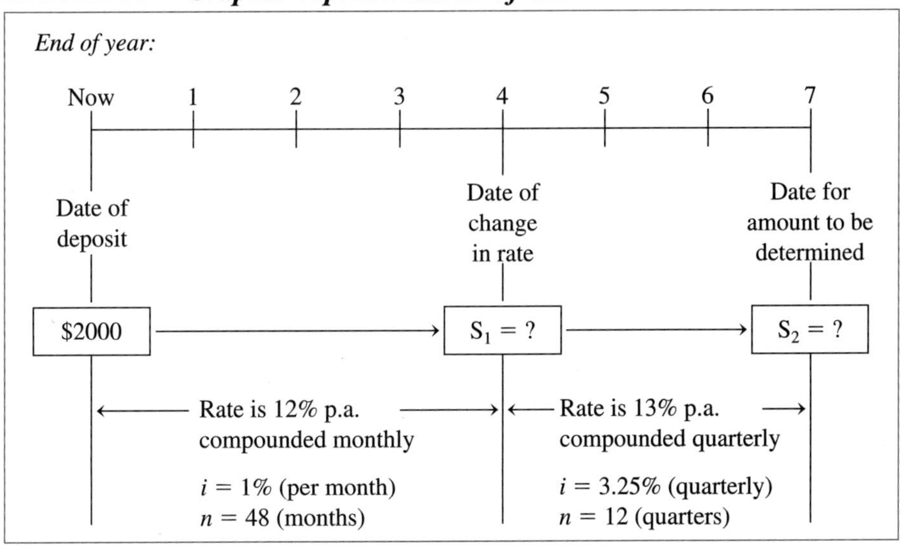

STEP 1 Determine the accumulated value of the original deposit at the time the interest rate changes, that is, after 4 years.

$$P = 2000.00;\ i = 1\% = 0.01;\ n = 48$$

$$S_1 = 2000.00(1 + 0.01)^{48} = 2000.00(1.6122261) = \$3224.45$$

STEP 2 Use the accumulated value after four years as new principal and calculate its accumulated value three years later using the new rate of interest.

$$P = 3224.45;\ i = 3.25\% = 0.0325;\ n = 12$$

$$S_2 = 3224.45(1 + 0.0325)^{12} = 3224.45(1.4678468) = \$4733.00$$

Solution by preprogrammed calculator

STEP 1	*Key in*	*Press*	*Display shows*	
	0	PMT	0	
	2000	PV	2000	
	1	%*i*	1	
	48	N	48	
		CPT	←(if no CPT, press 2nd)	
		FV	3224.4522	←answer to Step 1

STEP 2

	PV	3224.4522	← this step enters the new principal
3.25	%*i*	3.25	
12	N	12	
	CPT		
	FV	4733.00	← final answer

***Example* 9.2e** A debt of \$500 accumulates interest at 12% p.a. compounded quarterly from April 1, 1995, to July 1, 1996, and 9% p.a. compounded monthly thereafter. Determine the compound amount of the debt on December 1, 1997.

Solution

STEP 1 Determine the accumulated value of the debt on July 1, 1996.

$$P = 500.00;\ i = 3\% = 0.03;$$

the period April 1, 1995, to July 1, 1996, contains 15 months: $n = 5$

$$S_1 = 500.00(1.03)^5 = 500.00(1.1592741) = \$579.64$$

STEP 2 Use the result of Step 1 as new principal and find its accumulated value on December 1, 1997.

$$P = 579.64;\ i = 0.75\% = 0.0075;$$

the period July 1, 1996, to December 1, 1997, contains 17 months: $n = 17$

$$S_2 = 579.64(1.0075)^{17} = 579.64(1.1354446) = \$658.15$$

Programmed solution

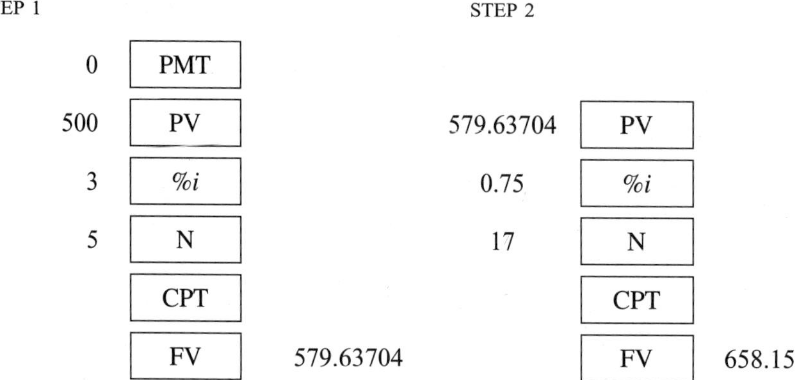

***Example* 9.2f** Jay opened a Registered Retirement Savings Plan account with his credit union on February 1, 1994, with a deposit of \$2000.00. He added \$1900.00 on February 1, 1995, and another \$1700.00 on February 1, 1998. What will his account amount to on August 1, 2004, if the plan earns a fixed rate of interest of 11% p.a. compounded semi-annually?

Solution

FIGURE 9.2 ***Graphic representation of data***

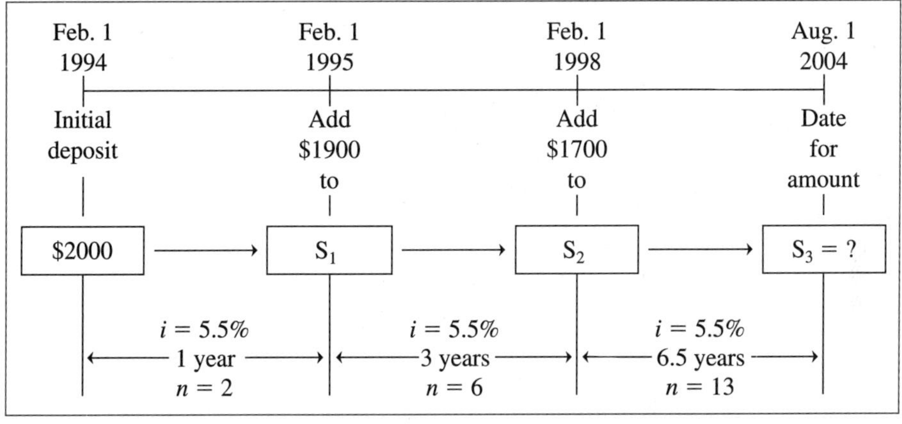

STEP 1 Determine the amount of the initial deposit on February 1, 1995.

$$P = 2000.00;\ i = 5.5\% = 0.055;$$
the period Feb. 1, 1994, to Feb. 1, 1995, contains 1 year: $n = 2$

$$S_1 = 2000.00(1.055)^2 = 2000.00(1.113025) = \$2226.05$$

STEP 2 Add the deposit of \$1900.00 to the amount of \$2226.05 to obtain the new principal as of February 1, 1995, and determine its amount on February 1, 1998.

$$P = 2226.05 + 1900.00 = 4126.05;\ i = 0.055;$$
the period Feb. 1, 1995, to Feb. 1, 1998, contains 3 years: $n = 6$

$$S_2 = 4126.05(1.055)^6 = 4126.05(1.3788428) = \$5689.17$$

STEP 3 Add the deposit of \$1700.00 to the amount of \$5689.17 to obtain the new principal as of February 1, 1998, and determine its amount on August 1, 2004.

$$P = 5689.17 + 1700.00 = 7389.17;\ i = 0.055;$$
the period Feb. 1, 1998, to Aug. 1, 2004, contains 6.5 years: $n = 13$

$$S_3 = 7389.17(1.055)^{13} = 7389.17(2.0057739) = \$14\ 821.00$$

Programmed solution

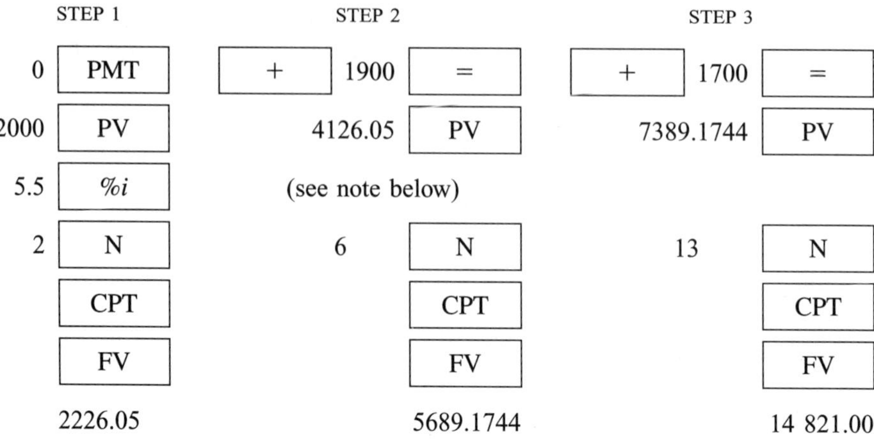

Note: There is no need to key in the rate in steps 2 and 3—it is already programmed from step 1.

Example 9.2g A demand loan of $10 000.00 is repaid by payments of $5000.00 in one year, $6000.00 in four years, and a final payment in six years. Interest on the loan is 16% p.a. compounded quarterly during the first year, 14% p.a. compounded semi-annually for the next three years, and 13.5% p.a. compounded annually for the remaining years. Determine the final payment.

Solution

FIGURE 9.3 ***Graphic representation of data***

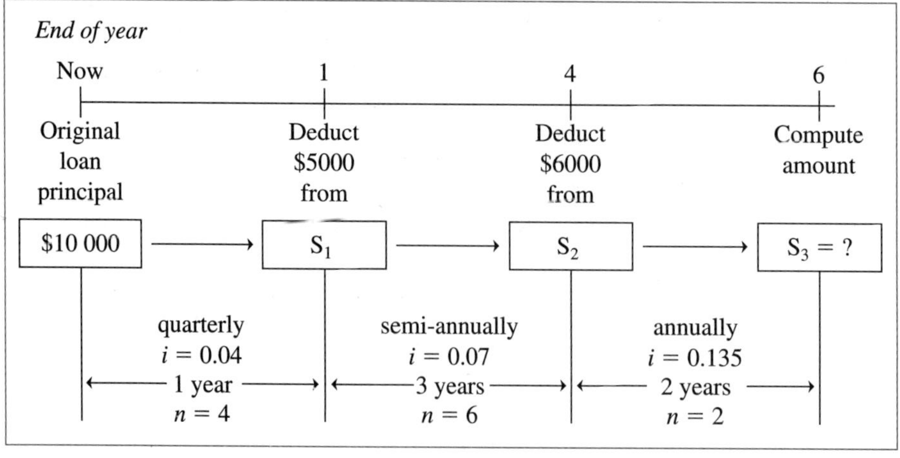

STEP 1 Determine the accumulated value of the debt at the time of the first payment.

$$P = 10\ 000.00;\ i = 4\% = 0.04;\ n = 4$$

$S_1 = 10\ 000.00(1.04)^4 = 10\ 000.00(1.1698586) = \$11\ 698.59$

STEP 2 Subtract the payment of $5000.00 from the accumulated value of $11 698.59 to obtain the debt balance. Now determine its accumulated value at the time of the second payment three years later.

$$P = 11\ 698.59 - 5000.00 = 6698.59;\ i = 7\% = 0.07;\ n = 6$$

$S_2 = 6698.59(1.07)^6 = 6698.59(1.5007304) = \$10\ 052.78$

STEP 3 Subtract the payment of $6000.00 from the accumulated value of $10 052.78 to obtain the debt balance. Now determine its accumulated value two years later.

$$P = 10\ 052.78 - 6000.00 = 4052.78;\ i = 13.5\% = 0.135;\ n = 2$$

$S_3 = 4052.78(1.135)^2 = 4052.78(1.288225) = \$5220.89$

The final payment after six years is $5220.89.

Programmed solution

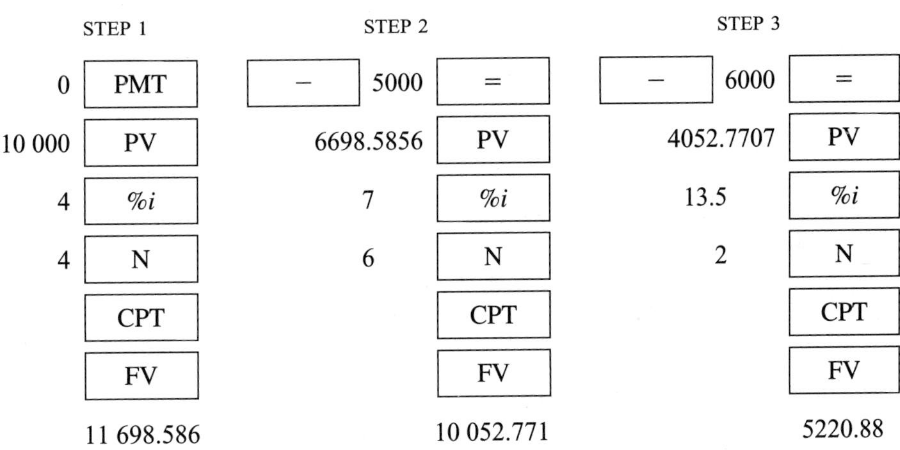

Exercise 9.2

A. Find the compound amount for each of the following.

	Principal	Nominal rate	Frequency of conversion	Time
1.	$ 400.00	7.5%	annually	8 years
2.	1000.00	12.5%	semi-annually	12 years
3.	1250.00	6.5%	quarterly	9 years
4.	500.00	12%	monthly	3 years
5.	1700.00	8%	quarterly	14.75 years
6.	840.00	15%	semi-annually	8.5 years
7.	2500.00	16%	monthly	12.25 years
8.	150.00	13.25%	quarterly	27 months
9.	480.00	15.75%	semi-annually	42 months
10.	1400.00	14.4%	monthly	18.75 years

B. Answer each of the following questions.

1. What is the maturity value of a five-year term deposit of $5000.00 at 12.5% compounded semi-annually? How much interest did the deposit earn?

2. How much will a registered retirement savings deposit of $1500.00 be worth in 15 years at 8% compounded quarterly? How much of the amount is interest?

3. You made a registered retirement savings plan deposit of $1000.00 on December 1, 1988, at a fixed rate of 11% compounded monthly. If you withdraw the deposit on August 1, 1995, how much will you receive?

4. Roy's parents made a trust deposit of $500.00 on October 31, 1978, to be withdrawn on Roy's eighteenth birthday on July 31, 1996. To what will the deposit amount on that date at 13% compounded quarterly?

5. What is the accumulated value of $100.00 invested for eight years at 15% p.a. compounded
(a) annually? **(b)** semi-annually? **(c)** quarterly? **(d)** monthly?

6. To what will a principal of $500.00 amount in five years at 13% p.a. compounded
(a) annually? **(b)** semi-annually? **(c)** quarterly? **(d)** monthly?

7. What is the accumulated value of and the amount of compound interest for $100.00 invested at 14% compounded quarterly for
(a) five years? **(b)** 10 years? **(c)** 20 years?

8. Find the compound amount of and the compound interest on $500.00 invested at 12% compounded monthly for
(a) 3.5 years; **(b)** 6 years; **(c)** 11.5 years.

9. The Canadian consumer price index was approximately 120 at the beginning of 1990. If inflation continues at an average annual rate of 3%, what will the index be at the beginning of 2000?

10. Peel Credit Union expects an average annual growth rate of 20% for the next five years. If the assets of the credit union currently amount to $2.50 million, what will the forecasted assets be in five years?

11. A local bank offers $5000.00 five-year certificates at 13.75% compounded semi-annually. Your credit union makes the same type of deposit available at 13.5% compounded monthly.

(a) Which investment gives more interest over the five years?

(b) What is the difference in the amount of interest?

12. The Continental Bank advertises capital savings at 12.25% compounded semi-annually while National Trust offers premium savings at 12% compounded monthly. If you have $1000.00 to invest for two years,

(a) which deposit will earn more interest?

(b) what is the difference in the amount of interest?

C. Answer each of the following questions.

1. A deposit of $2000.00 earns interest at 14% p.a. compounded quarterly. After two and a half years, the interest rate is changed to 13.5% compounded monthly. How much is the account worth after six years?

2. An investment of $2500.00 earns interest at 9% p.a. compounded monthly for three years. At that time the interest rate is changed to 9% compounded quarterly. How much will the accumulated value be one and a half years after the change?

3. A debt of $800.00 accumulates interest at 13% compounded semi-annually from February 1, 1996, to August 1, 1998, and 14% compounded quarterly thereafter. Determine the amount of the debt on November 1, 2001.

4. Accumulate $1300.00 at 13.5% p.a. compounded monthly from March 1, 1995, to July 1, 1997, and thereafter at 13% p.a. compounded quarterly. What is the amount on April 1, 2000?

5. Pat opened an RRSP deposit account on December 1, 1994, with a deposit of $1000.00. He added $1000.00 on July 1, 1995, and $1000.00 on November 1, 1996. How much is in his account on January 1, 1998, if the deposit earns 12% p.a. compounded monthly?

6. Terri started an RRSP on March 1, 1992, with a deposit of $2000.00. She added $1800.00 on December 1, 1994, and $1700.00 on September 1, 1996. What is the accumulated value of her account on December 1, 1999, if interest is 11.5% compounded quarterly?

7. A debt of \$4000.00 is repaid by payments of \$1500.00 in nine months, \$2000.00 in 18 months, and a final payment in 27 months. If interest was 10% compounded quarterly, what was the amount of the final payment?

8. Sheridan Service has a line of credit loan with the Bank of Nova Scotia. The initial loan balance was \$6000.00. Payments of \$2000.00 and \$3000.00 were made after four months and nine months respectively. At the end of one year, Sheridan Service borrowed an additional \$4000.00. Six months later, the line of credit loan was converted into a collateral mortgage loan. What was the amount of the mortgage if interest was 18% compounded monthly?

9. A demand loan of \$3000.00 is repaid by payments of \$1500.00 after two years, \$1500.00 after four years, and a final payment after seven years. Interest is 14% compounded quarterly for the first year, 15% compounded semi-annually for the next three years, and 15% compounded monthly thereafter. What is the size of the final payment?

10. A variable rate demand loan showed an initial balance of \$12 000.00, payments of \$5000.00 after eighteen months, \$4000.00 after thirty months, and a final payment after five years. Interest was 13% compounded semi-annually for the first two years and 15% compounded monthly for the remaining time. How much was the size of the final payment?

9.3 *Present value and compound discount*

A. *The present value concept and related terms*

***Example* 9.3a** Find the principal that will amount in six years to \$17 715.61 at 10% p.a. compounded annually.

Solution

The problem may be graphically represented as shown in Figure 9.4.

FIGURE 9.4 ***Graphic representation of data***

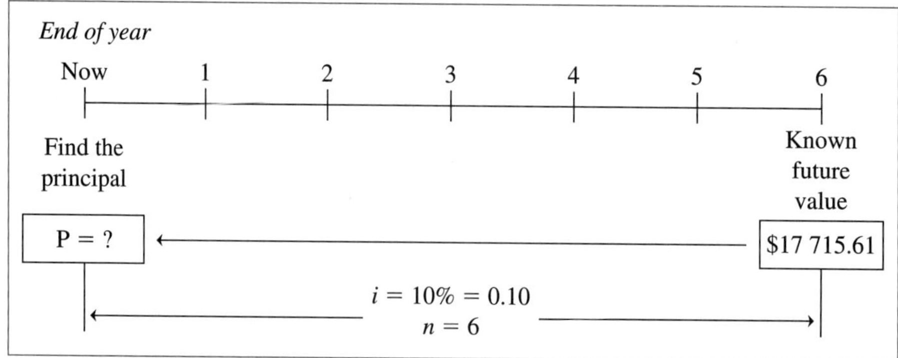

This problem is the inverse of the problem used to illustrate the meaning of compound interest. Instead of knowing the value of the principal and finding its future value, we know that the future value is \$17 715.61. What we want to determine is the value of the principal.

To solve the problem, we use the amount formula $S = P(1 + i)^n$ and substitute the known values.

$$S = 17\,715.61;\ i = 10\% = 0.10;\ n = 6$$

$$17\,715.61 = P(1.10)^6 \longleftarrow \text{by substituting in } S = P(1 + i)^n$$

$$17\,715.61 = P(1.771561) \longleftarrow \text{computing } (1.10)^6$$

$$P = \frac{17\,715.61}{1.771561} \longleftarrow \text{solve for P by dividing both sides by 1.771561}$$

$$P = \$10\,000.00$$

The principal that will grow to \$17 715.61 in six years at 10% p.a. compounded annually is \$10 000.00.

This principal is called the **present value** or **discounted value** or **proceeds** of the known future amount.

The difference between the known future amount of \$17 715.61 and the computed present value (principal) of \$10 000.00 is the **compound discount** and represents the compound interest accumulating on the computed present value.

The process of computing the present value or discounted value or proceeds is called **discounting.**

B. The present value formula

The present value of an amount at a given time at compound interest is defined as the principal that will grow to the given amount if compounded at a given periodic rate of interest over a given number of conversion periods.

Since the problem of finding the present value is equivalent to finding the principal when the amount, the periodic rate of interest, and the number of conversion periods are given, the compound amount formula $S = P(1 + i)^n$ applies.

However, because the problem of finding the present value of an amount is frequently encountered in financial analysis, it is useful to solve the compound amount formula for P to obtain the present value formula.

$$S = P(1 + i)^n \longleftarrow \text{start with the compound amount formula, Formula 9.1}$$

$$\frac{S}{(1 + i)^n} = \frac{P(1 + i)^n}{(1 + i)^n} \longleftarrow \text{divide both sides by the compounding factor } (1 + i)^n$$

$$\frac{S}{(1 + i)^n} = P \longleftarrow \text{reduce the fraction } \frac{(1 + i)^n}{(1 + i)^n} \text{ to 1}$$

$$P = \frac{S}{(1+i)^n}$$ ⟵ present value formula for compound interest ⟵ *Formula* **9.2A**

Example **9.3b** Find the present value of $11 593.11 due in nine years at 12% p.a. compounded quarterly.

Solution

$$S = 11\ 593.11;\ i = 3\% = 0.03;\ n = 36$$

$$P = \frac{S}{(1+i)^n}$$ ⟵ using the present value formula

$$= \frac{11\ 593.11}{(1+0.03)^{36}}$$ ⟵ by substitution

$$= \frac{11\ 593.11}{2.8982783}$$

$$= \$4000.00$$

Note: The division of 11 593.11 by 2.8982783, like any division, may be changed to a multiplication by using the reciprocal of the divisor.

$$\frac{11\ 593.11}{2.8982783}$$ ⟵ the division to be changed into a multiplication

$$= 11\ 593.11\left(\frac{1}{2.8982783}\right)$$ ⟵ the reciprocal of the divisor 2.8982783 is found by dividing 1 by 2.8982783

$$= 11\ 593.11(0.3450324)$$ ⟵ computed value of the reciprocal

$$= \$4000.00$$

For calculators equipped with the reciprocal function key $\boxed{\frac{1}{x}}$, converting the division into a multiplication is easily accomplished by first computing the compounding factor and then using the $\boxed{\frac{1}{x}}$ key to obtain the reciprocal.

Example **9.3c** What principal will amount to $5000.00 seven years from today if interest is 9% p.a. compounded monthly?

Solution

Finding the principal that amounts to a future sum of money is equivalent to finding the present value.

$$S = 5000.00;\ i = 0.75\% = 0.0075;\ n = 84$$

$$P = \frac{5000.00}{(1.0075)^{84}} \longleftarrow \text{using Formula 9.2A}$$

$$= \frac{5000.00}{1.8732019} \longleftarrow \text{computing the factor } (1.0075)^{84}$$

$$= 5000.00(0.5338453) \longleftarrow \text{using the reciprocal function key}$$

$$= \$2669.23$$

Using the reciprocal of the divisor to change division into multiplication is reflected in the practice of stating the present value formula with a *negative* exponent.

$$\frac{1}{a^n} = a^{-n} \longleftarrow \text{negative exponent rule}$$

$$\frac{1}{(1 + i)^n} = (1 + i)^{-n}$$

$$\frac{S}{(1 + i)^n} = S(1 + i)^{-n}$$

Formula 9.2A, the present value formula, can be restated in multiplication form using a negative exponent.

$$\boxed{P = S(1 + i)^{-n}} \longleftarrow \textbf{\textit{Formula} 9.2B}$$

The factor $(1 + i)^{-n}$ is called the **discount factor** and is the reciprocal of the compounding factor $(1 + i)^n$.

C. *Using preprogrammed financial calculators to find present value*

As explained in Section 9.2B, preprogrammed calculators provide quick solutions to compound interest calculations. Three of the four variables are entered and the value of the fourth variable is retrieved.

To solve Example 9.3c, in which S = 5000, i = 0.75%, n = 84, and P is to be determined, use the following procedure.

	Press	*Display shows*	
0	PMT	0	⟵ this step ensures that the calculator performs a compound interest calculation
5000	FV	5000	⟵ this enters the future value amount S
0.75	%i	0.75	⟵ this enters the conversion rate i
84	N	84	⟵ this enters the number of compounding periods n

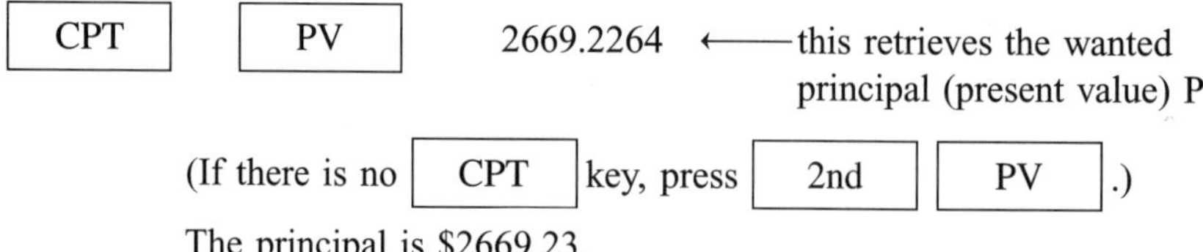

(If there is no CPT key, press 2nd PV .)

The principal is $2669.23.

Exercise 9.3

A. Find the present value of each of the following amounts.

	Amount	*Nominal rate*	*Frequency of conversion*	*Time*
1.	$1000.00	8%	quarterly	7 years
2.	1500.00	13.5%	semi-annually	10 years
3.	600.00	15%	monthly	6 years
4.	350.00	7.5%	annually	8 years
5.	1200.00	9%	monthly	12 years
6.	3000.00	12.25%	semi-annually	5 years, 6 months
7.	900.00	6.4%	quarterly	9 years, 3 months
8.	500.00	15.6%	monthly	15 years

B. Answer each of the following questions.

1. Find the present value and the compound discount of $1600.00 due four and a half years from now if money is worth 18.5% compounded semi-annually.

2. Find the present value and the compound discount of $2500.00 due in six years, three months, if interest is 6% compounded quarterly.

3. Find the principal that will amount to $1250.00 in four years at 10% p.a. compounded quarterly.

4. What sum of money will grow to $2000.00 in seven years at 15% compounded monthly?

5. A debt of $5000.00 is due November 1, 2000. What is the value of the obligation on February 1, 1994, if money is worth 7% compounded quarterly?

6. How much would you have to deposit in an account today to have $3000.00 in a five-year term deposit at maturity if interest is 12.75% compounded annually?

9.4 *Discounting promissory notes at compound interest*

A. *Discounting long-term promissory notes*

Long-term promissory notes (written for a term longer than one year) are usually subject to compound interest. As with short-term promissory notes, long-term promissory notes are negotiable and can be bought and sold (*discounted*) at any time before maturity.

The principles involved in discounting long-term promissory notes are similar to those used in discounting short-term promissory notes by the simple discount method except that no requirement exists to add three days of grace in determining the legal due date of a long-term promissory note.

The discounted value or proceeds of a long-term promissory note is the present value at the date of discount of the maturity value of the note. It is found using the present value formulae $P = \frac{S}{(1+i)^n}$ or $P = S(1+i)^{-n}$.

For non-interest-bearing notes, the maturity value is the face value. However, for interest-bearing promissory notes, the maturity value must be determined first by using the amount formula $S = P(1+i)^n$.

B. Discounting non-interest-bearing promissory notes

Since the face value of a non-interest-bearing note is also its maturity value, the proceeds of a non-interest-bearing note are the present value of its face value at the date of discount.

Example **9.4a** Determine the proceeds of a non-interest-bearing note for $1500.00 discounted two and a quarter years before its due date at 15% p.a. compounded monthly.

Solution

The maturity value S = 1500.00;

the rate of discount $i = \left(\frac{15}{12}\right)\% = 1.25\% = 0.0125$;

the number of conversion periods $n = (2.25)(12) = 27$.

$P = S(1+i)^{-n}$ ← using Formula 9.2B

$= 1500.00(1 + 0.0125)^{-27}$

$= 1500.00\left(\frac{1}{1.3985109}\right)$

$= 1500.00(0.7150463)$

$= \$1072.57$

Programmed solution

0	PMT		
1500	FV		
1.25	%*i*		
27	N		
	CPT	PV	1072.57

C. *Discounting interest-bearing promissory notes*

The proceeds of an interest-bearing note is the present value at the date of discount of the value of the note at maturity. Therefore, the maturity value of an interest-bearing promissory note must be determined before finding the discounted value.

Example **9.4b** Determine the proceeds of a promissory note for \$3600.00 with interest at 12% p.a. compounded quarterly, issued September 1, 1994, due on June 1, 2000, and discounted on December 1, 1996, at 15% p.a. compounded semi-annually.

Solution

STEP 1 Find the maturity value of the note using Formula 9.1, $S = P(1 + i)^n$.

$P = 3600.00$; the interest rate $i = 3\% = 0.03$; the interest period, September 1, 1994, to June 1, 2000, contains 5 years and 9 months:

$$n = \left(5\frac{9}{12}\right)(4) = 23.$$

$$S = 3600.00(1 + 0.03)^{23}$$
$$= 3600.00(1.9735865)$$
$$= \$7104.91$$

STEP 2 Find the present value at the date of discount of the maturity value found in Step 1 using $P = S(1 + i)^{-n}$.

$S = 7104.91$; the rate of discount, $i = 7.5\% = 0.075$;
the discount period, December 1, 1996, to June 1, 2000, contains 3 years and 6 months: $n = \left(3\frac{6}{12}\right)(2) = 7.$

$$P = 7104.91(1 + 0.075)^{-7}$$
$$= 7104.91(0.6027549)$$
$$= \$4282.52$$

The proceeds of the note on December 1, 1996, are \$4282.52. The method and the data are represented graphically in Figure 9.5.

$$X = \frac{P(1+i_1)^{N_1}}{(1+i_2)^{N_2}}$$

$$X = P(1+i)^{N}(1+i_2)^{-N_2}$$

FIGURE 9.5 ***Graphic representation of method and data***

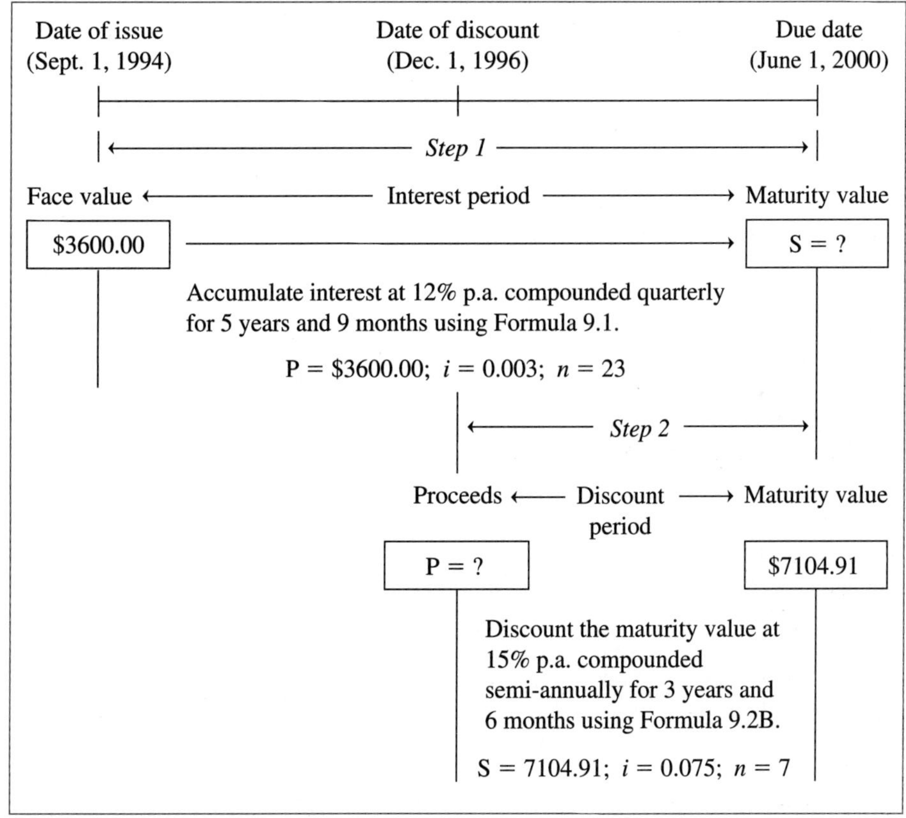

Programmed solution

STEP 1

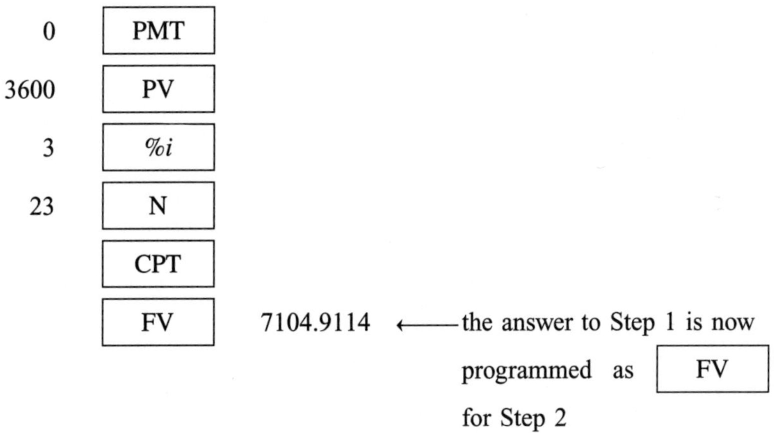

STEP 2

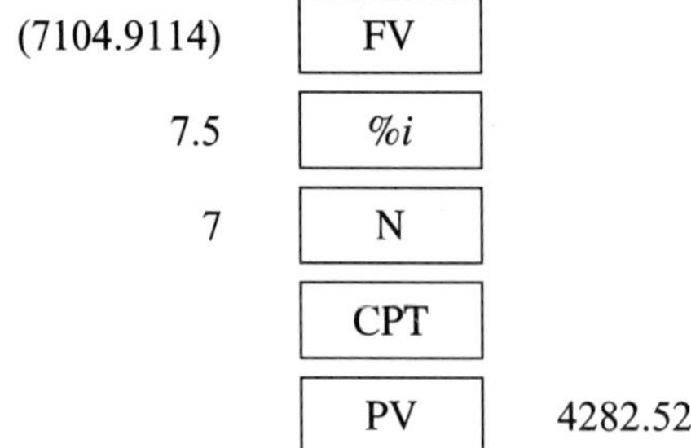

Exercise 9.4

A. Find the proceeds and the compound discount for each of the following long-term promissory notes.

	Face value	*Date issue*	*Term*	*Int. rate*	*Frequency of conversion*	*Date of discount*	*Disct rate*	*Frequency of conversion*
1.	$2000	1992-06-30	5 years	—	—	1994-12-31	12%	semi-annual
2.	700	1990-04-01	10 years	—	—	1995-07-01	15%	quarterly
3.	1500	1991-05-31	8 years	13.5%	annually	1996-05-31	16%	semi-annual
4.	4000	1993-09-30	4 years	11%	semi-annual	1995-03-31	15%	quarterly
5.	800	1992-02-01	7 yrs, 9 mo	14%	quarterly	1997-11-01	12%	monthly
6.	2200	1990-10-31	8.25 years	12%	monthly	1993-01-31	10%	quarterly

B. Find the proceeds of each of the following promissory notes.

1. a non-interest-bearing promissory note for $6000.00 discounted 54 months before its due date at 11% compounded quarterly
2. a $4200.00, non-interest-bearing note due August 1, 1999, discounted on March 1, 1995, at 7.5% compounded monthly
3. a promissory note with a maturity value of $1800.00 due on September 30, 1999, discounted at 15% compounded semi-annually on March 31, 1996
4. a fifteen-year promissory note discounted after six years at 9% compounded quarterly with a maturity value of $7500.00
5. a five-year promissory note for $3000.00 with interest at 12% compounded semi-annually, discounted 21 months before maturity at 14% compounded quarterly
6. a $5000.00, seven-year note bearing interest at 8.0% compounded quarterly, discounted two and a half years after the date of issue at 6.0% compounded monthly

7. a six-year, \$900.00 note bearing interest at 10% compounded quarterly, issued June 1, 1990, discounted on December 1, 1995, to yield 12.5% compounded semi-annually

8. a ten-year promissory note dated April 1, 1992, with a face value of \$1300.00 bearing interest at 7% compounded semi-annually, discounted seven years later when money was worth 9% compounded quarterly

9.5 *Equivalent values*

A. Equations of value

As discussed in Chapter 7, sums of money have different values at different times. Because of their time value, sums of money coming due at different times are not directly comparable. To make such sums of money comparable, a specific time, the **comparison date** or **focal date**, must be chosen. Allowance must be made for interest from the due dates of the sums of money to the selected focal date; that is, the dated values of the sums of money must be determined.

When compounding, any time may be chosen as the focal date. The selection of the focal date does not affect the answers; it only determines which formula has to be used. For compound interest, equations of value can be set up using the amount formula $S = P(1 + i)^n$ or the present value formula $P = S(1 + i)^{-n}$.

As with simple interest, the appropriate formula depends on the position of the due dates relative to the focal date:

(a) If the due date falls *before* the focal date, use the *amount* formula (see Figure 9.6).

(b) If the due date falls *after* the focal date, use the *present value* formula (see Figure 9.7).

B. Finding the equivalent single payment

Example 9.5a \$4000.00 is payable three years from now. If money is worth 14% p.a. compounded semi-annually, determine the equivalent value

(i) seven years from now; (ii) now.

Solution

(i) Using "seven years from now" as the focal date, the method and the data can be represented graphically as shown in Figure 9.6.

FIGURE 9.6 ***Graphic representation of method and data***

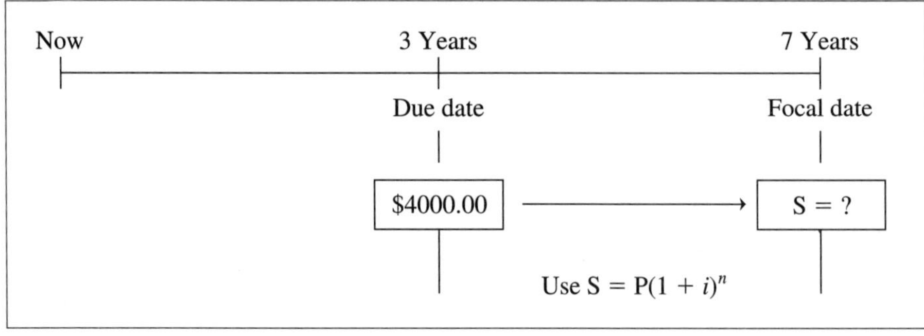

Since the due date falls *before* the focal date, use the amount formula.

$$P = 4000.00;\ i = \frac{14\%}{2} = 0.07;\ n = 4(2) = 8$$

$$S = 4000.00(1 + 0.07)^8 = 4000.00(1.7181862) = \$6872.74$$

The equivalent value of the $4000.00 seven years from now is $6872.74.

(ii) Using "now" as the focal date, the method and the data can be represented graphically as shown in Figure 9.7.

FIGURE 9.7 ***Graphic representation of method and data***

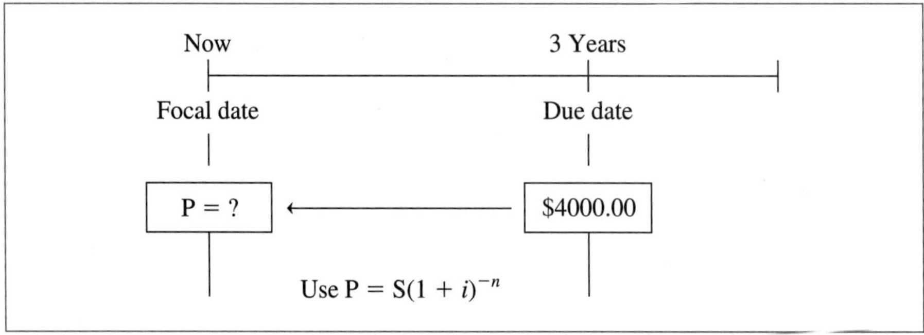

Since the due date falls *after* the focal date, use the present value formula.

$$S = 4000.00;\ i = \frac{14\%}{2} = 0.07;\ n = 3(2) = 6$$

$$P = 4000.00(1 + 0.07)^{-6} = 4000.00(0.6663422) = \$2665.37$$

The equivalents value of the $4000.00 now is $2665.37.

Programmed solution

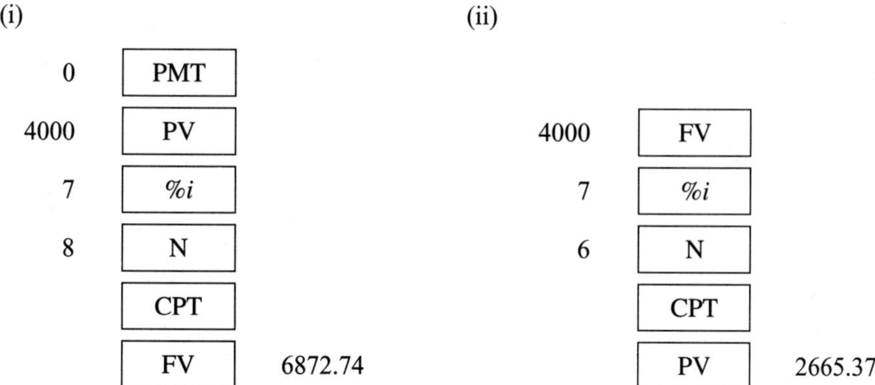

Example **9.5b** Joanna plans to pay off a debt by payments of \$1600.00 one year from now, \$1800.00 eighteen months from now, and \$2000.00 thirty months from now. Determine the single payment now that would settle the debt if money is worth 8% p.a. compounded quarterly.

Solution

While any date may be selected as the focal date, a logical choice for the focal date is the time designated 'now' since the single payment 'now' is wanted. As is shown in Figure 9.8, the due dates of the three payments are *after* the focal date. Therefore, the present value formula $P = S(1 + i)^{-n}$ is appropriate for finding the equivalent values of the three payments.

FIGURE 9.8 ***Graphic representation of method and data***

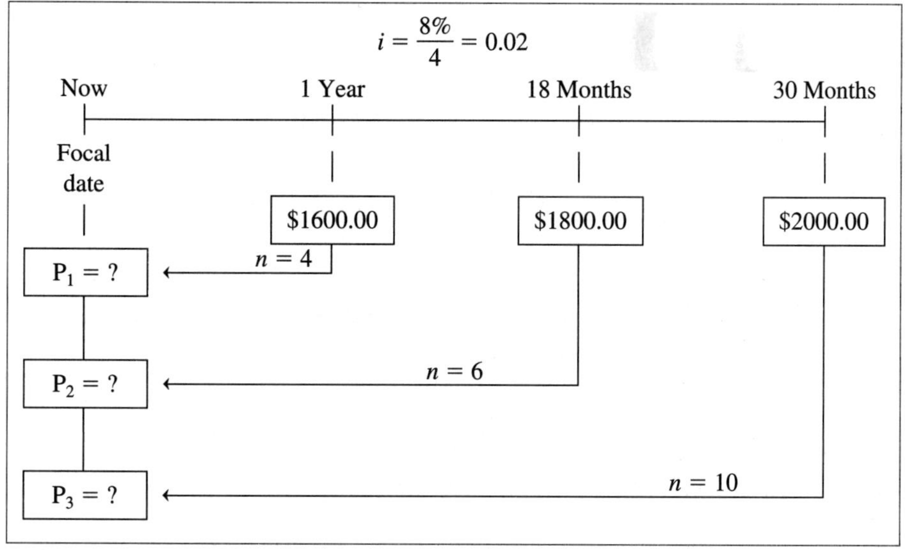

The equivalents of the three payments at the selected focal date are

$P_1 = 1600.00(1 + 0.02)^{-4} = 1600.00(0.9238454) = \$1478.15$
$P_2 = 1800.00(1 + 0.02)^{-6} = 1800.00(0.8879714) = \$1598.35$
$P_3 = 2000.00(1 + 0.02)^{-10} = 2000.00(0.8203483) = \$1640.70$

The equivalent single payment to settle the debt now is $4717.20.

Programmed solution

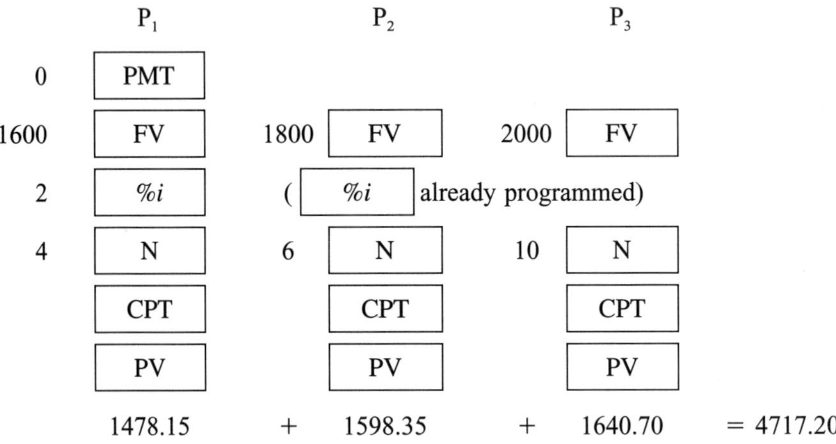

Example **9.5c** Debt payments of $400.00 due five months ago, $600.00 due today, and $800 due in nine months are to be combined into one payment due three months from today at 15% p.a. compounded monthly.

Solution

The logical choice for the focal date is '3 months from now,' the date when the equivalent single payment is to be made.

As shown in Figure 9.9, the first two payments are due *before* the focal date; the amount formula $S = P(1 + i)^n$ should be used. However, the third payment is due *after* the focal date which means that, for it, the present value formula $P = S(1 + i)^{-n}$ applies.

The equivalent values (designated E_1, E_2, E_3) of the debt payments at the selected focal date are

$E_1 = 400.00(1 + 0.0125)^8 = 400.00(1.1044861) = \$\ 441.79$
$E_2 = 600.00(1 + 0.0125)^3 = 600.00(1.0379707) = \$\ 622.78$
$E_3 = 800.00(1 + 0.0125)^{-6} = 800.00(0.9281749) = \$\ 742.54$

The equivalent single payment to settle the debt three months from now is $1807.11

FIGURE 9.9 ***Graphic representation of method and data***

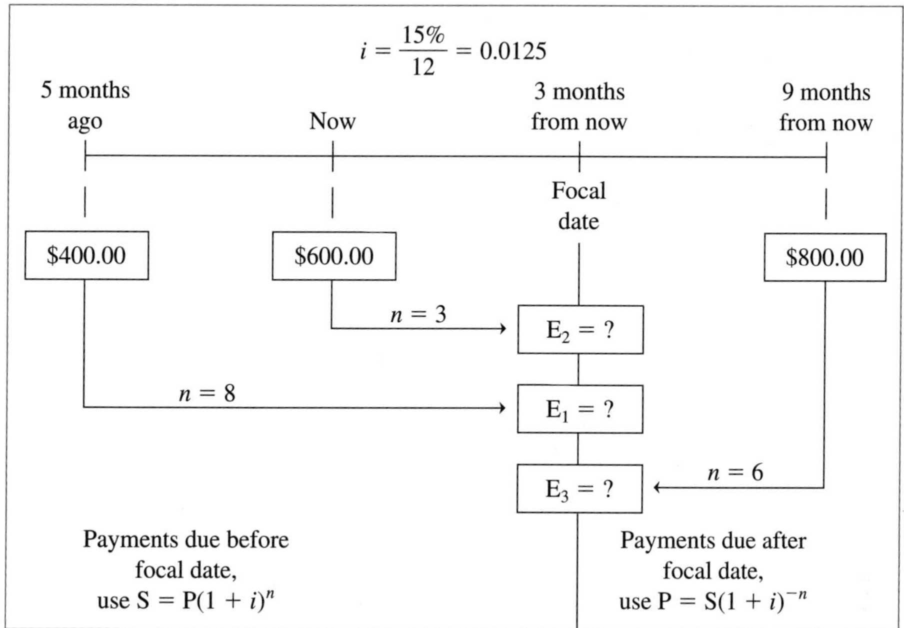

Programmed solution

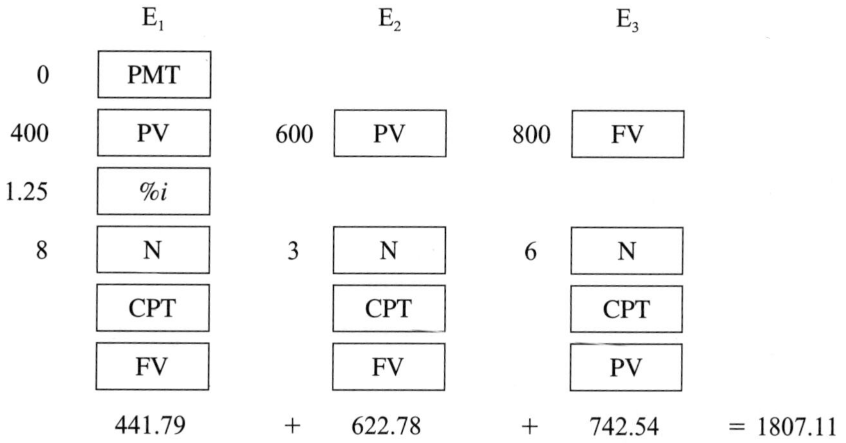

Example **9.5d** Payments of \$500.00 are due at the end of each of the next five years. Determine the equivalent single payment five years from now (just after the last payment is due) if money is worth 13% p.a. compounded annually.

Solution

Select as the focal date 'five years from now.'

Let the equivalent single payment be represented by E and the dated values of the first four payments be represented by E_1, E_2, E_3, E_4 as indicated in Figure 9.10. Then the following equation of values can be set up.

$$\begin{aligned} E &= 500.00 + E_4 + E_3 + E_2 + E_1 \\ &= 500.00 + 500.00(1.13) + 500.00(1.13)^2 + 500.00(1.13)^3 + 500.00(1.13)^4 \\ &= 500.00[1 + (1.13) + (1.13)^2 + (1.13)^3 + (1.13)^4] \\ &= 500.00(1 + 1.13 + 1.2769 + 1.442897 + 1.6304736) \\ &= 500.00(6.4802706) \\ &= 3240.14 \end{aligned}$$

The equivalent single payment after five years is $3240.14.

FIGURE 9.10 ***Graphic representation of method and data***

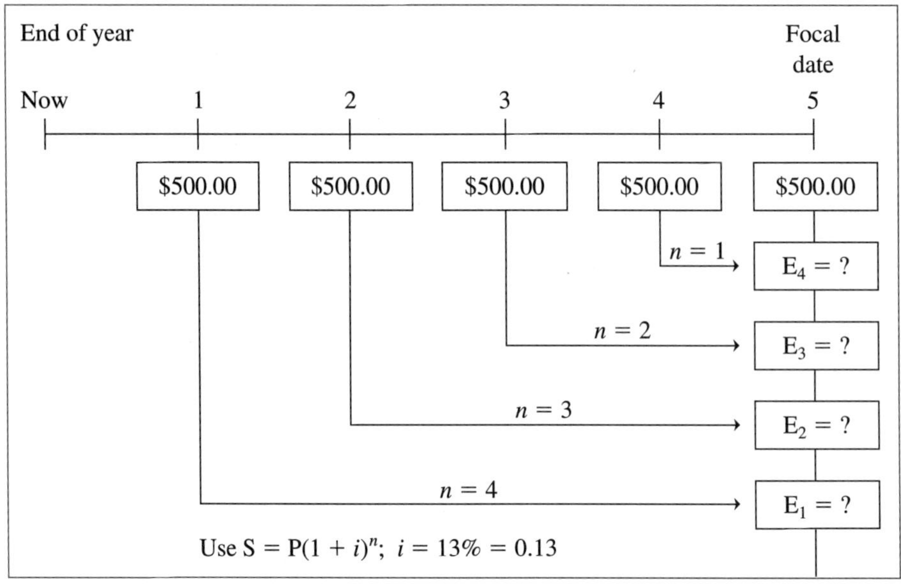

Example **9.5e** Payments of $200.00 are due at the end of each of the next five quarters. Determine the equivalent single payment that will settle the debt now if interest is 15% p.a. compounded quarterly.

Solution

Select as the focal date 'now.'

Let the equivalent single payment be represented by E and the dated values of the five payments by E_1, E_2, E_3, E_4, E_5 respectively as shown in Figure 9.11. Then the following equation of values can be set up.

$$\begin{aligned}
E &= E_1 + E_2 + E_3 + E_4 + E_5 \\
&= 200.00(1.0375)^{-1} + 200.00(1.0375)^{-2} + 200.00(1.0375)^{-3} + 200.00(1.0375)^{-4} \\
&\quad + 200.00(1.0375)^{-5} \\
&= 200.00[(1.0375)^{-1} + (1.0375)^{-2} + (1.0375)^{-3} + (1.0375)^{-4} + (1.0375)^{-5}] \\
&= 200.00(0.9638554 + 0.9290173 + 0.8954383 + 0.8630731 + 0.8318777) \\
&= 200.00(4.4832618) \\
&= 896.65
\end{aligned}$$

The equivalent single payment now is $896.65.

FIGURE 9.11 ***Graphic representation of method and data***

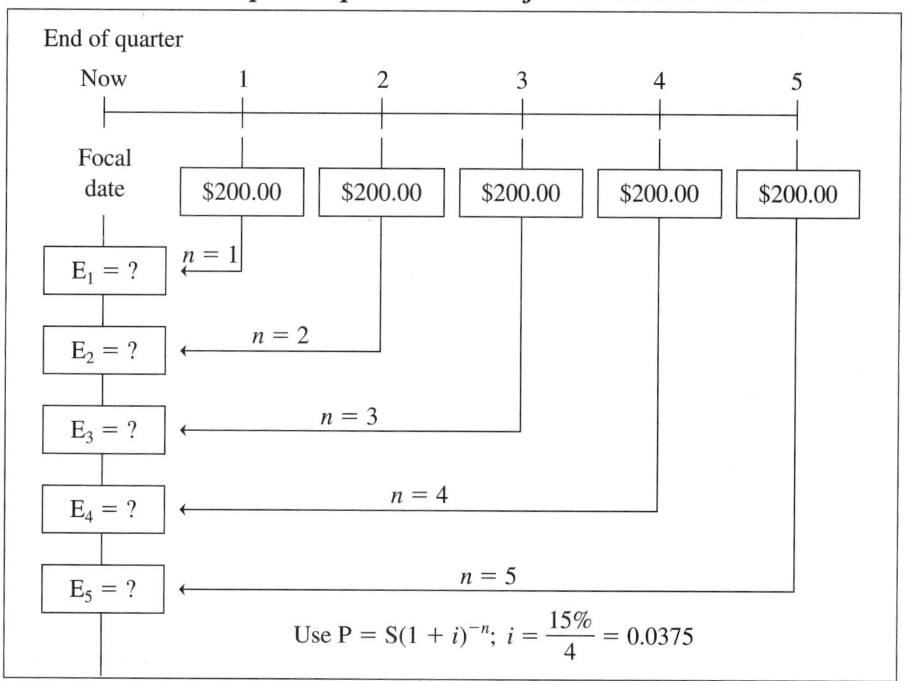

C. Finding the value of two or more equivalent payments

When two or more equivalent payments are needed, an equation of values matching the dated values of the original debt payments against the dated values of the proposed replacement payments on a selected focal date should be set up. This procedure is similar to the one used for simple interest in Chapter 7.

Example **9.5f** Debt payments of \$1000.00 due today and \$2000.00 due one year from now are to be settled by a payment of \$1500.00 three months from now and a final payment eighteen months from now. Determine the size of the final payment if interest is 10% p.a. compounded quarterly.

Solution

Let the size of the final payment be \$$x$. The logical focal date is the date of the final payment.

FIGURE 9.12 ***Graphic representation of method and data***

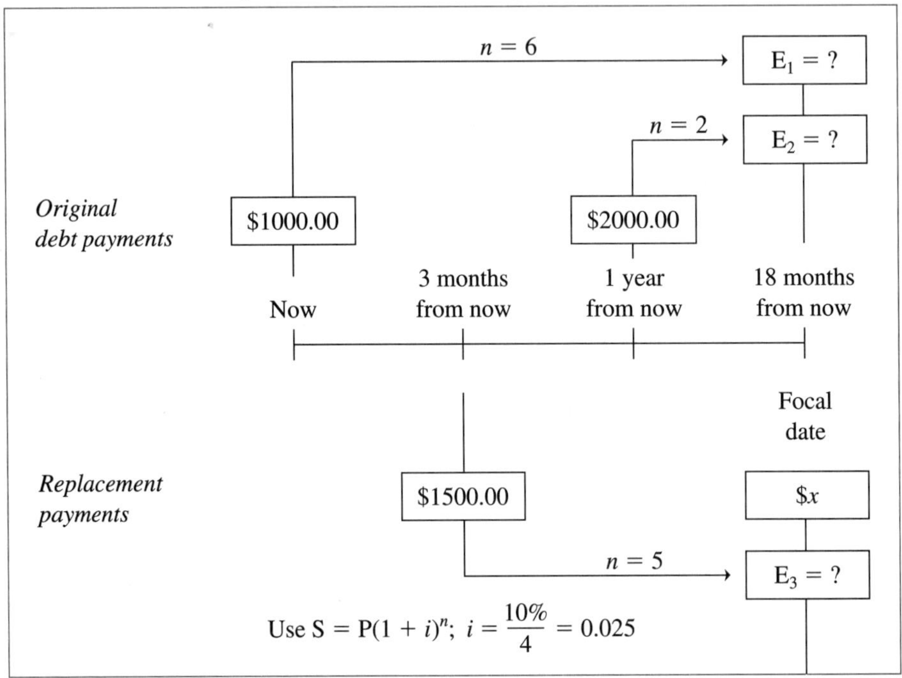

As shown in Figure 9.12, the two original debt payments and the first replacement payment are due before the selected focal date. The amount formula $S = P(1 + i)^n$ applies. Because the final payment is dated on the focal date, its dated value is \$$x$.

The equivalent values of the original debt payments at the selected focal date, designated E_1 and E_2, are matched against the equivalent values of the replacement payments, designated E_3 and x, giving rise to the equation of values.

$$E_1 + E_2 = x + E_3$$

$$1000.00(1.025)^6 + 2000.00(1.025)^2 = x + 1500.00(1.025)^5$$

$$1000.00(1.1596934) + 2000.00(1.050625) = x + 1500.00(1.1314082)$$

$$1159.69 + 2101.25 = x + 1697.11$$

$$x = 1563.83$$

The final payment is $1563.83.

Programmed solution

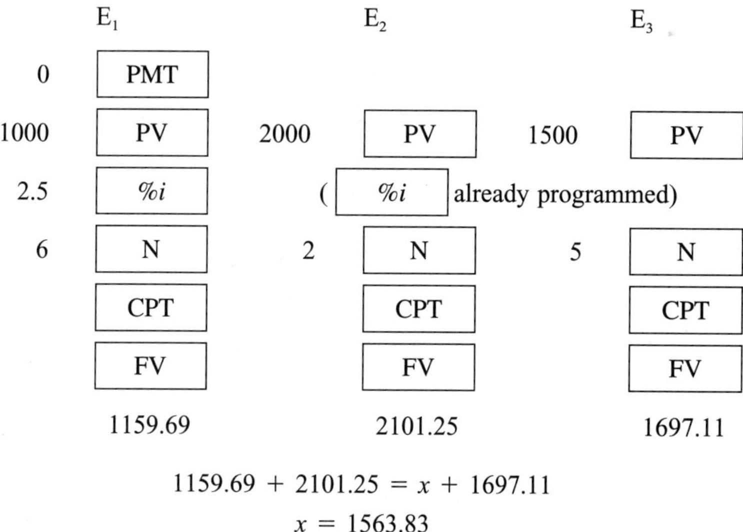

$$1159.69 + 2101.25 = x + 1697.11$$

$$x = 1563.83$$

Example **9.5g** Debt payments of $750.00 due seven months ago, $600.00 due two months ago, and $900.00 due in five months are to be settled by two equal payments due now and three months from now respectively. Determine the size of the equal payments at 15% p.a. compounded monthly.

Solution

Let the size of the equal payments be represented by $$x$ and choose 'now' as the focal date.

$$i = \frac{15\%}{12} = 0.0125.$$

First, consider the dated values of the original debt payments at the chosen focal date.

The due dates of the debt payments of \$750.00 and \$600.00 are seven months and two months respectively before the focal date. Their dated values at the focal date are $750.00(1.0125)^7$ and $600.00(1.0125)^2$ respectively.

The due date of the \$900.00 payment is five months after the focal date. Its dated value is $900.00(1.0125)^{-5}$.

Second, consider the dated values of the replacement payments at the selected focal date.

The first replacement payment due at the focal date is $\$x$. The second replacement payment is due three months after the focal date. Its dated value is $x(1.0125)^{-3}$.

Now equate the dated values of the replacement payments with the dated values of the original debt payments to set up the equation of values.

$$x + x(1.0125)^{-3} = 750.00(1.0125)^7 + 600.00(1.0125)^2 + 900.00(1.0125)^{-5}$$

$$x + 0.9634183x = 750.00(1.0908505) + 600.00(1.0251563) + 900.00(0.9397771)$$

$$1.9634183x = 818.14 + 615.09 + 845.80$$

$$1.9634183x = 2279.03$$

$$x = \frac{2279.03}{1.9634183}$$

$$x = 1160.75$$

The size of the two equal payments is \$1160.75.

Programmed solution

$x + x(1.0125)^{-3}$		= $750(1.0125)^7$		+ $600(1.0125)^2$		+ $900(1.0125)^{-5}$	
	⇓		⇓		⇓		⇓
0	PMT						
1	FV	750	PV	600	PV	900	FV
1.25	%i		(	%i	already programmed)		
3	N	7	N	2	N	5	N
	CPT		CPT		CPT		CPT
	PV		FV		FV		PV
	0.9634183						
	⇓		⇓		⇓		⇓
$x + 0.9634183x =$			818.14	+	615.09	+	845.80

$$1.9634183x = 2279.03$$
$$x = 1160.75$$

Note: In $x(1.025)^{-3}$, | FV | is not known. To obtain the factor $(1.025)^{-3}$, use | FV | = 1.

***Example* 9.5h** Two debts, one of \$4000 due in three months with interest at 17% compounded quarterly and the other of \$3000 due in eighteen months with interest at 16.5% compounded semi-annually, are to be discharged by making two equal payments. What is the size of the equal payments if the first is due one year from now, the second two years from now, and money is worth 18% compounded monthly?

Solution

Let the size of the equal payments be represented by \$$x$ and choose 'one year from now' as the focal date.

Since the two debts are interest bearing, first determine the maturity value of the two debts.

The maturity value of \$4000 due in three months at 17% compounded quarterly $= 4000(1.0425)^1 = \$4170.00$

The maturity value of \$3000 due in eighteen months at 16.5% compounded semi-annually $= 3000(1.0825)^3$
$= 3000(1.2684803) = \$3805.44$

Now determine the dated values of the two maturity values at the selected focal date subject to 18% compounded monthly.

The first debt matures nine months before the selected focal date. Its dated value

$$= 4170.00(1.015)^9 = 4170.00(1.14339) = \$4767.94$$

The second debt matures six months after the selected focal date. Its dated value

$$= 3805.44(1.015)^{-6} = 3805.44(0.9145422) = \$3480.24$$

The dated values of the two replacement payments at the selected focal date are \$$x$ and \$$x(1.015)^{-12}$. Therefore, the equation of values is

$$x + x(1.015)^{-12} = 4767.94 + 3480.24$$
$$x + 0.8363874x = 8248.18$$
$$x = \frac{8248.18}{1.8363874}$$
$$x = 4491.53$$

The size of the two equal payments is \$4491.53.

Programmed solution

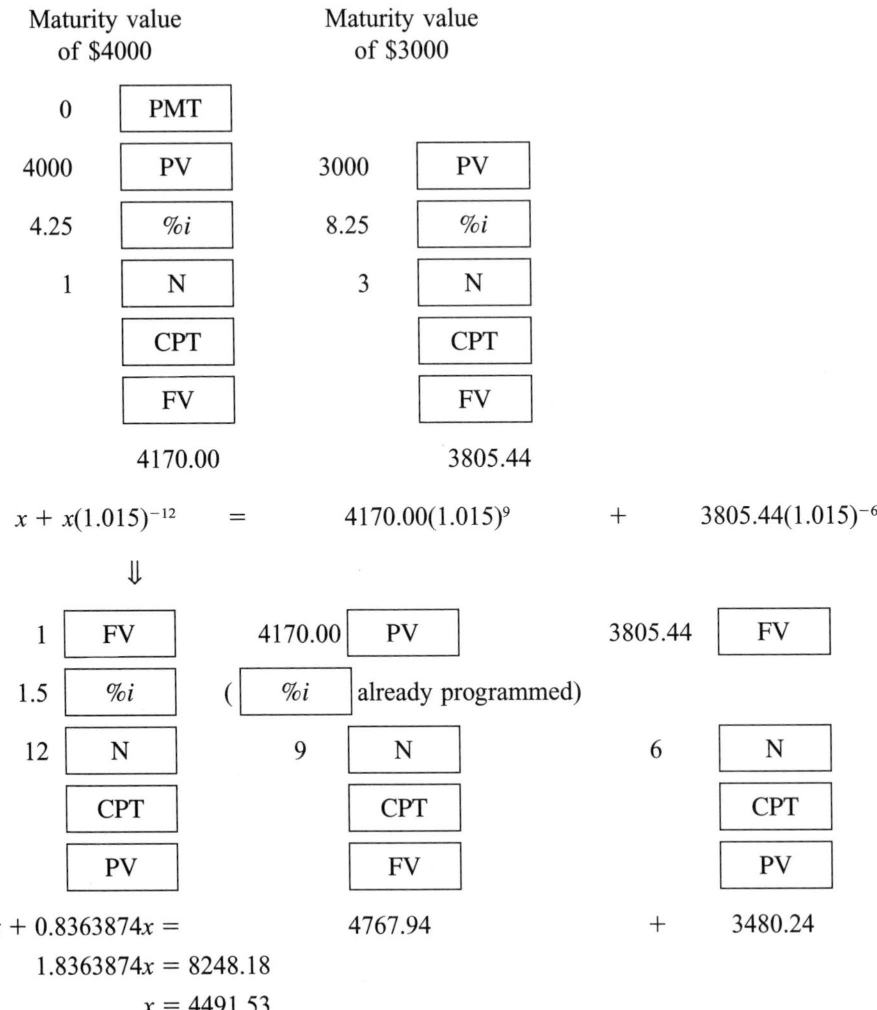

Example **9.5i** What is the size of the equal payments that must be made at the end of each of the next five years to settle a debt of $5000.00 due in five years if money is worth 9% p.a. compounded annually?

Solution

Select as the focal date 'five years from now.' Let the equal payments be represented by $x and let the dated values of the first four payments be represented by E_1, E_2, E_3, E_4 respectively as shown in Figure 9.13.

FIGURE 9.13 ***Graphic representation of method and data***

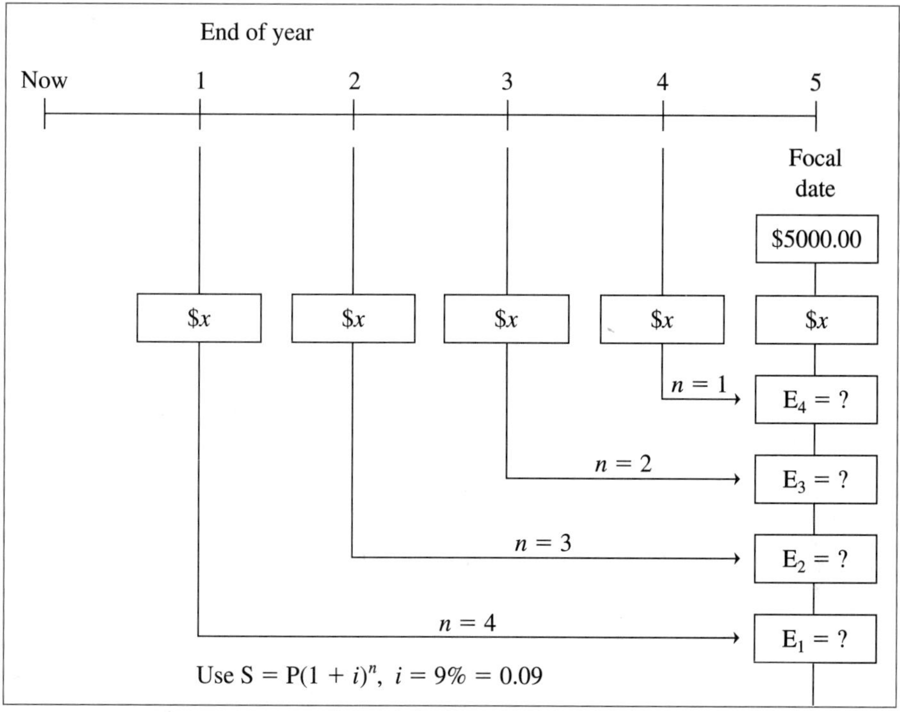

Then the equation of values may be set up.

$5000.00 = x + E_4 + E_3 + E_2 + E_1$

$5000.00 = x + x(1.09) + x(1.09)^2 + x(1.09)^3 + x(1.09)^4$

$5000.00 = x[1 + (1.09) + (1.09)^2 + (1.09)^3 + (1.09)^4]$

$5000.00 = x(1 + 1.09 + 1.881 + 1.295029 + 1.4115816)$

$5000.00 = 5.9847106x$

$$x = \frac{5000.00}{5.9847106}$$

$$x = 835.46$$

The size of the equal payments is $835.46.

Example 9.5j What is the size of the equal payments that must be made at the end of each of the next five quarters to settle a debt of $3000.00 due now if money is worth 12% p.a. compounded quarterly?

Solution

Select as the focal date 'now.' Let the size of the equal payments be represented by $\$x$ and let the dated values of the five payments be represented by E_1, E_2, E_3, E_4, E_5 respectively as shown in Figure 9.14.

FIGURE 9.14 ***Graphic representation of method and data***

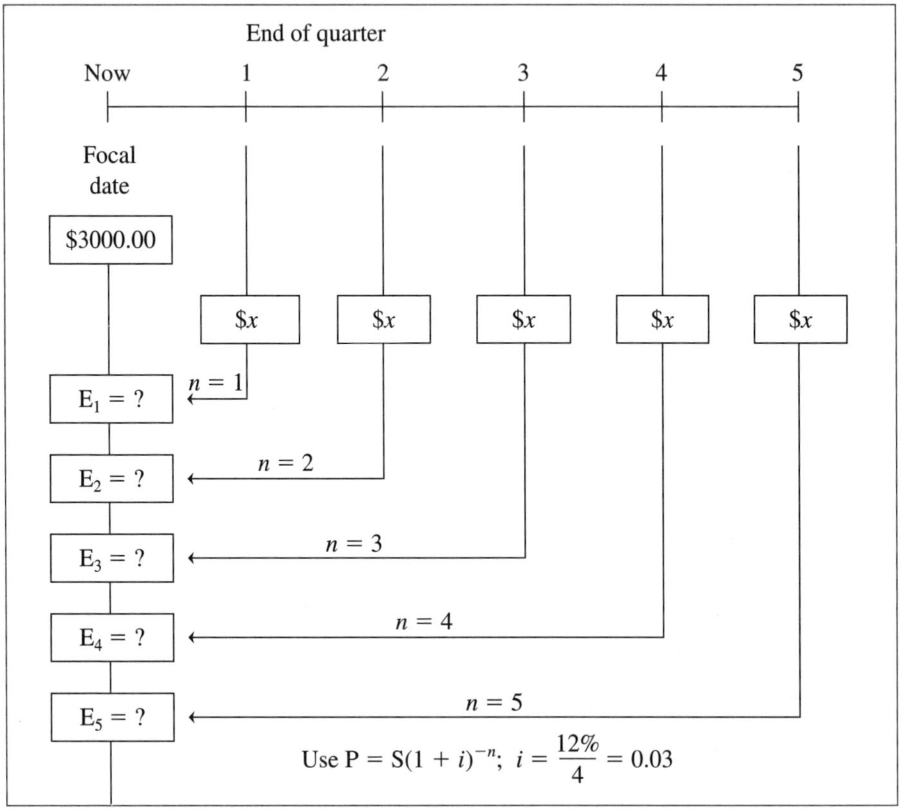

End of quarter

Now	1	2	3	4	5
Focal date					
\$3000.00	\$x	\$x	\$x	\$x	\$x
E_1 = ? ← $n = 1$					
E_2 = ? ← $n = 2$					
E_3 = ? ← $n = 3$					
E_4 = ? ← $n = 4$					
E_5 = ? ← $n = 5$					

Use $P = S(1 + i)^{-n}$; $i = \frac{12\%}{4} = 0.03$

Then the equation of values may be set up.

$$3000.00 = E_1 + E_2 + E_3 + E_4 + E_5$$
$$3000.00 = x(1.03)^{-1} + x(1.03)^{-2} + x(1.03)^{-3} + x(1.03)^{-4} + x(1.03)^{-5}$$
$$3000.00 = x[(1.03)^{-1} + (1.03)^{-2} + (1.03)^{-3} + (1.03)^{-4} + (1.03)^{-5}]$$
$$3000.00 = x(0.9708737 + 0.9425959 + 0.9151417 + 0.8884871 + 0.8626088)$$
$$3000.00 = 4.5797073x$$
$$x = \frac{3000.00}{4.5797073}$$
$$x = 655.06$$

The size of the equal payments is \$655.06.

Exercise 9.5

A. Find the equivalent single payment on the given focal date for each of the following.

	Original payments	*Int. rate*	*Frequency of conversion*	*Focal date*
1.	$5000.00 due in 2 years	12%	monthly	5 years from now
2.	$1600.00 due in 18 months	14%	quarterly	42 months from now
3.	$3400.00 due in 4 years	10%	semi-annually	one year from now
4.	$2700.00 due in 60 months	7%	quarterly	6 months from now
5.	$800.00 due in 6 months and $700.00 due in 15 months	13%	monthly	2 years from now
6.	$1000.00 due in 9 months and $1200.00 due in 18 months	16%	quarterly	3 years from now
7.	$400.00 due in 3 years and $600.00 due in 5 years	11%	semi-annually	now
8.	$2000.00 due in 20 months and $1500.00 due in 40 months	15%	monthly	9 months from now
9.	$800.00 due today and $1400.00 due in 3 years with interest at 12% compounded annually	13.5%	quarterly	one year from now
10.	$500.00 due in 6 months with interest at 14% compounded quarterly and $800.00 due in 18 months with interest at 16% compounded semi-annually	9%	monthly	9 months from now

B. Find the equivalent replacement payments for each of the following.

	Original payments	*Int. rate*	*Frequency of conversion*	*Replacement payments*	*Focal date*
1.	$2000.00 due now and $2000.00 due in 4 years	14.5%	annually	$2000.00 due in 2 years, a second payment due in 7 years	7 years from now
2.	$1500.00 due in 6 months and $1900.00 due in 21 months	7%	quarterly	$2000.00 due in 3 years, the remainder due in 45 months	45 months from now
3.	$800.00 due 2 years ago and $1000.00 due in 5 years	12%	semi-annually	2 equal payments; first payment due in 4 years, second payment due in 8 years	4 years from now
4.	$3000.00 due 1 year ago and $2500.00 due in 4 years	15%	monthly	2 equal payments; first due now, second payment due in 6 years	now
5.	$900.00 due in 3 months and $800.00 due in 30 months with interest at 15% compounded quarterly	9%	monthly	2 equal payments; first due today, second due in 3 years	today
6.	$1400.00 due today and $1600.00 due in 5 years with interest at 14.5% compounded annually	14%	quarterly	2 equal payments; first due in 18 months, second due in 4 years	18 months from now

C. Solve each of the following problems.

1. $4000.00 is due in five years. If money is worth 12% compounded annually, find the equivalent payment that would settle the debt

   (a) now; **(b)** in 2 years; **(c)** in 5 years; **(d)** in 10 years.

2. A debt payment of \$5500 is due in 27 months. If money is worth 16% p.a. compounded quarterly, what is the equivalent payment

   (a) now? **(b)** 15 months from now? **(c)** 27 months from now?

   (d) 36 months from now?

3. A debt can be paid by payments of \$2000.00 today, \$2000.00 in three years, and \$2000.00 in six years. What single payment would settle the debt four years from now if money is worth 10% compounded semi-annually?

4. \$600.00, \$800.00, and \$1200.00 are due in one year, three years, and six years respectively. What is the equivalent single sum of money due two and a half years from now if interest is 12% compounded monthly?

5. Debt payments of \$400.00 due today and \$700.00 due in eight months with interest at 12% compounded monthly are to be settled by a payment of \$500.00 six months from now and a final payment in fifteen months. Determine the size of the final payment if money is worth 6% compounded monthly.

6. Payments of \$1200.00 due one year ago and \$1000.00 due six months ago are to be replaced by a payment of \$800.00 now, a second payment of \$1000.00 nine months from now, and a final payment eighteen months from now. What is the size of the final payment if interest is 14% compounded quarterly?

7. An obligation of \$8000.00 due one year ago is to be settled by four equal payments due at the beginning of each of the next four years respectively. What is the size of the equal payments if interest is 12% compounded semi-annually?

8. A loan of \$3000.00 made today is to be repaid in three equal instalments due in one year, three years, and five years respectively. What is the size of the equal instalments if money is worth 12% compounded monthly?

9. Payments of \$500.00 each are due at the end of each of the next five years. If money is worth 11% compounded annually, what is the single equivalent payment

   (a) five years from now? **(b)** now?

10. Rework Problem 9 with payments due at the beginning of each of the next five years. (You can obtain the solution directly from your solution to Problem 9.)

11. What is the size of the equal payments that must be made at the end of each of the next four years to settle a debt of \$3000.00 subject to interest at 10% p.a. compounded annually

    (a) due four years from now? **(b)** due now?

12. Rework Problem 11 with payments made at the beginning of each of the next four years. (You can obtain the solution directly from your solution to Problem 11.)

Review exercise

1. What is the accumulated value of \$500.00 in fifteen years at 6% compounded
   (a) annually? **(b)** quarterly? **(c)** monthly?

2. What is the amount of \$10 000.00 at 10.5% compounded monthly
   (a) in four years? **(b)** in eight and one-half years? **(c)** in twenty years?

3. Landmark Trust offers five-year investment certificates at 7.5% compounded semi-annually.
   (a) What is the value of a \$2000 certificate at maturity?
   (b) How much of the maturity value is interest?

4. Western Savings offers three-year term deposits at 9.25% compounded annually while your credit union offers such deposits at 9.0% compounded quarterly. If you have \$5000 to invest, what is the maturity value of your deposit
   (a) at Western Savings? **(b)** at your credit union?

5. Find the compound amount and the compound interest of
   (a) \$1800.00 invested at 14% compounded quarterly for 15.5 years;
   (b) \$1250.00 invested at 13.5% compounded monthly for 15 years.

6. Find the present value and the compound discount of
   (a) \$3600.00 due in 9 years if interest is 8% compounded semi-annually;
   (b) \$9000.00 due in 5 years if money is worth 6.8% compounded quarterly.

7. The Peel Company borrowed \$20 000.00 at 10% compounded semi-annually and made payments toward the loan of \$8000.00 after two years and \$10 000.00 after three and a half years. How much is required to pay off the loan one year after the second payment?

8. Ted deposited \$1750.00 in an RRSP on March 1, 1986, at 10% compounded quarterly. Subsequently the interest rate was changed to 12% compounded monthly on September 1, 1988, and to 11% compounded semi-annually on June 1, 1990. What will the value of the RRSP deposit be on December 1, 1996, if no further changes in interest are made?

9. A non-interest-bearing note for \$1500.00 is due on June 30, 2000. The note is discounted at 15% compounded quarterly on September 30, 1994. What are the proceeds of the note?

10. An investment of \$2500 is accumulated at 5% compounded quarterly for two and one-half years. At that time the interest rate is changed to 6% compounded monthly. How much is the investment worth two years after the change in interest rate?

11. To ensure that funds are available to repay the principal at maturity, a borrower deposits \$2000 each year for three years. If interest is 13% compounded quarterly, how much will the borrower have on deposit four years after the first deposit was made?

12. Cindy started a registered retirement savings plan on February 1, 1989, with a deposit of $2500. She added $2000 on February 1, 1990, and $1500 on February 1, 1991. What is the accumulated value of her RRSP account on August 1, 1999, if interest is 10% compounded quarterly?

13. A demand loan of $8000 is repaid by payments of $3000 after fifteen months, $4000 after thirty months, and a final payment after four years. If interest was 15% for the first two years and 16% for the remaining time, and compounding is quarterly, what is the size of the final payment?

14. Find the present value and the compound discount of $4000 due in seven years and six months if interest is 14.8% compounded quarterly.

15. Find the principal that will accumulate to $6000 in fifteen years at 15% compounded monthly.

16. Find the proceeds of a non-interest-bearing promissory note for $75 000 discounted 42 months before maturity at 16.5% compounded semi-annually.

17. A ten-year promissory note for $1750.00 dated May 1, 1988, bearing interest at 13% compounded semi-annually is discounted on August 1, 1994, to yield 14% compounded quarterly. Determine the proceeds of the note.

18. A seven-year, $10 000 promissory note bearing interest at 12% compounded quarterly is discounted four years after the date of issue at 16% compounded semi-annually. What are the proceeds of the note?

19. A $40 000, 15-year promissory note dated June 1, 1991, bearing interest at 15% compounded semi-annually is discounted on September 1, 1995, at 11% compounded quarterly. What are the proceeds of the note?

20. A sum of money has a value of $3000 eighteen months from now. If money is worth 18% compounded monthly, what is its equivalent value

(a) now? **(b)** one year from now? **(c)** three years from now?

21. Payments of $1000, $1200, and $1500 are due in six months, eighteen months, and thirty months from now respectively. What is the equivalent single payment two years from now if money is worth 16% compounded quarterly?

22. An obligation of $10 000 is due one year from now with interest at 13% compounded semi-annually. The obligation is to be settled by a payment of $6000 in six months and a final payment in fifteen months. What is the size of the second payment if interest is 18% compounded monthly?

23. Waldon Toys owes $3000 due in two years with interest at 16% compounded semi-annually and $2500 due in fifteen months at 13% compounded quarterly. If the company wants to discharge these debts by making two equal payments, the first one now and the second eighteen months from now, what is the size of the two payments if money is worth 15% compounded monthly?

24. Debt payments of $400.00 due today, $500.00 due in eighteen months, and $900.00 due in three years are to be combined into a single payment due two years from now. What is the size of the single payment if interest is 16% p.a. compounded quarterly?

25. Debt payments of \$2600.00 due one year ago and \$2400.00 due two years from now are to be replaced by two equal payments due one year from now and four years from now respectively. What is the size of the equal payments if money is worth 13.5% p.a. compounded semi-annually?

26. A loan of \$7000.00 taken out two years ago is to be repaid by three equal instalments due now, two years from now, and three years from now respectively. What is the size of the equal instalments if interest on the debt is 12% p.a. compounded monthly?

Self-test

1. What sum of money invested at 12% compounded quarterly will grow to \$3300 in 11 years?

2. Find the compound interest earned by \$1300 invested at 13.5% compounded monthly for seven years.

3. Determine the compounding factor for a sum of money invested for 14.5 years at 7% compounded semi-annually.

4. Five years after Anne deposited \$3600 in a savings account that earned interest at 10.2% compounded monthly, the rate of interest was changed to 9% compounded semi-annually. How much was in the account twelve years after the deposit was made?

5. A debt can be repaid by payments of \$4000 today, \$4000 in five years, and \$3000 in six years. What single payment would settle the debt one year from now if money is worth 19% compounded semi-annually?

6. A \$10 200 debt will accumulate for five years at 13% compounded semi-annually. For how much will the debt sell three years after it was incurred if the buyer of the debt charges 10% compounded quarterly?

7. What is the present value of \$5900 payable in 15 years if the current interest rate is 14% compounded semi-annually?

8. Determine the compound discount on \$8800 due in 7.5 years if interest is 9.6% compounded monthly.

9. Two debt payments, the first for \$800 due today and the second for \$600 due in nine months with interest at 10.5% compounded monthly, are to be settled by a payment of \$800 six months from now and a final payment in 24 months. Determine the size of the final payment if money is worth 13.5% compounded quarterly.

10. A note dated July 1, 1990, promises to pay \$8000 with interest at 16.5% compounded quarterly on January 1, 1999. Find the proceeds from the sale of the note on July 1, 1994, if money is then worth 12% compounded semi-annually.

11. Adam borrowed \$5000 at 13% compounded semi-annually. He repaid \$2000 after two years and \$2500 after three years. How much will he owe after five years?

12. A debt of \$7000 due today is to be settled by three equal payments due three months from now, 15 months from now, and 27 months from now respectively. What is the size of the equal payments at 21% compounded quarterly?

CASE STUDY

You are employed by the sales and marketing division of a large auto manufacturer. The company is about to introduce a new solar-powered car. Your responsibility is to work with the dealers to forecast sales and deal with potential problems that the dealers may have. The car will be introduced in 1996.

1. The first-year sales are estimated to be 18 000 units and the growth rate is expected to be 0.5% per month. Forecast the sales for 1999.

2. **(a)** Calculate the estimated increase in car sales from 1997 to 1998.

(b) What percent increase per annum does this number represent?

3. The sales of the model that this car is to replace have been declining. This year, sales were 23 400 cars. Sales have been declining at 1% per month from their height six years ago. Calculate the number of cars sold six years ago.

4. A new marketing study indicates that young people are marrying later and waiting several years before having children. This trend will affect sales of the new two-seater car. The marketers now predict growth rates of 0.5% per month for the first two years, 1% per month for the three following years, and a levelling off of 1.25% per month for the next five years. Project the sales for the year 2004.

5. To entice dealers to place large orders for the new car, the manufacturer is willing to put a car on dealers' lots interest free for three months. Dealers can then make payments of $2000 at three months, $3000 at six months, or $4000 at one year. Assuming that the dealer has sufficient money in a non-interest-paying current account, when is the best time for a dealer to pay for the car? How much can a dealer save by paying cash at this time if interest is 9% compounded monthly?

6. JLW Dealers wants to pass this incentive on to the customers and offers the car for four equal payments of $2500 at three, six, nine, and twelve months. If a customer buys the car and pays in cash at three months, what percent markup based on cost does the dealer make if interest is 9% compounded monthly? Assume the dealer paid cash for the car.

7. To obtain cash and make room for the new models, a dealer sells a repossessed van that had a dealer cost of $8900. The payments were to be $3000 every three months for a year. The first two payments have not been received and the third is due.

(a) Calculate the value of the payments as of now. Interest is 12% compounded monthly.

(b) Calculate the percent discount that can be offered on this van if the dealer wants to make a 20% markup based on cost.

8. A customer wants to order a new car. The trade-in value for the old car is $3000 and the customer wants to pay cash now rather than use the four-equal-payments plan. How much does the dealer have to sell the used car for to realize a 20% markup based on cost? Interest is 9% compounded monthly.

Summary of formulae used

Formula 9.1

$S = P(1 + i)^n$ — Finding the compound amount (or future value or maturity value) when the original principal, the rate of interest, and the time period are known

Formula 9.2A

$P = \frac{S}{(1 + i)^n}$ — Finding the present value (or principal or proceeds or discounted value) when the compound amount, the rate of interest, and the time period are known

Formula 9.2B

$P = S(1 + i)^{-n}$ — Finding the present value by means of the discount factor (the reciprocal of the compounding factor)

Glossary of terms used

Accumulation factor see *Compounding factor*

Amount see *Compound amount*

Comparison date see *Focal date*

Compound amount the sum of money to which a principal will grow at compound interest in a specific number of compounding or conversion periods at a specified periodic rate of interest

Compound discount the difference between a given amount and its present value (or proceeds or discounted value) at a specified time

Compound interest a procedure for computing interest whereby interest earned during an interest period is added onto the principal at the end of the interest period

Compounding factor the factor $(1 + i)^n$ found in compound interest formulae

Compounding period the time between two successive interest dates

Conversion period see *Compounding period*

Discount factor the factor $(1 + i)^{-n}$; the reciprocal of the compounding factor

Discounted value see *Present value*

Discounting the process of computing the present value (or proceeds or discounted value) of a future sum of money

Equivalent values the dated values of an original sum of money

Focal date a specific date chosen to compare the time values of one or more dated sums of money

Future value see *Compound amount*

Maturity value see *Compound amount*

Nominal rate of interest the stated rate at which the compounding is done one or more times per year; usually stated as an annual rate

Present value the principal at any time that will grow at compound interest to a given amount over a given number of compounding periods at a given rate of interest

Proceeds see *Present value*

10 Compound interest—further topics

Introduction

The two basic problems of computing compound amount and present value were considered in the previous chapter. Additional problems involving compound interest are considered in this chapter. The topics include computations with fractional conversion periods, finding interest rates, finding the number of conversion periods, computing equated dates and equivalent rates, and using continuous compounding.

In this and following chapters, you will use the power function and the natural logarithm function to determine values that you will use for further computation. It is useful to use the memory to retain such values. When doing so, you need to be aware that the number of digits retained in the registers is greater than the number of digits displayed. Thus, slight differences may result depending on whether the memory or the displayed digits are used. Any such differences are insignificant and should not concern you. For the worked examples in this text, we have used the memory whenever it was convenient to do so.

Objectives

Upon completing this chapter using an electronic calculator equipped with the universal power and universal root function, the natural logarithm function, and the antilogarithm function, you will be able to

1. find the compound amount when n is a fractional value;
2. find discounted values for fractional compounding periods;
3. discount promissory notes involving fractional compounding periods;
4. compute periodic, nominal, and effective rates of interest and determine the number of conversion periods;
5. find equated dates and equivalent rates and solve problems involving continuous compounding.

10.1 *Finding the compound amount when* n *is a fractional value*

A. *Two methods for solving the problem*

The value of n in the compounding factor $(1 + i)^n$ is not restricted to integral values; n may take any *fractional* value. The compound amount can be determined by means of the formula $S = P(1 + i)^n$ whether the time period contains an integral number of conversion periods or not.

Using the formula with n as a fractional value is the theoretically correct method to give the exact accumulated value. Historically, however, the computation when using a fractional n was laborious and required the use of logarithms. To avoid using logarithms, in practice an *approximation* method using simple interest for the fractional conversion period was used.

With the advent of electronic calculators equipped with an exponential function, the problem of computing with fractional values of n no longer exists. In fact, using the exact method with an electronic calculator is more direct than the approximation method. Except for the specific application of the practical method used in bond valuation (see Chapter 15), only the exact method is used in this text.

B. *Examples using the exact method*

Use Formula 9.1, $S = P(1 + i)^n$, where n is a fractional value representing the entire time period.

***Example* 10.1a** Find the accumulated value of \$1000.00 invested for two years and nine months at 15% p.a. compounded annually using the exact method.

Solution

The entire time period is 2 years and 9 months; the number of whole conversion periods is 2; the fractional conversion period is $\frac{9}{12}$ of a year.

$$P = 1000.00;\ i = 15\% = 0.15;\ n = 2\frac{9}{12} = 2.75$$

$$S = 1000.00(1.15)^{2.75} = 1000.00(1.4686525) = \$1468.65$$

Programmed solution

0	1000	15	2.75			
PMT	PV	%i	N	CPT	FV	1468.65

Example **10.1b** Determine the compound amount of \$400.00 invested at 14% p.a. compounded quarterly for three years and five months using the exact method.

Solution

$$P = 400.00;\ i = 3.5\% = 0.035;$$

$$n = \left(3\frac{5}{12}\right)(4) = \left(\frac{41}{12}\right)(4) = \frac{41}{3} = 13\frac{2}{3} = 13.666667$$

$S = 400.00(1.035)^{13.666667} = 400.00(1.6002388) = \$640.10$

Programmed solution

0	400	3.5	13.666667			
PMT	PV	%i	N	CPT	FV	640.10

Example **10.1c** Find the maturity value of a promissory note for \$2000.00 dated February 1, 1990, and due on October 1, 1996, if interest is 13% p.a. compounded semi-annually.

Solution

$$P = 2000.00;\ i = 6.5\% = 0.065;$$

the time period February 1, 1990, to October 1, 1996, contains 6 years and 8 months: $n = \left(6\frac{8}{12}\right)(2) = \left(\frac{80}{12}\right)(2) = 13.3333333.$

$S = 2000.00(1.065)^{13.3333333} = 2000.00(2.3155888) = \$4631.18$

Programmed solution

0	2000	6.5	13.3333333			
PMT	PV	%i	N	CPT	FV	4631.18

Example **10.1d** A debt of \$3500.00 dated August 31, 1994, is payable together with interest at 15% p.a. compounded quarterly on June 30, 1997. Determine the amount to be paid.

Solution

$P = 3500.00$; $i = 3.75\% = 0.0375$; the time period August 31, 1994, to June 30, 1997, contains 2 years and 10 months; the number of quarters $n = 11.333333$.

$$\begin{aligned} S &= 3500.00(1.0375)^{11.333333} \\ &= 3500.00(1.517744) \\ &= \$5312.10 \end{aligned}$$

Programmed solution

0	3500	3.75	11.333333			
PMT	PV	%i	N	CPT	FV	5312.10

Exercise 10.1

A. 1. Find the accumulated value of each of the following.

	Principal	*Rate*	*Frequency of conversion*	*Time*
(a)	$2500.00	7%	annually	7 years, 6 months
(b)	400.00	9%	quarterly	3 years, 8 months
(c)	1300.00	12%	semi-annually	9 years, 3 months
(d)	4500.00	15%	monthly	7.5 months

2. Find the compound interest for each of the following.

	Principal	*Rate*	*Frequency of conversion*	*Time*
(a)	$ 600.00	12.5%	annually	4 years, 7 months
(b)	1400.00	17.5%	semi-annually	15 years, 2 months
(c)	950.00	8.0%	quarterly	9 years, 10 months
(d)	3000.00	10.5%	annually	50 months

B. Solve each of the following problems.

1. A demand loan for $5000.00 with interest at 15% compounded semi-annually is repaid after five years, ten months. What is the amount of interest paid?
2. $4000.00 is invested for four years, eight months at 8.5% compounded annually. What is the compounded amount?
3. Determine the maturity value of a $600.00 promissory note dated August 1, 1992, and due on June 1, 1997, if interest is 13% p.a. compounded semi-annually.
4. Find the maturity value of a promissory note for $3200.00 dated March 31, 1991, and due on August 31, 1997, if interest is 14% compounded quarterly.
5. A debt of $8000.00 is payable in seven years and five months. Determine the accumulated value of the debt at 22% p.a. compounded annually.
6. A $6000.00 investment matures in three years, eleven months. Find the maturity value if interest is 9% p.a. compounded quarterly.

10.2 *Discounted value for a fractional compounding period*

A. Exact method for solving the problem

Using fractional values of n when finding the compound amount is relevant to finding the present value or discounted value of a future sum of money for a fractional time period. Only the exact method is used in this text.

Use Formula 9.1, $S = P(1 + i)^n$, or Formula 9.2A, $P = \frac{S}{(1 + i)^n}$, or Formula 9.2B, $P = S(1 + i)^{-n}$ where n is a fractional value representing the *entire* time period, S is a known value, and P is to be determined.

B. Examples

***Example* 10.2a** Find the present value of \$2000.00 due in three years and eight months if money is worth 13% p.a. compounded quarterly.

Solution

$$S = 2000.00;\ i = \frac{13\%}{4} = 3.25\% = 0.0325;\ n = \left(3\frac{8}{12}\right)(4) = 14\frac{2}{3} = 14.666667$$

$$P = \frac{S}{(1 + i)^n}$$ ← using Formula 9.2A

$$= \frac{2000.00}{(1 + 0.0325)^{14.666667}}$$ ← use as many decimals as are available in your calculator

$$= \frac{2000.00}{1.5985303}$$

$$= 2000.00(0.6255746)$$ ← multiply by the reciprocal

$$= \$1251.15$$

Programmed solution

0	2000	3.25	14.666667			
PMT	FV	%i	N	CPT	PV	1251.15

***Example* 10.2b** Determine the principal that will accumulate to \$3358.33 from September 1, 1992, to April 1, 1996, at 15% p.a. compounded semi-annually.

Solution

Finding the principal that will grow to the given amount of \$3358.33 is equivalent to finding the present value or discounted value of this amount.

The time period September 1, 1992, to April 1, 1996, contains three years and seven months; that is, it consists of seven whole conversion periods of six months each and a fractional conversion period of one month.

Use $P = \frac{S}{(1 + i)^n}$.

$S = 3358.33$; $i = 7.5\% = 0.075$; $n = \left(3\frac{7}{12}\right)(2) = 7\frac{1}{6} = 7.1666667$

$$
\begin{aligned}
P &= \frac{3358.33}{(1.075)^{7.1666667}} \\
&= \frac{3358.33}{1.6791674} \\
&= 3358.33(0.5955332) \\
&= \$2000.00
\end{aligned}
$$

Programmed solution

0	3358.33	7.5	7.1666667			
PMT	FV	%*i*	N	CPT	PV	2000.00

Exercise 10.2

A. 1. Find the present value of each of the following.

	Amount	*Rate*	*Frequency of conversion*	*Time due*
(a)	$1500.00	15.5%	annually	in 15 years, 9 months
(b)	900.00	11.5%	semi-annually	in 8 years, 10 months
(c)	6400.00	7%	quarterly	in 5 years, 7 months
(d)	7200.00	18%	monthly	in 21.5 months

2. Find the compound discount for each of the following.

	Amount	*Rate*	*Frequency of conversion*	*Time due*
(a)	$7500.00	12%	quarterly	in 4 years, 5 months
(b)	4800.00	14.5%	semi-annually	in 9 years, 9 months
(c)	870.00	9%	monthly	in 45.5 months
(d)	1250.00	5.5%	annually	in 12 years, 4 months

B. Solve each of the following problems.

1. What is the principal that will grow to $3000.00 in eight years, eight months at 15% compounded semi-annually?

2. Find the sum of money that accumulates to $1600.00 at 22% compounded quarterly in six years, four months.

3. Determine the proceeds of an investment with a maturity value of \$10 000.00 if discounted at 9% compounded monthly 22.5 months before the date of maturity.

4. Compute the discounted value of \$7000.00 due in three years, five months if money is worth 16% compounded quarterly.

5. Find the discounted value of \$3800.00 due in six years, eight months if interest is 7.5% compounded annually.

6. Calculate the proceeds of \$5500.00 due in seven years, eight months discounted at 13.5% compounded semi-annually.

10.3 *Discounting promissory notes involving fractional conversion periods*

A. Non-interest-bearing notes

***Example* 10.3a** A four-year, non-interest-bearing promissory note for \$6000.00 dated August 31, 1996, is discounted on October 31, 1997, at 14% p.a. compounded quarterly. Determine the proceeds of the note.

Solution

The due date of the note is August 31, 2000; the discount period October 31, 1997, to August 31, 2000, contains 2 years and 10 months.

$$S = 6000.00;\ i = 3.5\% = 0.035;$$

$$n = \left(2\frac{10}{12}\right)(4) = 11\frac{1}{3} = 11.333333$$

$$\begin{aligned} P &= S(1 + i)^{-n} \\ &= 6000.00(1 + 0.035)^{-11.333333} \\ &= 6000.00(0.6771362) \\ &= \$4062.82 \end{aligned}$$

Programmed solution

0	6000	3.5	11.333333			
PMT	FV	%i	N	CPT	PV	4062.82

***Example* 10.3b** You signed a promissory note at the Continental Bank for \$3000.00 due in 27 months. If the bank charges interest at 16% p.a. compounded semi-annually, determine the proceeds of the note.

Solution

The amount shown on the note is the sum of money due in 27 months, that is, the maturity value of the note.

$$S = 3000.00;\ i = 8\% = 0.08;\ n = \left(\frac{27}{12}\right)(2) = 4.5$$

$$\begin{aligned} P &= S(1 + i)^{-n} \\ &= 3000.00(1 + 0.08)^{-4.5} \\ &= 3000.00(0.7072828) \\ &= \$2121.85 \end{aligned}$$

Programmed solution

0	3000	8	4.5			
PMT	FV	%i	N	CPT	PV	2121.85

B. *Interest-bearing notes*

Example **10.3c** A five-year note for \$8000.00 bearing interest at 12% p.a. compounded monthly is discounted two years and five months before the due date at 14% p.a. compounded semi-annually. Determine the proceeds of the note.

Solution

STEP 1 Find the maturity value using $S = P(1 + i)^n$.

$$P = 8000.00;\ i = 1\% = 0.01;\ n = 60$$

$$\begin{aligned} S &= 8000.00(1.01)^{60} \\ &= 8000.00(1.8166967) \\ &= \$14\,533.57 \end{aligned}$$

STEP 2 Find the present value of the maturity value found in Step 1 using $P = S(1 + i)^{-n}$.

$$S = 14\,533.57;\ i = 7\% = 0.07;\ n = \left(\frac{29}{12}\right)(2) = 4.8333333$$

$$\begin{aligned} P &= 14\,533.57(1.07)^{-4.8333333} \\ &= 14\,533.57(0.7210716) \\ &= \$10\,479.75 \end{aligned}$$

Programmed solution

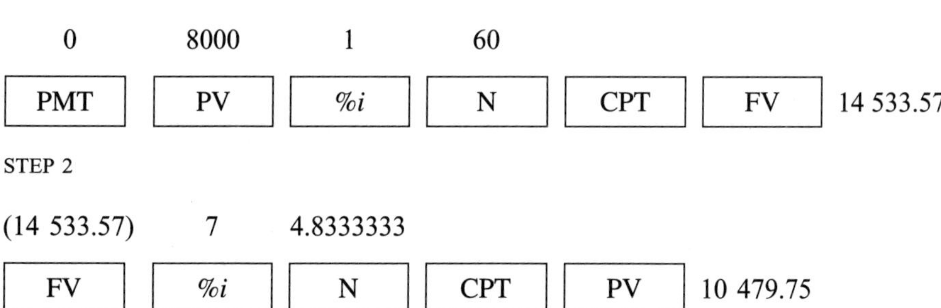

Exercise 10.3

A. Find the proceeds of each of the following promissory notes.

	Face value	*Date of issue*	*Term*	*Int. rate*	*Frequency of conversion*	*Date of discount*	*Disct rate*	*Frequency of conversion*
1	$5000	1990-04-01	10 years	—	—	1995-08-01	15%	annually
2	900	1991-08-31	8 years	—	—	1996-06-30	12%	quarterly
3	3200	1992-03-31	6 years	—	—	1995-10-31	8%	quarterly
4	1450	1989-10-01	9 years	—	—	1994-12-01	14%	semi-annually
5	780	1993-09-30	10 years	14%	annually	1997-04-30	16%	quarterly
6	2100	1987-02-01	12 years	6%	monthly	1994-07-01	7%	semi-annually
7	1850	1995-11-01	5 years	12%	quarterly	1997-10-01	14%	semi-annually
8	3400	1991-01-31	7 years	18%	monthly	1995-12-31	16%	quarterly

B. Solve each of the following problems.

1. A four-year non-interest-bearing promissory note for $3750.00 is discounted thirty-two months after the date of issue at 13.5% compounded semi-annually. Find the proceeds of the note.

2. A seven-year non-interest-bearing note for $5200.00 is discounted three years, eight months before its due date at 16% compounded quarterly. Find the proceeds of the note.

3. A non-interest-bearing eight-year note for $4500.00 issued August 1, 1990, is discounted April 1, 1994, at 14.5% compounded annually. Find the compound discount.

4. A $2800.00 promissory note issued without interest for five years on September 30, 1993, is discounted on July 31, 1996, at 8% compounded quarterly. Find the compound discount.

5. A six-year note for \$1750.00 issued on December 1, 1992, with interest at 13.5% compounded annually is discounted on March 1, 1995, at 15% compounded semi-annually. What are the proceeds of the note?

6. A ten-year note for \$1200.00 bearing interest at 15% compounded monthly is discounted at 16% compounded quarterly three years and ten months after the date of issue. Find the proceeds of the note.

7. Four years, seven months before its due date, a seven-year note for \$2650.00 bearing interest at 12% compounded quarterly is discounted at 8% compounded semi-annually. Find the compound discount.

8. On April 15, 1992, a ten-year note dated June 15, 1987, is discounted at 18% compounded quarterly. If the face value of the note is \$4000.00 and interest is 16% compounded quarterly, find the compound discount.

10.4 *Finding* i *and* n

A. Finding the nominal rate of interest

If the original principal P, the compound amount S, and the number of conversion periods n are known, the periodic rate of interest (conversion rate) i can be determined by substituting in Formula 9.1, $S = P(1 + i)^n$ and solving for i.

Example **10.4a** What is the annual compounding rate if \$200 accumulates to \$495.19 in eight years?

Solution

$$P = 200.00;\ S = 495.19;\ n = 8$$

$$\begin{aligned} 495.19 &= 200.00(1 + i)^8 \longleftarrow i \text{ is an } annual \text{ rate} \\ (1 + i)^8 &= 2.47595 \\ [(1 + i)^8]^{\frac{1}{8}} &= 2.47595^{\frac{1}{8}} \longleftarrow \text{raise each side to the power } \tfrac{1}{8} \\ 1 + i &= 2.47595^{0.125} \\ 1 + i &= 1.1199993 \\ i &= 0.1199993 \\ &= 11.99993\% \longleftarrow \text{the desired annual rate} \end{aligned}$$

The annual compounding rate is 12.0%.

Programmed solution

You can use preprogrammed financial calculators to find i by the same procedure used previously to determine S or P. That is, select the compound interest mode, enter the given variables S, P, and n, and retrieve the fourth variable i.

0	200	495.19	8			
PMT	PV	FV	N	CPT	$\%i$	11.999925 (annual)

Example **10.4b** Find the nominal annual rate of interest compounded quarterly if \$1200.00 accumulates to \$2505.78 in five years.

Solution

$$P = 1200.00;\ S = 2505.78;\ n = 20$$

$$\begin{aligned} 2505.78 &= 1200.00(1+i)^{20} \longleftarrow i \text{ is a } \textit{quarterly} \text{ rate} \\ (1+i)^{20} &= 2.08815 \\ 1+i &= 2.08815^{0.05} \longleftarrow \text{raise both sides to the power } \tfrac{1}{20}\text{, that is, } 0.05 \\ 1+i &= 1.0374999 \\ i &= 0.0374999 \\ &= 3.74999\% \end{aligned}$$

The quarterly compounding rate is 3.75%.

Programmed solution

0	1200	2505.78	20			
PMT	PV	FV	N	CPT	$\%i$	3.74999

Since 3.75% is a quarterly rate, the nominal annual rate of interest is (3.75%)(4) = 15.0%.

Example **10.4c** At what nominal rate of interest compounded quarterly will money double in four years?

Solution

While neither P nor S are given, any sum of money may be used as principal. For this calculation, a convenient value for the principal is \$1.00.

$$P = 1;\ S = 2;\ n = 16$$

$$\begin{aligned} 2 &= 1(1+i)^{16} \longleftarrow i \text{ is a } \textit{quarterly} \text{ rate} \\ (1+i)^{16} &= 2 \\ 1+i &= 2^{\frac{1}{16}} \\ 1+i &= 2^{0.0625} \\ 1+i &= 1.0442738 \\ i &= 0.0442738 \\ &= 4.42738\% \end{aligned}$$

Programmed solution

0	1	2	16			
PMT	PV	FV	N	CPT	%*i*	4.42738 (quarterly)

The nominal annual rate is 4(4.42738%) = 17.71% (approximately).

***Example* 10.4d** If $1000.00 earns interest of $195.62 in one year,

(i) what is the annual rate of interest?

(ii) what is the nominal annual rate of interest compounded monthly?

Solution

(i) P = 1000.00; I = 195.62; S = P + I = 1195.62; n = 1

$$1195.62 = 1000.00(1 + i)^1 \longleftarrow i \text{ is an } \textit{annual} \text{ rate}$$
$$1 + i = 1.19562$$
$$i = 0.19562$$
$$= 19.562\%$$

Programmed solution

0	1000	1195.62	1			
PMT	PV	FV	N	CPT	%*i*	19.562%

The annual rate of interest is 19.562%.

(ii)
$$1195.62 = 1000.00(1 + i)^{12} \longleftarrow i \text{ is a } \textit{monthly} \text{ rate}$$
$$(1 + i)^{12} = 1.19562$$
$$1 + i = 1.19562^{\frac{1}{12}}$$
$$1 + i = 1.19562^{0.0833333}$$
$$1 + i = 1.015$$
$$i = 0.015$$
$$= 1.5\%$$

Programmed solution

0 1000 1195.62 12

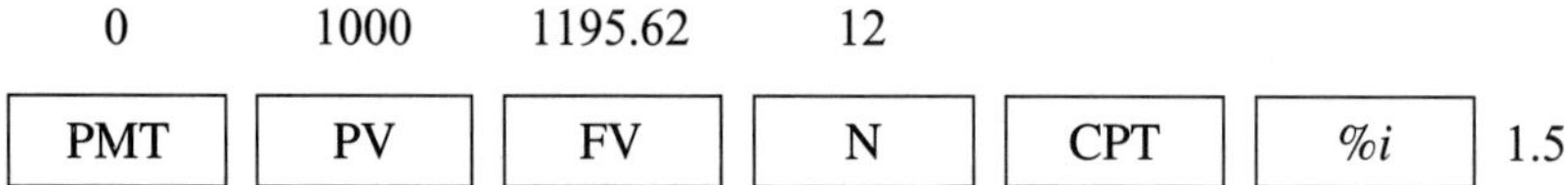

The nominal annual rate of interest compounded monthly is (1.5%)(12) = 18.0%.

B. *Effective rate of interest*

In Example 10.4d, compounding at an annual rate of interest of 19.562% has the same effect as compounding at 18% p.a. compounded monthly since, in both cases, the interest amounts to $195.62.

The annual rate of 19.562% is called the **effective rate of interest**. This rate is defined as the rate of interest compounded annually that yields the same amount of interest as a nominal annual rate of interest compounded a number of times per year other than one.

A formula for finding the effective rate of interest can be obtained as follows:

Let the nominal annual rate of interest be compounded m times per year and let the interest rate per conversion period be i.

Then the accumulated amount after one year is $S_1 = P(1 + i)^m$.

Let the corresponding effective annual rate of interest be f.

Then the accumulated amount after one year is $S_1 = P(1 + f)^1$.

$P(1 + f)^1 = P(1 + i)^m$ ⟵ the amounts are equal by definition

$1 + f = (1 + i)^m$ ⟵ divide both sides by P

$$f = (1 + i)^m - 1$$ ⟵ *Formula* **10.1**

Example **10.4e** Determine the effective rate of interest corresponding to 18% p.a. compounded (i) monthly; (ii) quarterly; (iii) semi-annually; (iv) annually; (v) daily.

Solution

(i) $i = \left(\frac{18\%}{12}\right) = 0.015; m = 12$

$f = (1 + i)^m - 1$ ⟵ using Formula 10.1

$= (1 + 0.015)^{12} - 1$

$= 1.1956182 - 1$

$= 0.1956182$

$= 19.562\%$ ⟵ see Example 10.4d

(ii) $i = \left(\frac{18\%}{4}\right) = 0.045; m = 4$

$f = (1.045)^4 - 1$

$= 1.1925186 - 1$

$= 0.1925186$

$= 19.252\%$

(iii) $i = \left(\frac{18\%}{2}\right) = 0.09; m = 2$

$f = (1.09)^2 - 1$

$= 1.18810 - 1$

$= 18.810\%$

(iv) $i = 18\% = 0.18; m = 1$

$$f = (1.18)^1 - 1$$
$$= 18.000\%$$

(v) $i = \left(\frac{18\%}{365}\right) = 0.00049315; m = 365$

$$f = (1.00049315)^{365} - 1$$
$$= 1.1971641 - 1$$
$$= 19.716\%$$

Summary of Results

For a nominal annual rate of 18% p.a., effective rates are

when compounding annually ($m = 1$) $\longrightarrow f = 18.000\%$
when compounding semi-annually ($m = 2$) $\longrightarrow f = 18.810\%$
when compounding quarterly ($m = 4$) $\longrightarrow f = 19.252\%$
when compounding monthly ($m = 12$) $\longrightarrow f = 19.562\%$
when compounding daily ($m = 365$) $\longrightarrow f = 19.716\%$

Interpretation of Results

(a) The nominal annual rate is the effective rate of interest if the number of conversion periods per year is 1, that is, if compounding annually.

(b) For a given nominal annual rate, the effective rate of interest increases as the number of conversion periods per year increases.

Example **10.4f** You have money to invest in interest-earning deposits. You have determined that suitable deposits are available at your bank paying 6.5% p.a. compounded semi-annually, at a local trust company paying 6.625% p.a., and at your credit union paying 6.45% p.a. compounded monthly. What institution offers the best rate of interest?

Solution

Since the methods of conversion differ, the interest rates are not directly comparable. To make the rates comparable, determine the effective rates of interest corresponding to the nominal annual rates.

For the bank

$$i = \left(\frac{6.5\%}{2}\right) = 0.0325; m = 2$$

$$f = (1 + 0.0325)^2 - 1 = 1.0660563 - 1 = 0.0660563 = 6.606\%$$

For the trust company

$$i = 6.625 = 0.0625; m = 1$$

$$f = i = 6.625\%$$

For the credit union

$$i = \left(\frac{6.45\%}{12}\right) = 0.005375;\ m = 12$$

$$f = (1.005375)^{12} - 1 = 1.0664414 - 1 = 0.0664414 = 6.644\%$$

While the nominal rate offered by the credit union is lowest, the corresponding effective rate of interest is highest due to the higher frequency of conversion. The rate offered by the credit union is best.

C. *Finding the number of conversion periods*

If the principal P, the compound amount S, and the periodic rate of interest i are known, the number of conversion periods n can be determined by substituting the known values in $S = P(1 + i)^n$ and solving for n.

Example **10.4g** In how many years will \$2000.00 grow to \$5306.60 at 20% compounded quarterly?

Solution

$$P = 2000.00;\ S = 5306.60;\ i = 5\% = 0.05$$

$5306.60 = 2000.00(1.05)^n$ ⟵ substituting in Formula 9.1

$(1.05)^n = 2.65330$

$n \ln 1.05 = \ln 2.65330$ ⟵ solve for n using the natural logarithm

$0.0487902n = 0.9758041$ ⟵ obtain the numerical values using the [lnx] key

$$n = \frac{0.9758041}{0.0487902} = 20.000018 = 20 \text{ (quarters)}$$

Programmed solution

You can use preprogrammed financial calculators to find n by the same procedure previously used to find S, P, or i.

0	2000	5306.60	5			
PMT	PV	FV	%i	CPT	N	20.0

At 20% compounded quarterly, \$2000.00 will grow to \$5306.60 in five years.

***Example* 10.4h** How long does it take for money to double

(i) at 10% p.a.?

(ii) at 12% p.a. compounded monthly?

(iii) at 16% p.a. compounded semi-annually?

(iv) at 20% p.a. compounded quarterly?

Solution

While neither P nor S is given, any sum of money may be used as principal. For this calculation, a convenient value for the principal is \$1.00.

$$P = 1.00; S = 2.00$$

(i) At 10% p.a., $i = 10\% = 0.10$

$$2 = 1(1 + 0.10)^n$$
$$1.10^n = 2$$
$$n \ln 1.10 = \ln 2$$
$$0.0953102n = 0.6931472$$
$$n = 7.2725409 \text{ (years)}$$

Programmed solution

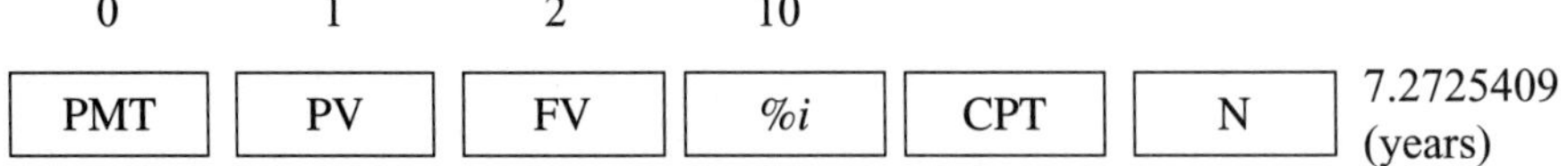

0 PMT | 1 PV | 2 FV | 10 %i | CPT | N | 7.2725409 (years)

At 10% p.a., money doubles in approximately 7 years and 3 months.

(ii) At 12% p.a. compounded monthly, $i = 1\% = 0.01$

$$2 = 1(1.01)^n$$
$$1.01^n = 2$$
$$n \ln 1.01 = \ln 2$$
$$0.0099503n = 0.6931472$$
$$n = 69.660717 \text{ (months)}$$

Programmed solution

Since [PV] = 1 and [FV] = 2 are already programmed from part (i), proceed with

1 [%i] [CPT] [N] 69.66017 (months)

At 12% p.a. compounded monthly, money doubles in approximately 5 years and 10 months.

(iii) At 16% p.a. compounded semi-annually, $i = 8\% = 0.08$

$$\begin{aligned} 1.08^n &= 2 \\ n \ln 1.08 &= \ln 2 \\ 0.0769610n &= 0.6931472 \\ n &= 9.0064683 \text{ (half-year periods)} \end{aligned}$$

Programmed solution

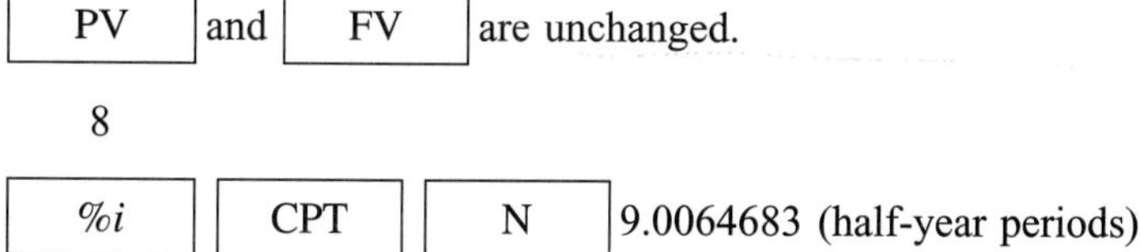

PV and FV are unchanged.

8

%i CPT N 9.0064683 (half-year periods)

At 16% p.a. compounded semi-annually, money doubles in approximately 4.5 years.

(iv) At 20% p.a. compounded quarterly, $i = 5\% = 0.05$

$$\begin{aligned} 1.05^n &= 2 \\ n \ln 1.05 &= \ln 2 \\ 0.0487902n &= 0.6931472 \\ n &= 14.206699 \text{ (quarters)} \end{aligned}$$

Programmed solution

5

%i CPT N 14.206699 (quarters)

At 20% p.a. compounded quarterly, money doubles in approximately 3.5 years.

Note: A quick estimator of the number of conversion periods needed to double money in value is given by the **Rule of 70**. It states that the number of conversion periods required to double money is 70 divided by the periodic rate of interest i. A comparison of the results using the Rule of 70 with the computed values obtained in Example 10.4h is shown below.

	Periodic rate	*Estimated number of conversion periods*	*Computed number of conversion periods*
(i)	10%	$\frac{70}{10} = 7$	7.27
(ii)	1%	$\frac{70}{1} = 70$	69.66
(iii)	8%	$\frac{70}{8} = 8.75$	9.01
(iv)	5%	$\frac{70}{5} = 14$	14.21

Example **10.4i** How long will it take for money to triple at 6% compounded monthly?

Solution

$$\text{Let } P = 1\text{; then } S = 3\text{; } i = 0.5\%$$

$$3 = 1(1.005)^n$$
$$1.005^n = 3$$
$$n \ln 1.005 = \ln 3$$
$$0.0049875n = 1.0986123$$
$$n = 220.271 \text{ (months)}$$

Programmed solution

0	1	3	0.5			
PMT	PV	FV	%i	CPT	N	220.271

At 6% compounded monthly, money triples in approximately 18 years and 4 months.

Exercise 10.4

A. Compute the rate of interest or the number of interest periods as indicated.

1. Compute the effective rate of interest for each of the following.
   - **(a)** 9.5% compounded semi-annually
   - **(b)** 14.5% compounded quarterly
   - **(c)** 15.0% compounded monthly
   - **(d)** 7.2% compounded monthly
   - **(e)** 14.6% compounded quarterly
   - **(f)** 21.2% compounded semi-annually

2. Find the nominal annual rate of interest for each of the following.

	Principal	*Amount*	*Time*	*Frequency of conversion*
(a)	$1400.00	$3192.98	7 years	annually
(b)	2350.00	4676.00	5 years	quarterly
(c)	690.00	1812.00	6 years	monthly
(d)	1240.00	4720.80	12 years	semi-annually
(e)	3160.00	5000.00	4 years, 9 months	quarterly
(f)	785.00	1200.00	3 years, 8 months	monthly

3. Determine the number of compounding periods for each of the following.

	Principal	*Amount*	*Interest rate*	*Frequency of conversion*
(a)	$2600.00	$6437.50	7%	annually
(b)	1240.00	3249.00	14%	quarterly
(c)	560.00	1350.00	9%	monthly
(d)	3480.00	4715.80	13%	semi-annually
(e)	950.00	1900.00	14%	quarterly
(f)	1300.00	3900.00	6%	semi-annually

B. Solve each of the following.

1. What is the nominal rate of interest compounded quarterly at which $420.00 will accumulate to $1000.00 in nine years and six months?

2. A principal of $1250.00 compounded monthly amounts to $2800.00 in 7.25 years. What is the nominal annual rate of interest?

3. At what nominal rate of interest will money double itself in
   (a) six years, nine months if compounded quarterly?
   (b) nine years, two months if compounded monthly?

4. What is the nominal rate of interest at which money will triple itself in
   (a) twelve years if compounded annually?
   (b) seven years and six months if compounded semi-annually?

5. What is the effective rate of interest if $100.00 grows to $150.00 in six years compounded quarterly?

6. If $1100.00 accumulates to $1850.00 in four years, six months compounded semi-annually, what is the effective rate of interest?

7. Find the nominal annual rate of interest compounded quarterly that is equal to an effective rate of 19.25%.

8. If the effective rate of interest on an investment is 16.4%, what is the nominal rate of interest compounded monthly?

9. How long will it take $400.00 to accumulate to $760.00 at 7% p.a. compounded semi-annually?

10. In how many days will $540.00 grow to $600.00 at 13.5% p.a. compounded monthly?

11. In how many years will money quadruple at 8% compounded quarterly?

12. In how many months will money triple at 15% compounded semi-annually?

13. If an investment of \$800.00 earned interest of \$320.00 at 12% compounded monthly, for how many years was the money invested?

14. A loan of \$2000.00 was repaid together with interest of \$1164.00. If interest was 14% compounded quarterly, for how many months was the loan taken out?

15. If you borrowed \$1000.00 on May 1, 1996, at 10% compounded semi-annually and interest on the loan amounts to \$157.63, on what date is the loan due?

16. A promissory note for \$600.00 dated May 15, 1995, requires an interest payment of \$150.00 at maturity. If interest is at 15% compounded monthly, determine the due date of the note.

17. A non-interest-bearing promissory note for \$1500.00 was discounted at 13% p.a. compounded quarterly. If the proceeds of the note were \$1199.11, how many months before the due date was the note discounted?

18. A five-year, \$1000.00 note bearing interest at 11% compounded annually was discounted at 15% compounded semi-annually yielding proceeds of \$1416.56. How many months before the due date was the discount date?

10.5 *Special problems—equated date, equivalent rates, continuous compounding*

A. Equated date

Chapter 9, section 9.5, considered the concept of *equivalence* of values when using the compound interest method. In solving problems of equivalence, the unknown value was always the size of a payment at the selected focal date. While this type is the most frequently arising problem, occasionally the value to be found is the focal date or the interest rate.

The **equated date** is the date on which a single sum of money is equal to the sum of two or more dated sums of money. To find an equated date, an equation of values can be set up by the same technique used in Section 9.5. However, solving the equation for n requires the same technique as used in Section 10.4C. Since this method involves the use of logarithms, you can solve the problem using an electronic calculator as long as the calculator is equipped with the natural logarithm function (lnx key).

***Example* 10.5a** A financial obligation requires the payment of \$2000.00 in six months, \$3000.00 in fifteen months, and \$5000.00 in 24 months. When can the obligation be discharged by the single payment equal to the sum of the required payments if money is worth 15% p.a. compounded monthly?

Solution

The single payment equal to the sum of the required payments is \$2000.00 plus \$3000.00 plus \$5000.00, or \$10 000.00. Select as the focal date 'now.' Let the number of compounding periods from the focal date to the equated date be represented by n. Since the compounding is done monthly, n will be a number of months and $i = \frac{15\%}{12} = 1.25\% = 0.0125$. The method and data are shown graphically in Figure 10.1.

Let E_1, E_2, E_3 represent the equivalent values of the original payments at the focal date as shown in Figure 10.1.

Let E_4 represent the equivalent value of the single payment of \$10 000.00 at the focal date.

The equation of values can now be set up.

$$E_4 = E_1 + E_2 + E_3$$

$$10\,000.00(1.0125)^{-n} = 2000.00(1.0125)^{-6} + 3000.00(1.0125)^{-15} + 5000.00(1.0125)^{-24}$$

$$10\,000.00(1.0125)^{-n} = 2000.00(0.9281749) + 3000.00(0.8299932) + 5000.00(0.7421971)$$

$$10\,000.00(1.0125)^{-n} = 1856.35 + 2489.98 + 3710.99$$

$$10\,000.00(1.0125)^{-n} = 8057.32$$

$$(1.0125)^{-n} = \frac{8057.32}{10\,000.00}$$

$$(1.0125)^{-n} = 0.805732$$

$$-n(\ln 1.0125) = \ln 0.805732$$

$$-n(0.0124225) = -0.2160041$$

$$n = \frac{0.2160041}{0.0124225}$$

$$n = 17.388107$$

FIGURE 10.1 ***Graphic representation of method and data***

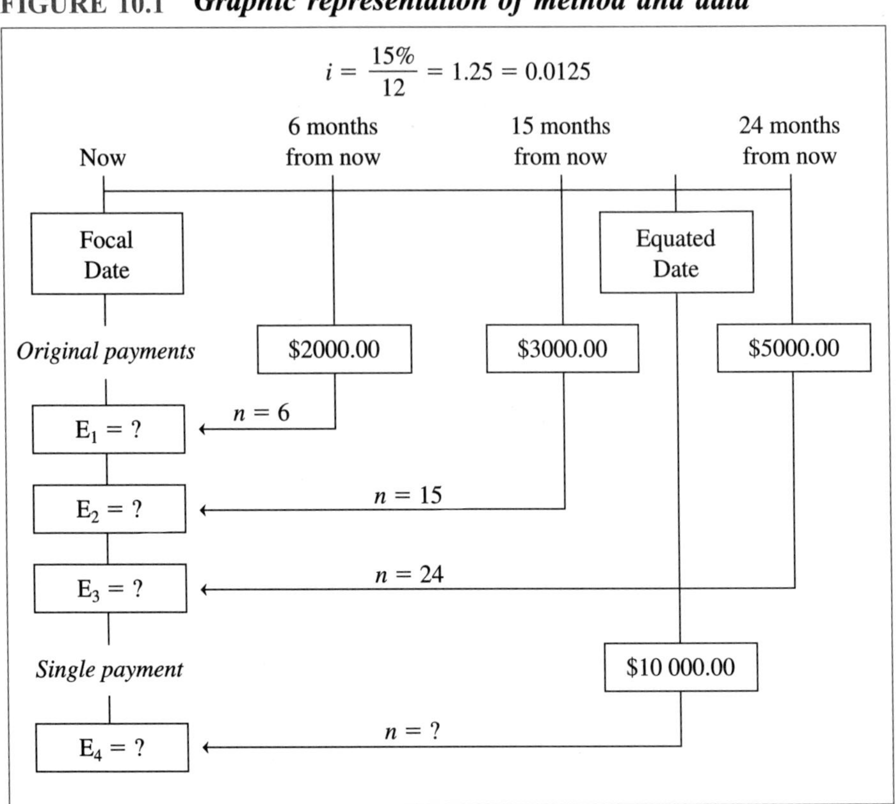

Programmed solution

First simplify the equation $E_4 = E_1 + E_2 + E_3$.

$$10\,000(1.0125)^{-n} = 2000.00\,(1.0125)^{-6} + 3000\,(1.0125)^{-15} + 5000\,(1.0125)^{-24}$$

	⇓		⇓		⇓
0	PMT				
2000	FV	3000	FV	5000	FV
1.25	%i	(	%i	already programmed)	
6	N	15	N	24	N
	CPT		CPT		CPT
	PV		PV		PV

$10\,000(1.0125)^{-n}$ = 1856.35 + 2489.98 + 3710.99

Now solve the simplified equation

$$10\,000(1.0125)^{-n} = 8057.32$$

in which S = 10 000; P = 8057.32; i = 1.25%

10 000	8057.32	1.25			
FV	PV	%i	CPT	N	17.388107

The equated date is about 17.4 months or 529 days from now.

While the definition of equated date requires that the single sum of money be equal to the sum of the dated sums of money considered, the method used in solving the problem can be applied to problems in which the single sum of money does not equal the sum of the dated sums of money considered.

***Example* 10.5b** A loan is to be repaid by three equal payments of \$1500.00 due now, two years from now, and four years from now respectively. When can the obligation be paid off by a single payment of \$5010.00 if interest is 10% compounded annually?

Solution

Select as the focal date 'now.' Let the number of compounding periods from the focal date to the equated date be represented by n. Since the compounding is done annually, n will be a number of years and i = 10% = 0.10.

Let E_1, E_2, E_3 represent the equivalent values of the original payments at the focal date.

$$\begin{aligned} E_1 &= 1500.00 && = 1500.00 \\ E_2 &= 1500.00(1.10)^{-2} = 1500.00(0.8264463) && = 1239.67 \\ E_3 &= 1500.00(1.10)^{-4} = 1500.00(0.6830135) && = \underline{1024.52} \\ && E_1 + E_2 + E_3 &= 3764.19 \end{aligned}$$

Let E_4 represent the equivalent value of the single payment of \$5010.00 at the focal date.

$$\begin{aligned} E_4 &= 5010.00(1.10)^{-n} \\ E_4 &= E_1 + E_2 + E_3 \\ 5010.00(1.10)^{-n} &= 3764.19 \\ (1.10)^{-n} &= 0.7513353 \\ -n(\ln 1.10) &= \ln 0.7513353 \\ -0.0953102n &= -0.2859033 \\ n &= 3 \end{aligned}$$

Programmed solution

$$E_4 = E_1 + E_2 + E_3$$

$5010.00(1.10)^{-n} = 1500.00 + 1500(1.10)^{-2} + 1500(1.10)^{-4}$

⇓

0 [PMT]

1500 [FV] ([FV] and [%i] already programmed)

10 [%i]

2 [N] 4 [N]

[CPT] [CPT]

[PV] [PV]

$5010.00(1.10)^{-n} = 1500.00 + 1239.67 + 1024.52$

$5010.00(1.10)^{-n} = 3764.19$

5010 [FV] 3764.19 [PV] ([%i] already programmed) [CPT] [N] 3.0

The single payment should be made three years from now.

***Example* 10.5c** A loan of \$2000.00 taken out today is to be repaid by a payment of \$1200.00 in six months and a final payment of \$1000.00. If interest is 15% compounded monthly, when should the final payment be made?

Solution

Let the focal point be 'now'; $i = \dfrac{15\%}{12} = 1.25\% = 0.0125.$

$$2000.00 = 1200.00(1.0125)^{-6} + 1000.00(1.0125)^{-n}$$
$$2000.00 = 1200.00(0.9281749) + 1000.00(1.0125)^{-n}$$
$$2000.00 = 1113.81 + 1000.00(1.0125)^{-n}$$
$$886.19 = 1000.00(1.0125)^{-n}$$
$$(1.0125)^{-n} = 0.88619$$
$$-n(\ln 1.0125) = \ln 0.88619$$
$$-0.0124225n = -0.1208239$$
$$n = 9.7261997 \text{ (months)}$$

Programmed solution

$$2000.00 = 1200.00(1.0125)^{-6} + 1000(1.0125)^{-n}$$

$$\Downarrow$$

0	1200	1.25	6			
PMT	FV	%i	N	CPT	PV	1113.81

$$2000.00 = 1113.81 + 1000(1.0125)^{-n}$$
$$886.19 = 1000(1.0125)^{-n}$$

886.19	1000	1.25			
PV	FV	%i	CPT	N	9.72619 (months)

$$n = 296\ days \longleftarrow \left(\frac{9.7261997}{12}\right)(365)$$

The final payment should be made in 296 days.

B. Equivalent rates

Interest rates that increase a given principal to the same compound amount over the same period of time are called **equivalent rates.**

***Example* 10.5d** Find the compound amount after one year of $100.00 accumulated at

(i) 12.55% compounded annually; (ii) 12.18% compounded semi-annually;
(iii) 12.00% compounded quarterly; (iv) 11.88% compounded monthly.

Solution

	(i)	*(ii)*	*(iii)*	*(iv)*
Principal	100.00	100.00	100.00	100.00
Nominal rate	12.55%	12.18%	12.00%	11.88%
i	0.1255	0.0609	0.03	0.0099
n	1	2	4	12
Amount	$100.00(1.1255)^1$ 100.00(1.1255) $112.55	$100.00(1.0609)^2$ 100.00(1.1255088) $112.55	$100.00(1.03)^4$ 100.00(1.1255088) $112.55	$100.00(1.0099)^{12}$ 100.00(1.1254870) $112.55

Note: The four different nominal annual rates produce the same compound amount of $112.55 for the same principal of $100.00 over the same time period of one year. By definition, the four nominal rates are equivalent rates.

To find equivalent rates, we need to equate the accumulated values of $1 for the rates under consideration based on a selected time period, usually one year.

Example **10.5e** Find the nominal annual rate compounded semi-annually that is equivalent to an effective annual rate of 12%.

Solution

Let the semi-annual rate of interest be represented by i.
For P = 1, n = 2, the accumulated value $S_1 = (1 + i)^2$.
For the given effective rate, the accumulated value $S_2 = (1 + 0.12)^1$.
By definition, to be equivalent, $S_1 = S_2$.

$$(1 + i)^2 = 1.12$$
$$1 + i = 1.12^{0.5}$$
$$1 + i = 1.0583005$$
$$i = 0.0583005 \longleftarrow \text{semi-annual rate}$$

Programmed solution

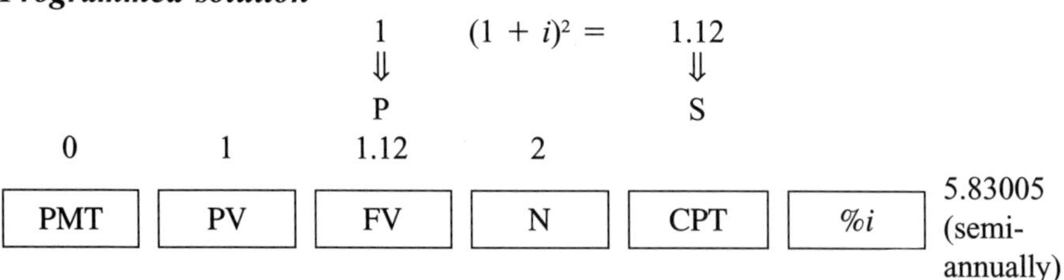

The nominal annual rate is 2(0.0583005) = 0.1166010 = 11.66%.

Example **10.5f** What nominal rate compounded quarterly is equivalent to 16.2% p.a. compounded monthly?

Solution

Let the quarterly rate be i; P = 1; n = 4.
The accumulated value of $1 after one year $S_1 = (1 + i)^4$.
For the given rate $i = \dfrac{16.2\%}{12} = 1.35\% = 0.0135$; $n = 12$.
The accumulated value of $1 after one year $S_2 = (1.0135)^{12}$.
To be equivalent, $S_1 = S_2$.

$$(1 + i)^4 = (1.0135)^{12}$$
$$1 + i = (1.0135)^3$$
$$1 + i = 1.0410492$$
$$i = 0.0410492 \longleftarrow \text{quarterly rate}$$

Programmed solution

$$(1 + i)^4 = (1.0135)^{12}$$

⇓

0 1 1.35 12

PMT | PV | %i | N | CPT | FV | 1.1745866

$$1(1 + i)^4 = 1.1745866$$

1 1.1745866 4

PV | FV | N | CPT | %i | 4.10492 (quarterly)

The nominal annual rate is 4(0.0410492) = 0.1641968 = 16.42%.

Example **10.5g** Peel Credit Union offers premium savings deposits at 12% interest paid semi-annually. The Board of Directors wants to change to monthly payment of interest. What nominal rate should the board set to maintain the same effective rate?

Solution

Let the monthly rate be i; $n = 12$; P = 1.
The accumulated value of \$1 after one year $S_1 = (1 + i)^{12}$.
For the existing rate, $n = 2$, $i = 0.06$.
The accumulated value of \$1 in one year $S_2 = (1.06)^2$.
To yield the same effective rate, the two rates must be equivalent.

$$\begin{aligned}(1 + i)^{12} &= (1.06)^2\\ 1 + i &= (1.06)^{\frac{1}{6}}\\ 1 + i &= 1.0097588\\ i &= 0.0097588 \longleftarrow \text{monthly rate}\end{aligned}$$

Programmed solution

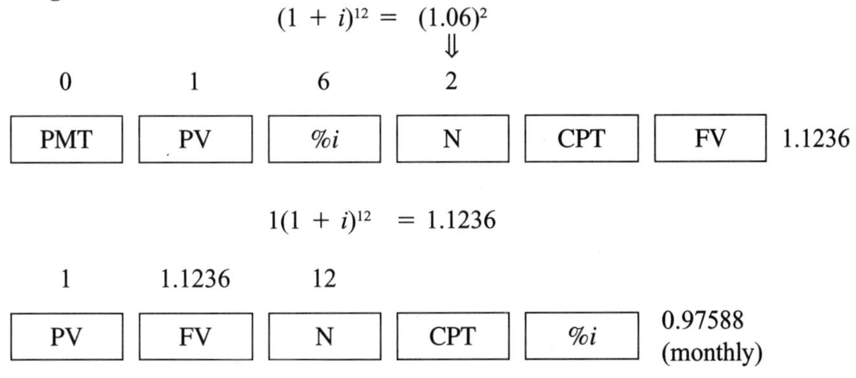

The nominal rate is 12(0.0097588) = 0.117106 = 11.71%.

Note: The effective annual rate of interest using Formula 10.1, $f = (1 + i)^m - 1$, for the existing rate is

$$f = (1 + 0.06)^2 - 1 = 1.1236 - 1 = 0.1236 = 12.36\%$$

and for the new nominal rate compounded monthly is

$$f = (1 + 0.0097588)^{12} - 1 = 1.1236001 - 1 = 0.1236001 = 12.36\%$$

C. Continuous compounding

Compounding is not restricted to the commonly used annual, semi-annual, quarterly and monthly intervals. Rather, it can be done at any time interval. Daily compounding has become quite feasible with the widespread installation of computers in financial institutions. Shorter and shorter time intervals can be used until the limiting case, known as **continuous compounding**, is reached.

Formulae for continuous compounding have been developed and are listed below (formulae 10.2, 10.3, and 10.4). You can solve problems involving continuous compounding using an electronic calculator equipped with an antilog function (e^x key). This function is normally available on calculators equipped with an lnx key.

Caution: The programming feature CANNOT be used for continuous compounding.

(a) *Finding the compound amount*

$$S = Pe^{nj} \quad \longleftarrow \textit{Formula } \mathbf{10.2}$$

e = the universal constant 2.7182818 (approximately);
n = the number of years for compounding;
j = the nominal annual rate of interest.

(b) *Finding the present value*

$$P = Se^{-nj} \quad \longleftarrow \textit{Formula } \mathbf{10.3}$$

(c) *Finding the effective rate of interest*

$$f = e^j - 1 \quad \longleftarrow \textit{Formula } \mathbf{10.4}$$

***Example* 10.5h** To how much will \$100.00 grow at 10% compounded continuously in

(i) one year? (ii) two years? (iii) eight years?

Solution

(i) $P = 100.00; \quad n = 1; \quad j = 10\% = 0.10$

$$\begin{aligned} S &= 100.00[e^{1(0.10)}] \longleftarrow \text{substituting in Formula 10.2} \\ &= 100.00(e^{0.10}) \\ &= 100.00(1.1051709) \longleftarrow \text{enter 0.10 in keyboard and} \\ &= \$110.52 \qquad\qquad \text{use } \boxed{\;e^x\;} \text{ key} \end{aligned}$$

(ii) $P = 100.00; \quad n = 2; \quad j = 10\% = 0.10$

$$S = 100.00[e^{2(0.10)}] = 100.00(e^{0.20}) = 100.00(1.2214028) = \$122.14$$

(iii) $P = 100.00; \quad n = 8; \quad j = 10\% = 0.10$

$$S = 100.00[e^{8(0.10)}] = 100.00(e^{0.80}) = 100.00(2.2255409) = \$222.55$$

***Example* 10.5i** What is the present value of \$1000.00 at 12% compounded continuously due in

(i) 2.5 years? (ii) 5 years, 9 months? (iii) 12 years, 8 months?

Solution

(i) $S = 1000.00; \quad n = 2.5; \quad j = 12\% = 0.12$

$$\begin{aligned} P &= 1000.00[e^{-2.5(0.12)}] \longleftarrow \text{substituting in Formula 10.3} \\ &= 1000.00(e^{-0.30}) \\ &= 1000.00(0.7408182) \\ &= \$740.82 \end{aligned}$$

(ii) $S = 1000.00; \quad n = 5.75; \quad j = 12\% = 0.12$

$$\begin{aligned} P &= 1000.00[e^{-5.75(0.12)}] \\ &= 1000.00(e^{-0.69}) \\ &= 1000.00(0.5015761) \\ &= \$501.58 \end{aligned}$$

(iii) $S = 1000.00; \quad n = 12.666667; \quad j = 12\% = 0.12$

$$\begin{aligned} P &= 1000.00[e^{-12.666667(0.12)}] \\ &= 1000.00(e^{-1.52}) \\ &= 1000.00(0.2187119) \\ &= \$218.71 \end{aligned}$$

***Example* 10.5j** Find the effective rate of interest for each of the following nominal rates compounded continuously: (i) 10% (ii) 15%

Solution

(i) $f = e^{j} - 1$ ⟵ substituting in Formula 10.4

$= e^{0.10} - 1$

$= 1.1051709 - 1$

$= 0.1051709$

$= 10.517\%$ (approximately)

(ii) $f = e^{0.15} - 1$

$= 1.1618342 - 1$

$= 0.1618342$

$= 16.18\%$ (approximately)

Example **10.5k** How long will it take money to double if compounded continuously at (i) 10%? (ii) 18%?

Solution

$$P = 1.00;\ S = 2.00$$

$2.00 = 1.00(e^{nj})$ ⟵ substituting in Formula 10.2

$e^{nj} = 2$

$nj(\ln e) = \ln 2$ ⟵ using the natural logarithm

$nj = \dfrac{\ln 2}{\ln e}$

$nj = \ln 2$ ⟵ $\ln e = 1$

$n = \dfrac{\ln 2}{j}$ ⟵ a general solution for doubling money

(i) $j = 10\% = 0.10$

$n = \dfrac{\ln 2}{0.10}$

$= \dfrac{0.6931472}{0.10}$

$= 6.9314718$ (years)

$= 83$ months approximately

(ii) $j = 18\% = 0.18$

$n = \dfrac{\ln 2}{0.18}$

$= \dfrac{0.6931472}{0.18}$

$= 3.8508177$ (years)

$= 46$ months approximately

Note: The Rule of 70 referred to in Section 10.4, used to estimate the number of conversion periods required to double money, originates from the general solution for doubling money when compounding continuously. Since $\ln 2 = 0.69314718$ or approximately 0.70, an estimate of n is given by $n = \dfrac{0.70}{j}$. To convert the interest to percent form, multiply 0.70 by 100—the Rule of 70. Similar rules could have been established for tripling, quadrupling, etc.

To triple money, $n = \frac{\ln 3}{j} = \frac{1.0986123}{j}$ or approximately $\frac{110}{\text{rate of interest}}$ → Rule of 110.

For $j = 10\%$, money triples in about $\frac{110}{10} = 11$ compounding periods.

To quadruple money, $n = \frac{\ln 4}{j} = \frac{1.3862944}{j}$ or approximately $\frac{139}{\text{rate of interest}}$.

For $j = 10\%$, money quadruples in about $\frac{139}{10} = 14$ periods.

Example **10.5l** What is the nominal rate compounded continuously that is equivalent to 12% compounded quarterly?

Solution

Let the nominal rate compounded continuously be represented by j.
For P = 1 and $n = 1$, the accumulated value in one year $S_1 = e^j$.
For 12% compounded quarterly, the accumulated value in one year $S_2 = (1.03)^4$.
To be equivalent, $S_1 = S_2$.

$$e^j = (1.03)^4$$
$$e^j = 1.1255088$$
$$j(\ln e) = \ln 1.1255088$$
$$j = 0.1182352 \longleftarrow \ln e = 1$$
$$j = 11.82\% \text{ (approximately)}$$

Exercise 10.5

A. Answer each of the following.

1. Find the equated date at which the original payments are equivalent to the single payment for each of the following.

	Original payments	*Int. rate*	*Frequency of conversion*	*Single payment*
(a)	\$400 due in 9 months and \$700 due in 21 months	12%	quarterly	\$1256.86
(b)	\$1200 due today and \$2000 due in 5 years	15%	semi-annually	\$3808.70
(c)	\$1000 due 8 months ago, \$1200 due in 6 months, and \$1500 due in 16 months	15%	monthly	\$3500.00
(d)	\$600 due in 2 years, \$800 due in 3.5 years, and \$900 due in 5 years	20%	quarterly	\$1800.00

2. Find the nominal annual rate of interest equivalent to each of the following.

   (a) 12.5% compounded semi-annually

   (b) 6% compounded monthly

   (c) 14.2% compounded quarterly

   (d) 16.2% compounded monthly

3. Find the accumulated value of each of the following sums of money compounded continuously.

   (a) \$400.00 at 7% for six years

   (b) \$2700.00 at 14.5% for 12 years

   (c) \$1800.00 at 5.5% for four years, seven months

   (d) \$3700.00 at 13.4% for three years, ten months

4. Find the present value of each of the following amounts if interest is compounded continuously.

   (a) \$6000.00 due in 18 years at 7.75%

   (b) \$3400.00 due in nine years, six months at 9.8%

   (c) \$4500.00 due in two years, five months at 16.25%

   (d) \$1000.00 due in one year, nine months at $12\frac{3}{8}$%.

5. Find the effective rate of each of the following nominal rates compounded continuously.

   (a) 22.5%

   (b) 14.25%

B. Solve each of the following problems.

1. A contract requires payments of \$4000.00 today, \$5000.00 in three years, and \$6000.00 in five years. When can the contract be fulfilled by a single payment equal to the sum of the required payments if money is worth 15% p.a. compounded monthly?

2. A financial obligation requires the payment of \$500.00 in nine months, \$700.00 in fifteen months, and \$600.00 in 27 months. When can the obligation be discharged by a single payment of \$1600.00 if interest is 17% compounded quarterly?

3. When Brenda bought Sheridan Service from Ken, she agreed to make three payments of \$6000.00 each in one year, three years, and five years respectively. Because of initial cash flow difficulties, Brenda offered to pay \$8000.00 in two years and a second payment of \$10 000.00 at a later date. When should she make the second payment if interest is 13% compounded semi-annually?

4. Leo sold a property and is to receive \$3000.00 in six months, \$4000.00 in 24 months, and \$5000.00 in 36 months. The deal was renegotiated after nine months at which time Leo received a payment of \$7000.00; he was to receive a further payment of \$6000.00 later. When should Leo receive the second payment if money is worth 14% compounded quarterly?

5. The Central Bank pays 7.5% compounded semi-annually on certain types of deposits. If interest is compounded monthly, what nominal rate of interest will maintain the same effective rate of interest?

6. The treasurer of Sheridan Credit Union proposes changing the method of compounding interest on premium savings accounts to daily compounding. If the current rate is 12% compounded quarterly, what nominal rate should the treasurer suggest to the Board of Directors to maintain the same effective rate of interest?

7. You have invested \$1000.00 for five years at 8% compounded quarterly. How much more interest would you earn if interest were compounded continuously?

8. A private lender requires interest of 16.5% compounded continuously. A local bank charges 16.5% compounded monthly. How much more is the private lender's interest on a loan of \$8000.00 taken out for eight years?

9. What single payment made today would pay off two debt payments of \$1600.00 each, due in 15 months and 30 months respectively, if interest is 14% compounded continuously?

10. A contract offers \$4000.00 in three years, \$7000.00 in six years, and \$9000.00 in eight years. What single sum of money paid today would satisfy the contract if money is worth 11.75% compounded continuously?

11. What nominal rate of interest compounded quarterly is equivalent to 5% compounded continuously?

12. Compute the nominal rate of interest compounded monthly that is equivalent to 15.5% compounded continuously.

13. How long will it take money to double if compounded continuously at

    (a) 6%?

    (b) 15.4%?

14. What length of time will it take money

    (a) to triple at 9% compounded continuously?

    (b) to quadruple at 15.4% compounded continuously?

15. What nominal rate compounded continuously is equivalent to 14% compounded quarterly?

16. Find the nominal rate compounded continuously that is equivalent to 7.50% compounded monthly.

Review exercise

1. If \$6000.00 is invested for six years and seven months at 15% compounded semi-annually, what is the interest that the investment earns?
2. Determine the sum of money that will grow to \$14 000 in four years, eight months at 5% compounded quarterly.
3. Compute the maturity value of a \$5000 promissory note dated November 15, 1986, and due on June 15, 1996, if interest is 8% compounded quarterly.
4. Determine the proceeds of \$9000 three years and ten months before the due date if interest is 7% compounded semi-annually.
5. A fifteen-year promissory note for \$16 500 bearing interest at 15% compounded monthly is discounted at 9% compounded semi-annually three years and four months after the date of issue. Compute the proceeds of the note.
6. An eight-year promissory note for \$20 000 dated May 2, 1994, bearing interest at 17% compounded quarterly, is discounted on September 2, 1996, at 16.5% compounded semi-annually. Determine the proceeds of the note.
7. An investment of \$2000.00 is made for three years, four months at 12.5% compounded semi-annually. What is the amount of interest?
8. Determine the discounted value now of \$5200.00 due in forty months at 6.5% compounded quarterly.
9. Compute the proceeds of a non-interest-bearing promissory note for \$1600.00 two years and eight months before the due date if money is worth 17.5% compounded annually.
10. At what nominal rate of interest compounded monthly will \$400.00 earn \$300.00 interest in four years?
11. What nominal rate of interest compounded monthly is equivalent to an effective rate of 6.2%?
12. Find the equated date at which two payments of \$500.00 due six months ago and \$600.00 due today could be settled by a payment of \$1300.00 if interest is 15% compounded monthly.
13. Find the accumulated value of \$700.00 at 8.5% compounded continuously for seven years.
14. Find the principal that will grow to \$1450.00 at 11% compounded continuously in six years and nine months.
15. In what period of time will money triple at 10% compounded semi-annually?
16. Find the effective rate equivalent to 16.75% compounded continuously.
17. Find the amount of
    (a) \$3500 compounded continuously for six years at 24%;
    (b) \$8400 compounded continuously for three years, eight months at 28%.

18. Find the present value of

(a) \$10 000 due in ten years if interest is 4% compounded continuously;

(b) \$7000 due in four years, four months if interest is 15.5% compounded continuously.

19. Find the nominal annual rate of interest correct to two decimals

(a) at which \$2500 will grow to \$7000 in eight years compounded quarterly;

(b) at which money will double in five years compounded semi-annually;

(c) if the effective annual rate of interest is 9.2% and compounding is done monthly;

(d) which is equivalent to 16% compounded quarterly;

(e) which is equivalent to 16% compounded continuously.

20. Compute the effective annual rate of interest correct to two decimals

(a) for 10.5% compounded monthly;

(b) at which \$2000 will grow to \$4800 in seven years compounded quarterly;

(c) for 9% compounded continuously.

21. **(a)** What is the nominal annual rate of interest compounded monthly that is equivalent to 18.5% compounded quarterly?

(b) What is the nominal annual rate of interest compounded quarterly that is equivalent to an effective annual rate of 20%?

22. **(a)** How many years will it take for \$7500 to accumulate to \$23 855.95 at 15% compounded semi-annually?

(b) Over what period of time will money triple at 18% compounded quarterly?

(c) How long will it take for a loan of \$10 000 to amount to \$16 350 at 16.5% compounded monthly?

(d) In how many years will money double if compounded continuously at 13%?

23. A financial obligation requires the payment of \$2000 now, \$2500 in six months, and \$4000 in one year. When will a single payment of \$8000 discharge the obligation if interest is 18% compounded monthly?

24. Gitu owes two debt payments — a payment of \$5000 due in six months and a payment of \$6000 due in fifteen months. If Gitu makes a payment of \$5000 now, when should he make a second payment of \$6000 if money is worth 17% compounded semi-annually?

25. Payment of a debt of \$10 000 incurred on December 1, 1993, with interest at 15% compounded semi-annually is due on December 1, 1996. If a payment of \$7500 is made on December 1, 1995, on what date should a second payment of \$7500 be made if money is worth 18% compounded quarterly?

26. Debts of \$700 due in six months, \$500 due in fifteen months, and \$900 due in two years are to be settled by a single payment one year from now. What is the size of that single payment if interest is 14.5% compounded continuously?

27. Three years and five months after its date of issue, a six-year promissory note for $3300.00 bearing interest at 18% compounded monthly is discounted at 17% compounded semi-annually. Find the proceeds of the note.

28. A seven-year, $1500.00 promissory note with interest at 12.5% compounded semi-annually was discounted at 14% compounded quarterly yielding proceeds of $2150.00. How many months before the due date was the discount date?

29. A contract requires payments of $2000.00 in one year and $4000.00 in five years. The contract was renegotiated and met by a payment of $3000.00 in two years and a final payment of $4500.00. If interest was 15.5% compounded continuously, when was the second payment made?

30. What is the nominal rate compounded continuously which is equivalent to 7% compounded semi-annually?

Self-test

1. A ten-year, $9200 promissory note with interest at 21% compounded monthly is discounted at 15% compounded semi-annually yielding proceeds of $34 524.63. How many months before the due date was the date of discount?

2. Determine the maturity value of $1400 due in 71 months compounding annually at 7.75%.

3. Determine the effective annual rate of interest equivalent to 15% compounded monthly.

4. What is the nominal rate of interest compounded continuously that is equivalent to 13% compounded quarterly?

5. How many months from now can a payment of $1000 due twelve months ago and a payment of $400 due six months from now be settled by a payment of $2213.44 if interest is 21% compounded monthly?

6. At what nominal rate of interest compounded semi-annually will $6900 earn $6400 interest in five years?

7. In how many years will money double at 7.2% compounded quarterly?

8. What is the nominal rate of interest compounded semi-annually that is equivalent to an effective rate of 10.25%?

9. Seven years and two months after its date of issue, an eleven-year promissory note for $8200 bearing interest at 13.5% compounded monthly is discounted at 10.5% compounded semi-annually. Find the proceeds of the note.

10. Find the accumulated value of $5100 invested at 8.9% compounded continuously for ten years and six months.

11. Compute the proceeds of a non-interest-bearing note for $1100 three years and seven months before the due date if money is worth 11% p.a. compounded annually.

12. Find the principal that will grow to $7400 at 15% compounded continuously in ten years and eight months.

CASE STUDY

You have an opportunity to buy a franchise for a fresh-cut French fry store. The franchise licence costs $100 000; it includes the equipment for a small outlet in a mall. Before borrowing or investing this sum of money, it is advisable to complete several operational and financial calculations to see if the franchise will be profitable.

1. The licence fee will be financed by a $75 000 bank loan at 8.5% compounded quarterly. To keep expenses low at first, you will pay only the interest on the amount for the first year and seven months.

   (a) Calculate the interest due at that time.

   (b) This amount is to be paid in 19 equal monthly instalments. Calculate the monthly payment.

2. The company has advised you that the deep fryers will last six years and five months. At that time, new fryers must be installed at a cost of $8900.

   (a) How much money do you have to set aside now to ensure that the $8900 is available? Interest is 9.75% compounded semi-annually.

   (b) To estimate monthly expenses, assume that you will pay the $8900 by making 77 equal monthly payments into a bank account. Calculate the monthly payment. Why will this payment be high?

3. The company projects that sales for the first month will be 3700 units. Growth is expected to be ¾% per month. The average store becomes profitable at 4200 units per month. How many months will it be before this outlet shows a profit?

4. The $25 000 down payment will be financed by a personal loan with interest compounded semi-annually. In five years, this loan is to be repaid by a lump sum of $37 000.

   (a) Calculate the effective rate of interest.

   (b) To estimate monthly expenses, assume this loan will be paid back in equal monthly payments over the five years. What are the payments?

5. The company has done an extensive cost-profit analysis and advises that each unit should contain 1¾ potatoes. The cost to the store for these special potatoes is $3.45 for 15 potatoes.

   (a) Calculate the cost per unit.

   (b) Calculate the cost of potatoes for the first month.

6. You will draw a salary of $600 per month until the store is profitable. Other expenses such as rent and staff amount to $3000 per month. The chips must sell for $1.50 per unit.

   (a) How much money will be gained or lost in the first month?

   (b) How many units must be sold to pay all expenses?

Summary of formulae used

Formula 9.1

$S = P(1 + i)^n$ Finding the compound amount when n is a fractional value using the exact method

Formula 9.2

$P = \frac{S}{(1 + i)^n}$ Finding the present value (discounted value or proceeds) when n is a fractional value using the exact method

or $P = S(1 + i)^{-n}$

Formula 10.1

$f = (1 + i)^m - 1$ Finding the effective rate of interest f for a nominal annual rate compounded m times per year

Formula 10.2

$S = Pe^{nj}$ Finding the compound amount when using continuous compounding

Formula 10.3

$P = Se^{-nj}$ Finding the present value when using continuous compounding

Formula 10.4

$f = e^j - 1$ Finding the effective rate of interest for a nominal rate compounded continuously

Glossary of terms used

Continuous compounding the limiting case in compounding with regard to the length of the conversion period

Effective rate of interest the annual rate of interest that yields the same amount of interest per year as a nominal rate compounded a number of times per year

Equated date the date at which a single sum of money is equal to the sum of two or more dated sums of money

Equivalent rates interest rates that accumulate a given principal to the same amount over the same period of time

Rule of 70 a quick estimator of the number of conversion periods needed to double money at a given periodic rate of interest

11 *Ordinary simple annuities*

Introduction

An annuity is a series of payments, usually of equal size, made at periodic time intervals. The word annuity implies yearly payments but the term applies to all periodic payment plans, the most frequent of which require annual, semi-annual, quarterly, or monthly payments. Practical applications of annuities are widely encountered in the finances of businesses and individuals alike. Payments or receipts of money relating to rent, leases, pensions, family allowances, wages and salaries, insurance premiums, mortgages, loans, interest on bonds, and other investments are examples of annuities. Various types of annuities are identified based on the term of an annuity, the date of payment, and the length of the conversion period. In this chapter, we will deal only with ordinary simple annuities.

Objectives

Upon completing this chapter, you will be able to

1. distinguish between types of annuities based on term, payment date, and conversion period;
2. compute the amount (or accumulated value) of ordinary annuities;
3. compute the present value (or discounted value) of ordinary annuities;
4. find the periodic rent when either the amount or the present value of an ordinary annuity is known;
5. find the term of an annuity when either the amount or the present value of the annuity is known;
6. find the interest rate when either the amount or the present value of an ordinary annuity is known.

11.1 *Introduction to annuities*

A. Basic concepts

An **annuity** is a series of payments, usually of equal size, made at periodic intervals. The length of time between the successive payments is called the **payment interval** or **payment period**. The length of time from the beginning of the first payment interval to the end of the last payment interval is called the **term of the annuity**. The size of each of the regular payments is the **periodic rent** and the sum of the periodic payments in one year is the **annual rent**.

B. Types of annuities

Several time variables affect annuities and annuities are classified according to the time variable considered. Depending on whether the term of the annuity is fixed or indefinite, annuities are classified as **annuities certain** or **contingent annuities**.

Typical examples of annuities certain (annuities for which the term is fixed, that is, for which both the beginning date and the ending date are known) include rental payments for real estate, lease payments on equipment, instalment payments on loans, mortgage payments, and interest payments on bonds and debentures.

Examples of contingent annuities (annuities for which the beginning date or the ending date or both are uncertain) are life insurance premiums and pension payments or payments from an RRSP converted into a life annuity at the age of 71. The ending date is unknown for these annuities since they terminate with the death of the recipient. Some contingent annuities are the result of clauses in wills, where the beginning date of periodic payments to a beneficiary is unknown, or of payments from a trust fund for the remaining life of a surviving spouse since neither the beginning date nor the ending date is known.

A special type of annuity is the **perpetuity**, an annuity for which the payments continue forever. Perpetuities result when the size of the period rent is equal to or less than the periodic interest earned by a fund, such as a scholarship fund or an endowment fund to a university.

Variations in the date of payment are another way to classify annuities certain. If payments are made at the end of each payment period, we are dealing with an **ordinary annuity**. If, on the other hand, payments are made at the beginning of each payment period, we are dealing with an **annuity due**.

Typical examples of ordinary annuities are instalment payments on loans, mortgage payments, and interest payments on bonds and debentures, while rent payments on real estate and lease payments on equipment rentals are examples of annuities due.

Deferring the first payment for a specified period of time gives rise to a **deferred annuity**. This type may be either an ordinary annuity or an annuity due depending on whether the future payments are at the beginning or at the end of each payment interval.

A third time variable used to classify annuities is the length of the conversion period relative to the payment period. We distinguish between **simple annuities** and **general annuities** depending on whether or not the conversion period coincides with the payment interval.

An example of a simple annuity is the monthly payments on a loan for which the interest is compounded monthly, since the interest period coincides with the payment period. However, the typical mortgage on homes is compounded semi-annually but repaid by monthly payments. It is an example of a general annuity since the conversion period is different from the payment period.

Example **11.1a** Classify each of the following by

(i) term; (ii) date of payment; (iii) conversion period.

(a) Deposits of $150.00 earning interest at 12% compounded quarterly are made at the beginning of each quarter for four years.

Solution

(i) annuity certain (the term is fixed: four years)

(ii) annuity due (payments are made at the beginning of each quarter)

(iii) simple annuity (the quarterly conversion period equals the quarterly payment period)

(b) Payments of $200.00 are made at the end of each month for five years. Interest is 16% compounded semi-annually.

Solution

(i) annuity certain (the term is fixed: five years)

(ii) ordinary annuity (payments are made at the end of each month)

(iii) general annuity (semi-annual conversion period does not match the monthly payment period)

(c) A fund of $10 000.00 is deposited in a trust account earning interest compounded annually. Starting five years from the date of deposit, the interest earned for the year is to be paid out as a scholarship.

Solution

(i) perpetuity (the payments can go on forever)

(ii) deferred annuity (the first payment is deferred for 5 years)

(iii) simple annuity (the annual conversion period equals the annual interest period)

(d) In his will, Dr. C. directed that part of his estate be invested in a trust fund earning interest compounded quarterly. His surviving wife was to be paid for the remainder of her life $2000.00 at the end of every three months starting three months after his death.

Solution

(i) contingent annuity (both the starting date and ending date are uncertain)

(ii) ordinary annuity (payments at the end of every three months)

(iii) simple annuity (the quarterly conversion period equals the quarterly payment period)

Note: In this chapter, we will deal only with annuities that have a fixed term with payments at the end of each payment period and with conversion periods that coincide with the payment periods; that is, with ordinary simple annuities that are also annuities certain. We will use the word annuity to mean this type of annuity. Other types of annuities are considered in chapters 12 and 13.

Exercise 11.1

A. Classify each of the following by (a) term; (b) date; (c) conversion period.

1. Payments of $50.00 are made at the beginning of each month for five years at 12% compounded semi-annually.

2. Deposits of $500.00 are made at the end of each quarter for nine years earning interest at 7% compounded quarterly.

3. A fund with an initial deposit of $50 000.00 is set up to provide annual scholarships to eligible business students in an amount not exceeding the annual interest earned by the fund. Scholarship payments are to begin three years from the date of deposit. Interest earned by the fund is compounded semi-annually.

4. The Saskatoon Board of Education introduced a long-term disability plan for its employees. The plan provides for monthly payments equal to 90 percent of regular salary starting one month after the beginning of the disability. Assume that the plan is subject to monthly compounding.

5. Gary invested $10 000.00 in an account paying interest compounded monthly with the provision that equal monthly payments be made to him from the account for fifteen years at the beginning of each month starting ten years from the date of deposit.

6. Ms. X set up a trust fund earning interest compounded semi-annually to provide equal monthly support payments for her surviving husband starting one month after her death.

11.2 *Amount of an annuity*

A. Amount of a series of payments—basic computation

Example 11.2a Find the amount of deposits of $2000.00, $4000.00, $5000.00, $1000.00, and $3000.00 made at the end of each of five consecutive years respectively at 12% compounded annually just after the last deposit was made.

Solution

The series of deposits can be represented on a time graph as shown:

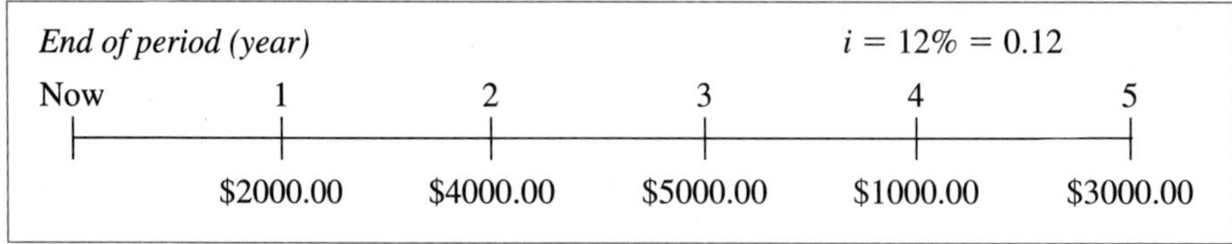

To find the amount of the series of deposits, we need to determine the combined value of the five deposits, including interest, at the focal point *five years from now*. This can be done using Formula 9.1, $S = P(1 + i)^n$. A graphic representation of the method and data is shown in Figure 11.1 below.

FIGURE 11.1 ***Graphic representation of method and data***

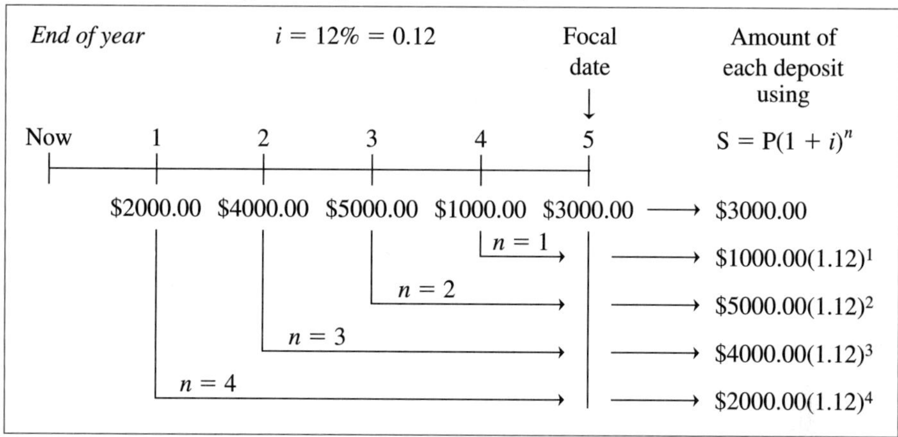

Explanations regarding the amount of each deposit:
The deposit of $3000.00 has just been made and has a value of $3000.00 at the focal date. The deposit of $1000.00 has been in for one year ($n = 1$) and has earned interest for one year at the focal date. Similarly, the deposit of $5000.00 has been in for two years ($n = 2$), the deposit of $4000.00 for three years ($n = 3$), and the deposit of $2000.00 for four years ($n = 4$).

The problem can now be solved by computing the amount of the individual deposits and adding.

Deposit 5	3000.00	=	$ 3 000.00
Deposit 4	$1000.00(1.12)^1 = 1000.00(1.12)$	=	1 120.00
Deposit 3	$5000.00(1.12)^2 = 5000.00(1.2544)$	=	6 272.00
Deposit 2	$4000.00(1.12)^3 = 4000.00(1.4049280)$	=	5 619.71
Deposit 1	$2000.00(1.12)^4 = 2000.00(1.5735194)$	=	3 147.04
	TOTAL		$19 158.75

***Example* 11.2b** Find the amount of five deposits of $3000.00 each made at the end of each of five consecutive years respectively at 12% compounded annually, just after the last deposit has been made.

Solution

This example is basically the same as Example 11.2a except that all deposits are equal in size. The problem can be solved in the same way.

FIGURE 11.2 *Graphic representation of method and data*

End of year			$i = 12\% = 0.12$		Focal date ↓	Amount of each deposit using
Now	1	2	3	4	5	$S = P(1+i)^n$
	\$3000.00	\$3000.00	\$3000.00	\$3000.00	\$3000.00	→ \$3000.00
				$n = 1$ →		→ $3000.00(1.12)^1$
			$n = 2$ →			→ $3000.00(1.12)^2$
		$n = 3$ →				→ $3000.00(1.12)^3$
	$n = 4$ →					→ $3000.00(1.12)^4$

While the approach to solving the problem is fundamentally the same as in Example 11.2a, the fact that the deposits are *equal in size* permits a useful mathematical simplification. The equal deposit of \$3000.00 can be taken out as a common factor and the individual compounding factors can be added. This method avoids computing the amount of each individual deposit.

Deposit 5	3000.00(1)		(1)		(1.)
Deposit 4	$3000.00(1.12)^1$		$(1.12)^1$		(1.12)
Deposit 3	$3000.00(1.12)^2$	= 3000.00	$(1.12)^2$	= 3000.00	(1.2544)
Deposit 2	$3000.00(1.12)^3$		$(1.12)^3$		(1.404928)
Deposit 1	$3000.00(1.12)^4$		$(1.12)^4$		(1.5735194)
				= 3000.00	(6.3528474)
				= \$19 058.54	

Since the deposits in Example 11.2b are equal in size and are made at the end of each period, the problem is an ordinary annuity. Because this type of problem occurs frequently, it is useful to carry the mathematical simplification beyond taking out the common factor. To illustrate the simplification, the solution to Example 11.2b can be rewritten in equation form and manipulated as shown below.

The amount of the ordinary annuity

$= 3000.00 + 3000.00(1.12)^1 + 3000.00(1.12)^2 + 3000.00(1.12)^3 + 3000.00(1.12)^4$

$= 3000.00(1 + 1.12^1 + 1.12^2 + 1.12^3 + 1.12^4)$

= 3000.00 (the sum of the first five terms of a geometric progression whose first term $t_1 = 1$ with a common ratio 1.12. This sum may be computed using the formula

$$S = a\left(\frac{r^n - 1}{r - 1}\right) \text{ for } r > 1$$

where a = the first term
r = the common ratio
n = the number of terms

$$= 3000.00\left[1\left(\frac{1.12^5 - 1}{1.12 - 1}\right)\right] \longleftarrow a = t_1 = 1;\ r = 1.12;\ n = 5$$

$$= 3000.00\left(\frac{1.7623417 - 1}{0.12}\right)$$

$$= 3000.00\left(\frac{0.7623417}{0.12}\right)$$

$$= 3000.00(6.3528475)$$

$$= \$19\,058.54$$

***Example* 11.2c** Use the geometric progression method to determine the accumulated value of payments of \$200.00 made at the end of each of six consecutive years if interest is 10% compounded annually.

Solution

Since the payments are equal in size and are made at the end of each compounding period, the problem is an ordinary simple annuity and the accumulated value of the payments may be written in equation form.

Let the accumulated value be represented by S. Then

$$S = 200.00 + 200.00(1.10) + 200.00(1.10)^2 + 200.00(1.10)^3 + 200.00(1.10)^4 + 200.00(1.10)^5$$

$$= 200.00(1 + 1.10 + 1.10^2 + 1.10^3 + 1.10^4 + 1.10^5)$$

= 200.00 (the sum of the first six terms of a geometric progression with the first term 1 and common ratio 1.10)

$$= 200.00\left(\frac{1.10^6 - 1}{1.10 - 1}\right)$$

$$= 200.00\left(\frac{1.7715610 - 1}{0.10}\right)$$

$$= 200.00\left(\frac{0.7715610}{0.10}\right)$$

$$= 200.00(7.71561)$$

$$= \$1543.12$$

B. *Formula for finding the amount of an ordinary annuity*

Because annuities are geometric progressions, a general formula can be developed for finding the accumulated value of this type of series of payments.

The following notation has been generally adopted in dealing with annuities:

S_n = the amount (accumulated value) of an ordinary annuity;
R = the size of the periodic payment (rent);
i = the interest rate per conversion period;
n = the number of periodic payments (which for simple annuities is also the number of conversion periods).

Using the above notation, the general problem is represented in Figure 11.3.

FIGURE 11.3 ***Graphic representation of the general form of an ordinary annuity***

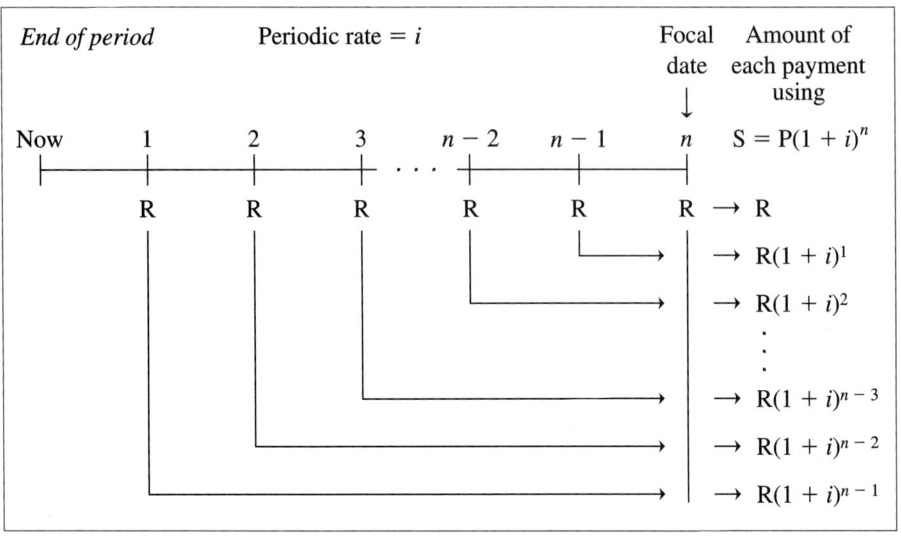

The addition of the amount of the individual payments at the focal date gives rise to the equation

$$S_n = R + R(1 + i)^1 + R(1 + i)^2 + \ldots + R(1 + i)^{n-3} + R(1 + i)^{n-2} + R(1 + i)^{n-1}$$

$$= R[1 + (1 + i)^1 + (1 + i)^2 + \ldots + (1 + i)^{n-3} + (1 + i)^{n-2} + (1 + i)^{n-1}]$$

= R (the sum of the first n terms of a geometric progression with first term 1 and common ratio $1 + i$)

$$= R\left[\frac{(1 + i)^n - 1}{(1 + i) - 1}\right] \longleftarrow \text{substituting in the formula } S = \frac{a(r^n - 1)}{r - 1}$$

$$S_n = R\left[\frac{(1 + i)^n - 1}{i}\right]$$ ⟵ *Formula* **11.1** ⟵ amount of an ordinary annuity

The factor $\frac{(1 + i)^n - 1}{i}$ is called the **compounding** or **accumulation factor for annuities** or the **accumulated value of one dollar per period**.

Example **11.2d** Find the accumulated value of quarterly payments of $50.00 made at the end of each quarter for ten years just after the last payment has been made if interest is 8% compounded quarterly.

Solution

Since the payments are of equal size made at the end of each quarter, the problem is an ordinary annuity.

$$R = 50.00; \quad i = \frac{8\%}{4} = 2\% = 0.02; \quad n = 10(4) = 40$$

$$S_n = 50.00\left[\frac{(1 + 0.02)^{40} - 1}{0.02}\right] \longleftarrow \text{substituting in Formula 11.1}$$

$$= 50.00\left(\frac{2.2080397 - 1}{0.02}\right)$$

$$= 50.00\left(\frac{1.2080397}{0.02}\right)$$

$$= 50.00(60.401985)$$

$$= \$3020.10$$

Example **11.2e** You deposit \$10.00 at the end of each month for five years in an account paying 12% compounded monthly.

(i) How much will be the balance in your account at the end of the five-year term?

(ii) How much of the amount will you have contributed?

(iii) How much is interest?

Solution

(i) $R = 10.00; \quad i = 1\% = 0.01; \quad n = 60$

$$S_n = 10.00\left[\frac{(1 + i)^n - 1}{i}\right]$$

$$= 10.00\left(\frac{1.01^{60} - 1}{0.01}\right)$$

$$= 10.00\left[\frac{(1.8166967 - 1)}{0.01}\right]$$

$$= 10.00(81.66967)$$

$$= \$816.70$$

(ii) Your contribution is \$10.00 per month for 60 months, or 10.00(60) = \$600.00.

(iii) Since your contribution is \$600.00, the interest earned is 816.70 − 600.00 = \$216.70.

C. *Using preprogrammed financial calculators*

You can use preprogrammed financial calculators efficiently to solve annuity problems by selecting the financial mode, entering the given values, and retrieving the answer.

The five variables used in annuity calculations are S_n, A_n, R, i, n. They are programmed into the calculator and are used by pressing keys as follows. Make sure the calculator is set in the financial mode.

Key	*Press to enter or retrieve*
FV	the future value or amount S_n
PV	the present value A_n
PMT	the periodic payment or rent R
%*i*	the periodic rate (conversion rate) i
N	the number of periodic payments n

To begin an ordinary annuity calculation, enter the given values in any order. The value of the wanted variable is then retrieved by pressing CPT (in some models 2nd) followed by the key representing the unknown wanted variable.

When performing an annuity calculation, only one of the present value A_n *or* the amount S_n is involved. To avoid incorrect answers, the present value PV should be set to zero when determining the future value FV and vice versa.

To solve Example 11.2e, in which R = 10.00, i = 1%, and n = 60, use the following procedure.

	Press	Display shows	
0	PV	0	⟵ a precaution to avoid incorrect answers
10	PMT	10	⟵ this enters the periodic payment R
1	%*i*	1	⟵ this enters the conversion rate i
60	N	60	⟵ this enters the number of payments n
CPT	FV	816.6967	⟵ this retrieves the wanted amount S_n

The future value is $816.70.

D. *Applications*

***Example* 11.2f** Jim West set up a savings plan with City Trust of Victoria whereby he deposits $300.00 at the end of each quarter for eight years. The amount in his account at that time will become a term deposit withdrawable after a further five years. If interest throughout the total time period is 11% compounded quarterly,

(i) how much will be in Jim's account just after he makes his last deposit?

(ii) how much will the balance of his account be when he can withdraw the deposit?

(iii) how much of the total at the time of withdrawal did Jim contribute?

(iv) how much is the interest earned?

Solution

As Figure 11.4 shows, problems of this type may be solved in stages. The first stage involves finding the amount of an *ordinary annuity*. This amount becomes the principal for the second stage, which involves finding the amount of a *single* sum of money invested for five years.

FIGURE 11.4 ***Graphic representation of method and data***

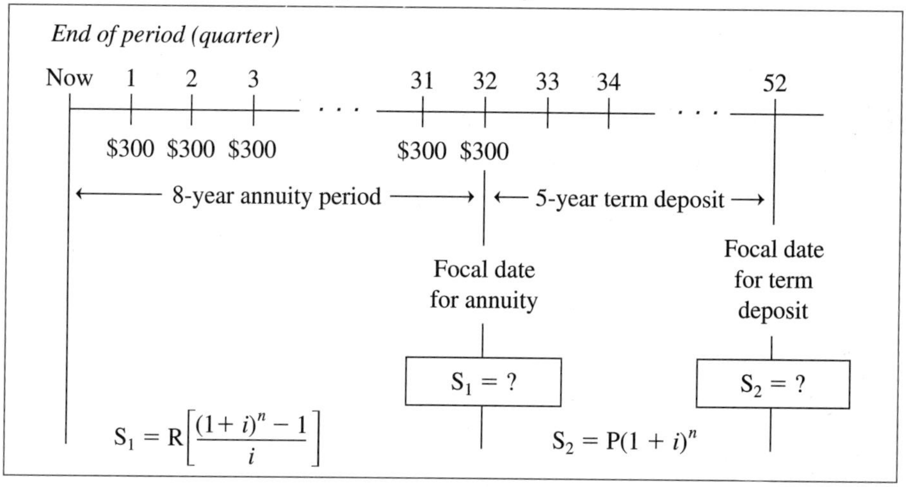

(i) $R = 300.00; \quad i = \frac{11\%}{4} = 2.75\% = 0.0275; \quad n = 8(4) = 32$

$$S_1 = 300.00\left[\frac{(1.0275^{32} - 1)}{0.0275}\right] \longleftarrow \text{Formula 11.1}$$

$$= 300.00\left[\frac{(2.3824214 - 1)}{0.0275}\right]$$

$$= 300.00(50.269869)$$

$$= \$15\ 080.96$$

(ii) $P = S_1 = 15\ 080.96; \quad i = 0.0275; \quad n = 5(4) = 20$

$$S_2 = 15\ 080.96(1.0275)^{20} \longleftarrow \text{Formula 9.1}$$

$$= 15\ 080.96(1.7204284)$$

$$= \$25\ 945.71$$

(iii) Jim's contribution = 32(300.00) = \$9600.00.

(iv) The amount of interest earned = 25 945.71 − 9600.00 = \$16 345.71.

Programmed solution for parts (i) and (ii)

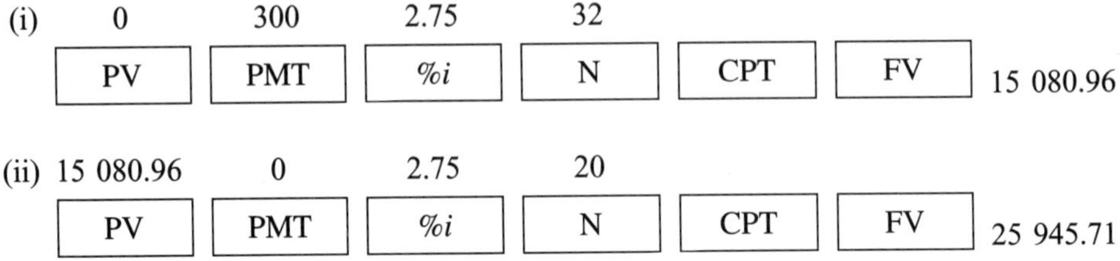

Example **11.2g** The Gordons saved for the purchase of their dream home by making deposits of \$1000.00 per year for ten consecutive years in an account with Cooperative Trust in Saskatoon. The account earned interest at 10.75% compounded annually. At the end of the ten-year contribution period, the deposit was left for a further six years earning interest at 11.5% compounded semi-annually.

(i) What down payment were the Gordons able to make on their house?

(ii) How much of the down payment was interest?

Solution

(i) First, find the amount in the account at the end of the term of the ordinary annuity formed by the yearly deposits.

$$R = 1000.00; \quad i = 10.75\% = 0.1075; \quad n = 10$$

$$S_1 = 1000.00\left[\frac{(1.1075^{10} - 1)}{0.1075}\right]$$

$$= 1000.00\left[\frac{(2.7761143 - 1)}{0.1075}\right]$$

$$= 1000.00(16.521994)$$

$$= \$16\,521.99$$

Second, compute the accumulated value of S_1 in six years.

$$P = S_1 = 16\,521.99; \quad i = \frac{11.5\%}{2} = 5.75\% = 0.0575; \quad n = 12$$

$S_2 = 16\,521.99(1.0575)^{12}$

$= 16\,521.99(1.9559805)$

$= \$32\,316.69$

The Gordons made a down payment of \$32 316.69.

(ii) Since the Gordons contributed (1000.00)(10) = \$10 000.00, the amount of interest in the down payment is \$22 316.69.

Programmed solution for part (i)

0	1000	10.75	10			
PV	PMT	%i	N	CPT	FV	16 521.99
16 521.99	0	5.75	12			
PV	PMT	%i	N	CPT	FV	32 316.69

Example **11.2h** Marise has contributed \$1500.00 per year for the last twelve years into an RRSP deposit account with her caisse populaire in Quebec City. Interest earned by these deposits was 9.5% compounded annually for the first eight years and 10.5% compounded annually for the last four years. Five years after the last deposit, she converted her RRSP into a Registered Retirement Income Fund (RRIF). How much was the beginning balance in the RRIF if interest for those five years remained at 10.5%?

Solution

As Figure 11.5 shows, the problem may be divided into two annuities. The first annuity covers the deposits for the first eight years; the second annuity covers the next four payments.

The focal date for the first annuity is at the end of year 8 (Focal date 1).

The accumulated value of this annuity is computed using Formula 11.1.

FIGURE 11.5 ***Graphic representation of method and data***

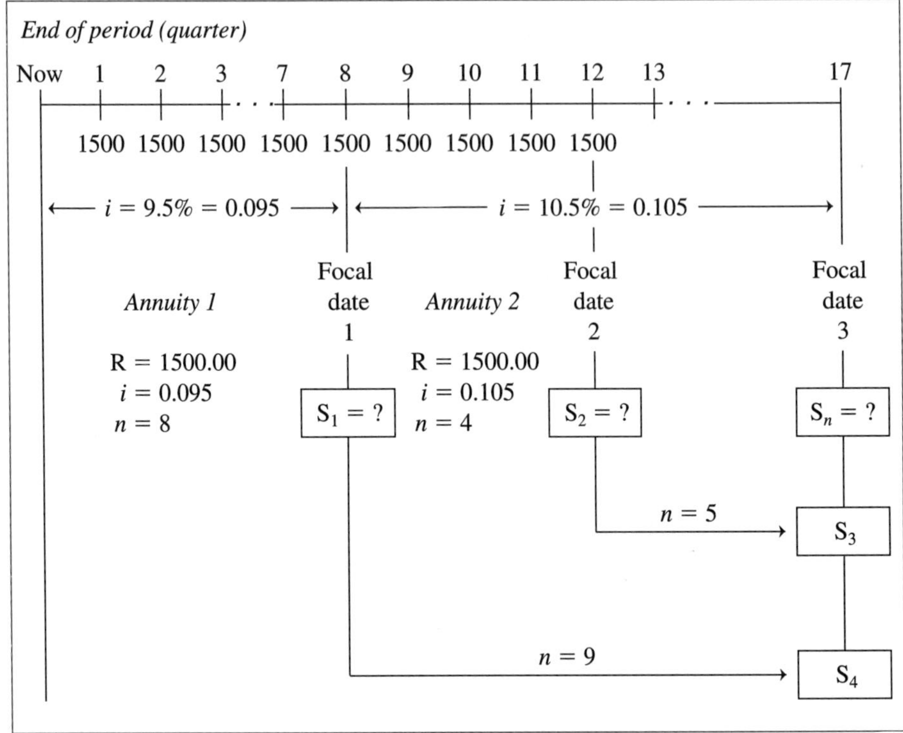

$$S_1 = 1500\left[\frac{(1.095^8 - 1)}{0.095}\right]$$

$$= 1500.00\left[\frac{(2.0668690 - 1)}{0.095}\right]$$

$$= 1500.00(11.230200)$$

$$= \$16\,845.30$$

S_1 now accumulates for nine years (to the end of Year 17) at 10.5% to obtain S_4 at the focal date for the beginning balance in the RRIF (Focal date 3).

$$S_4 = 16\,845.30(1.105)^9$$

$$= 16\,845.30(2.4561818)$$

$$= \$41\,375.12$$

The focal date for the second annuity is at the end of Year 12 (Focal date 2).

$$S_2 = 1500.00\left[\frac{(1.105^4 - 1)}{0.105}\right]$$

$$= 1500.00\left[\frac{(1.4909021 - 1)}{0.105}\right]$$

$$= 1500.00(4.6752576)$$

$$= \$7012.89$$

S_2 now accumulates for five years (to the end of Year 17) to obtain S_3 at Focal date 3.

$$S_3 = 7012.89(1.105)^5$$

$$= 7012.89(1.6474468)$$

$$= \$11\,553.36$$

The beginning balance S_n in the RRIF is now obtained by adding S_3 and S_4.

$$S_n = 11\,553.36 + 41\,375.12$$

$$= \$52\,928.48$$

Programmed solution

S_1	0	1500	9.5	8			
	PV	PMT	%i	N	CPT	FV	16 845.30
S_4	16 845.30	0	10.5	9			
	PV	PMT	%i	N	CPT	FV	41 375.12
S_2	0	1500	10.5	4			
	PV	PMT	%i	N	CPT	FV	7 012.89
S_3	7012.89	0	10.5	5			
	PV	PMT	%i	N	CPT	FV	11 553.36

$S_n = S_3 + S_4 = 11\,553.36 + 41\,375.12 = 52\,928.48$

Exercise 11.2

A. Find the amount of the ordinary annuity for each of the following.

	Periodic payment	*Payment interval*	*Term*	*Interest rate*	*Conversion period*
1.	$1500.00	1 quarter	$7\frac{1}{2}$ years	5%	quarterly
2.	$20.00	1 month	6.75 years	12%	monthly
3.	$700.00	6 months	20 years	7%	semi-annually
4.	$10.00	1 month	15 years	15%	monthly
5.	$320.00	3 months	8 years, 9 months	10.4%	quarterly
6.	$2000.00	$\frac{1}{2}$ year	11 years, 6 months	8.8%	semi-annually

B. Answer each of the following questions.

1. Find the accumulated value of payments of $200.00 made at the end of every three months for twelve years if money is worth 13% compounded quarterly.
2. To what will deposits of $60.00 made at the end of each month amount to after six years if interest is 10.8% compounded monthly?
3. How much interest is included in the amount of an ordinary annuity of $1500.00 paid every six months at 12% compounded semi-annually if the term of the annuity is fifteen years?
4. Jane Alleyre made ordinary annuity payments of $15.00 per month for sixteen years earning 9% compounded monthly. How much interest is included in the amount of the annuity?
5. Saving for his retirement 25 years from now, Jimmy Olsen set up a savings plan whereby he will deposit $25.00 at the end of each month for the next 15 years. Interest is 12% compounded monthly.
   (a) How much money will be in Mr. Olsen's account on the date of his retirement?
   (b) How much will Mr. Olsen contribute?
   (c) How much is interest?
6. The Wolfs have each contributed $1000.00 per year for the last ten years into RRSP accounts earning 6% compounded annually. If they leave their accumulated contributions for another five years in the RRSP at the same rate of interest,
   (a) how much will Mr. and Mrs. Wolf have in total in their RRSP accounts?
   (b) how much did the Wolfs contribute?
   (c) how much will be interest?

7. Ms. Pitt has made quarterly payments of $1375.00 at the end of each quarter into an RRSP for the last seven years earning interest at 7% compounded quarterly. If she leaves the accumulated money in the RRSP for another three years at 8% compounded semi-annually, how much will she be able to transfer at the end of the three years into a Registered Retirement Income Fund?

8. For the last six years Joe Borelli has made deposits of $300.00 at the end of every six months earning interest at 5% compounded semi-annually. If he leaves the accumulated balance for another ten years at 6% compounded quarterly, what will the balance be in Joe's account?

11.3 *Present value of an annuity*

A. Present value of a series of payments—basic computation

Example **11.3a** Find the single sum of money whose value now is equivalent to payments of $2000.00, $4000.00, $5000.00, $1000.00, and $3000.00 made at the end of each of five consecutive years respectively at 12% compounded annually.

Solution

The series of payments can be represented on a time graph.

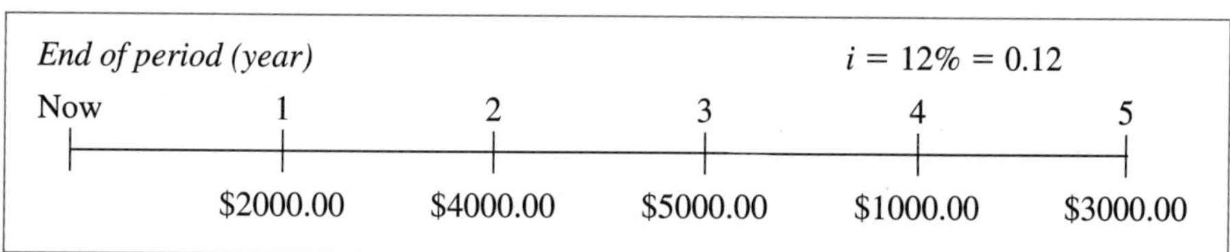

To find the present value of the series of payments, we need to determine the *combined* present value of the five payments at the focal point 'now.' This can be done using Formula 9.2B, $P = S(1 + i)^{-n}$. A graphic representation of the method and data is shown in Figure 11.6.

The solution to the problem can be completed by computing the present value of the individual payments and adding.

Payment 1	$2000.00(1.12)^{-1} = 2000.00(0.8928571)$	=	$1 785.71
Payment 2	$4000.00(1.12)^{-2} = 4000.00(0.7971939)$	=	3 188.78
Payment 3	$5000.00(1.12)^{-3} = 5000.00(0.7117802)$	=	3 558.90
Payment 4	$1000.00(1.12)^{-4} = 1000.00(0.6355181)$	=	635.52
Payment 5	$3000.00(1.12)^{-5} = 3000.00(0.5674269)$	=	1 702.28
	TOTAL		$10 871.19

FIGURE 11.6 ***Graphic representation of method and data***

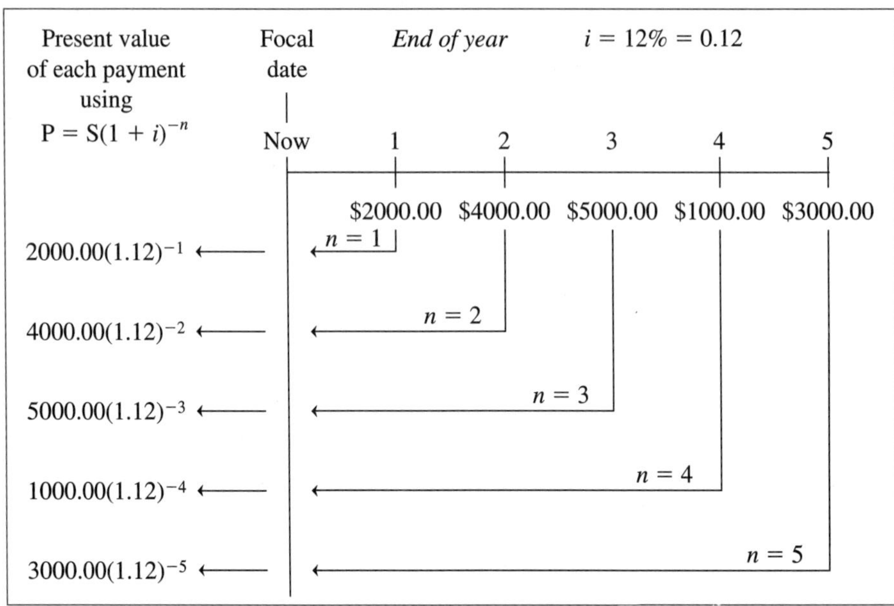

Example **11.3b** Find the present value of five payments of \$3000.00 made at the end of each of five consecutive years respectively if money is worth 12% compounded annually.

Solution

This example is basically the same as Example 11.3a except that all payments are equal in size.

While the approach to solving the problem is fundamentally the same as in Example 11.3a, the fact that the payments are equal in size permits the same mathematical simplification used for Example 11.2b.

Payment 1	$3000.00(1.12)^{-1}$		$(1.12)^{-1}$		(0.8928571)
Payment 2	$3000.00(1.12)^{-2}$		$(1.12)^{-2}$		(0.7971939)
Payment 3	$3000.00(1.12)^{-3}$	=	$3000.00(1.12)^{-3}$	=	$3000.00(0.7117802)$
Payment 4	$3000.00(1.12)^{-4}$		$(1.12)^{-4}$		(0.6355181)
Payment 5	$3000.00(1.12)^{-5}$		$(1.12)^{-5}$		(0.5674269)

$$= 3000.00(3.6047762)$$
$$= \$10\ 814.33$$

Since the payments in Example 11.3b are equal in size and are made at the end of each period, the problem is an ordinary annuity. Finding the sum of the present values of the individual payments at the beginning of the term of an annuity is defined as finding the **present value of an annuity**. It is useful to carry the mathematical simplification beyond simply taking out the common factor 3000.00.

FIGURE 11.7 ***Graphic representation of method and data***

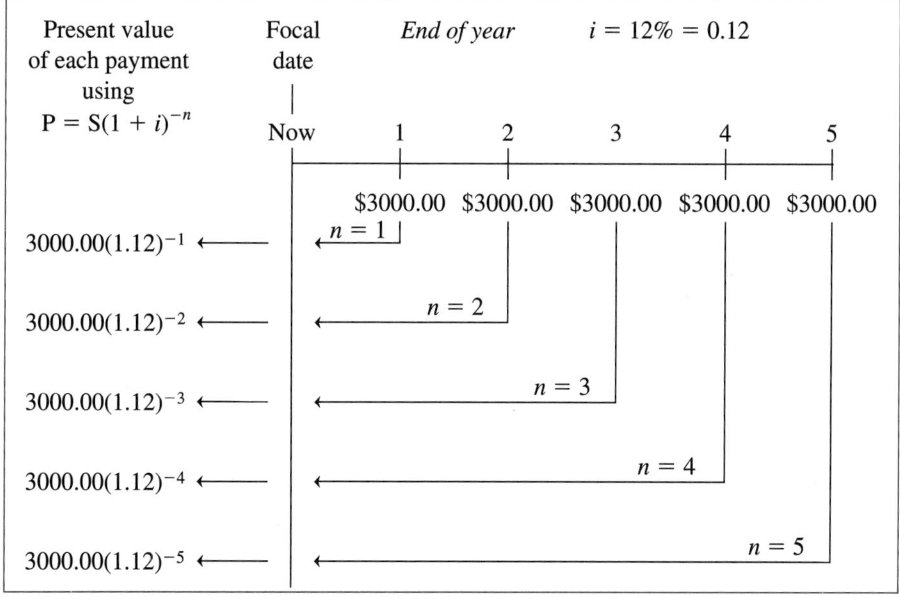

To illustrate the simplification, the solution to Example 11.3b can be rewritten in equation form and manipulated as shown below.

The present value of the ordinary annuity

$= 3000.00(1.12)^{-1} + 3000.00(1.12)^{-2} + 3000.00(1.12)^{-3} + 3000.00(1.12)^{-4} + 3000.00(1.12)^{-5}$

$= 3000.00(1.12^{-1} + 1.12^{-2} + 1.12^{-3} + 1.12^{-4} + 1.12^{-5})$ ⟵ taking out the common factor 3000.00

$= 3000.00(1.12^{-1})(1 + 1.12^{-1} + 1.12^{-2} + 1.12^{-3} + 1.12^{-4})$ ⟵ taking out the common factor 1.12^{-1}

$= 3000.00(1.12^{-1})$ (the sum of the first five terms of a geometric progression with the first term 1 and common ratio 1.12^{-1}.) This sum may be computed using the formula

$$S = a\left(\frac{1 - r^n}{1 - r}\right) \text{ for } r < 1 \text{ where } a = \text{the first term}$$

r = the common ratio

n = the number of terms

$$= 3000.00(1.12^{-1})\left[1\left(\frac{1 - (1.12^{-1})^5}{1 - (1.12^{-1})}\right)\right]$$ ⟵ $a = t_1 = 1;\ r = 1.12^{-1};\ n = 5$

$$= 3000.00\left(\frac{1}{1.12}\right)\left(\frac{1 - 1.12^{-5}}{1 - \frac{1}{1.12}}\right) \longleftarrow \text{convert } 1.12^{-1} \text{ to } \frac{1}{1.12}$$

$$= 3000.00\left(\frac{1}{1.12}\right)\left(\frac{1 - 1.12^{-5}}{\frac{1.12 - 1}{1.12}}\right) \longleftarrow \text{convert } 1 - \frac{1}{1.12} \text{ to } \frac{1.12 - 1}{1.12}$$

$$= 3000.00\left(\frac{1}{1.12}\right)\left[\frac{(1.12)(1 - 1.12^{-5})}{1.12 - 1}\right] \longleftarrow \text{simplify the complex fraction}$$

$$= 3000.00\left(\frac{1}{1}\right)\left(\frac{1 - 1.12^{-5}}{0.12}\right) \longleftarrow \text{reduce by } 1.12$$

$$= 3000.00\left[\frac{(1 - 0.5674269)}{0.12}\right]$$

$$= 3000.000\left(\frac{0.4325731}{0.12}\right)$$

$$= 3000.00(3.6047762)$$

$$= \$10\ 814.33$$

Example **11.3c** Use the geometric progression method to determine the present value at the beginning of the first deposit period of deposits of \$600.00 made at the end of each of four consecutive years if money is worth 10% compounded annually.

Solution

The deposits are equal in size and are made at the end of each period. Since the focal date is at the beginning of the first deposit period, the problem is an ordinary annuity. In equation form, the combined present value of the deposits, represented by A_n, can be written as

$$A_n = 600.00(1.10)^{-1} + 600.00(1.10)^{-2} + 600.00(1.10)^{-3} + 600.00(1.10)^{-4}$$

$$= 600.00(1.10^{-1} + 1.10^{-2} + 1.10^{-3} + 1.10^{-4}) \longleftarrow \text{common factor } 600.00$$

$$= 600.00(1.10^{-1})(1 + 1.10^{-1} + 1.10^{-2} + 1.10^{-3}) \longleftarrow \text{common factor } 1.10^{-1}$$

$$= 600.00(1.10^{-1})\left(\begin{array}{l}\text{the sum of the first four terms of a}\\ \text{geometric progression with first}\\ \text{term 1 and common ratio } 1.10^{-1}\end{array}\right)$$

$$= 600.00(1.10^{-1})\left(\frac{1 - 1.10^{-4}}{1 - 1.10^{-1}}\right)$$

$$= 600.00\left(\frac{1}{1.10}\right)\left(\frac{1 - 1.10^{-4}}{1 - \frac{1}{1.10}}\right)$$

$$= 600.00\left(\frac{1}{1.10}\right)\left[\frac{(1.10)(1 - 1.10^{-4})}{1.10 - 1}\right]$$

$$= 600.00\left(\frac{1 - 1.10^{-4}}{0.10}\right)$$

$$= 600.00\left[\frac{(1 - 0.6830135)}{0.10}\right]$$

$$= 600.00(3.1698654)$$

$$= \$1901.92$$

B. *Formula for finding the present value of an ordinary annuity*

Because annuities are geometric progressions and because the present value of an annuity is the sum of the present values of the periodic payments at the beginning of the term of the annuity, a general formula for finding the present value of an annuity can be developed.

Figure 11.8 presents the general problem using the following generally adopted notation.

A_n = the present value (discounted value) of an ordinary annuity;

R = the size of the periodic payment (rent);

i = the interest rate per conversion period;

n = the number of periodic payments (which for simple annuities equals the number of conversion periods).

FIGURE 11.8 ***Graphic representation of the general problem of finding the present value of an ordinary annuity***

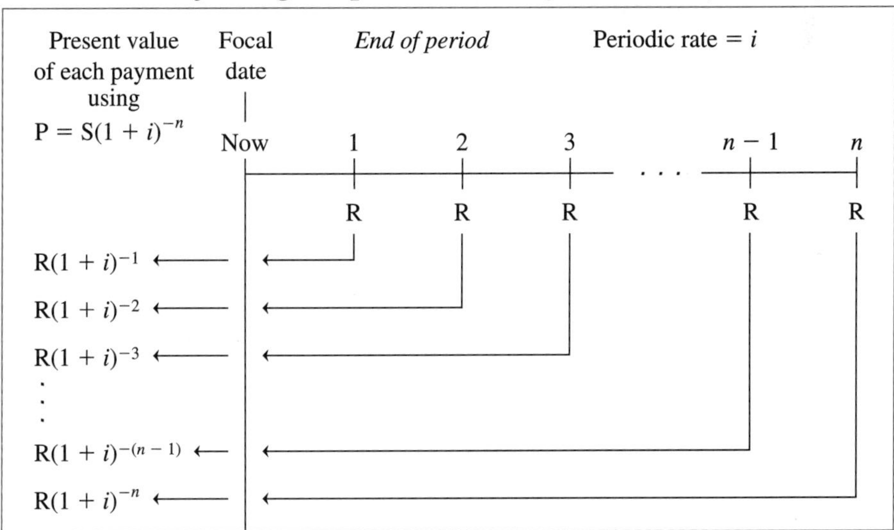

Adding the present values of the individual payments at the focal date gives rise to the following equation.

$$
\begin{aligned}
A_n &= R(1+i)^{-1} + R(1+i)^{-2} + R(1+i)^{-3} + \ldots + R(1+i)^{-(n-1)} + R(1+i)^{-n} \\
&= R[(1+i)^{-1} + (1+i)^{-2} + (1+i)^{-3} + \ldots + (1+i)^{-(n-1)} + (1+i)^{-n}] \\
&= R(1+i)^{-1}[1 + (1+i)^{-1} + (1+i)^{-2} + \ldots + (1+i)^{-(n-2)} + (1+i)^{-(n-1)}] \\
&= R(1+i)^{-1}\begin{bmatrix}\text{the sum of the first } n \text{ terms of a geometric progression} \\ \text{with first term 1 and common ratio } (1+i)^{-1}\end{bmatrix} \\
&= R(1+i)^{-1}\left(\frac{1-[(1+i)^{-1}]^n}{1-(1+i)^{-1}}\right) \longleftarrow \text{substituting in the formula } S = \frac{a(1-r^n)}{1-r} \\
&= R\left(\frac{1}{1+i}\right)\left[\frac{1-(1+i)^{-n}}{1-\frac{1}{1+i}}\right] \longleftarrow \text{convert } (1+i)^{-1} \text{ to } \frac{1}{1+i} \\
&= R\left(\frac{1}{1+i}\right)\left[\frac{1-(1+i^{-n}}{\frac{(1+i)-1}{1+i}}\right] \longleftarrow \text{convert } 1-\frac{1}{1+i} \text{ to } \frac{(1+i)-1}{(1+i)} \\
&= R\left(\frac{1}{1+i}\right)\left[\frac{(1+i)[1-(1+i)^{-n}]}{1+i-1}\right] \\
&= R\left[\frac{1-(1+i)^{-n}}{i}\right] \longleftarrow \text{reduced by } (1+i)
\end{aligned}
$$

$$
\boxed{A_n = R\left[\frac{1-(1+i)^{-n}}{i}\right]} \longleftarrow \textit{Formula } \mathbf{11.2} \longleftarrow \text{Present value of an ordinary annuity}
$$

The factor $\frac{1-(1+i)^{-n}}{i}$ is called the **present value factor** or **discount factor for annuities** or the **discounted value of one dollar per period.**

***Example* 11.3d** Find the present value at the beginning of the first payment period of payments of \$50.00 made at the end of each quarter for ten years, if interest is 16% compounded quarterly.

Solution

Because the payments are of equal size made at the end of each quarter, the problem is an ordinary annuity. Since the focal date is the beginning of the term of the annuity, the formula for finding the present value of an ordinary annuity applies.

$$R = 50.00; \quad i = \frac{16\%}{4} = 0.04; \quad n = 10(4) = 40$$

$$A_n = 50.00\left[\frac{1-(1+0.04)^{-40}}{0.04}\right] \longleftarrow \text{substituting in Formula 11.2}$$

$$= 50.00\left(\frac{1-0.2082890}{0.04}\right)$$

$$= 50.00\left(\frac{0.7917110}{0.04}\right)$$

$$= 50.00(19.792774)$$

$$= \$989.64$$

***Example* 11.3e** If you want to withdraw \$100.00 at the end of each month for five years from an account paying 12% compounded monthly,

(i) how much must you have on deposit at the beginning of the month in which the first withdrawal is made?

(ii) how much will you receive in total?

(iii) how much of what you will receive is interest?

Solution

(i) $$R = 100.00; \quad i = 1\% = 0.01; \quad n = 60$$

$$A_n = 100.00\left[\frac{1-(1+i)^{-n}}{i}\right]$$

$$= 100.00\left[\frac{(1-1.01^{-60})}{0.01}\right]$$

$$= 100.00\left[\frac{(1-0.5504496)}{0.01}\right]$$

$$= 100.00\left(\frac{0.4495504}{0.01}\right)$$

$$= 100.00(44.95504)$$

$$= \$4495.50$$

(ii) Total receipts will be \$100.00 per month for 60 months or \$6000.00.

(iii) Since the initial balance must be \$4495.50, the interest received will be 6000.00 − 4495.50 = \$1504.50.

C. Present value using preprogrammed financial calculators

To find the present value of the ordinary annuity in Example 11.3e in which R = 100.00, i = 1%, and n = 60, proceed as follows.

	Press	Display shows	
0	FV	0	←—a precaution
100	PMT	100	
1	%i	1	
60	N	60	
CPT	PV	4495.5039	←—pressing the PV key retrieves the wanted present value A_n

You must have $4495.50 on deposit.

D. Applications

***Example* 11.3f** Mr. and Mrs. Hong bought a vacation property for $3000.00 down and $1000.00 every half-year for twelve years. If interest is 13% compounded semi-annually, what was the cash value of the property?

Solution

The cash value is the price of the property at the date of purchase and represents the dated value of all payments at that date.

$$\text{CASH VALUE} = \text{DOWN PAYMENT} + \begin{matrix}\text{PRESENT VALUE OF}\\ \text{THE PERIODIC PAYMENTS}\end{matrix}$$

Since the first half-yearly payment is due at the end of the first six-month period, the present value of the periodic payments is the present value of an ordinary annuity.

$$R = 1000.00; \quad i = \frac{13\%}{2} = 6.5\% = 0.065; \quad n = 12(2) = 24$$

$$A_n = 1000.00\left[\frac{(1 - 1.065^{-24})}{0.065}\right]$$

$$= 1000.00\left[\frac{(1 - 0.2206020)}{0.065}\right]$$

$$= 1000.00\left(\frac{0.7793980}{0.065}\right)$$

$$= 1000.00(11.990739)$$

$$= \$11\ 990.74$$

Programmed solution

0	1000	6.5	24			
FV	PMT	%i	N	CPT	PV	11 990.74

The cash value = 3000.00 + 11 990.74 = \$14 990.74.

Example 11.3g Armand Rice expects to retire in seven years and would like to receive \$500.00 per month for ten years starting at the end of the first month after his retirement. To achieve this goal, he deposited part of the proceeds of \$50 000.00 from the sale of a property into a fund earning 10.5% compounded monthly.

(i) How much must be in the fund at the date of his retirement?

(ii) How much of the proceeds did he deposit in the fund?

(iii) How much does he expect to receive from the fund?

(iv) How much of what he will receive is interest?

Solution

As Figure 11.9 shows, problems of this type should be solved in stages. The first stage involves finding the present value of an annuity. This sum of money becomes the future amount for the second stage which involves finding the present value of that future amount at the date of deposit.

FIGURE 11.9 ***Graphic representation of method and data***

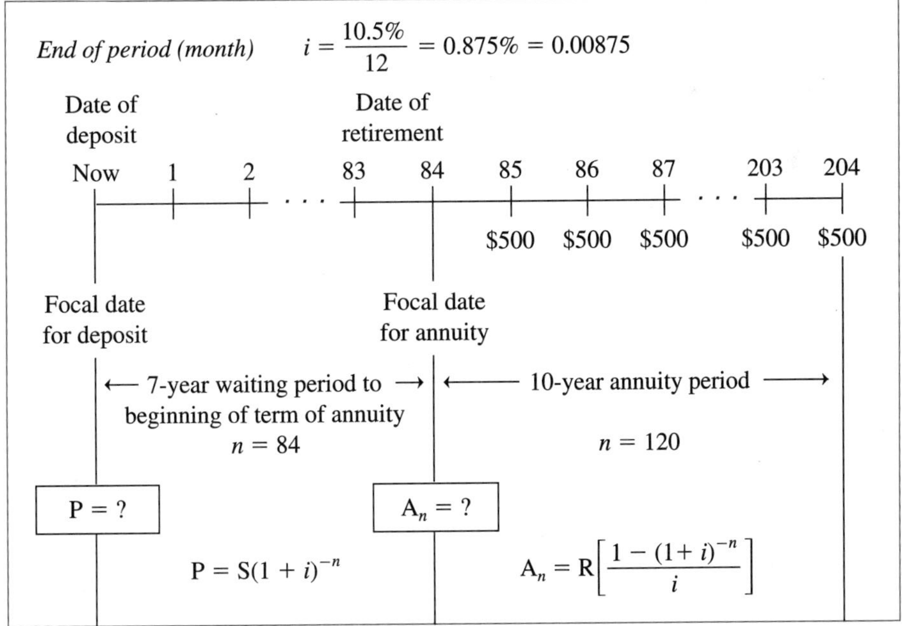

(i) $R = 500.00; \quad i = 0.00875; \quad n = 120$

$$A_n = 500.00\left[\frac{(1 - 1.00875^{-120})}{0.00875}\right]$$

$$= 500.00\left[\frac{(1 - 0.3515396)}{0.00875}\right]$$

$$= 500.00(74.109758)$$

$$= \$37\ 054.88$$

(ii) $S = A_n = 37\ 054.88; \quad i = 0.00875; \quad n = 84$

$$P = 37\ 054.88(1.00875)^{-84}$$

$$= 37\ 054.88(0.4810409)$$

$$= \$17\ 824.91$$

(iii) He expects to receive 500.00(120) = \$60 000.00.

(iv) Interest received will be 60 000.00 − 17 824.91 = \$42 175.09.

Programmed solution for parts (i) and (ii)

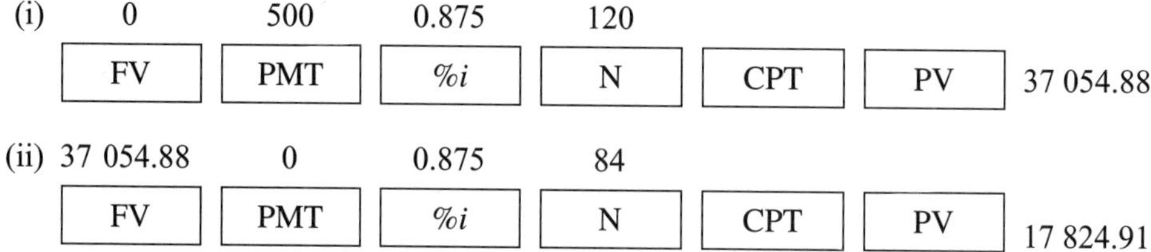

***Example* 11.3h** Sheila Davidson borrowed money from her credit union and agreed to repay the loan in blended monthly payments of \$180.90 over a four-year period. Interest on the loan was 15% compounded monthly.

(i) How much did she borrow?

(ii) If she missed the first eleven payments, how much would she have to pay at the end of the first year to bring her payments up to date?

(iii) If the credit union demanded payment in full after one year, how much money would Sheila Davidson need?

(iv) If the loan is paid off after one year, what would have been its total cost?

(v) How much of the total loan cost is additional interest paid on the missed payments?

Solution

(i) The amount borrowed is the present value (or discounted value) of the 48 payments as the time diagram shows.

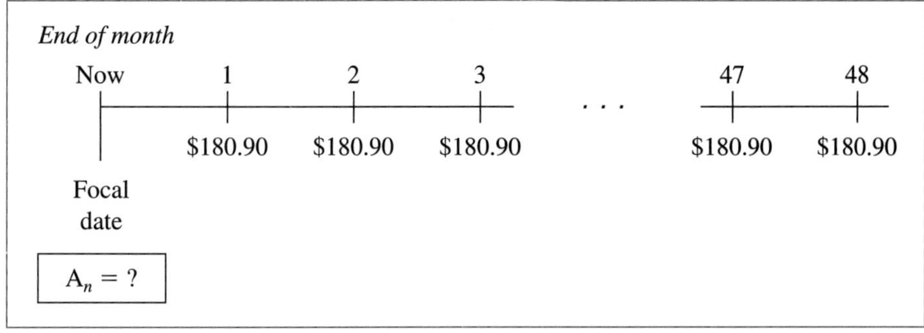

$$R = 180.90; \quad i = \frac{15\%}{12} = 1.25\% = 0.125; \quad n = 4(12) = 48$$

$$A_n = 180.90\left[\frac{(1 - 1.0125^{-48})}{0.0125}\right] \longleftarrow \text{using Formula 11.2}$$

$$= 180.90\left[\frac{(1 - 0.5508565)}{0.0125}\right]$$

$$= 180.90(35.93148)$$

$$= \$6500.00$$

Programmed solution

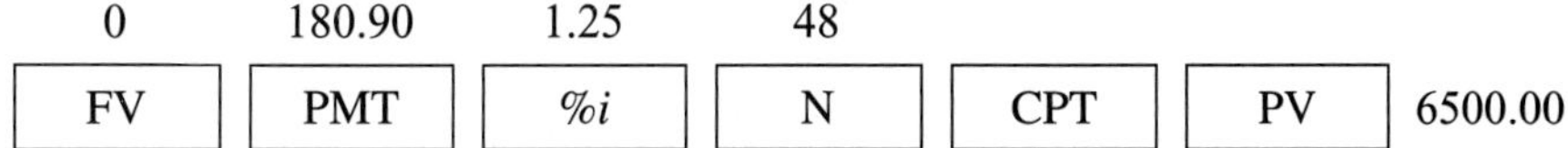

(ii) As the diagram below shows, Sheila Davidson must pay the accumulated value of the first twelve payments to bring her payments up to date after one year.

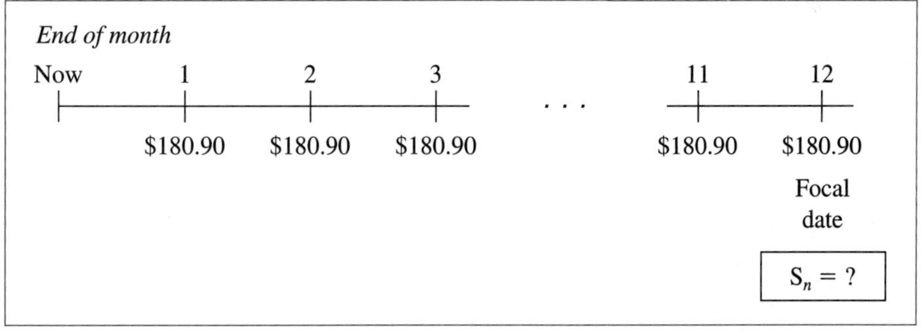

$$R = 180.90; \quad i = 0.0125; \quad n = 12$$

$$S_n = 180.90\left[\frac{(1.0125^{12} - 1)}{0.0125}\right] \longleftarrow \text{using Formula 11.1}$$

$$= 180.90\left[\frac{(1.1607545 - 1)}{0.0125}\right]$$

$$= 180.90(12.860361)$$

$$= \$2326.44$$

Programmed solution

0	180.90	1.25	12			
PV	PMT	%*i*	N	CPT	FV	2326.44

(iii) The sum of money required to pay off the loan in full is the sum of the accumulated values of the first twelve payments plus the discounted values of the remaining 36 payments.

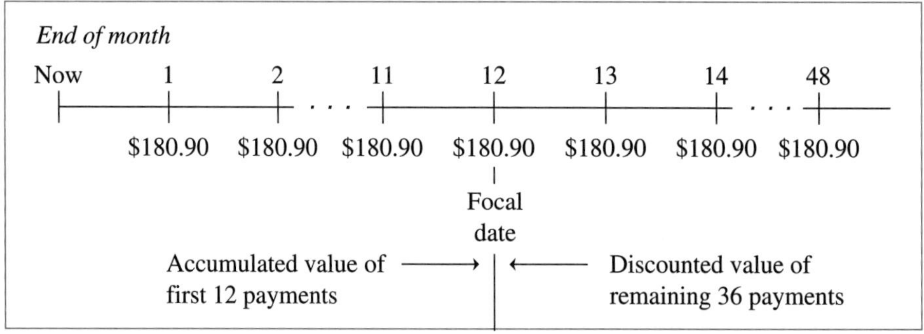

The accumulated value of the first 12 payments, as computed in part (ii) above, is $2326.44. The discounted value of the remaining payments is found using Formula 11.2.

$$R = 180.90; \quad i = 0.0125; \quad n = 36$$

$$A_n = 180.90\left[\frac{(1 - 1.0125^{-36})}{0.0125}\right]$$

$$= 180.90\left[\frac{(1 - 0.6394092)}{0.0125}\right]$$

$$= 180.90(28.847267)$$

$$= \$5218.47$$

Programmed solution

0	180.90	1.25	36			
FV	PMT	%*i*	N	CPT	PV	5218.47

The amount of money needed is 5218.47 + 2326.44 = \$7544.91.

(iv) The total cost of the loan if paid off after one year is 7544.91 − 6500.00 = \$1044.91.

(v) \$2326.44 is needed to bring the payments up to date. Since the normal amount paid during the first year would have been 180.90(12) = \$2170.80, the additional interest paid is 2326.44 − 2170.80 = \$155.64.

Exercise 11.3

A. Determine the present value of the ordinary annuity for each of the following.

	Periodic payment	*Payment interval*	*Term*	*Interest rate*	*Compounding period*
1.	\$1600.00	6 months	$3\frac{1}{2}$ years	8.5%	semi-annually
2.	\$700.00	1 quarter	4 years, 9 months	15%	quarterly
3.	\$4000.00	1 year	12 years	12.5%	annually
4.	\$45.00	1 month	18 years	6.6%	monthly
5.	\$250.00	3 months	14 years, 3 months	14.4%	quarterly
6.	\$80.00	1 month	9.25 years	15.6%	monthly

B. Answer each of the following questions.

1. Find the present value of payments of \$375.00 made at the end of every six months for fifteen years if money is worth 7% compounded semi-annually.

2. What is the discounted value of deposits of \$60.00 made at the end of each month for nine years if interest is 4.5% compounded monthly?

3. You want to receive \$600.00 at the end of every three months for five years. Interest is 7.6% compounded quarterly.

   (a) How much would you have to deposit at the beginning of the five-year period?

   (b) How much of what you receive is interest?

4. An instalment contract for the purchase of a car requires payments of \$270.60 at the end of each month for the next three years. If interest is 13.8% p.a. compounded monthly,

   (a) what is the amount financed?

   (b) how much is the interest cost?

5. For home entertainment equipment, Ted paid \$400.00 down and signed an instalment contract that required payments of \$69.33 at the end of each month for three years. If interest is 15% compounded monthly,

   (a) what was the cash price of the equipment?

   (b) how much was the cost of financing?

6. Elynor bought a vacation property for $2500.00 down and quarterly mortgage payments of $633.25 at the end of each quarter for five years. If interest is 14% compounded quarterly,

   (a) what was the purchase price of the property?

   (b) how much interest will Elynor pay?

7. Ed intends to retire in eight years. To supplement his pension he would like to receive $450.00 every three months for fifteen years. If he is to receive the first payment three months after his retirement and interest is 13% p.a. compounded quarterly, how much must he invest today to achieve his goal?

8. Planning for their son's college education, Vivien and Adrian Marsh opened an account paying 6.3% compounded monthly. If ordinary annuity payments of $200.00 per month are to be paid out of the account for three years starting seven years from now, how much did the Marshes deposit?

9. Kimiko signed a chattle mortgage requiring payments of $253.74 at the end of every month for six years at 15% compounded monthly.

   (a) How much was the original mortgage balance?

   (b) If Kimiko missed the first five payments, how much would she have to pay after six months to bring the mortgage payments up to date?

   (c) How much would Kimiko have to pay after six months to pay out the mortgage?

   (d) If the mortgage were paid out, what would the total interest cost be?

   (e) How much of the total interest cost is additional interest because of the missed payments?

10. Field Construction agreed to lease payments of $642.79 on construction equipment to be made at the end of each month for three years. Financing is at 18% compounded monthly.

   (a) What is the value of the original lease contract?

   (b) If, due to delays, the first eight payments were deferred, how much money would be needed after nine months to bring the lease payments up to date?

   (c) How much money would be required to pay out the lease after nine months?

   (d) If the lease were paid off, what would be the total interest included in the payout figure?

   (e) How much of the total interest would be due to deferring the first eight payments?

11.4 *Finding the periodic rent*

A. Finding the periodic payment when the amount of the annuity is known

If S_n, i, and n are known, you can determine R by substituting the given values in the formula for finding the amount of an ordinary annuity and solving for R.

Example **11.4a** What quarterly deposit will accumulate to \$10 000.00 in four years at 14% compounded quarterly?

Solution

$$S_n = 10\ 000.00; \quad i = \frac{14\%}{4} = 3.5\% = 0.035; \quad n = 16$$

$$10\ 000.00 = R\left(\frac{1.035^{16} - 1}{0.035}\right) \longleftarrow \text{substituting in Formula 11.1}$$

$$10\ 000.00 = R\left(\frac{1.733986 - 1}{0.035}\right)$$

$$10\ 000.00 = R(20.97103)$$

$$R = \frac{10\ 000.00}{20.97103}$$

$$R = \$476.85$$

B. *Finding the periodic payment when the present value of the annuity is known*

If A_n, i, and n are known, you can determine R by substituting the given values in the formula for finding the present value of the annuity and solving for R.

Example **11.4b** What semi-annual payment is required to pay off a loan of \$8000.00 in ten years if interest is 16% compounded semi-annually?

Solution

$$A_n = 8000.00; \quad i = \frac{16\%}{2} = 8\% = 0.08; \quad n = 10(2) = 20$$

$$8000.00 = R\left(\frac{1 - 1.08^{-20}}{0.08}\right) \longleftarrow \text{substituting in Formula 11.2}$$

$$8000.00 = R\left(\frac{1 - 0.2145482}{0.08}\right)$$

$$8000.00 = R(9.8181474)$$

$$R = \frac{8000.00}{9.8181474}$$

$$R = \$814.82$$

C. *Finding R using preprogrammed calculators*

You can find the periodic payment R by entering the three known values (S_n, n, i or A_n, n, i) and then retrieving the answer by pressing [CPT] [PMT].

Example **11.4c** If you want to have $5000.00 on deposit in your bank account in three years, how much must you deposit at the end of each month if interest is 16.5% compounded monthly?

Solution

$$S_n = 5000.00; \quad i = 1.375\%; \quad n = 36$$

	Press	Display shows
0	PV	0
5000	FV	5000
1.375	%*i*	1.375
36	N	36
CPT	PMT	108.27191

The monthly deposit required is $108.27.

Example **11.4d** Derek bought a new car valued at $9500. He paid $2000 down and financed the remainder over five years at 15% compounded monthly. How much must Derek pay each month?

Solution

$$A_n = 9500 - 2000 = 7500; \quad i = \frac{15\%}{12} = 1.25\%; \quad n = 60$$

	Press	Display shows
0	FV	0
7500	PV	7500
1.25	%*i*	1.25
60	N	60
CPT	PMT	178.42448

Derek's monthly payment is $178.42.

D. Applications

***Example* 11.4e** Cecile Tremblay, age 37, expects to retire at age 62. To plan for her retirement, she intends to deposit \$1500.00 at the end of each of the next 25 years in a registered retirement savings plan. After her last contribution, she intends to convert the existing balance into a registered retirement income fund from which she expects to make 20 equal annual withdrawals. If she makes the first withdrawal one year after her last contribution and interest is 10.5% compounded annually, how much is the size of the annual withdrawal?

Solution

As the time diagram below shows, the problem can be broken into two steps.

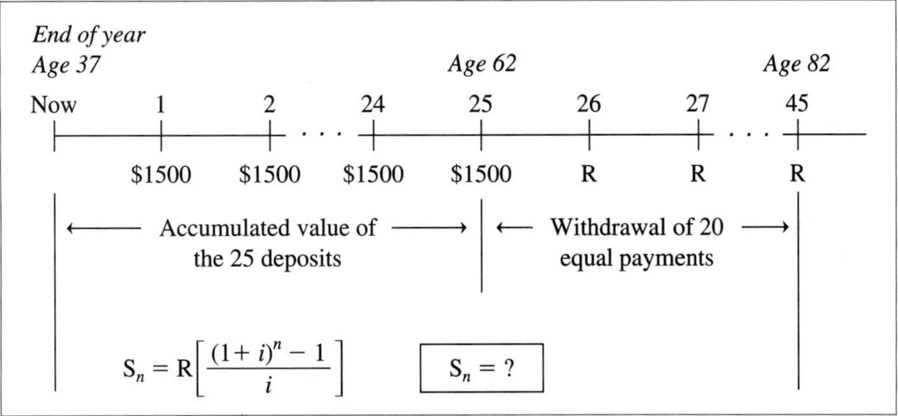

STEP 1 Compute the *accumulated* value S_n of the 25 annual deposits of \$1500.00 into the RRSP.

$$R = 1500.00; \quad i = 10.5\% = 0.105; \quad n = 25$$

$$S_n = 1500.00\left(\frac{1.105^{25} - 1}{0.105}\right) \longleftarrow \text{substituting in Formula 11.1}$$

$$= 1500.00(106.05219)$$

$$= \$159\ 078.28$$

STEP 2 Compute the annual payment that can be withdrawn from the RRIF which has an initial balance of \$159 078.28.

$$A_n = 159\ 078.28; \ i = 0.105; \ n = 20$$

$$159\ 078.28 = R\left(\frac{1 - 1.105^{-20}}{0.105}\right) \longleftarrow \text{using Formula 11.2}$$

$$159\ 078.28 = R(8.2309089)$$

$$R = 19\ 326.94$$

Programmed Solution

STEP 1

0	1500	10.5	25			
PV	PMT	%*i*	N	CPT	FV	159 078.28

STEP 2

0	159 078.28	10.5	20			
FV	PV	%*i*	N	CPT	PMT	19 326.94

The sum of money that Cecile can withdraw each year is $19 326.94.

Note: While special formulae for finding R could be developed by solving Formulae 11.1 and 11.2 for R, no useful purpose is served by such formulae because of the availability of electronic calculators. No special formulae for finding R are developed or used in this text.

Exercise 11.4

A. For each of the following ordinary annuities, determine the size of the periodic rent.

	Amount S_n	*Present value* A_n	*Payment period*	*Term of annuity*	*Int. rate*	*Conversion period*
1.	$15 000.00		6 months	7 years, 6 months	5.5%	semi-annually
2.	$6 000.00		1 quarter	9 years, 9 months	13%	quarterly
3.		$12 000.00	12 months	15 years	14.5%	annually
4.		$7 000.00	6 months	12.5 years	17.5%	semi-annually
5.	$8 000.00		3 months	6 years	6.8%	quarterly
6.		$20 000.00	1 month	20 years	21%	monthly

B. Answer each of the following questions.

1. What deposit made at the end of each quarter for 15 years will accumulate to $20 000.00 at 6% compounded quarterly?

2. What payment is required at the end of each month for five years to repay a loan of $8000.00 at 16.5% compounded monthly?

3. A contract can be fulfilled by making an immediate payment of $7500.00 or equal payments at the end of every six months for ten years. What is the size of the semi-annual payments at 19.6% compounded semi-annually?

4. What payment made at the end of each month for eighteen years will amount to $16 000.00 at 9.5% compounded monthly?

5. Olivia bought a car priced at \$10 600.00 for 10% down and the balance in equal monthly payments over four years at 16.2% compounded monthly. How much does Olivia have to pay each month?

6. The Watsons bought a rental property valued at \$50 000.00 by paying 20% down and mortgaging the balance over 25 years through equal quarterly payments at 14% compounded quarterly. What was the size of the quarterly payments?

7. George plans to deposit \$1200.00 at the end of every six months for fifteen years into an RRSP account. After the last deposit, he intends to convert the existing balance into an RRIF and withdraw equal amounts at the end of every six months for twenty years. If interest is expected to be 7.5% compounded semi-annually, how much will George be able to collect every six months?

8. Starting three months after her grandson Robin's birth, Mrs. Devine made deposits of \$60.00 into a trust fund every three months until Robin was twenty-one years old. The trust fund provides for equal withdrawals at the end of each quarter for four years beginning three months after the last deposit. If interest is 10% compounded quarterly, how much will Robin receive every three months?

9. On the day of his daughter's birth, Mr. Dodd deposited \$2000.00 in a trust fund with his credit union at 5% compounded quarterly. Following her eighteenth birthday, the daughter is to receive equal payments at the end of each month for four years while she is at college. If interest is to be 6.0% compounded monthly after the daughter's eighteenth birthday, how much will she receive every month?

10. Equal payments are to be made at the end of each month for fifteen years with interest at 9% compounded monthly. After the last payment, the fund is to be invested for seven years at 10% compounded quarterly and have a maturity value of \$20 000.00. What is the size of the monthly payment?

11.5 *Finding the term of an annuity*

A. *Finding the term when the amount of the annuity is known*

If S_n, R, and i are known, you can determine n by substituting the given values in the formula for finding the amount of an annuity and solving for n.

***Example* 11.5a** How long will it take for \$200.00 deposited at the end of each quarter to amount to \$6885.29 at 12% compounded quarterly?

Solution

$$S_n = 6885.29; \quad i = \frac{12\%}{4} = 3\% = 0.03; \quad R = 200.00$$

$$6885.29 = 200.00\left(\frac{1.03^n - 1}{0.03}\right) \longleftarrow \text{substituting in Formula 11.1}$$

$$34.42645 = \frac{1.03^n - 1}{0.03} \longleftarrow \text{divide both sides by 200.00}$$

$$1.0327935 = 1.03^n - 1 \longleftarrow \text{multiply both sides by 0.03}$$

$$1.03^n = 2.0327935 \longleftarrow \text{add 1 to both sides}$$

$$n \ln 1.03 = \ln 2.0327935 \longleftarrow \text{solve for } n \text{ using natural logarithms}$$

$$0.0295588n = 0.709411$$

$$n = \frac{0.709411}{0.0295588}$$

$$n = 24 \text{ (quarters)}$$

It will take six years for \$200.00 per quarter to grow to \$6885.29.

B. *Finding the term when the present value of the annuity is known*

If A_n, R, and i are known, you can determine n by substituting the given values in the formula for finding the present value of an annuity and solving for n.

Example **11.5b** How many quarterly payments of \$600.00 are required to repay a loan of \$5400.00 at 14% compounded quarterly?

Solution

$$A_n = 5400.00; \quad R = 600.00; \quad i = \frac{14\%}{4} = 3.5\% = 0.035$$

$$5400.00 = 600.00\left(\frac{1 - 1.035^{-n}}{0.035}\right) \longleftarrow \text{substituting in Formula 11.2}$$

$$9.00 = \frac{1 - 1.035^{-n}}{0.035} \longleftarrow \text{divide both sides by 600.00}$$

$$0.315 = 1 - 1.035^{-n} \longleftarrow \text{multiply both sides by 0.035}$$

$$1.035^{-n} = 0.685$$

$$-n \ln 1.035 = \ln 0.685 \longleftarrow \text{solve for } n \text{ using natural logarithms}$$

$$-0.0344014n = -0.3783364$$

$$n = \frac{0.3783364}{0.0344014}$$

$$n = 10.997696$$

$$n = 11 \text{ quarters}$$

C. *Finding* n *using preprogrammed calculators*

Finding the number of periodic payments n is accomplished by entering the three known values (S_n, R, i or A_n, R, i) and then retrieving the answer by pressing CPT N. When S_n is given, R must be keyed in as a negative number in some models.

Example **11.5c** In how many months will your bank account grow to $3000.00 if you deposit $150.00 at the end of each month and the account earns 9% compounded monthly?

Solution

$$S_n = 3000.00; \quad R = 150.00; \quad i = \frac{9\%}{12} = 0.75\%$$

	Press	Display shows
0	PV	0
3000	FV	3000
150 (or −150)	PMT	150 (or −150)
0.75	%i	0.75
CPT	N	18.70472 ←— months

It will take about 19 months to accumulate $3000.

Interpretation of result

When S_n, R, and i are known, it is unlikely that n will be a whole number. The fractional time period of 0.7 month indicates that the accumulated value of 18 deposits of $150.00 will be less than $3000.00, while the accumulated value of 19 deposits will be more than $3000.00. This point can be verified by computing S_{18} and S_{19}.

$$S_{18} = 150.00\left(\frac{1.0075^{18} - 1}{0.0075}\right) = 150.00(19.194717) = \$2879.21$$

$$S_{19} = 150.00\left(\frac{1.0075^{19} - 1}{0.0075}\right) = 150.00(20.338677) = \$3050.80$$

The definition of an annuity does not provide for making payments at unequal time intervals. The appropriate answer to problems in which n is a fractional value is a whole number. The usual approach is to round upwards so that in this case $n = 19$.

Rounding upwards implies that the deposit made at the end of the nineteenth month is smaller than the usual deposit of $150.00. The method of computing the size of the final deposit or payment when the term of the annuity is a fractional value rounded upwards is considered in Chapter 14.

Example **11.5d** On his retirement, Art received a gratuity of $8000.00 from his employer. Taking advantage of the existing tax legislation, he invested the money in an income averaging annuity that provides for semi-annual payments of $1200.00 at the end of every six months. If interest is 11.5% compounded semi-annually, how long will the annuity exist?

Solution

$$A_n = 8000.00; \quad R = 1200.00; \quad i = \frac{11.5\%}{2} = 5.75\%$$

	Press	Display shows
0	FV	0
8000	PV	8000
1200	PMT	1200
5.75	%*i*	5.75
CPT	N	8.6468812 ← half-year periods

The annuity will be in existence for four and a half years. Art will receive eight payments of $1200.00 and a final payment that will be less than $1200.00.

Note: While special formulae for finding n could be developed by solving Formulae 11.1 and 11.2 for n, no useful purpose is served by such formulae because of the availability of electronic calculators. No special formulae for finding n are developed or used in this text.

Exercise 11.5

A. Find the term of each of the following ordinary annuities. (State your answer in years and months).

	Amount S_n	Present value A_n	Periodic rent	Payment interval	Interest rate	Compounding period
1.	\$20 000.00		\$800.00	1 year	7.5%	annually
2.	\$17 000.00		\$ 35.00	1 month	12%	monthly
3.		\$14 500.00	\$190.00	1 month	15%	monthly
4.		\$ 5 000.00	\$300.00	3 months	20%	quarterly
5.	\$ 3 600.00		\$175.00	6 months	17.4%	semi-annually
6.		\$ 9 500.00	\$740.00	1 quarter	5.2%	quarterly

B. Answer each of the following questions.

1. How long would it take you to save \$4500.00 by making deposits of \$50.00 at the end of every month into a savings account earning 6% compounded monthly?

2. In what period of time could you pay back a loan of \$3600.00 by making monthly payments of \$96.00 if interest is 19.5% compounded monthly?

3. A deposit of \$4000.00 is made today for a five-year period. For how long can \$500.00 be withdrawn from the account at the end of every three months starting three months after the end of the five-year term if interest is 11% compounded quarterly?

4. If \$646.56 is deposited into an account earning 6.5% compounded semi-annually at the end of every six months and the balance in the account four years after the last deposit is to be \$20 000.00, how many deposits are needed?

11.6 *Finding the rate of interest using preprogrammed calculators*

Finding the rate of interest i per conversion period is accomplished by entering the three known values (S_n, R, n or A_n, R, n) and then retrieving the answer by pressing [CPT] [%i]. You can then obtain the nominal annual rate of interest by multiplying i by the number of compounding periods per year.

A. *Finding* i *when the amount* S_n *is known*

***Example* 11.6a** Compute the nominal rate of interest at which \$50 deposited at the end of each month for ten years will amount to \$15 000.

Solution

$$S_n = 15\ 000; \quad R = 50; \quad n = 120$$

	Press	Display shows
0	PV	0
15000	FV	15000
50 (or −50)	PMT	50 (or −50)
120	N	120
CPT	%*i*	1.3672477 ← allow several seconds for the computation

The monthly conversion rate is 1.3672477%. The nominal rate of interest is (12)(1.3672477%) = 16.41% approximately.

B. *Finding* i *when the present value* A_n is known

***Example* 11.6b** A loan of \$6000 is paid off over five years by monthly payments of \$157.30. What is the nominal rate of interest on the loan?

Solution

$$A_n = 6000; \quad R = 157.30; \quad n = 60$$

	Press	Display shows
0	FV	0
6000	PV	6000
157.30	PMT	157.30
60	N	60
CPT	%*i*	1.6250333 ← wait several seconds for the answer

The monthly compounding rate is 1.6250333%. The nominal rate of interest is 19.5%.

Note: The usefulness of preprogrammed calculators is underlined when finding the conversion rate i. Determining i requires an iterative process that may take several seconds even when using a preprogrammed calculator. The process is very lengthy when done by hand. It is illustrated in the Appendix.

Exercise 11.6

A. Compute the nominal rate of interest for each of the following ordinary annuities.

	Amount S_n	*Present value* A_n	*Periodic rent*	*Payment interval*	*Term*	*Compounding period*
1.	$9000.00		$143.54	3 months	8 years	quarterly
2.	$4800.00		$49.00	1 month	5 years	monthly
3.		$7400.00	$119.06	1 month	7 years	monthly
4.		$5540.00	$800.00	6 months	5 years	semi-annually

B. Answer each of the following questions.

1. Compute the nominal rate of interest at which $350.00 paid at the end of every three months for six years accumulates to $12 239.76.

2. What is the nominal rate of interest if a four-year loan of $6000.00 is repaid by monthly payments of $171.58?

3. Rene contributed $250.00 every three months into an RRSP for ten years. What nominal rate of interest did the RRSP earn if the balance in Rene's account just after he made his last contribution was $19 955.40?

4. Rita converted a RRSP balance of $199 875.67 into an RRIF that will pay her $1800.00 at the end of every month for nine years. What is the nominal rate of interest?

5. A car valued at $11 400.00 can be bought for 10% down and monthly payments of $318.56 for three and a half years. What is the effective cost of financing?

6. A property worth $40 000.00 can be purchased for 20% down and quarterly mortgage payments of $1100.00 for 25 years. What effective rate of interest is charged?

Review exercise

1. Payments of $360.00 are made into a fund at the end of every three months for twelve years. If the fund earns interest at 7% compounded quarterly,

   (a) what will the balance in the fund be after twelve years?

   (b) how much of the balance is deposits?

   (c) how much of the balance is interest?

2. A trust fund is set up to make payments of $950.00 at the end of each month for seven and a half years. If interest on the fund is 13.8% compounded monthly,
   (a) how much money must be deposited into the fund?
   (b) how much will be paid out of the fund?
   (c) how much interest is earned by the fund?
3. A loan of $4500.00 is to be repaid in equal quarterly payments over two and a half years. If interest is 16% compounded quarterly, how much is the quarterly payment?
4. What semi-annual investment will accumulate to $6600.00 in seven and a half years at 4.5% compounded semi-annually?
5. How much interest is included in the accumulated value of $75.90 paid at the end of each month for four years if interest is 9% compounded monthly?
6. If a loan was repaid by quarterly payments of $320.00 in five years at 15% compounded quarterly, how much money had been borrowed?
7. Mr. Arnold borrowed $15 200.00 which he agreed to repay in semi-annual payments of $2000.00 each. If interest on the loan is 17% compounded semi-annually, how long will it take Mr. Arnold to pay off the loan?
8. What nominal rate of interest is paid on quarterly RRSP contributions of $750.00 made for fifteen years if the balance just after the last contribution is $106 000.00?
9. What nominal rate of interest was charged on a loan of $5600.00 repaid in monthly instalments of $148.90 in four and a half years?
10. Terry bought a car valued at $9300.00 for 20% down and the balance in equal monthly instalments over three and a half years at 15.9% compounded monthly. What was the size of his monthly payment?
11. How long will it take to build up a fund of $10 000.00 by saving $300.00 every six months at 10.5% compounded semi-annually?
12. What is the term of a mortgage of $35 000.00 repaid by monthly payments of $475.00 if interest is 13.5% compounded monthly?
13. An income averaging annuity of $1050.00 per quarter for six years is paid from an initial retirement gratuity of $21 000.00. What nominal rate of interest is paid by the annuity?
14. Donna's annual RRSP contribution of $5500.00 amounted to $100 000.00 after eleven years. What annual interest rate did the contributions earn?
15. If you contribute $1500.00 into an RRSP every six months for twelve years and interest on the deposits is 8% compounded semi-annually, how much would the balance in the RRSP be seven years after the last contribution?
16. Doris purchased a piano with $300.00 down and monthly payments of $124.00 for two and a half years at 15% compounded monthly. What was the purchase price of the piano?

17. A truck valued at $9650.00 was bought for 20% down and monthly payments for five years. If interest is 16.2% compounded monthly, what is the size of the monthly payment?

18. The amount of $10 000.00 is put into a five-year term deposit paying 11.5% compounded semi-annually. After five years the deposit is converted into an ordinary annuity of equal semi-annual payments of $2000.00 each. If interest remains the same, what is the term of the annuity?

19. A trailer valued at $24 000.00 can be bought for 15% down and monthly payments of $470.00 over five years. What is the effective interest rate paid?

20. Glenn has made contributions of $250.00 every three months into an RRSP for ten years. Interest for the first four years was 10% compounded quarterly. Since then the interest rate has been 11% compounded quarterly. How much will Glenn have in his RRSP three years after the last contribution?

21. Avi expects to retire in twelve years. Beginning one month after his retirement he would like to receive $500.00 per month for twenty years. How much must he deposit into a fund today to be able to do so if the rate of interest on the deposit is 6% compounded monthly?

22. Mirielle has deposited $125.00 at the end of each month for 15 years at 7.5% compounded monthly. After her last deposit she converted the balance into an ordinary annuity paying $1200.00 every three months for twelve years. If interest on the annuity is compounded quarterly, what is the effective rate of interest paid by the annuity?

23. Anne received $45 000.00 from her mother's estate. She wants to set aside part of her inheritance for her retirement nine years from now. At that time she would like to receive a pension supplement of $600.00 at the end of each month for 25 years. If the first payment is due one month after her retirement and interest is 10% compounded monthly, how much must Anne set aside?

24. Ty received a separation payment of $5000.00 at age 35. He invested that sum of money at 11.5% compounded semi-annually until he was 65. At that time he converted the existing balance into an ordinary annuity paying $8000.00 every three months with interest at 11% compounded quarterly. For how long will the annuity run?

25. Sally contributed $500.00 every six months for fourteen years into an RRSP earning interest at 6.5% compounded semi-annually. Seven years after the last contribution, Sally converted the RRSP into an RRIF that is to pay her equal quarterly amounts for sixteen years. If the first payment is due three months after the conversion into the RRIF and interest on the RRIF is 7% compounded quarterly, how much will Sally receive every three months?

26. Wendy deposited $500.00 into an RRSP every three months for 25 years. Upon her retirement she converted the RRSP balance into an RRIF that is to pay her equal quarterly amounts for twenty years. If the first payment is due three months after her retirement and interest is 9% compounded quarterly, how much will Wendy receive every three months?

27. A contract is signed requiring payments of $750.00 at the end of every three months for eight years.
    - **(a)** How much is the cash value of the contract if money is worth 18% compounded quarterly?
    - **(b)** If the first three payments are missed, how much would have to be paid after one year to bring the contract up to date?
    - **(c)** If, because of the missed payments, the contract has to be paid out at the end of one year, how much money is needed?
    - **(d)** How much of the total interest paid is due to the missed payments?
28. Aaron deposited $900.00 every six months for twenty years into a fund paying 15.5% compounded semi-annually. Five years after the last deposit he converted the existing balance in the fund into an ordinary annuity paying him equal monthly payments for fifteen years. If interest on the annuity is 15% compounded monthly, what is the size of the monthly payment he will receive?
29. $8000.00 is invested at a fixed rate of 12.5% compounded semi-annually for seven years. After seven years, the fund is converted into an ordinary annuity paying $750.00 per month. If interest on the annuity is 12% compounded monthly, what is the term of the annuity?
30. A savings plan requiring quarterly deposits of $400.00 for twenty years provides for a lump sum payment of $92 000.00 just after the last deposit has been made.
    - **(a)** What is the effective rate of interest on the savings plan?
    - **(b)** If, instead of the lump sum, monthly ordinary annuity payments of $1350.00 may be accepted at the same nominal rate of interest (correct to two decimals) but compounded monthly, what is the term of the annuity?

Self-test

1. A sum of money is deposited at the end of every month for ten years at 7.5% compounded monthly. After the last deposit, interest for the account is to be 6% compounded quarterly and the account is to be paid out by quarterly payments of $4800 over six years. What is the size of the monthly deposit?
2. You won $100 000 in a lottery and you want to set some of that sum aside for ten years. After ten years, you would like to receive $2400 at the end of every three months for eight years. How much of your winnings must you set aside if interest is 10.5% compounded quarterly?
3. A debt can be repaid by payments of $2000 today, $4000 in five years, and $3000 in eight years. What single payment would settle the debt three years from today if money is worth 9% compounded quarterly?
4. Compute the nominal annual rate of interest on a loan of $48 000 repaid in semi-annual instalments of $4000 in ten years.
5. A loan of $14 400 is to be repaid in quarterly payments of $600. How many payments are required to repay the loan at 10.5% compounded quarterly?

6. Wen borrowed $7500 at 21.5% compounded quarterly. He repaid $4500 after two years and $7500 after five years. How much will Wen owe at the end of nine years?

7. Determine the effective annual rate of interest earned by quarterly deposits of $3000 made for eight years if the balance just after the last deposit is $120 000.

8. A loan was repaid in seven years by monthly payments of $450. If interest was 12% compounded monthly, how much interest was paid?

9. Ms. Simms made quarterly deposits of $540 into a savings account. For the first five years interest was 12% compounded quarterly. Since then the rate of interest has been 10.8% compounded quarterly. How much is the account balance after thirteen years?

10. How much interest is included in the accumulated value of $3200 paid at the end of every six months for four years if the interest rate is 10.5% compounded semi-annually?

11. The amount of $46 200 is invested at 9.5% compounded quarterly for four years. After four years the balance in the fund is converted into an annuity. If interest on the annuity is 6.5% compounded semi-annually and payments are made at the end of every six months for seven years, what is the size of the payments?

12. An obligation of $5000 due in four years is to be settled by four equal payments due today, fifteen months from now, twenty-seven months from now, and thirty-six months from now respectively. What is the size of the equal payments at 16.5% compounded quarterly?

13. What is the size of semi-annual deposits that will accumulate to $67 200 after eight years at 13.5% compounded semi-annually?

14. Sue contributed $800 every three months for five years into an RRSP earning 19.5% compounded quarterly. Six years after the last contribution, she converted the RRSP into an annuity which is to pay her monthly for thirty years. If the first payment is due one month after the conversion into the annuity and interest on the annuity is 13.5% compounded monthly, how much will Sue receive every month?

CASE STUDY

A young couple is considering buying a house, a car, and new appliances. Many payment options are available. The couple's combined yearly gross income is $41 000; deductions amount to 35% of this amount. Based on the following data, calculate how much money per month the couple will have left over for entertainment.

1. The house has a list price of $133 000 and requires a minimum down payment of 5%. There are two payment options.

   (a) Finance the balance at 9% per annum compounded monthly and amortized over 25 years. Calculate the monthly payment and the interest paid over 25 years.

(b) Finance the balance at 9% per annum compounded monthly and make a monthly payment of \$1150 per month. Calculate how much interest is saved by paying the extra amount per month.

2. The car that the couple is considering has a list price of \$18 900. The trade-in value of their old car is \$3500. G.S.T. of 7% on the list price and P.S.T. of 8% on the difference must be added. There are three options.

(a) Use the car manufacturer's payment plan—2.9% interest per annum compounded monthly over 48 months. Calculate the monthly payment.

(b) Accept a \$1250 cash-back offer on the list price and finance the balance with a bank loan of 8¾% per annum compounded monthly over 48 months. Calculate the monthly payment.

(c) The dealer advertises an "interest added," 6% per annum compounded monthly offer. The interest for the 48 months is added to the balance and then the total is divided into 48 equal payments. Calculate the monthly payment.

3. Different manufacturers offer specials on appliance combinations. The list price for similar units is \$3200. There are three payment options.

(a) Pay cash and receive a 15% discount. Calculate the cash price.

(b) Pay \$400 down and then make 36 payments of \$77.78.

(i) Calculate the cash price if interest is 9% per annum compounded monthly.

(ii) What is the total amount of interest paid?

(c) Pay cash by borrowing from the bank for 36 months at 10% per annum compounded monthly. Calculate the monthly payment.

(d) Is option B or C less expensive?

4. How much money is left over per month if the couple decides to make all purchases on a payment plan? Choose the lowest monthly payments.

Summary of formulae used

Formula 9.1

$S = P(1 + i)^n$ — Finding the compound amount (or future value or maturity value) when the original principal, the rate of interest, and the time period are known

Formula 9.2B

$P = S(1 + i)^{-n}$ — Finding the present value by means of the discount factor (the reciprocal of the compounding factor)

Formula 11.1

$$S_n = R\left[\frac{(1 + i)^n - 1}{i}\right]$$

Finding the amount (accumulated value) of an ordinary simple annuity

Formula 11.2

$$A_n = R\left[\frac{1 - (1 + i)^{-n}}{i}\right]$$

Finding the present value (discounted value) of an ordinary annuity

Glossary of terms used

Accumulated value of one dollar per period see *Accumulation factor*

Accumulation factor for annuities the factor $\frac{(1 + i)^n - 1}{i}$

Amount of an annuity the sum of the accumulated values of the periodic payments at the end of the term of the annuity

Annual rent the sum of the periodic payments in one year

Annuity a series of payments, usually equal in size, made at equal periodic time intervals

Annuity certain an annuity for which the term is fixed

Annuity due an annuity in which the periodic payments are made at the beginning of each payment interval

Compounding factor for annuities see *Accumulation factor*

Contingent annuity an annuity in which the term is uncertain; that is, either the beginning date of the term or the ending date of the term or both are unknown

Deferred annuity an annuity in which the first payment is delayed for a number of payment periods

Discount factor of annuities see *Present value factor*

Discounted value of one dollar per period see *Present value factor*

General annuity an annuity in which the conversion (or compounding) period is different from the payment interval

Ordinary annuity an annuity in which the payments are made at the end of each payment interval

Payment interval the length of time between successive payments

Payment period see *Payment interval*

Periodic rent the size of the regular periodic payment

Perpetuity an annuity for which the payments continue forever

Present value factor for annuities the factor $\frac{1 - (1 + i)^{-n}}{i}$

Present value of an annuity the sum of the present values (or discounted values) of the periodic payments at the beginning of the term of the annuity

Simple annuity an annuity in which the conversion period is the same as the payment interval

Term of annuity the length of time from the beginning of the first payment interval to the end of the last payment interval

12 *Other simple annuities*

Introduction

The basic type of annuity—the ordinary annuity in which the payments are made at the end of each payment period—was considered in Chapter 11.

In this chapter we will consider other simple annuities resulting from variations in the payment dates. These include annuities due in which payments are made in advance, deferred annuities in which the first payment is made after the end of the first payment interval, and perpetuities in which payments continue indefinitely.

Objectives

Upon completing this chapter, you will be able to

1. determine the amount and present value of annuities due;
2. find the periodic rent, the term, and the interest rate for annuities due;
3. determine the present value of ordinary deferred annuities and deferred annuities due;
4. find the periodic rent, the term, and the interest rate for deferred annuities;
5. determine the present value of simple perpetuities.

12.1 *Annuities due—amount and present value*

A. Amount of an annuity due

By definition, an **annuity due** is an annuity in which the periodic payments are made at the beginning of each payment interval.

Finding the amount of such an annuity is similar to finding the amount of an ordinary annuity. In fact, the amount of an annuity due is closely related to the amount of an ordinary annuity. This same close relationship also holds for the present value.

Example **12.1a** Find the accumulated value at the end date of the last payment period of deposits of $3000.00 each made at the beginning of five consecutive years respectively at 12% compounded annually.

Solution

As for any problem involving a series of payments, the method of solution and the data can be shown on a time diagram.

FIGURE 12.1 ***Graphic representation of method and data***

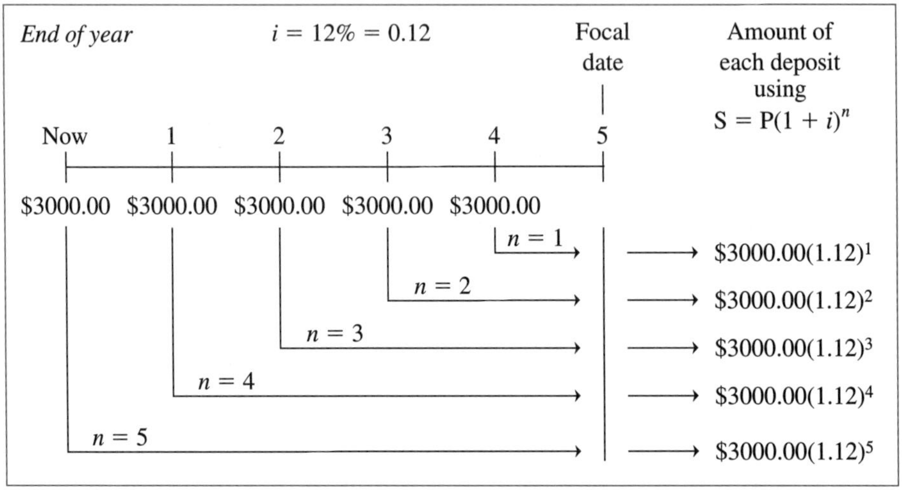

End of year $i = 12\% = 0.12$ Focal date

Amount of each deposit using $S = P(1 + i)^n$

Now 1 2 3 4 5

\$3000.00 \$3000.00 \$3000.00 \$3000.00 \$3000.00

$n = 1$ → \$3000.00(1.12)[1]

$n = 2$ → \$3000.00(1.12)[2]

$n = 3$ → \$3000.00(1.12)[3]

$n = 4$ → \$3000.00(1.12)[4]

$n = 5$ → \$3000.00(1.12)[5]

As shown in the diagram, the first deposit is located at the beginning of Year 1, which is the same as 'now'; the second deposit is located at the beginning of Year 2, which is the same as the end of Year 1; the third at the beginning of Year 3; the fourth at the beginning of Year 4; and the fifth and last deposit at the beginning of Year 5, which is also the beginning of the last payment period. The focal date, however, is located at the *end* of the last payment period.

The accumulated values of the individual deposits are obtained by using Formula 9.1, $S = P(1 + i)^n$. Finding the combined total of the five accumulated values is made easier by taking out the common factors 3000.00 and 1.12 as shown below.

$$
\begin{array}{llllll}
\textit{Deposit 5} & 3000.00(1.12)^1 & & (1.12) & & (1.\ \ ) & & (1.\qquad\ ) \\
\textit{Deposit 4} & 3000.00(1.12)^2 & & (1.12)^2 & & (1.12) & & (1.12\qquad) \\
\textit{Deposit 3} & 3000.00(1.12)^3 & = 3000.00 & (1.12)^3 & = 3000.00(1.12) & (1.12)^2 & = 3000.00(1.12) & (1.12544\ \ ) \\
\textit{Deposit 2} & 3000.00(1.12)^4 & & (1.12)^4 & & (1.12)^3 & & (1.404928\ ) \\
\textit{Deposit 1} & 3000.00(1.12)^5 & & (1.12)^5 & & (1.12)^4 & & (1.5735194)
\end{array}
$$

$$
\begin{aligned}
&= 3000.00(1.12)(6.3528474) \\
&= 19\ 058.54(1.12) \\
&= \$21\ 345.56
\end{aligned}
$$

Note: This example is the same as Example 11.2b except that the deposits are made at the beginning of each payment period rather than at the end. The answer to Example 11.2b was \$19 058.54. We could have obtained the answer to this example simply by multiplying the answer to Example 11.2b by 1.12. This method can be verified by writing the problem in equation form and using the geometric series method.

The amount of the series of deposits

$= 3000.00(1.12)^1 + 3000.00(1.12)^2 + 3000.00(1.12)^3 + 3000.00(1.12)^4 + 3000.00(1.12)^5$

$= 3000.00(1.12 + 1.12^2 + 1.12^3 + 1.12^4 + 1.12^5)$

$= 3000.00(1.12)(1 + 1.12 + 1.12^2 + 1.12^3 + 1.12^4)$

= 3000.00(1.12)(the sum of the first five terms of a geometric progression whose first term is 1 with a common ratio 1.12)

$= 3000.00(1.12)\left(\frac{1.12^5 - 1}{1.12 - 1}\right) \longleftarrow$ substitute in $S = \frac{a(r^n - 1)}{r - 1}, r > 1$

= 3000.00(1.12)(6.3528474)

= 19 058.54(1.12)

= \$21 345.56

***Example* 12.1b** Use the geometric progression method to determine the accumulated value of payments of \$200.00 made at the beginning of each of six consecutive years if interest is 10% compounded annually.

Solution

Since the payments are equal in size and are made at the beginning of each payment period, the problem is an annuity due and the focal date for finding the amount is the end point of the last payment period. The accumulated value of the payments can be written in equation form.

Let the accumulated value of the annuity due be represented by S_n(due).

$S_n(\text{due}) = 200.00(1.10)^1 + 200.00(1.10)^2 + 200.00(1.10)^3 + 200.00(1.10)^4 + 200.00(1.10)^5 + 200.00(1.10)^6$

$= 200.00(1.10 + 1.10^2 + 1.10^3 + 1.10^4 + 1.10^5 + 1.10^6)$

$= 200.00(1.10)(1 + 1.10 + 1.10^2 + 1.10^3 + 1.10^4 + 1.10^5)$

= 200.00(1.10)(the sum of the first six terms of a geometric progression with first term 1 and common ratio 1.10)

$= 200.00(1.10)\left(\frac{1.10^6 - 1}{1.10 - 1}\right)$

= 200.00(1.10)(7.71561)

= 1543.12(1.10)

= \$1697.43

Note: Example 12.1b is the same as Example 11.2c except that the payments have been made at the beginning of each payment period. The answer to Example 11.2c was $1543.12. Again, we could have used this answer to find the solution to Example 12.1b simply by multiplying by the factor 1.10. The factor 1.10 consists of 1 + 0.10 and, since 0.10 = i, 1.10 is the factor $(1 + i)$.

Furthermore, the annuity in Example 11.2c was an ordinary annuity while the answer in Example 12.1b is an annuity due. It appears that the amount of the annuity due can be obtained by multiplying the amount of the ordinary annuity by the factor $(1 + i)$. We can verify this implication by solving the simple annuity due in a general way.

The general notation for annuities due is the same as for ordinary annuities except that the accumulated value of the annuity due is represented by the symbol S_n(due). The simple annuity due is represented in Figure 12.2 and the general solution follows.

FIGURE 12.2 ***Graphic representation of the general problem of finding the amount of an annuity due***

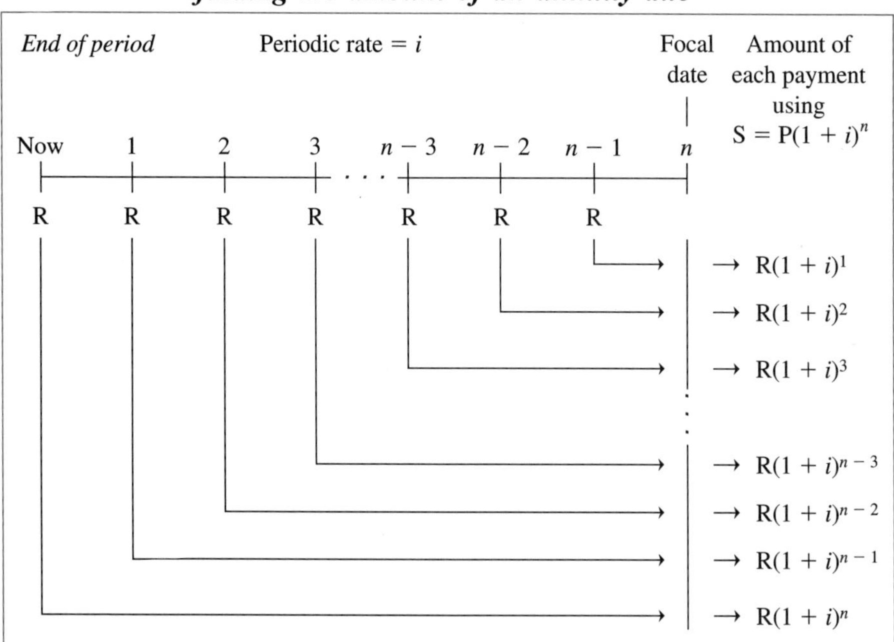

Adding the accumulated values of the individual payments at the focal date gives rise to the following equation.

$$\begin{aligned}S_n(\text{due}) &= R(1+i)^1 + R(1+i)^2 + R(1+i)^3 + \ldots + R(1+i)^{n-2} + \\ &\quad R(1+i)^{n-1} + R(1+i)^n \\ &= R[(1+i)^1 + (1+i)^2 + (1+i)^3 + \ldots + (1+i)^{n-2} + \\ &\quad (1+i)^{n-1} + (1+i)^n] \\ &= R(1+i)[1 + (1+i)^1 + (1+i)^2 + \ldots + (1+i)^{n-3} + (1+i)^{n-2} + \\ &\quad (1+i)^{n-1}] \\ &= R(1+i)(\text{the sum of the first } n \text{ terms of a geometric progression with first} \\ &\qquad \text{term 1 and common ratio } 1+i) \\ &= R(1+i)\left[\frac{(1+i)^n - 1}{(1+i) - 1}\right]\end{aligned}$$

$$S_n(\text{due}) = R(1+i)\left[\frac{(1+i)^n - 1}{i}\right]$$ ⟵ ***Formula*** **12.1** ⟵ amount of an annuity due

Note: Formula 12.1, the amount of an annuity due, differs from Formula 11.1, the amount of an ordinary annuity, only by the factor $(1 + i)$.

$$\text{AMOUNT OF AN ANNUITY DUE} = (1+i) \times \text{AMOUNT OF THE ORDINARY ANNUITY}$$

The relationship between an annuity due and the corresponding ordinary annuity is graphically illustrated in the comparison of the line diagrams.

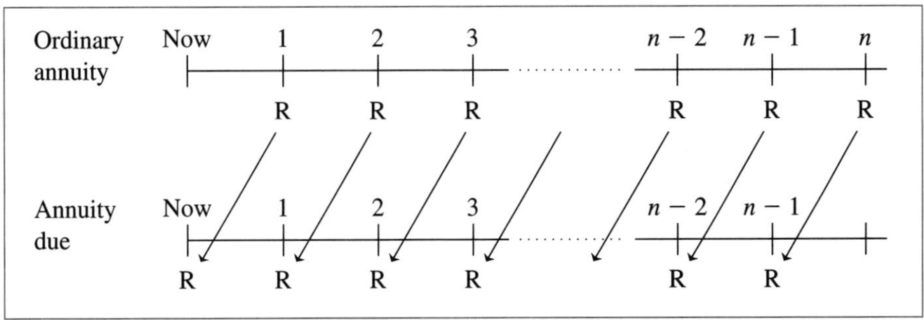

The two line graphs show the shift of the payments by one period. In an annuity due, every payment earns interest for one more period than in an ordinary annuity and this explains the factor $(1 + i)$.

Example **12.1c** Find the accumulated value at the end of the last payment period of quarterly payments of $50.00 made at the beginning of each quarter for ten years if interest is 6% compounded quarterly.

Solution

Since the payments are of equal size made at the beginning of each period, the payment series is an annuity due and since the focal date is the end of the last payment period, the amount of the annuity due is to be found.

$$R = 50.00; \quad i = \frac{6\%}{4} = 0.015; \quad n = 10(4) = 40$$

$$\begin{aligned} S_n(\text{due}) &= 50.00(1.015)\left(\frac{1.015^{40} - 1}{0.015}\right) \longleftarrow \text{ substituting in Formula 12.1} \\ &= 50.00(1.015)(54.2678939) \\ &= 2713.39(1.015) \\ &= \$2754.10 \end{aligned}$$

***Example* 12.1d** You deposit $10.00 at the beginning of each month for five years in an account paying 12% compounded monthly.

(i) How much will the balance in your account be at the end of five years?

(ii) How much of the amount will you have contributed?

(iii) How much of the balance will be interest?

Solution

(i)

$$R = 10.00; \quad i = \frac{12\%}{12} = 1\% = 0.01; \quad n = 5(12) = 60$$

$$\begin{aligned} S_n(\text{due}) &= 10.00(1.01)\left(\frac{1.01^{60} - 1}{0.01}\right) \\ &= 10.00(1.01)(81.66967) \\ &= 816.6967(1.01) \\ &= 824.86 \end{aligned}$$

(ii) Your contribution is (10.00)(60) = $600.00.

(iii) The interest earned = 824.86 − 600.00 = $224.86.

B. *Present value of an annuity due*

***Example* 12.1e** Find the present value of five payments of $3000.00 each made at the beginning of each of five consecutive years respectively if money is worth 12% compounded annually.

Solution

As Figure 12.3 shows, the present value of the individual payments are obtained using Formula 9.2B, $P = S(1 + i)^{-n}$. The sum of the individual present values is easier to find when the common factor 3000.00 is taken out.

FIGURE 12.3 ***Graphic representation of method and data***

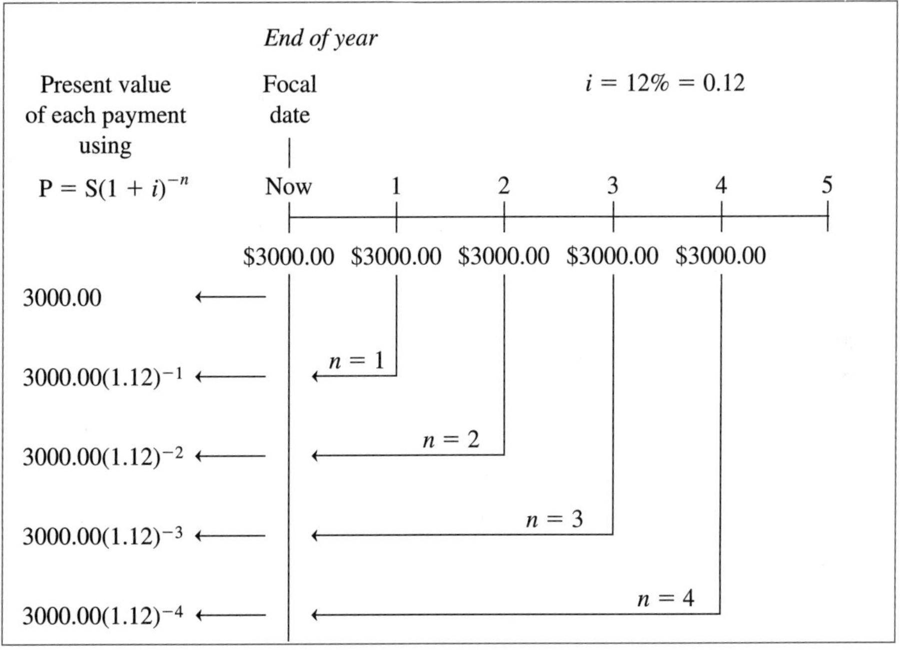

Payment 1	3000.00	(1)	(1.0000000)
Payment 2	$3000.00(1.12)^{-1}$	$(1.12)^{-1}$	(0.8928571)
Payment 3	$3000.00(1.12)^{-2}$ =	$3000.00(1.12)^{-2}$ =	3000.00(0.7971939)
Payment 4	$3000.00(1.12)^{-3}$	$(1.12)^{-3}$	(0.7117802)
Payment 5	$3000.00(1.12)^{-4}$	$(1.12)^{-4}$	(0.6355181)
		=	3000.00(4.0373493)
		=	\$12 112.05

As in previous examples, the problem may be set up in an equation form that leads to a solution using the formula for the sum of a geometric progression.

$$\begin{aligned}
A_n(\text{due}) &= 3000.00 + 3000.00(1.12)^{-1} + 3000.00(1.12)^{-2} + 3000.00(1.12)^{-3} + 3000.00(1.12)^{-4} \\
&= 3000.00(1 + 1.12^{-1} + 1.12^{-2} + 1.12^{-3} + 1.12^{-4}) \\
&= 3000.00(\text{the sum of the first five terms of a geometric progression with first term 1 and common ratio } 1.12^{-1}) \\
&= 3000.00\left[\frac{1 - (1.12^{-1})^5}{1 - 1.12^{-1}}\right] \longleftarrow \text{substituting in } S = \frac{a(1 - r^n)}{1 - r}, r < 1 \\
&= 3000.00\left(\frac{1 - 1.12^{-5}}{1 - 1.12^{-1}}\right) \\
&= 3000.00\left(\frac{1 - 0.5674269}{1 - 0.8928571}\right) \\
&= 3000.00\left(\frac{0.4325731}{0.1071429}\right) \\
&= 3000.00(4.0373473) \\
&= \$12\,112.04
\end{aligned}$$

Note: Example 12.1e is the same as Example 11.3b, except that the payments are made at the beginning of each payment period. The answer to Example 11.3b was \$10 814.33. If this amount is multiplied by 1.12, the result is \$12 112.05, the answer to Example 12.1e.

This result implies that we could have obtained the present value of the annuity due in Example 12.1e by multiplying the present value of the ordinary annuity in Example 11.3b by the factor 1.12 which is the factor $(1 + i)$.

This implication can be verified by solving the simple annuity due for its present value, represented by the symbol A_n(due), as Figure 12.4 shows.

Adding the present values of the individual payments at the focal date gives rise to the following equation.

$$\begin{aligned}
A_n(\text{due}) &= R + R(1 + i)^{-1} + R(1 + i)^{-2} + R(1 + i)^{-3} + \ldots + R(1 + i)^{n-2} + R(1 + i)^{n-1} \\
&= R[1 + (1 + i)^{-1} + (1 + i)^{-2} + (1 + i)^{-3} + \ldots + (1 + i)^{n-2} + (1 + i)^{n-1}] \\
&= R\left(\begin{matrix}\text{the sum of the first } n \text{ terms of a geometric progression} \\ \text{with first term 1 and common ratio } (1 + i)^{-1}\end{matrix}\right) \\
&= R\left(\frac{1 - [(1 + i)^{-1}]^n}{1 - (1 + i)^{-1}}\right)
\end{aligned}$$

FIGURE 12.4 ***Graphic representation of the general problem of finding the present value of an annuity due***

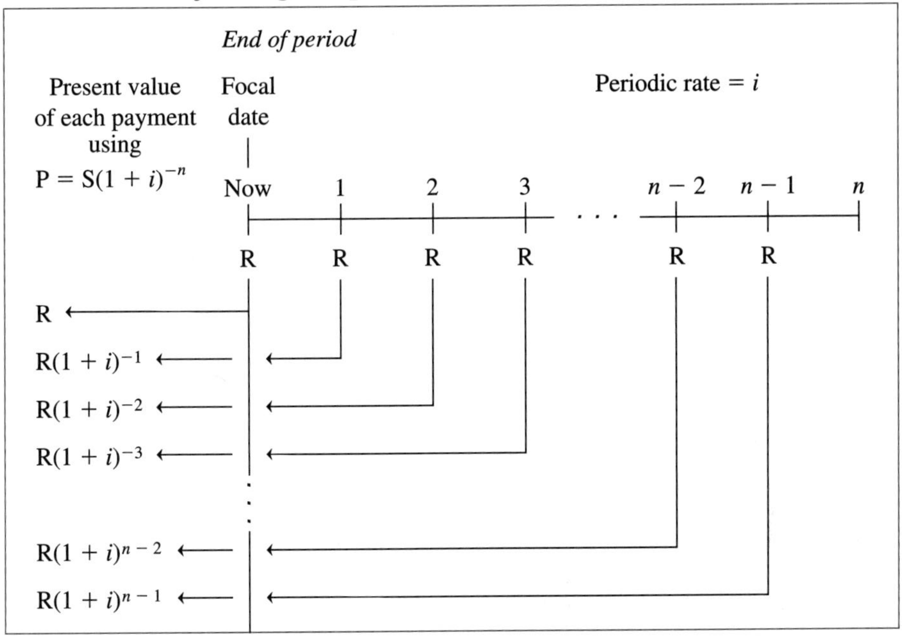

$$= R\left[\frac{1-(1+i)^{-n}}{1-(1+i)^{-1}}\right]$$

$$= R\left[\frac{1-(1+i)^{-n}}{1-\frac{1}{1+i}}\right]$$

$$= R\left[\frac{1-(1+i)^{-n}}{\frac{(1+i)-1}{1+i}}\right]$$

$$= R\left(\frac{(1+i)[1-(1+i)^{-n}]}{i}\right)$$

$$A_n(\text{due}) = R(1+i)\left[\frac{1-(1+i)^{-n}}{i}\right]$$ ⟵ ***Formula* 12.2** ⟵ present value of an annuity due

Note: Formula 12.2, present value of an annuity due, differs from Formula 11.2, present value of an ordinary annuity, only by the factor $(1 + i)$.

$$\text{PRESENT VALUE OF AN ANNUITY DUE} = (1 + i) \times \text{PRESENT VALUE OF THE ORDINARY ANNUITY}$$

***Example* 12.1f** Find the present value of payments of \$50.00 made at the beginning of each quarter for ten years if interest is 6% compounded quarterly.

Solution

$$R = 50.00; \quad i = \frac{6\%}{4} = 1.5\% = 0.015; \quad n = 10(4) = 40$$

$$A_n(\text{due}) = 50.00(1.015)\left[\frac{1 - (1.015)^{-40}}{(0.015)}\right] \longleftarrow \text{substituting in Formula 12.2}$$

$$= 50.00(1.015)(29.9158452)$$

$$= 1495.79(1.015)$$

$$= \$1518.23$$

***Example* 12.1g** What is the cash value of a three-year lease of office facilities renting for \$536.50 payable at the beginning of each month if money is worth 15% compounded monthly?

Solution

Since the payments are at the beginning of each payment period, the problem involves an annuity due and since we want the cash value, the present value of the annuity due is required.

$$R = 536.50; \quad i = \frac{15\%}{12} = 1.25\% = 0.0125; \quad n = 3(12) = 36$$

$$A_n(\text{due}) = 536.50(1.0125)\left[\frac{1 - (1.0125)^{-36}}{0.0125}\right]$$

$$= 536.50(28.847267)(1.0125)$$

$$= 15\,476.56(1.0125)$$

$$= \$15\,670.02$$

The cash value of the lease is \$15 670.02.

C. *Using preprogrammed financial calculators*

You can easily determine the amount S_n(due) or the present value A_n(due) using a preprogrammed financial calculator by finding the corresponding value for an ordinary annuity and multiplying by $(1 + i)$ or, if a [DUE] key is available, by pressing [DUE] instead of [CPT] (or [2nd]) when retrieving the answer. If [DUE] is a secondary function, press [2nd] followed by the primary function key.

Example **12.1h** Payments of $425 are to be made at the beginning of each quarter for 10 years. If money is worth 20% compounded quarterly, determine

(i) the accumulated value of the payments;

(ii) the present value of the payments.

Solution

(i) $R = 425; \quad i = 5\%; \quad n = 40$

	Press	Display shows	
0	[PV]	0	
425	[PMT]	425	
5	[%*i*]	5	
40	[N]	40	
[DUE] (or [2nd] [CPT])	[FV]	53906.899 ←	this retrieves the amount of an annuity due

The accumulated value of the annuity due is $53 906.90.

(ii)

	Press	Display shows	
0	[FV]	0	
425	[PMT]	425	
5	[%*i*]	5	
40	[N]	40	
[DUE] (or [2nd] [CPT])	[PV]	7657.2423 ←	this retrieves the present value of an annuity due

The present value of the annuity due is $7657.24.

Example **12.1i** Frank deposited monthly rent receipts of \$250.00 due at the beginning of each month in a savings account paying 10.5% compounded monthly for four years. Frank made no further deposits after four years but left the money in the account.

(i) How much will the balance be twelve full years after he made the first deposit?

(ii) How much of the total will be due to rent?

(iii) How much will be interest?

Solution

(i) First determine the balance at the end of four years. This problem involves finding the amount of an annuity due.

$$R = 250.00; \quad i = \frac{10.5\%}{12} = 0.875\%; \quad n = 48$$

$$\begin{aligned} S_n(\text{due}) &= 250.00(1.00875)\left(\frac{1.00875^{48} - 1}{0.00875}\right) \\ &= 250.00(1.00875)(59.335279) \\ &= 14\,833.82(1.00875) \\ &= \$14\,963.62 \end{aligned}$$

Now accumulate \$14 963.62 for another eight years.

$$P = 14\,963.62; \quad i = 0.00875; \quad n = 8(12) = 96$$

$$\begin{aligned} S &= 14\,963.62(1.00875)^{96} \quad \longleftarrow \text{substituting in Formula 9.1} \\ &= 14\,963.62(2.3079191) \\ &= \$34\,534.82 \end{aligned}$$

Programmed solution

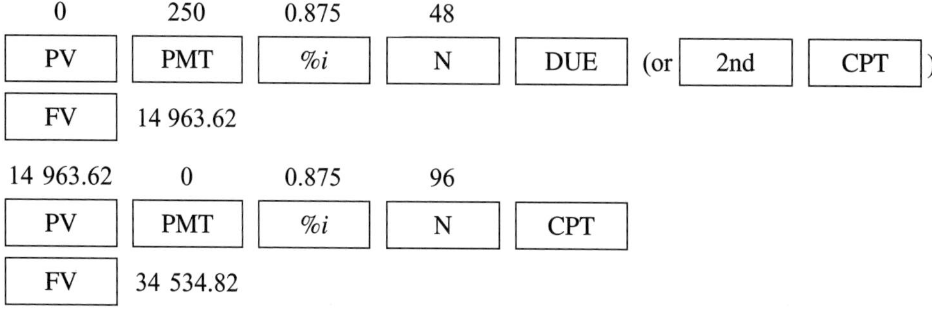

The balance in the account after 12 years is \$34 534.82.

(ii) The rent receipts in the total are 250.00(48) = \$12 000.00

(iii) Interest in the balance is 34 534.82 − 12 000.00 = \$22 534.82.

Example **12.1j** Ms. Willis would like to receive annuity payments of \$2000.00 at the beginning of each quarter for seven years. The annuity is to start five years from now and interest is 11.8% compounded quarterly.

(i) How much must Ms. Willis invest today?

(ii) How much will Ms. Willis receive from the annuity?

(iii) How much of what she receives will be interest?

Solution

(i) First, find the present value of the annuity due (the focal point is five years from now).

$$R = 2000.00; \quad i = \frac{11.8\%}{4} = 2.95\% = 0.0295; \quad n = 7(4) = 28$$

$$\begin{aligned} A_n(\text{due}) &= 2000.00(1.0295)\left[\frac{1-(1.0295)^{-28}}{0.0295}\right] \\ &= 2000.00(18.879335)(1.0295) \\ &= 37\,758.67(1.0295) \\ &= \$38\,872.55 \end{aligned}$$

Second, determine the present value of \$38 872.55 (the focal point is 'now').

$$S = 38\,872.55; \quad i = 2.95\%; \quad n\ 5(4) = 20$$

$$\begin{aligned} P &= 38\,872.55(1.0295)^{-20} \\ &= 38\,872.55(0.5590787) \\ &= \$21\,732.82 \end{aligned}$$

Programmed solution

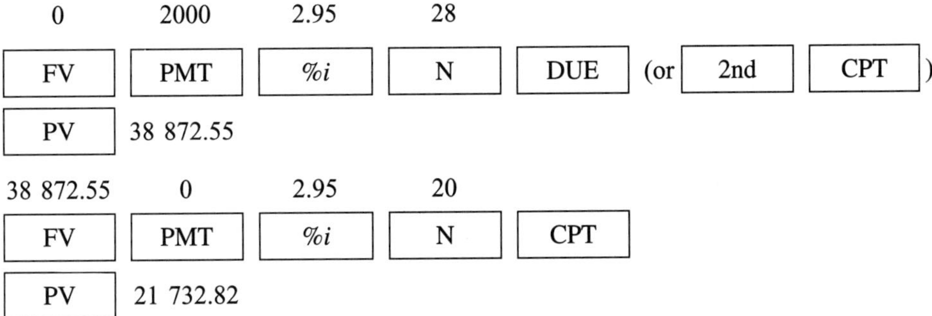

Ms. Willis will have to invest \$21 732.82.

(ii) Ms. Willis will receive 28(2000.00) = \$56 000.00.

(iii) Interest will be 56 000.00 − 21 732.82 = \$34 267.18.

Exercise 12.1

A. Find the amount and the present value of each of the following annuities due.

	Periodic payment	*Payment interval*	*Term*	*Interest rate*	*Conversion period*
1.	\$3000.00	3 months	8 years	8%	quarterly
2.	\$750.00	1 month	5 years	12%	monthly
3.	\$2000.00	6 months	12 years	15.6%	semi-annually
4.	\$450.00	3 months	15 years	14.4%	quarterly
5.	\$65.00	1 month	20 years	9%	monthly
6.	\$160.00	1 month	15 years	6%	monthly

B. Answer each of the following questions.

1. Find the amount of an annuity due of \$300.00 payable at the beginning of every month for seven years at 12% compounded monthly.

2. Determine the accumulated value after twelve years of deposits of \$360.00 made at the beginning of every three months and earning interest at 7% compounded quarterly.

3. Find the present value of payments of \$2500.00 made at the beginning of every six months for ten years if money is worth 9.5% compounded semi-annually.

4. What is the discounted value of deposits of \$240.00 made at the beginning of every three months for seven years if money is worth 8.8% compounded quarterly?

5. A washer-dryer combination can be bought by making monthly payments of \$52.50 for two and a half years. The first payment is due on the date of sale and interest is 21% compounded monthly.

   (a) What is the purchase price?

   (b) How much will be paid in instalments?

   (c) How much is the cost of financing?

6. Diane Wallace bought a living-room suite on time signing an instalment contract that requires monthly payments of \$62.25 for three years. The first payment is made on the date of signing and interest is 24% compounded monthly.

   (a) What was the cash price?

   (b) How much will Diane pay in total?

   (c) How much of what she pays will be interest?

7. Until he retires sixteen years from now, Mr. Lait plans to deposit $300.00 at the beginning of every three months in an account paying interest at 10% compounded quarterly.
   (a) What will the balance be in his account when he retires?
   (b) How much of the balance will be interest?

8. Ms. Jones contributes $750.00 at the beginning of every six months into an RRSP paying interest at 8% compounded semi-annually.
   (a) How much will her RRSP deposits amount to in twenty years?
   (b) How much of the amount will be interest?

9. The monthly premium on a three-year insurance policy is $64.00 payable in advance. What is the cash value of the policy if money is worth 13.8% compounded monthly?

10. The monthly rent payment on office space is $535.00 payable in advance. What yearly payment in advance would satisfy the lease if interest is 15.6% compounded monthly?

12.2 *Annuities due—finding R,* n, *and* i

A. *Finding the periodic payment when the amount S_n or the present value A_n is known*

If S_n(due), n, and i are known, you can find R by substituting the given values in Formula 12.1. If A_n(due), n, and i are known, you can find R by substituting the given values in Formula 12.2.

Example **12.2a** What semi-annual payment must be made into a fund at the beginning of every six months to accumulate to $9600.00 in ten years at 11% compounded semi-annually?

Solution

$$S_n(\text{due}) = 9600.00; \quad i = \frac{11\%}{2} = 5.5\% = 0.055; \quad n = 10(2) = 20$$

$$9600.00 = R(1.055)\left(\frac{1.055^{20} - 1}{0.055}\right) \longleftarrow \text{substituting in Formula 12.1}$$

$$9600.00 = R(1.055)(34.868318)$$

$$9600.00 = R(36.786075)$$

$$R = \frac{9600.00}{36.786075}$$

$$R = 9600.00(0.0271842)$$

$$R = \$260.97$$

Programmed solution

	Press	Display shows	
0	PV	0	
9600	FV	9600	
5.5	%i	5.5	
20	N	20	
DUE (or 2nd CPT)	PMT	260.96831 ⟵	this retrieves the periodic payment for an annuity due

The semi-annual payment is $260.97.

Example **12.2b** What monthly rent payment at the beginning of each month for four years is required to fulfill a lease contract worth $7000.00 if money is worth 18% compounded monthly?

Solution

$$A_n(\text{due}) = 7000.00; \quad i = \frac{18\%}{12} = 1.5\% = 0.015; \quad n = 4(12) = 48$$

$$7000.00 = R(1.015)\left(\frac{1 - 1.015^{-48}}{0.015}\right)$$ ⟵ substituting in Formula 12.2

$$7000.00 = R(1.015)(34.042554)$$

$$7000.00 = R(34.553192)$$

$$R = \frac{7000.00}{34.553192}$$

$$R = 7000.00(0.0289409)$$

$$R = \$202.59$$

Programmed solution

		Press	Display shows
	0	FV	0
	7000	PV	7000
	1.5	%i	1.5
	48	N	48
DUE	(or 2nd CPT)	PMT	202.58621

The monthly rent payment due at the beginning of each month is $202.59.

Note: While special formulae for finding R could be obtained by solving Formulae 12.1 and 12.2 for R, due to technology, no useful purpose is served by such formulae. No special formulae for finding R are developed or used in this text.

Example **12.2c** How much will you have to deposit into an account at the beginning of every three months for twelve years if you want to have a balance of $100 000.00 twenty years from now and interest is 8% compounded quarterly?

Solution

First, find the balance that you must have in the account at the end of the term of the annuity (after 12 years).

$$S = 100\ 000.00; \quad i = \frac{8\%}{4} = 2\% = 0.02; \quad n = 8(4) = 32$$

$$\begin{aligned} P &= 100\ 000.00(1.02)^{-32} \\ &= 100\ 000.00(0.5306333) \\ &= \$53\ 063.33 \end{aligned}$$

Next, find the quarterly payment needed at the beginning of each quarter to accumulate to $53 063.33.

$$S_n(\text{due}) = 53\,063.33; \quad i = 0.02; \quad n = 12(4) = 48$$

$$53\,063.33 = R(1.02)\left(\frac{1.02^{48} - 1}{0.02}\right)$$

$$53\,063.33 = R(1.02)(79.3535193)$$

$$53\,063.33 = R(80.94058968)$$

$$R = \frac{53\,063.33}{80.94058968}$$

$$R = 53\,063.33(0.01235474)$$

$$R = \$655.58$$

Programmed solution

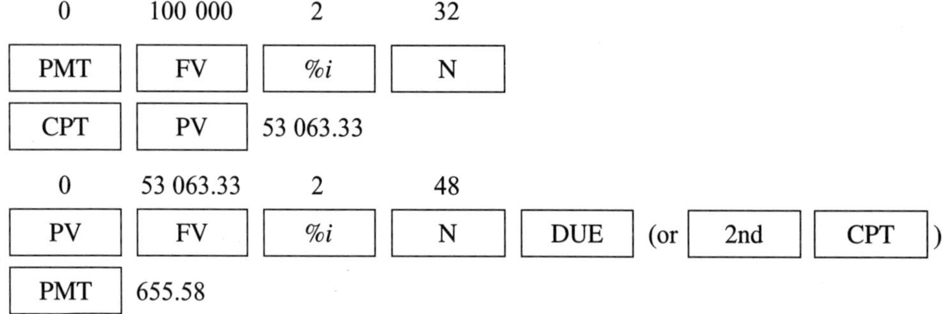

The quarterly deposit at the beginning of each payment period is $655.58.

***Example* 12.2d** What payment can be received at the beginning of each month for fifteen years if $10 000.00 is deposited in a fund ten years before the first payment is made and interest is 12% compounded monthly?

Solution

First, find the accumulated value of the initial deposit at the beginning of the term of the annuity due ten years after the deposit.

$$P = 10\,000.00; \quad i = \frac{12\%}{12} = 1\% = 0.01; \quad n = 10(12) = 120$$

$$\begin{aligned} S &= 10\,000.00(1.01)^{120} \\ &= 10\,000.00(3.3003869) \\ &= \$33\,003.87 \end{aligned}$$

Now determine the monthly withdrawal that can be made at the beginning of each month from the initial balance of $33 003.87.

$$A_n(\text{due}) = 33\,003.87; \quad i = 1\%; \quad = n = 15(12) = 180$$

$$33\,003.87 = R(1.01)\left[\frac{1 - (1.01)^{-180}}{0.01}\right]$$

$$33\,003.87 = R(1.01)(83.321664)$$

$$R = \frac{33\,003.87}{84.154881}$$

$$R = 33\,003.87(0.0118829)$$

$$R = \$392.18$$

Programmed solution

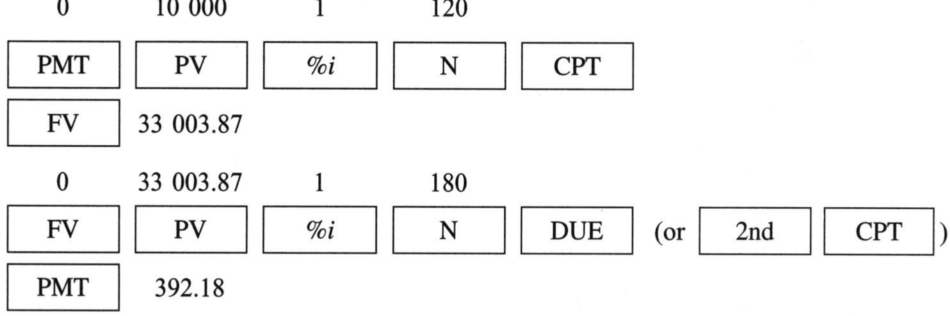

A payment of $392.18 can be made at the beginning of each month.

B. *Finding the term when the amount S_n or the present value A_n is known*

If S_n(due), R, and i are known, you can find n by substituting the given values in Formula 12.1 and solving for n. If A_n(due), R, and i are known, you can find n by substituting the given values in Formula 12.2 and solving for n.

1. *Finding* n *when S_n(due) is known*

Example 12.2e Over what length of time will $75.00 deposited at the beginning of each month grow to $6500.00 at 12% compounded monthly?

Solution

$$S_n(\text{due}) = 6500.00; \quad R = 75.00; \quad i = \frac{12\%}{12} = 1\% = 0.01$$

$$6500.00 = 75.00(1.01)\left(\frac{1.01^n - 1}{0.01}\right) \longleftarrow \text{substituting in Formula 12.1}$$

$$6500.00 = 7575.00(1.01^n - 1)$$

$$\frac{6500.00}{7575.00} = 1.01^n - 1$$

$$0.8580858 + 1 = 1.01^n$$

$$n \ln(1.01) = \ln 1.8580858 \longleftarrow \text{use natural logarithms to solve for } n$$

$$n(0.0099503) = 0.6195468$$

$$n = \frac{0.6195468}{0.0099503}$$

$$n = 62.263942$$

As discussed in Chapter 11, n should be rounded upwards.

$$n = 63 \text{ (months)}$$

It will take 5 years and 3 months to accumulate $6500.00.

Example **12.2f** Sheridan Credit Union intends to accumulate a building fund of $150 000.00 by depositing $3300.00 at the beginning of every three months at 13% compounded quarterly. How long will it take for the fund to reach the desired amount?

Solution

$$S_n(\text{due}) = 150\ 000.00; \quad R = 3300.00; \quad i = \frac{13\%}{4} = 3.25\%$$

Programmed solution

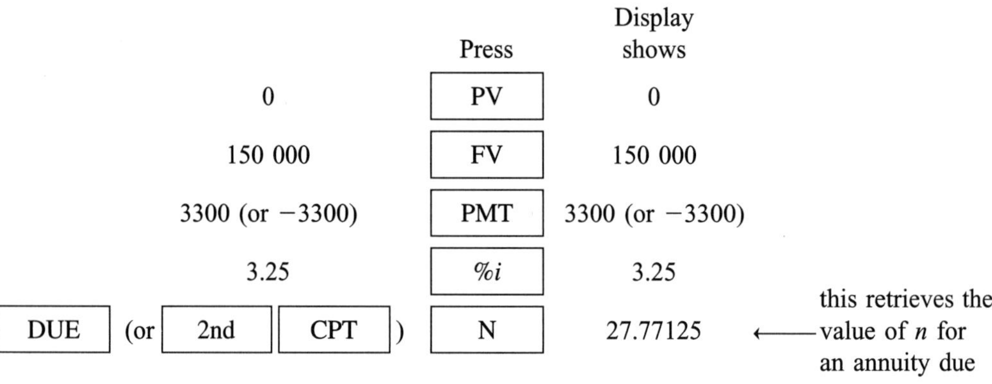

	Press	Display shows	
0	PV	0	
150 000	FV	150 000	
3300 (or −3300)	PMT	3300 (or −3300)	
3.25	%i	3.25	
DUE (or 2nd CPT)	N	27.77125	⟵ this retrieves the value of n for an annuity due

$$n = 28 \text{ quarters (approximately)}$$

It will take seven years to build up the fund.

2. *Finding* n *when A_n(due) is known*

Example 12.2g For how long can you withdraw $480.00 at the beginning of every three months from a fund of $9000.00 if interest is 10% compounded quarterly?

Solution

$$A_n(\text{due}) = 9000.00; \quad R = 480.00; \quad i = \frac{10\%}{4} = 2.5\% = 0.025$$

$$9000.00 = 480.00(1.025)\left(\frac{1 - 1.025^{-n}}{0.025}\right) \longleftarrow \text{substituting in Formula 12.2}$$

$$9000.00 = 19\,680.00(1 - 1.025^{-n})$$

$$\frac{9000.00}{19\,680.00} = 1 - 1.025^{-n}$$

$$0.4573171 = 1 - 1.025^{-n}$$

$$1.025^{-n} = 1 - 0.4573171$$

$$1.025^{-n} = 0.5426829$$

$$-n \ln 1.025 = \ln 0.5426829$$

$$-n(0.0246926) = -0.6112301$$

$$n = \frac{0.6112301}{0.0246926}$$

$$n = 24.753561$$

$$n = 25 \text{ (quarters)}$$

Withdrawals of $480.00 can be made for 6 years and 3 months. (The last withdrawal will be less than $480.00.)

Example 12.2h A lease contract valued at $7800.00 is to be fulfilled by rental payments of $180.00 due at the beginning of each month. If money is worth 21% compounded monthly, what should the term of the lease be?

Solution

$$A_n(\text{due}) = 7800.00; \quad R = 180.00; \quad i = \frac{21\%}{12} = 1.75\%$$

Programmed solution

	Press	Display shows
0	FV	0
7800	PV	7800
180	PMT	180
1.75	%i	1.75
DUE (or 2nd CPT)	N	78.832271

n = 79 months (approximately)

The term of the lease should be 6 years and 7 months.

Note: While special formulae for finding n could be obtained by solving Formulae 12.1 and 12.2 for n, due to the technology, no useful purpose is served by such formulae. No special formulae for finding n are developed or used in this text.

C. *Finding the rate of interest* i *when either S_n(due) or A_n(due) is known using a preprogrammed calculator*

Finding the rate of interest per conversion period i is accomplished by entering the three known values S_n(due), R, n or A_n(due), R, n and then retrieving the answer by pressing DUE %i. You can then obtain the nominal annual rate of interest by multiplying i by the number of compounding periods per year.

1. *Finding* i *when the amount S_n(due) is known*

Example 12.2i Compute the nominal rate of interest at which $50 deposited at the beginning of each month for ten years will amount to $15 000.

Solution

$$S_n(\text{due}) = 15\ 000; \quad R = 50; \quad n = 120$$

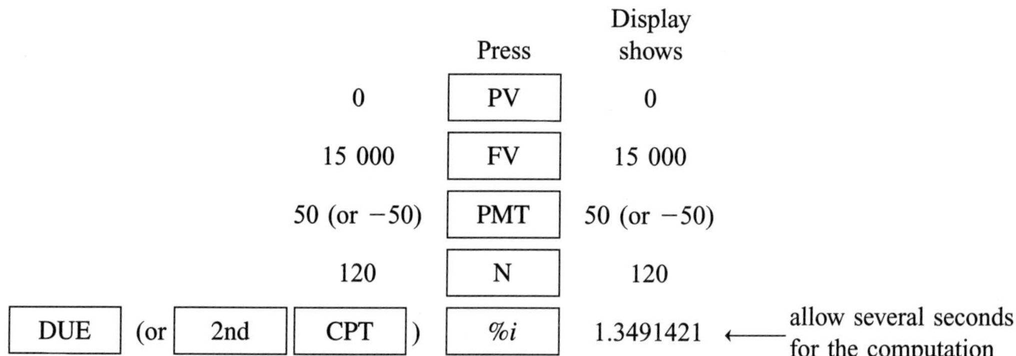

	Press	Display shows	
0	PV	0	
15 000	FV	15 000	
50 (or −50)	PMT	50 (or −50)	
120	N	120	
DUE (or 2nd CPT)	%i	1.3491421	← allow several seconds for the computation

The monthly conversion rate is 1.3491421%.
The nominal rate of interest is (12)(1.3491421%) = 16.19% approximately.

2. *Finding* i *when the present value* A_n*(due) is known*

***Example* 12.2j** A lease agreement valued at $7500 requires payment of $620 at the beginning of every quarter for five years. What is the nominal rate of interest charged?

Solution

$$A_n(\text{due}) = 7500; \quad R = 620; \quad n = 20$$

	Press	Display shows	
0	FV	0	
7500	PV	7500	
620	PMT	620	
20	N	20	
DUE (or 2nd CPT)	%i	6.0706197	← allow several seconds for the computation

The quarterly compounding rate is 6.0706197%.

The nominal rate of interest is (4)(6.0706197%) = 24.28% approximately.

Note: For an annuity due you can compute the conversion rate i without using a preprogrammed calculator by the trial and error approach shown in the Appendix. The needed modifications to Formulae 12.1 and 12.2 and the computation itself are also illustrated in the Appendix.

Exercise 12.2

A. Find the unknown value in each of the following annuities due.

	Amount	*Present value*	*Periodic payment*	*Payment period*	*Term*	*Int. rate*	*Conversion period*
1.	$20 000.00		?	3 months	15 years	16%	quarterly
2.		$12 000.00	?	1 year	8 years	7%	annually
3.		$18 500.00	?	6 months	12 years	13%	semi-annually
4.	$9400.00		?	1 month	5 years	12%	monthly
5.	$5300.00		$35.00	1 month	?	6%	monthly
6.		$8400.00	$440.00	3 months	?	14%	quarterly
7.		$6450.00	$1120.00	1 year	?	10%	annually
8.	$15 400.00		$396.00	6 months	?	5%	semi-annually
9.	$70 000.00		$367.00	1 year	25 years	?	annually
10.		$42 000.00	$528.00	1 month	10 years	?	monthly
11.		$28 700.00	$2015.00	6 months	15 years	?	semi-annually
12.	$36 000.00		$235.00	3 months	12 years	?	quarterly

B. Answer each of the following questions.

1. Elspeth McNab bought a boat valued at $12 500.00 on the instalment plan requiring equal monthly payments for four years. If the first payment is due on the date of purchase and interest is 16.5% compounded monthly, what is the size of the monthly payment?

2. How much does a depositor have to save at the beginning of every three months for nine years to accumulate $35 000.00 if interest is 8% compounded quarterly?

3. Quarterly payments of $1445.00 are to be made at the beginning of every three months on a lease valued at $25 000.00. What should the term of the lease be if money is worth 16% compounded quarterly?

4. Tom is saving $600.00 at the beginning of each month. How soon can he retire if he wants to have a retirement fund of $120 000.00 and interest is 12% compounded monthly?

5. What nominal rate of interest was paid if contributions of $250.00 made into an RRSP at the beginning of every three months amounted to $14 559.00 after ten years?

6. A vacation property valued at $25 000.00 was bought for fifteen payments of $2750.00 due at the beginning of every six months. What nominal rate of interest was charged?

7. Julia deposited \$1500.00 in an RRSP at the beginning of every six months for twenty years. The money earned interest at 11% compounded semi-annually. After twenty years, she converted the RRSP into an RRIF from which she wants to withdraw equal amounts at the beginning of each month for fifteen years. If interest on the RRIF is 12% compounded monthly, how much does she receive each month?

8. Mr. Clark wants to receive payments of \$900.00 at the beginning of every three months for twenty years starting on the date of his retirement. If he retires in twenty-five years, how much must he deposit in an account at the beginning of every three months if interest on the account is 10% compounded quarterly?

9. If you save \$75.00 at the beginning of every month for ten years, for how long can you withdraw \$260.00 at the beginning of each month starting ten years from now, assuming that interest is 12% compounded monthly?

10. Ali deposits \$450.00 at the beginning of every three months. He wants to build up his account so that he can withdraw \$1000.00 every three months starting three months after the last deposit. If he wants to make the withdrawals for fifteen years and interest is 10% compounded quarterly, for how long must Ali make the quarterly deposits?

11. What is the effective rate of interest on a lease contract valued at \$13 500.00 if payments of \$1500.00 are made at the beginning of every six months for seven years?

12. An insurance policy provides a benefit of \$250 000.00 twenty years from now. Alternatively, the policy pays \$4220.00 at the beginning of each year for twenty years. What is the effective rate of interest paid?

12.3 *Deferred annuities*

A. *Basic concepts and computation*

A **deferred annuity** is one in which the first payment is made at a time *later* than the end of the first payment interval. The time period from the time referred to as 'now' to the starting point of the term of the annuity is called the **period of deferment.** The number of compounding periods in the period of deferment is designated by the letter symbol *d*. The amount of a deferred annuity (designated by the symbol S_n (defer)) is the accumulated value of the periodic payments at the end of the term of the annuity.

The **present value of a deferred annuity** (designated by the symbol A_n (defer)) is the discounted value of the periodic payment at the beginning of the period of deferment.

Example 12.3a Payments of \$500.00 are due at the end of each year for ten years. If the annuity is deferred for four years and interest is 12% compounded annually, determine

(i) the amount of the deferred annuity;

(ii) the present value of the deferred annuity.

Solution

$$R = 500.00; \quad i = 12\% = 0.12; \quad n = 10; \quad d = 4$$

(i)
$$S_n(\text{defer}) = S_n = 500.00\left(\frac{1.12^{10} - 1}{0.12}\right) \longleftarrow \text{using Formula 11.1}$$
$$= 500.00(17.548735)$$
$$= \$8774.37$$

Note: The period of deferment does *not* affect the solution to the problem of finding the amount of a deferred annuity: $S_n(\text{defer}) = S_n$. Therefore, the problem of finding the amount of a deferred annuity is identical to the problem of finding the amount of an annuity. No further consideration is given in this text to the problem of finding the amount of a deferred annuity.

FIGURE 12.5 ***Graphic representation of method and data***

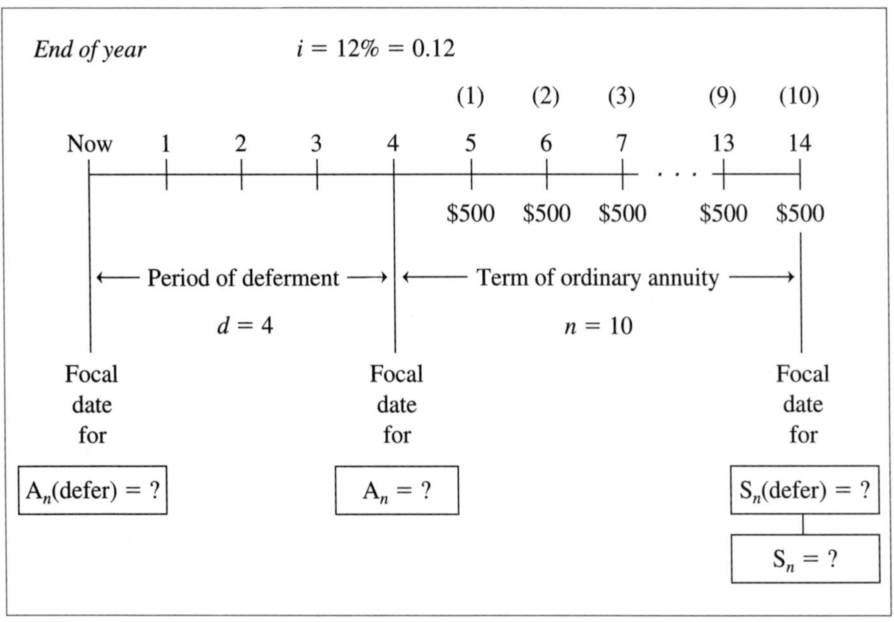

(ii) The problem of finding the present value of a deferred annuity can be divided into two smaller problems. We have used this approach in solving Example 11.3g in Chapter 11 and Example 12.1j in Chapter 12 and we use it again in this problem to find the present value of the deferred annuity.

First, find the present value of the ordinary annuity (focal date at the beginning of the term of the annuity).

$$A_n = 500.00\left(\frac{1 - 1.12^{-10}}{0.12}\right) \longleftarrow \text{using Formula 11.2}$$
$$= 500.00(5.6502230)$$
$$= \$2825.11$$

Second, find the present value of A_n at the focal date 'now.'

$$A_n(\text{defer}) = P = 2825.11(1.12^{-4}) \longleftarrow \text{using Formula 9.2B}$$
$$= 2825.11(0.6355181)$$
$$= \$1795.41$$

Programmed solution

0	500	12	10			
FV	PMT	%i	N	CPT	PV	2825.11
0	2825.11	12	4			
PMT	FV	%i	N	CPT	PV	1795.41

Alternatively, you can find the present value of the deferred annuity by assuming that periodic payments were made during the period of deferment. This assumption shifts the beginning date of the term of the annuity to the focal date 'now,' as Figure 12.6 shows. To obtain the present value of the deferred annuity, deduct the present value of the annuity representing the assumed payments from the present value of the annuity representing all payments.

FIGURE 12.6 ***Graphic representation of method and data***

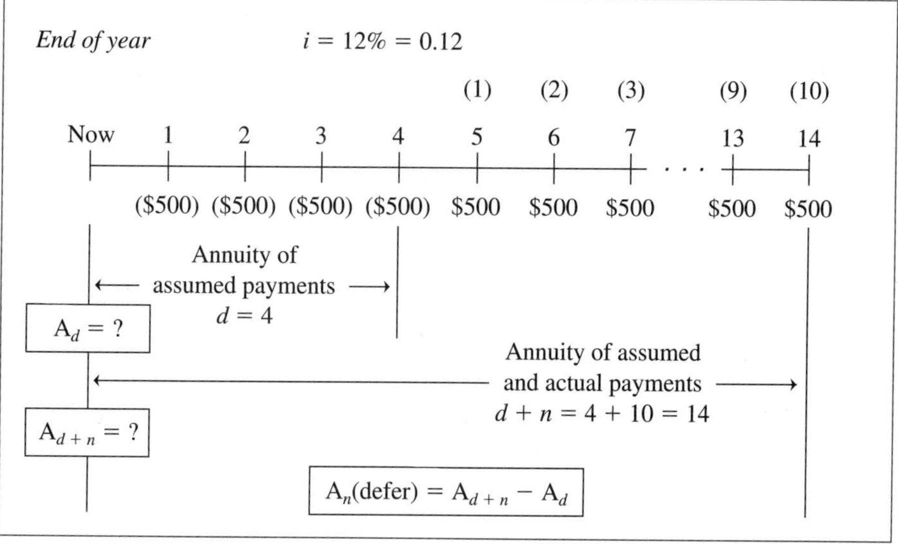

$$A_{d+n} = 500.00\left(\frac{1 - 1.12^{-14}}{0.12}\right) \longleftarrow \text{using Formula 11.2}$$
$$= 500.00(6.6281682)$$
$$= \$3314.08$$

$$A_d = 500.00\left(\frac{1 - 1.12^{-4}}{0.12}\right) \longleftarrow \text{using Formula 11.2}$$
$$= 500.00(3.0373493)$$
$$= \$1518.67$$

$$A_n(\text{defer}) = 3314.08 - 1518.67 = \$1795.41$$

Programmed alternative solution

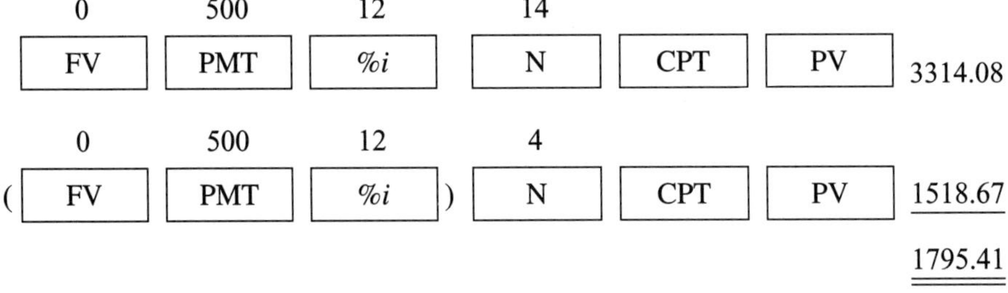

Example **12.3b** Mr. Peric wants to receive payments of \$800.00 at the end of each month for ten years after his retirement. If he retires in seven years, how much must Mr. Peric invest now if interest on the investments is 12% compounded monthly?

Solution

The monthly payments after retirement form an ordinary annuity.

$$R = 800.00; \quad i = \frac{12\%}{12} = 1\% = 0.01; \quad n = 10(12) = 120$$

The period of deferment is 7 years so $d = 7(12) = 84$.

The amount to be invested now is the present value of the deferred annuity.

$$A_n = 800\left(\frac{1 - 1.01^{-120}}{0.01}\right)$$
$$= 800(69.700522)$$
$$= 55\,760.42$$

$$A_n(\text{defer}) = 55\,760.42(1.01)^{-84}$$
$$= 55\,760.42(0.4335155)$$
$$= 24\,173.00$$

Programmed solution

0	800	1	120			
FV	PMT	%i	N	CPT	PV	55 760.42
55 760.42	0	1	84			
FV	PMT	%i	N	CPT	PV	24 173.00

Mr. Peric must invest $24 173.00.

B. Present value of a deferred annuity due

You can find the present value of a deferred annuity due by the approach used in Examples 12.3a and 12.3b except that Formula 12.2 is used in Step 1.

Example **12.3c** $2000.00 is to be withdrawn from a fund at the beginning of every three months for twelve years starting ten years from now. If interest is 10% compounded quarterly, what must be the balance in the fund today to permit the withdrawals?

Solution

The withdrawals form an annuity due.

$$R = 2000.00; \quad i = \frac{10\%}{4} = 2.5\% = 0.025; \quad n = 12(4) = 48$$

The period of deferment is 10 years so $d = (10)(4) = 40$.

$$\begin{aligned} A_n(\text{due}) &= 2000.00(1.025)\left[\frac{1-(1.025)^{-48}}{0.025}\right] \\ &= 2000(1.025)(27.773154) \\ &= 56\,934.97 \\ A_n(\text{defer}) &= 56.934.97(1.025)^{-40} \\ &= 56\,934.97(0.3724306) \\ &= 21\,204.33 \end{aligned}$$

Programmed solution

0	2000	2.5	48				
FV	PMT	%*i*	N	DUE	(or	2nd	CPT)
PV	56 934.97						

56 934.97	0	2.5	40	
FV	PMT	%*i*	N	CPT
PV	21 204.33			

The balance in the fund today must be $21 204.33.

Exercise 12.3

A. Find the present value of each of the following deferred annuities.

	Periodic payment	*Made at*	*Payment period*	*Period of deferment*	*Term*	*Int. rate*	*Conversion period*
1.	$850.00	beginning	1 year	3 years	10 years	7.5%	annually
2.	$45.00	end	1 month	5 years	7 years	12%	monthly
3.	$125.00	end	6 months	8 years	15 years	7%	semi-annually
4.	$720.00	beginning	3 months	6 years	12 years	14%	quarterly
5.	$85.00	beginning	1 month	20 years	15 years	18%	monthly
6.	$225.00	end	1 month	12 years	20 years	10.5%	monthly

B. Answer each of the following questions.

1. Calvin Jones bought his neighbour's farm for $10 000 down and payments of $5000.00 at the end of every three months for ten years. If the payments are deferred for two years and interest is 14% compounded quarterly, what was the purchase price of the farm?

2. Denise Kadawalski intends to retire in twelve years and would like to receive $2400.00 every six months for fifteen years starting on the date of her retirement. How much must Denise deposit in an account today if interest is 6.5% compounded semi-annually?

3. Arlene and Mario Dumont want to set up a fund to finance their daughter's university education. They want to be able to withdraw $400.00 from the fund at the beginning of each month for four years. Their daughter enters university in seven and a half years and interest is 12% compounded monthly.

(a) How much must the Dumonts deposit in the fund today?

(b) What will be the amount of the total withdrawals?

(c) How much of the amount withdrawn will be interest?

4. The Omega Venture Group needs to borrow to finance a project. Repayment of the loan involves payments of \$8500.00 at the end of every three months for eight years. No payments are to be made during the development period of three years. Interest is 20% compounded quarterly.
   (a) How much should the Group borrow?
   (b) What amount will be repaid?
   (c) How much of that amount will be interest?

12.4 *Deferred annuities—finding R,* n, *and* i

When the present value of either a deferred ordinary annuity or a deferred annuity due is known, you can find R, n, or i by methods similar to the ones used earlier in Chapters 11 and 12.

A. Finding the periodic payment R

You can find the periodic payment for deferred ordinary annuities and deferred annuities due, R, by first determining the future value of the known present value at the end of the period of deferment and then substituting in the appropriate annuity formula (Formula 11.2 for ordinary annuities or Formula 12.2 for annuities due).

***Example* 12.4a** Find the size of the payment required at the end of every three months to repay a five-year loan of \$25 000.00 if the payments are deferred for two years and interest is 14% compounded quarterly.

Solution

The payments form a deferred ordinary annuity.

$$A_n \text{ (defer)} = 25\,000.00;\ i = \frac{14\%}{4} = 3.5\% = 0.035;\quad n = 5(4) = 20;\quad d = 2(4) = 8$$

Value of \$25 000 at the end of the period of deferment,

$$\begin{aligned} S &= 25\,000(1.035)^8 \longleftarrow \text{using Formula 9.1} \\ &= 25\,000(1.3168090) \\ &= 32\,920.23 \end{aligned}$$

$$32\,920.33 = R\left(\frac{1 - 1.035^{-20}}{0.035}\right) \longleftarrow \text{substituting in Formula 11.2}$$

$$32\,920.33 = 14.212403R$$

$$R = \frac{32\,920.33}{14.212403}$$

$$R = 2316.30$$

Programmed solution

0	25 000	3.5	8			
PMT	PV	%i	N	CPT	FV	32 920.33

0	32 920.33	3.5	20			
FV	PV	%i	N	CPT	PMT	2316.30

The size of the required payment is \$2316.30.

Example **12.4b** What payment can be made at the beginning of each month for six years if \$5000.00 is invested today at 12% compounded monthly and the payments are deferred for ten years?

Solution

The payments form a deferred annuity due.

$$A_n(\text{defer}) = 5000.00;\ i = \frac{12\%}{12} = 1\% = 0.01;\quad n\ 6(12) = 72;\quad d = 10(12) = 120$$

Value of the \$5000 at the end of the period of deferment,

$$\begin{aligned} S &= 5000(1.01)^{120} \\ &= 5000(3.3003869) \\ &= 16\,501.94 \end{aligned}$$

$$16\,501.94 = R(1.01)\left(\frac{1 - 1.01^{-72}}{0.01}\right) \longleftarrow \text{substituting in Formula 12.2}$$

$$16\,501.94 = R(1.01)(51.150392)$$

$$16\,501.94 = 51.661896R$$

$$R = \frac{16\,501.94}{51.661896}$$

$$R = 319.42$$

Programmed solution

0	5000	1	120	
PMT	PV	%i	N	CPT
FV	16 501.94			

0	16 501.94	1	72				
FV	PV	%i	N	DUE	(or	2nd	CPT)
PMT	319.42						

The monthly payment is \$319.42.

B. *Finding the term* n *of a deferred annuity*

You can find the term for deferred ordinary annuities by the same approach used to determine the periodic payment R.

Example **12.4c** For how long can you pay $500.00 at the end of each month out of a fund of $10 000.00, deposited today at 10.5% compounded monthly, if the payments are deferred for nine years?

Solution

The payments form a deferred ordinary annuity.

$$A_n(\text{defer}) = 10\,000.00;\ R = 500.00;\ \ i = \frac{10.5\%}{12} = 0.875\% = 0.00875;$$

$$d = 9(12) = 108$$

The value of the $10 000 at the end of the period of deferment,

$$S = 10\,000.00(1.00875)^{108}$$
$$= 10\,000.00(2.5622598)$$
$$= 25\,622.60$$

$$25\,622.60 = 500.00\left(\frac{1 - 1.00875^{-n}}{0.00875}\right)$$

$$25\,622.60 = 57\,142.857(1 - 1.00875^{-n})$$

$$\frac{25\,622.60}{57\,142.857} = 1 - 1.00875^{-n}$$

$$0.4483955 = 1 - 1.00875^{-n}$$

$$1.00875^{-n} = 0.5516045$$

$$-n \ln 1.00875 = \ln 0.5516045$$

$$-n(0.0087119) = -0.5949239$$

$$n = \frac{0.5949239}{0.0087119}$$

$$n = 68.288334$$

$$n = 69 \text{ (months)}$$

Programmed solution

0	10 000	0.875	108			
PMT	PV	%i	N	CPT	FV	25 622.60
0	25 622.60	0.875	500			
FV	PV	%i	PMT	CPT	N	68.288334

Payments can be made for 5 years and 9 months.

***Example* 12.4d** A scholarship of \$3000.00 per year is to be paid at the beginning of each year from a scholarship fund of \$15 000.00 invested at 11% compounded annually. How long will the scholarship be paid if payments are deferred for five years?

Solution

The annual payments form a deferred annuity due.

$$A_n(\text{defer}) = 15\,000.00;\ R = 3000.00;\quad i = 11\% = 0.11;\quad d = 5$$

The value of the \$15 000.00 at the end of the period of deferment,

$$S = 15\,000.00(1.11)^5$$
$$= 15\,000.00(1.6850582)$$
$$= 25\,275.87$$

$$25\,275.87 = 3000.00(1.11)\left(\frac{1 - 1.11^{-n}}{0.11}\right)$$

$$25\,275.87 = 30\,272.727(1 - 1.11^{-n})$$

$$0.8349387 = 1 - 1.11^{-n}$$

$$1.11^{-n} = 0.1650613$$

$$-n \ln 1.11 = \ln 0.1650613$$

$$-0.10436n = -1.8014385$$

$$n = \frac{1.8014385}{0.10436}$$

$$n = 17.261769$$

$$n = 18 \text{ years (approximately)}$$

Programmed solution

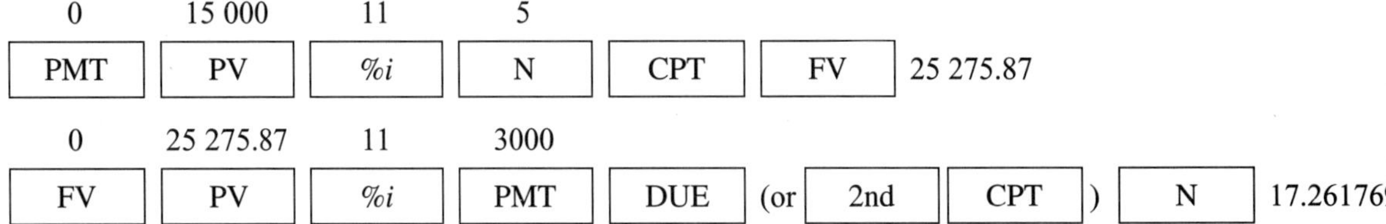

The scholarship fund will provide 17 payments of \$3000 and a final payment of less than \$3000.00.

C. Finding the conversion rate i *for deferred annuities*

You can determine the periodic rate of interest for deferred annuities by trial and error using the method explained in the Appendix.

Exercise 12.4

A. For each of the following deferred annuities, find the unknown value.

	Present value	*Periodic payment*	*Made at*	*Payment interval*	*Period of deferment*	*Term*	*Int. rate*	*Compounding period*
1.	$ 7 200.00	?	beginning	3 months	3 years	5 years	9%	quarterly
2.	$14 500.00	?	end	6 months	7 years	10 years	15%	semi-annually
3.	?	$ 220.00	end	1 month	2 years	4 years	18%	monthly
4.	?	$3600.00	beginning	1 year	10 years	15 years	13%	annually
5.	$21 000.00	$3485.00	beginning	3 months	8 years	?	16%	quarterly
6.	$ 8 800.00	$ 325.00	end	1 month	3 years	?	6%	monthly

B. Answer each of the following questions.

1. A deposit of $20 000 is made for a twenty-year term. After the term expires, equal withdrawals are to be made for twelve years at the end of every six months. What is the size of the semi-annual withdrawal if interest is 10% compounded semi-annually?

2. Payments on a seven-year lease valued at $12 200 are to be made at the beginning of each month during the last five years of the lease. If interest is 18% compounded monthly, what is the size of the monthly payments?

3. For how long can $1000 be withdrawn at the end of each month from an account containing $16 000 if the withdrawals are deferred for six years and interest is 12% compounded monthly?

4. Mrs. X paid $24 000 into a retirement fund paying interest at 11% compounded semi-annually. If she retires in seventeen years, for how long can Mrs. X withdraw $10 000 from the fund every six months? Assume that the first withdrawal is on the date of retirement.

5. What sum of money invested now will provide payments of $1200.00 at the end of every three months for six years if the payments are deferred for nine years and interest is 10% compounded quarterly?

6. An investment in a lease offers returns of $2500 per month due at the beginning of each month for five years. What investment is justified if the returns are deferred for two years and the interest required is 24% compounded monthly?

7. To finance the development of a new product, a company borrowed \$50 000.00 at 17% compounded quarterly. If the loan is to be repaid in equal quarterly payments over seven years and the first payment is due three years after the date of the loan, what is the size of the quarterly payment?

8. Mr. Talbot received a retirement gratuity of \$18 000.00 which he deposited in a RRSP. He intends to leave the money for fourteen years. At that time he plans to transfer the balance into a RRIF and make equal withdrawals at the end of every six months for twenty years. If interest is 10.5% compounded semi-annually, what will be the size of each withdrawal?

9. Greg borrowed \$6500.00 at 15% compounded monthly to help finance his education. He contracted to repay the loan in monthly payments of \$300.00 each. If the payments are due at the end of each month and the payments are deferred for four years, for how long will Greg have to make monthly payments?

10. A lease valued at \$32 000.00 requires payments of \$4000.00 every three months. If the first payment is due three years after the lease was signed and interest is 22% compounded quarterly, what is the term of the lease?

12.5 *Simple perpetuities*

A. *Basic concepts*

A **perpetuity** is an annuity in which the periodic payments begin on a fixed date and continue indefinitely. Interest payments on permanently invested sums of money are prime examples of perpetuities. Dividends on preferred shares fall into this category assuming that the issuing corporation has an indefinite life. Scholarships paid perpetually from an endowment fit the definition of perpetuity.

As there is no end to the term, it is *not* possible to determine the amount of a perpetuity. However, the present value of a perpetuity *is* a definite value and this section deals with the present value of simple perpetuities.

B. *Present value of ordinary perpetuities*

The following symbols are commonly used when dealing with perpetuities:

A = the present value of the perpetuity;

R = the periodic rent (or perpetuity payment);

i = the periodic rate of interest.

FIGURE 12.7 ***Graphic representation of an ordinary perpetuity***

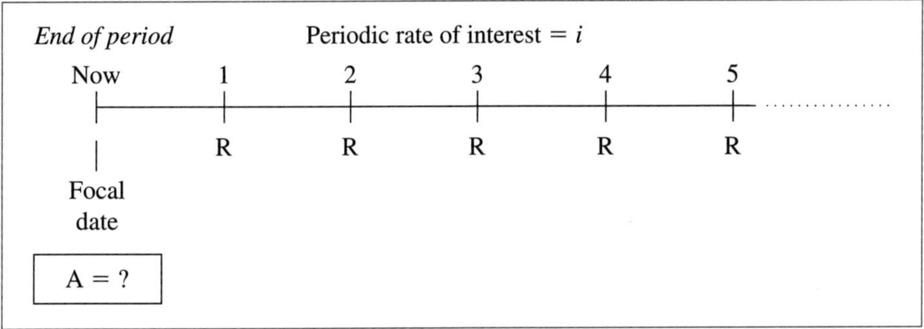

The **perpetuity payment R** is the interest earned by the present value of the perpetuity in one interest period.

$$R = iA$$

$$\boxed{A = \frac{R}{i}} \longleftarrow \textit{Formula } 12.3 \longleftarrow \text{present value of an ordinary perpetuity}$$

Example **12.5a** What sum of money invested today at 10% compounded annually will provide a scholarship of \$1500.00 at the end of every year?

Solution

$$R = 1500.00; \quad i = 10\% = 0.10$$

$$A = \frac{1500.00}{0.10} = \$15\,000.00 \longleftarrow \text{substituting in Formula 12.3}$$

Example **12.5b** The maintenance cost for Northern Railroad of a crossing with a provincial highway is \$2000.00 at the end of each month. Proposed construction of an overpass would eliminate the monthly maintenance cost. If money is worth 12% compounded monthly, how much should Northern be willing to contribute toward the cost of construction?

Solution

The monthly maintenance expense payments form an ordinary perpetuity.

$$R = 2000.00; \quad i = \frac{12\%}{12} = 0.01$$

$$A = \frac{2000.00}{0.01} = \$200\,000.00$$

Northern should be willing to contribute $200 000.00 toward construction.

***Example* 12.5c** A will gives an endowment of $50 000.00 to a college with the provision that a scholarship be paid at the end of each year. If the money is invested at 11% compounded annually, how much is the annual scholarship?

Solution

$$A = 50\,000.00; \quad i = 11\% = 0.11$$

$$R = 50\,000.00(0.11) = \$5500.00$$

C. *Present value of perpetuities due*

A perpetuity due differs from an ordinary perpetuity only in that the first payment is made at the focal date. Therefore, a perpetuity due may be treated as consisting of an immediate payment R followed by an ordinary perpetuity.

$$\boxed{A = R + \frac{R}{i}} \quad \longleftarrow \textit{Formula 12.4} \longleftarrow \text{present value of a perpetuity due}$$

***Example* 12.5d** A tract of land is leased in perpetuity at $1250.00 due at the beginning of each month. If money is worth 13.5% compounded monthly, what is the present value of the lease?

Solution

$$R = 1250.00; \quad i = \frac{13.5\%}{12} = 1.125\% = 0.01125$$

$$A = 1250.00 + \frac{1250.00}{0.01125} \longleftarrow \text{substituting in Formula 12.4}$$

$$= 1250.00 + 111\,111.11$$

$$= \$112\,361.11$$

***Example* 12.5e** How much money must be invested today in a fund earning 11.5% compounded annually to pay annual scholarships of $2000.00 starting

(i) one year from now?

(ii) immediately?

(iii) four years from now?

Solution

$$R = 2000.00; \quad i = 11.5\% = 0.115$$

(i) The annual scholarship payments form an ordinary perpetuity.

$$A = \frac{2000.00}{0.115} = \$17\,391.30$$

(ii) The annual scholarship payments form a perpetuity due.

$$A = 2000.00 + \frac{2000.00}{0.115}$$
$$= 2000.00 + 17\,391.30$$
$$= \$19\,391.30$$

(iii) The annual scholarship payments form an ordinary perpetuity deferred for three years.

$$A(\text{defer}) = A(1.115^{-3})$$
$$= 17\,391.30(0.7213988)$$
$$= \$12\,546.06$$

Exercise 12.5

A. Find the present value of each of the following perpetuities.

	Perpetuity payment	*Made at*	*Payment interval*	*Interest rate*	*Compounding period*
1.	$1250.00	end	3 months	6.8%	quarterly
2.	$ 985.00	beginning	6 months	11.5%	semi-annually
3.	$ 125.00	beginning	1 month	12.6%	monthly
4.	$3420.00	end	1 year	8.3%	annually

B. Answer each of the following questions.

1. Alain Rich wants to set up a scholarship fund for his alma mater. The annual scholarship payment is to be $2500.00 with the first such payment due four years after his deposit into the fund. If the fund pays 7.25% compounded annually, how much must Mr. Rich deposit?

2. A rental property provides a monthly income of $1150.00 due at the beginning of every month. What is the cash value of the property if money is worth 6.6% compounded monthly?

3. The faculty of Central College collected $1400.00 for the purpose of setting up a memorial fund from which an annual award is to be made to a qualifying student. If the money is invested at 14% compounded annually and the first annual award payment is to be made five years after the money was deposited, what is the size of the payment?

4. Barbara Katzman bought an income property for $28 000.00 three years ago. She has held the property for the three years without renting it. If she rents the property out now, what should the size of the monthly rent payment due in advance be if money is worth 15% compounded monthly?

Review exercise

1. Find the amount and the present value of semi-annual payments of $540.00 for seven and a half years if interest is 9.0% compounded semi-annually and the payments are made
   (a) at the end of every six months;
   (b) at the beginning of every six months.
2. Determine the amount and the present value of monthly payments of $50.00 each for eight years at 6% compounded monthly if
   (a) the payments form an annuity due;
   (b) the payments form an ordinary annuity.
3. A collateral mortgage can be discharged by making payments of $368.00 at the end of each month for fifteen years. If interest is 13.5% compounded monthly, what was the original principal borrowed?
4. Robert Deed deposited $100.00 in a trust account on the day of his son's birth and every three months thereafter. If interest paid is 14% compounded quarterly, what will the balance in the trust account be before the deposit is made on the son's twenty-first birthday?
5. If you would like to have $10 000.00 in your savings account and interest is 8% compounded quarterly, how much must you deposit every three months for five years if the deposits are made
   (a) at the end of each quarter?
   (b) at the beginning of each quarter?
6. Equal sums of money are withdrawn monthly from a fund of $20 000.00 for fifteen years. If interest is 9% compounded monthly, what is the size of each withdrawal
   (a) if made at the beginning of each month?
   (b) if made at the end of each month?
7. Annual rent of $6000.00 payable in advance is to be paid in equal monthly amounts at the beginning of each month. If money is worth 16.5% compounded monthly, what is the size of each monthly payment?
8. Agnes Bloch wants to save $5000.00 each year. If interest is 5% compounded quarterly, what deposit must she make
   (a) at the end of every three months?
   (b) at the beginning of every three months?

9. How long will it take to accumulate $18 000.00 at 12% compounded monthly if $125.00 is deposited in an account at the beginning of every month?

10. A contract valued at $11 500.00 requires payment of $1450.00 at the beginning of every six months. If interest is 15.5% compounded semi-annually, what is the term of the contract?

11. At what nominal rate of interest compounded semi-annually will $1200.00 deposited at the beginning of every six months accumulate to $40 000.00 in nine years?

12. What is the effective rate of interest charged on a lease valued at $9600.00 if payments of $300.00 are made at the beginning of each month for the four years?

13. Mr. Maxwell intends to retire in ten years and wishes to receive $4800.00 every three months for twenty years starting on the date of his retirement. How much must he deposit now to receive the quarterly payments from an account paying 6% compounded quarterly?

14. Tomac Swim Club bought electronic timing equipment on a contract requiring monthly payments of $725.00 for three years beginning eighteen months after the date of purchase. What was the cash value of the equipment if interest is 15% compounded monthly?

15. Frank invested a retirement gratuity of $15 000.00 in an income averaging annuity paying 12% compounded monthly. He withdraws the money in equal monthly amounts over five years. If the first withdrawal is made nine months after the deposit, what is the size of each withdrawal?

16. Mrs. Gold deposited an inheritance of $25 000.00 in a three-year term deposit. How much will she receive at the end of every three months for fifteen years after the deposit matures if interest is 11% compounded quarterly?

17. An income property is estimated to net $1750.00 per month continually. If money is worth 15.6% compounded monthly, what is the cash price of the property?

18. Western Pipelines pays $8000.00 at the beginning of each year for using a tract of land. What should the company offer the property owner as a purchase price if interest is 9.5% compounded annually?

19. Home entertainment equipment can be bought on time by making monthly payments of $82.00 for three and a half years. The first payment is due at the time of purchase and the financing cost is 16.5% compounded monthly.
    (a) What is the purchase price?
    (b) How much will be paid in instalments?
    (c) How much is the cost of financing?

20. Jim Wong makes deposits of $225.00 at the beginning of every three months. Interest earned by the deposits is 13% compounded quarterly.
    (a) How much will the balance in Jim's account be after eight years?
    (b) How much of the balance will Jim have contributed?
    (c) How much of the balance is interest?

21. For how long must $1000.00 be deposited at the beginning of every year to accumulate to $180 000.00 twelve years after the end of the year in which the last deposit was made if interest is 11.5% compounded annually?

22. Alicia Sidlo invested a retirement gratuity of $12 500.00 in a RRSP paying 10.5% compounded semi-annually for ten years. At the end of ten years, she rolled the RRSP balance over into a RRIF paying $500.00 at the beginning of each month starting with the date of rollover. If interest on the RRIF is 10.5% compounded monthly, for how long will Alicia receive monthly payments?

23. Mr. Smart wants to set up an annual scholarship of $3000.00. If the first payment is to be made in five years and interest is 7.0% compounded annually, how much must Mr. Smart pay into the scholarship fund?

24. Carla plans to invest in a property which after three years will yield $1200.00 at the end of each month indefinitely. How much should Carla be willing to pay if alternative investments yield 18% compounded monthly?

25. Mrs. Bean contributes $450.00 at the beginning of every three months to a RRSP. Interest on the account is 6% compounded quarterly.

    (a) What will the balance in the account be after seven years?

    (b) How much of the balance will be interest?

    (c) If Mrs. Bean converts the balance after seven years into a RRIF paying 5% compounded quarterly and makes equal quarterly withdrawals for twelve years starting three months after the conversion into the RRIF, what is the size of the quarterly withdrawal?

    (d) What is the combined interest earned by the RRSP and the RRIF?

26. Art will receive monthly payments of $850.00 from a trust account starting on the date of his retirement and continuing for twenty years. Interest is 10.5% compounded monthly.

    (a) What is the balance in the trust account on the date of Art's retirement?

    (b) How much interest will be included in the payments Art receives?

    (c) If Art made equal monthly deposits at the beginning of each month for fifteen years before his retirement, how much did he deposit each month?

    (d) How much interest will Art receive in total?

27. Kelly Farms bought a tractor priced at $10 500.00 on February 1. Kelly agreed to make monthly payments of $475.00 beginning December 1 of the same year. For how long will Kelly Farms have to make these payments if interest is 16.5% compounded monthly?

28. Okinagan Vineyards borrowed $75 000.00 on a five-year promissory note. It agreed to make payments of $6000.00 every three months starting on the date of maturity. If interest is 14% compounded quarterly, for how long will the company have to make the payments?

29. Mrs. Ball deposits $550.00 at the beginning of every three months. Starting three months after the last deposit, she intends to withdraw $3500.00 every three months for fourteen years. If interest is 8% compounded quarterly, for how long must Mrs. Ball make deposits?

30. Terry saves $50.00 at the beginning of each month for sixteen years. Beginning one month after his last deposit, he intends to withdraw $375.00 per month. If interest is 12% compounded monthly, for how long can Terry make withdrawals?

Self-test

1. Payments of $1080.00 are made into a fund at the beginning of every three months for eleven years. If the fund earns interest at 9.5% compounded quarterly, how much will the balance in the fund be after eleven years?

2. What sum of money must be deposited in a trust fund to provide a scholarship of $960.00 payable at the end of each month if interest is 7.5% compounded monthly?

3. How many months will it take to accumulate $142 400.00 at 14% compounded quarterly if $700.00 is deposited in an account at the beginning of every three months?

4. Find the present value of payments of $960.00 made at the beginning of every month for seven years if money is worth 18% compounded monthly.

5. Sally Smedley and Roberto Jones bought their neighbour's farm for $30 000.00 down and payments of $6000.00 at the end of every six months for six years. What is the purchase price of the farm if the semi-annual payments are deferred for four years and interest is 15% compounded semi-annually?

6. Western Pipelines pays $480.00 at the beginning of every half-year for using a tract of land. What should the company offer the property owner as a purchase price if interest is 11% compounded semi-annually?

7. What is the nominal annual rate of interest charged on a lease valued at $3840.00 if payments of $240.00 are made at the beginning of every three months for six years?

8. The amount of $57 426.00 is invested at 21% compounded monthly for six years. After the initial six-year period, the balance in the fund is converted into an annuity due paying $5600.00 every three months. If interest on the annuity is 10.5% compounded quarterly, what is the term of the annuity in months?

9. Tim bought a boat valued at $10 104.00 on the instalment plan. He made equal semi-annual payments for five years. If the first payment is due on the date of purchase and interest is 10.5% compounded semi-annually, what is the size of the semi-annual payments?

10. Deposits of $900.00 made at the beginning of every three months amount to $40 000.00 after six years. What is the effective annual rate of interest earned by the deposits if interest is compounded quarterly?

11. Eden would like to receive $3000.00 at the end of every six months for seven years after her retirement. If she retires ten years from now and interest is 13.5% compounded semi-annually, how much must she deposit into an account every six months starting now?

12. J.J. deposited $1680.00 at the beginning of every six months for eight years into a fund paying 15.5% compounded semi-annually. Fifteen years after the first deposit, he converted the existing balance into an annuity paying him equal monthly payments for twenty years. If the payments are made at the end of each month and interest is 15% compounded monthly, what is the size of the monthly payments?

CASE STUDY

The Adventure Group is a four-person partnership that specializes in white water rafting. After being in business for three years, the partners are considering selling shares. To estimate the worth of the business, it is necessary to calculate the total expenses and lost opportunity costs for the last three years. Shares will be sold based on this figure.

1. The business's rent is $650 per month in advance. If the interest rate for the first two years was 8% p.a. compounded monthly and for the last year was 9% p.a. compounded monthly, calculate the opportunity costs of renting the building.

2. The partners' initial investment was $120 000 in the ratio of 5:3:2:2.
   (a) Calculate each partner's investment.
   (b) Calculate the total opportunity costs of this investment if interest is 9% p.a. compounded monthly.

3. The partners have each deposited $150 at the beginning of every month for the past three years. This money was to be used to buy new equipment. Interest for the three years was 9% p.a. compounded monthly. The interest rate is now 6% p.a. compounded monthly.
   (a) How much is in the fund today?
   (b) The new equipment will require the money in the fund plus $3200 at the beginning of each quarter for 2½ years at 8% p.a. compounded quarterly. Calculate the cash value of the equipment.
   (c) The old equipment cost $1150 at the beginning of each month for three years at 12% p.a. compounded monthly. What is the percent change in the cost of equipment?

(d) This increase will be passed on to the consumer. What will be the new price for a \$350 trip?

4. At the beginning of every month, \$175 was taken from the profits and placed in an emergency fund paying 9% p.a. compounded monthly. The fund is now to be split according to each partner's investment. A monthly sum will be withdrawn at the end of each month for the next three years at 6% p.a. compounded monthly.

(a) How much of the fund is interest?

(b) Calculate the amount owed to each partner.

(c) Calculate the maximum withdrawal per month.

5. The partners need to borrow \$50 000 to upgrade facilities. The plan is to defer this loan for one year at 9% p.a. compounded monthly and then to make payments of \$4000 at the beginning of every quarter at 10% p.a. compounded quarterly.

(a) How many months will be required to pay off the loan?

(b) How much total interest will be paid on the loan?

6. The partners consider that their investment in the business consists of the total opportunity costs plus the cash value of the new equipment.

(a) If the business can be sold for \$315 000, what percent increase or decrease will they realize on their investment?

(b) If the partners had invested and kept their rent money, initial investment, and equipment money, how much money would they now have?

(c) Which investment had the higher return?

7. The business needs to buy new rafts. The rafts have a list price of \$3200 each and there are three payment methods.

(i) Make twelve end-of-month payments of \$279.84 each.

(ii) Make one payment of \$3500 at the end of one year.

(iii) Borrow the money from a bank, get a 15% discount on the list price, and make twelve payments of \$237.87 at the end of each month.

(a) Calculate the nominal rates of interest for each option.

(b) Calculate the maximum amount saved by choosing the least expensive option.

Summary of formulae used

Formula 9.1

$$S = P(1 + i)^n$$

Finding the compound amount (or future value or maturity value) when the original principal, the rate of interest, and the time period are known

Formula 9.2B

$$P = S(1 + i)^{-n}$$

Finding the present value by means of the discount factor (the reciprocal of the compounding factor) when the compound amount, the rate of interest, and the time period are known

Formula 11.1

$$S_n = R\left[\frac{(1 + i)^n - 1}{i}\right]$$

Finding the amount (accumulated value) of an ordinary simple annuity

Formula 11.2

$$A_n = R\left[\frac{1 - (1 + i)^{-n}}{i}\right]$$

Finding the present value (discounted value) of an ordinary annuity

Formula 12.1

$$S_n(\text{due}) = R(1 + i)\left[\frac{(1 + i)^n - 1}{i}\right]$$

Finding the amount of an annuity due

Formula 12.2

$$A_n(\text{due}) = R(1 + i)\left[\frac{1 - (1 + i)^{-n}}{i}\right]$$

Finding the present value of an annuity due

Formula 12.3

$$A = \frac{R}{i}$$

Finding the present value of an ordinary perpetuity

Formula 12.4

$$A = R + \frac{R}{i}$$

Finding the present value of a perpetuity due

Glossary of terms used

Annuity due an annuity in which the periodic payments are made at the beginning of each payment interval

Deferred annuity an annuity in which the first payment is made at a time later than the end of the first payment interval

Period of deferment the period from the time referred to as 'now' to the starting point of the term of the annuity

Perpetuity an annuity in which the periodic payments begin at a fixed date and continue indefinitely

Perpetuity payment the perpetual periodic payment which equals the interest earned by the present value of these payments in one interest period

Present value of a deferred annuity the discounted value of the periodic payments at the beginning of the period of deferment

13 *General annuities*

Introduction

Chapters 11 and 12 considered simple annuities in detail. Simple annuities are a special case in which the payment interval and the interest conversion period are the same length. However, interest is often compounded more or less frequently than payments are made. In Canada, for example, residential mortgages are usually compounded semi-annually while payments are made monthly.

Annuities in which the length of the interest conversion period is different from the length of the payment interval are discussed in this chapter. Such annuities are called general annuities; they may be ordinary annuities, annuities due, deferred annuities, or perpetuities.

Objectives

Upon completing this chapter, you will be able to

1. compute the amount (or accumulated value) of ordinary general annuities;
2. compute the present value (or discounted value) of ordinary general annuities;
3. compute the periodic payment, the term, and the interest rate of ordinary general annuities;
4. determine the amount, the present value, the periodic payment, the term, and the interest rate of general annuities due;
5. determine the present value, the periodic payment, the term, and the rate of interest of deferred general annuities;
6. determine the present value of general perpetuities.

13.1 *Amount of an ordinary general annuity*

A. *Basic concepts and computation*

The basic method of solving problems involving interest uses equivalent sets of financial obligations at a selected focal date. Thus, when dealing with any kind of annuity, the essential tool is an equation of value. This basic approach is equally applicable to **general annuities**; it is used to make the basic computations and develop useful formulae.

Example **13.1a** What is the accumulated value of \$100.00 deposited at the end of every six months for three years if interest is 12% compounded annually?

Solution

Since the payments are made semi-annually while the compounding is done annually, this annuity is classified as a general annuity. Furthermore, since the payments are at the end of each payment interval, the annuity is an ordinary general annuity. While the difference in the length of the payment period compared to the length of the compounding period introduces a mathematical complication, the basic approach to finding the amount of the ordinary general annuity is the same as is used in finding the amount of an ordinary simple annuity.

The basic solution and data for the problem are graphically shown in Figure 13.1. Since deposits are made at the end of every six months for three years, there are six deposits of \$100.00 at the times indicated. Because interest is compounded annually, $i = 12\% = 0.12$ and there are three conversion periods.

FIGURE 13.1 ***Graphic representation of method and data***

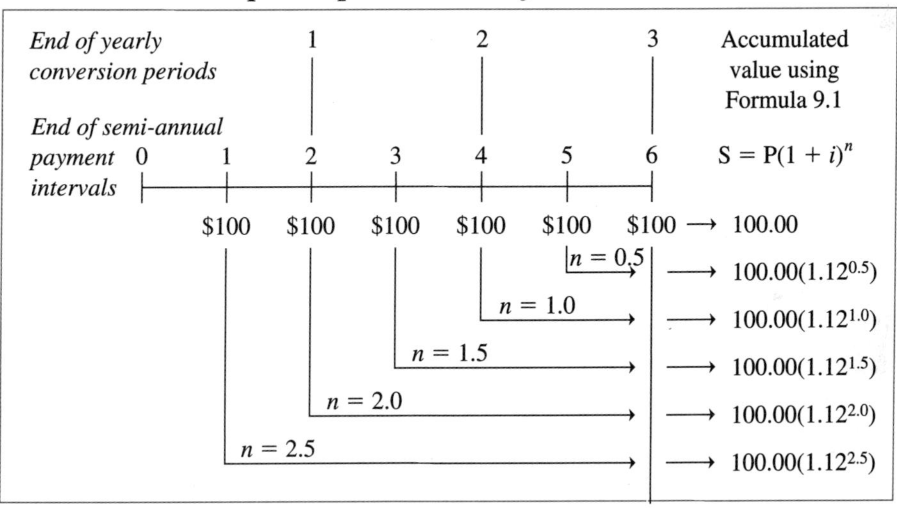

The focal point is at the end of Year 3. The last deposit is made at the focal date and has a value of \$100.00 on that date. The fifth deposit is made after 2.5 years and, in terms of conversion periods, has accumulated for a half conversion period ($n = 0.5$); its accumulated value is $100.00(1.12^{0.5}) = \$105.83$ at the focal date. The fourth deposit is made after two years and has accumulated for one conversion period ($n = 1.0$); its accumulated value at the focal date is $100.00(1.12^{1.0}) = \$112.00$. Similarly, the accumulated value of the third deposit is $100.00(1.12^{1.15}) = \$118.53$, while the accumulated value of the second deposit is $100.00(1.12^{2.0}) = \$125.44$. Finally, the accumulated value of the first deposit is $100.00(1.12^{2.5}) = \$132.75$. The total accumulated value after three years is \$694.55. This total could have been obtained by setting up the equation of values.

$$S_n = 100.00 + 100.00(1.12^{0.5}) + 100.00(1.12^{1.0}) + 100.00(1.12^{1.5}) + 100.00(1.12^{2.0}) + 100.00(1.12^{2.5})$$

$$= 100.00(1 + 1.12^{0.5} + 1.12^{1.0} + 1.12^{1.5} + 1.12^{2.0} + 1.12^{2.5})$$

$$= 100.00\left(\begin{array}{l}\text{the sum of the first six terms of a}\\ \text{geometric progression with first term 1}\\ \text{and common ratio } 1.12^{0.5}\end{array}\right)$$

$$= 100.00\left[\frac{(1.12^{0.5})^6 - 1}{1.12^{0.5} - 1}\right] \longleftarrow \text{substituting in the formula } S = \frac{a(r^n - 1)}{r - 1}, r > 1$$

$$= 100.00\left(\frac{1.4049280 - 1}{1.0583005 - 1}\right)$$

$$= 100.00\left(\frac{0.4049280}{0.0583005}\right)$$

$$= 100.00(6.9455322)$$

$$= \$694.55$$

The accumulated value is \$694.55.

Example **13.1b** What is the accumulated value of deposits of \$100.00 made at the end of each year for four years if interest is 12% compounded quarterly?

Solution

Since the deposits are made at the end of every year for four years, there are four payments of \$100.00 at the times shown in Figure 13.2. Since interest is compounded quarterly, $i = \frac{12\%}{4} = 3\% = 0.03$ and there are $4(4) = 16$ conversion periods. The focal point is the end of Year 4. The last payment is made at the focal point and has a value of \$100.00 at that date. The third payment is made after three years and, in terms of conversion periods, has accumulated for four conversion periods ($n = 4$); its accumulated value is $100.00(1.03^4) = \$112.55$. The second deposit has accumulated for 8 conversion periods ($n = 8$); its accumulated value is $100.00(1.03^8) = \$126.68$. The first deposit has accumulated for 12 conversion periods ($n = 12$); its accumulated value is $100.00(1.03^{12}) = \$142.58$. The total accumulated value of the deposits after four years is \$481.81. An equation of values can be set up to obtain this total.

FIGURE 13.2 ***Graphic representation of method and data***

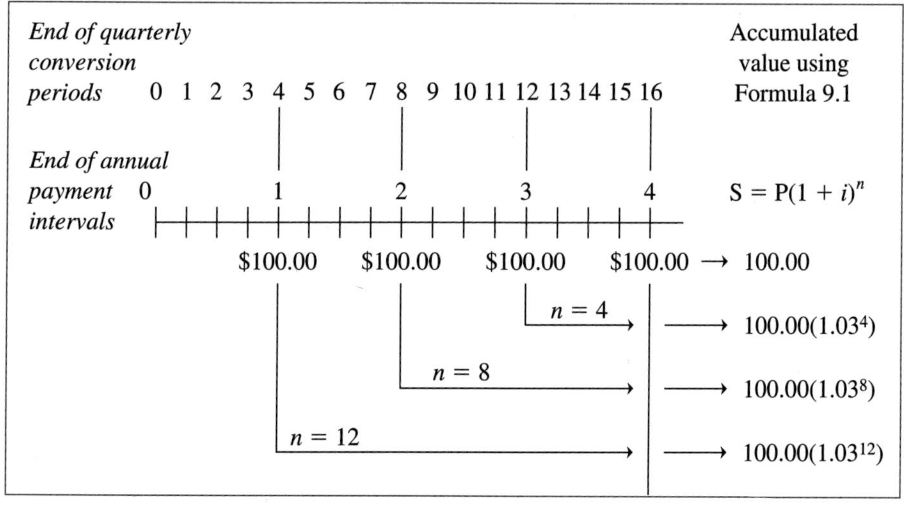

$$S = 100.00 + 100.00(1.03^4) + 100.00(1.03^8) + 100.00(1.03^{12})$$

$$= 100.00(1 + 1.03^4 + 1.03^8 + 1.03^{12})$$

$$= 100.00 \left(\begin{array}{l}\text{the sum of the first four terms of a} \\ \text{geometric progression with first term} \\ \text{1 and common ratio } 1.03^4\end{array}\right)$$

$$= 100.00\left[\frac{(1.03^4)^4 - 1}{1.03^4 - 1}\right] \longleftarrow \text{substituting in the formula } S = \frac{a(r^n - 1)}{r - 1}, r > 1$$

$$= 100.00\left(\frac{1.03^{16} - 1}{1.03^4 - 1}\right)$$

$$= 100.00\left(\frac{1.6047064 - 1}{1.1255088 - 1}\right)$$

$$= 100.00\left(\frac{0.6047064}{0.1255088}\right)$$

$$= 100.00(4.8180399)$$

$$= \$481.80$$

The accumulated value is $481.80.

B. Relationship between payment interval and interest conversion period

Examples 13.1a and 13.1b illustrate the two possible cases of general annuities.

CASE 1 The interest conversion period is *longer* than the payment period; each payment interval contains only a fraction of one conversion period.

CASE 2 The interest conversion period is *shorter* than the payment period; each payment period contains more than one conversion period.

The number of interest conversion periods per payment interval, designated by the letter c, can be determined from the following ratio.

$$c = \frac{\text{THE NUMBER OF INTEREST CONVERSION PERIODS PER YEAR}}{\text{THE NUMBER OF PAYMENT PERIODS PER YEAR}}$$

In dealing with general annuities it is important to understand clearly the relationship between the *payment interval* and the number of *interest conversion periods* per payment interval.

For Case 1 (see Example 13.1a.) c has a fractional value less than 1.

For Case 2 (see Example 13.1b.), c has a value greater than 1.

The following table provides a sampling of possible combinations of payment intervals and interest conversion periods you might encounter when dealing with general annuities. One of the most important is the monthly payment interval combined with semi-annual compounding since this combination is usually encountered with residential mortgages in Canada.

TABLE 13.1 *Some possible combinations of payment interval and interest conversion period*

Payment interval	*Interest conversion period*	*Number of interest conversion periods per payment interval*
semi-annually	monthly	$c = \frac{12}{2} = 6$
quarterly	monthly	$c = \frac{12}{4} = 3$
annually	quarterly	$c = \frac{4}{1} = 4$
semi-annually	annually	$c = \frac{1}{2} = 0.5$
quarterly	annually	$c = \frac{1}{4} = 0.25$
monthly	semi-annually	$c = \frac{2}{12} = \frac{1}{6}$
monthly	quarterly	$c = \frac{4}{12} = \frac{1}{3}$
monthly	annually	$c = \frac{1}{12}$

C. *Computing the equivalent effective rate of interest per payment period*

When using an electronic calculator equipped with a universal power key, the given periodic rate of interest i can be easily converted into the equivalent effective rate of interest per payment period.

Represent the equivalent effective rate of interest per payment period by f.

$$1 + f = (1 + i)^c \longleftarrow \text{Formula 10.1 except that } m \text{ is replaced by } c$$

Example **13.1c** Jean receives annuity payments at the end of every six months. If she deposits these payments in an account earning interest at 9% compounded monthly, what is the equivalent semi-annual rate of interest?

Solution

Since the payments are made at the end of every six months while interest is compounded monthly,

$$c = \frac{\text{THE NUMBER OF INTEREST CONVERSION PERIODS PER YEAR}}{\text{THE NUMBER OF PAYMENT PERIODS PER YEAR}} = \frac{12}{2} = 6$$

$$i = \frac{9\%}{12} = 0.75\% = 0.0075$$

$$1 + f = 1.0075^6$$
$$1 + f = 1.0458522$$
$$f = 0.0458522 = 4.58522\%$$

The equivalent semi-annual rate of interest is 4.58522%.

Example **13.1d** Peel Credit Union pays 6% compounded quarterly on its Premium Savings Accounts. If Roland Catchpole deposits $25.00 in his account at the end of every month, what is the equivalent monthly rate of interest?

Solution

Since the payments are made at the end of every month while interest is compounded quarterly,

$$c = \frac{4}{12} = \frac{1}{3}; \quad i = \frac{6\%}{4} = 1.5\% = 0.015$$

$$1 + f = 1.015^{\frac{1}{3}}$$
$$1 + f = 1.0049752$$
$$f = 0.0049752 = 0.49752\%$$

The equivalent monthly rate of interest is 0.49752%.

D. *Amount of an ordinary general annuity using the equivalent effective rate of interest per payment period*

Determining the equivalent rate per payment period f allows us to convert the ordinary general annuity problem into an ordinary simple annuity problem. Consistent with the symbols previously used for developing formulae for simple annuities, we will use the following notation:

S_{nc} = the amount (or accumulated value) of an **ordinary general annuity**;
R = the size of the periodic payment;
n = the number of periodic payments;
c = the number of interest conversion periods per payment interval;
i = the interest rate per interest conversion period;
f = the effective rate of interest per payment period.

Substituting f for i in Formula 11.1, we obtain

$$S_{nc} = R\left[\frac{(1+f)^n - 1}{f}\right] \text{ where } f = (1+i)^c - 1 \quad \longleftarrow \textit{Formula } \mathbf{13.1}$$

Example **13.1e** Determine the accumulated value after ten years of payments of \$2000.00 made at the end of each year if interest is 15% compounded monthly.

Solution

This problem is an ordinary general annuity.

$$R = 2000.00; \quad n = 10; \quad c = 12; \quad i = \frac{15\%}{12} = 1.25\% = 0.0125$$

The equivalent effective annual rate

$$f = 1.0125^{12} - 1 = 1.1607545 - 1 = 0.1607545 = 16.07545\%$$

The given ordinary general annuity can be converted into an ordinary simple annuity.

$$R = 2000.00; \quad n = 10; \quad f = 0.1607545$$

$$S_{nc} = 2000.00\left(\frac{1.1607545^{10} - 1}{0.1607545}\right) \longleftarrow \text{substituting in Formula 13.1}$$

$$= 2000.00(21.400412)$$

$$= \$42\ 800.82$$

The accumulated value after ten years is \$42 800.82.

***Example* 13.1f** Creditview Farms set aside \$1250.00 at the end of each month for the purchase of a combine. How much money will be available after five years if interest is 6.0% compounded semi-annually?

Solution

This problem involves an ordinary general annuity.

$$R = 1250.00; \quad n = 5(12) = 60; \quad c = \frac{2}{12} = \frac{1}{6}; \quad i = \frac{6.0\%}{2} = 3.0\% = 0.03$$

The equivalent effective monthly rate of interest

$$f = 1.03^{\frac{1}{6}} - 1 = 1.0049386 - 1 = 0.0049386 = 0.49386\%$$

$$S_{nc} = 1250.00\left(\frac{1.0049386^{60} - 1}{0.0049386}\right) \longleftarrow \text{substituting in Formula 13.1}$$

$$= 1250.00(69.638419)$$

$$= \$87\,048.02$$

After five years, the amount available is \$87 048.02.

E. *Using preprogrammed calculators to find the amount of an ordinary general annuity*

The use of f rather than i as the rate of interest is the only difference in the programmed solution for the general annuity compared to the programmed solution for a simple annuity.

***Example* 13.1g** Find the amount of \$2500.00 deposited at the end of every six months for ten years if interest is 10% compounded quarterly.

Solution

$$R = 2500.00; \quad n = 2(10) = 20; \quad c = \frac{4}{2} = 2;$$

$$i = \frac{10\%}{4} = 2.5\% = 0.025$$

STEP 1 Convert i into the equivalent effective rate of interest.

$$f = 1.025^2 - 1 = 1.050625 - 1 = 0.050625 = 5.0625\%$$

STEP 2 Using f as the interest rate per payment period, determine the amount of the ordinary annuity.

Key in	Press	Display shows	
	%i	5.0625	⟵ Step 2 begins with establishing the rate but the numerical value of f does not have to be keyed in again
0	PV	0	
2500	PMT	2500	
20	N	20	⟵ the number of payments
CPT	FV	83 213.027	

The amount on deposit after ten years will be \$83 213.03.

Example **13.1h** Determine the accumulated value of payments of \$1250.00 made at the end of each quarter for eight years if interest is 12.5% compounded annually.

Solution

$$R = 1250.00; \quad n = 8(4) = 32; \quad c = \frac{1}{4} = 0.25;$$

$$i = 12.5\% = 0.125$$

$$f = 1.125^{0.25} - 1 = 1.0298836 - 1 = 0.0298836 = 2.9883570\%$$

Key in	Press	Display shows	
	%i	2.988357	⟵ no need to key in f
0	PV	0	
1250	PMT	1250	
32	N	32	
CPT	FV	65 495.201	

The accumulated value of the payments is \$65 495.20.

Exercise 13.1

A. Find the amount of each of the following ordinary annuities.

	Periodic payment	*Payment interval*	*Term*	*Interest rate*	*Conversion period*
1.	$2500.00	6 months	7 years	8%	quarterly
2.	$900.00	3 months	5 years	12%	monthly
3.	$72.00	1 month	15 years	13%	semi-annually
4.	$225.00	3 months	10 years	15%	annually
5.	$1750.00	6 months	12 years	7%	semi-annually
6.	$680.00	1 month	3 years	9%	monthly
7.	$7500.00	1 year	4 years	16%	quarterly
8.	$143.00	1 month	9 years	14%	quarterly

B. Answer each of the following questions.

1. Find the amount of payments of $425.00 made at the end of every three months for nine years if interest is 9% compounded monthly.

2. What is the accumulated value of deposits of $1500.00 made at the end of every six months for six years if interest is 12% compounded quarterly?

3. How much will deposits of $15.00 made at the end of each month amount to after ten years if interest is 5% compounded quarterly?

4. What is the amount of payments of $250.00 made at the end of every three months in fifteen years if interest is 17.5% compounded annually?

5. Mr. Tomas has contributed $1000.00 at the end of each year into an RRSP paying 6% compounded quarterly.

   (a) How much will Mr. Tomas have in the RRSP after ten years?

   (b) How much of the amount is interest?

6. Alexa Sanchez saves $5.00 at the end of each month and deposits the money in an account paying 4% compounded quarterly.

   (a) How much will she accumulate in 25 years?

   (b) How much of the amount is interest?

7. Edwin Ng has made deposits of $500.00 into his savings account at the end of every three months for ten years. If interest is 13.5% compounded semi-annually and if he leaves the accumulated balance for another five years, what will be the balance in his account then?

8. Mrs. Cook has made deposits of $950.00 at the end of every six months for fifteen years. If interest is 12% compounded monthly, how much will Mrs. Cook have accumulated ten years after the last deposit?

13.2 *Present value of an ordinary general annuity*

A. *Present value of an ordinary general annuity using the equivalent effective rate of interest per payment period*

As with the amount of an ordinary general annuity, we can convert the given periodic rate of interest i into the equivalent effective rate of interest per payment period.

$$f = (1 + i)^c - 1$$

The use of f converts the ordinary general annuity problem into an ordinary simple annuity problem.

Substituting f for i in Formula 11.2, we obtain

$$A_{nc} = R\left[\frac{1 - (1 + f)^{-n}}{f}\right] \longleftarrow \textit{Formula } 13.2$$

Example **13.2a** A loan is repaid by making payments of \$2000.00 at the end of every six months for twelve years. If interest on the loan is 14% compounded quarterly, what was the principal of the loan?

Solution

$$R = 2000.00; \quad n = 12(2) = 24; \quad c = \frac{4}{2} = 2; \quad i = \frac{14\%}{4} = 3.5\% = 0.035$$

The equivalent effective semi-annual rate of interest

$$f = 1.035^2 - 1 = 1.071225 - 1 = 0.071225 = 7.1225\%$$

$$A_{nc} = 2000.00\left(\frac{1 - 1.071225^{-24}}{0.071225}\right) \longleftarrow \text{substituting in Formula 13.2}$$

$$= 2000.00(11.347049)$$

$$= \$22\ 694.10$$

The loan principal was \$22 694.10.

Example **13.2b** A second mortgage requires payments of \$370.00 at the end of each month for 15 years. If interest is 11% compounded semi-annually, what was the amount borrowed?

Solution

$$R = 370.00; \quad n = 15(12) = 180; \quad c = \frac{2}{12} = \frac{1}{6}; \quad i = \frac{11\%}{2} = 5.5\% = 0.055$$

The equivalent effective monthly rate of interest

$$f = 1.055^{\frac{1}{6}} - 1 = 1.0089634 - 1 = 0.0089634 = 0.89634\%$$

$$A_{nc} = 370.00\left(\frac{1 - 1.0089634^{-180}}{0.0089634}\right) \longleftarrow \text{substituting in Formula 13.2}$$

$$= 370.00(89.180057)$$

$$= \$32\ 996.62$$

The amount borrowed was \$32 996.62.

B. *Using preprogrammed calculators to find the present value of an ordinary general annuity*

STEP 1 Convert i into the equivalent effective rate of interest as shown in Section 13.1.

STEP 2 Using f as the interest rate per payment period, determine the present value of the ordinary annuity.

***Example* 13.2c** A contract is fulfilled by making payments of \$8500.00 at the end of every year for fifteen years. If interest is 13% compounded quarterly, what is the cash price of the contract?

Solution

$$R = 8500.00; \quad n = 15; \quad c = 4; \quad i = \frac{13\%}{4} = 3.25\%$$

STEP 1

$$f = 1.0325^4 - 1 = 1.1364759 - 1 = 0.1364759 = 13.647593\%$$

STEP 2

Key in	Press	Display shows	
	%i	13.647593	⟵ no need to key in f
0	FV	0	
8500	PMT	8500	
15	N	15	
CPT	PV	53 141.771	

The cash price of the contract is \$53 141.77.

Example **13.2d** A 25-year mortgage on a house requires payments of \$619.94 at the end of each month. If interest is 9.5% compounded semi-annually, what was the mortgage principal?

Solution

$$R = 619.94; \quad n = 25(12) = 300; \quad c = \frac{2}{12} = \frac{1}{6};$$

$$i = \frac{9.5\%}{2} = 4.75\%$$

$$f = 1.0475^{\frac{1}{6}} - 1 = 1.0077644 - 1 = 0.0077644 = 0.77644\%$$

Key in	Press	Display shows
	%*i*	0.77644
0	FV	0
619.94	PMT	619.94
300	N	300
CPT	PV	72 000.01

The mortgage principal was \$72 000.00.

Exercise 13.2

A. Find the present value of the following ordinary annuities.

	Periodic payment	*Payment interval*	*Term*	*Interest rate*	*Conversion period*
1.	\$1400.00	3 months	12 years	6%	monthly
2.	\$6000.00	1 year	9 years	10%	quarterly
3.	\$3000.00	3 months	4 years	16%	annually
4.	\$200.00	1 month	2 years	12%	semi-annually
5.	\$95.00	1 month	5 years	15%	monthly
6.	\$975.00	6 months	8 years	8%	semi-annually
7.	\$1890.00	6 months	15 years	7%	quarterly
8.	\$155.00	1 month	10 years	18%	quarterly

B. Answer each of the following questions.

1. Find the present value of payments of \$250.00 made at the end of every three months for twelve years if money is worth 12% compounded monthly.

2. What is the discounted value of \$1560.00 paid at the end of each year for nine years if interest is 16% compounded quarterly?

3. What cash payment is equivalent to making payments of \$825.00 at the end of every three months for 16 years if interest is 7% compounded semi-annually?

4. What is the principal from which \$175.00 can be withdrawn at the end of each month for twenty years if interest is 13% compounded quarterly?

5. A property was purchased for \$5000.00 down and payments of \$2500.00 at the end of every six months for six years. Interest is 12% compounded monthly.
   (a) What was the purchase price of the property?
   (b) How much is the cost of financing?

6. A car was bought for \$1500.00 down and payments of \$265.00 at the end of each month for four years. Interest is 15% compounded monthly.
   (a) What was the purchase price of the car?
   (b) How much will be the amount of interest paid?

7. Payments of \$715.59 are made at the end of each month to repay a 25-year mortgage. If interest is 10% compounded semi-annually, what is the original mortgage principal?

8. A 15-year mortgage is amortized by making payments of \$1031.61 at the end of every three months. If interest is 13.25% compounded annually, what was the original mortgage balance?

9. Cedomir Dale expects to retire in seven years. He bought a retirement annuity paying \$1200.00 every three months for twenty years. If the first payment is due three months after his retirement and interest is 12% compounded monthly, how much did Mr. Dale invest?

10. For her daughter's university education, Georgina Harcourt has invested an inheritance in a fund paying 11% compounded quarterly. If ordinary annuity payments of \$450.00 per month are to be made out of the fund for four years and the annuity begins twelve years from now, how much was the inheritance?

13.3 *Ordinary general annuities—finding* R, n, *or* i

A. *Finding the periodic rent R*

To determine the size of the periodic payment, use Formula 13.1 when S_{nc} is known and Formula 13.2 when A_{nc} is known. You can determine the equivalent effective rate of interest f by the procedure previously explained in this chapter and R by the procedure shown in Section 11.4.

Example **13.3a** What sum of money must be deposited at the end of every three months into an account paying 10% compounded monthly to accumulate to \$25 000.00 in ten years?

Solution

$$S_{nc} = 25\ 000.00; \quad n = 10(4) = 40; \quad c = \frac{12}{4} = 3;$$

$$i = \frac{10\%}{12} = \frac{5}{6}\% = 0.0083333$$

The equivalent effective quarterly rate of interest

$$f = 1.0083333^3 - 1 = 1.0252088 - 1 = 0.0252088 = 2.52088\%$$

$$25\ 000.00 = R\left(\frac{1.0252088^{40} - 1}{0.0252088}\right) \longleftarrow \text{substituting in Formula 13.1}$$

$$25\ 000.00 = R(67.715625)$$

$$R = \frac{25\ 000.00}{67.715625}$$

$$R = \$369.19$$

With a preprogrammed calculator, the procedure, after finding f, is

Key in	Press	Display shows
	%i	2.52088
0	PV	0
25 000	FV	25 000
40	N	40
2nd	PMT	369.19101

The required quarterly deposit is $369.19.

Example **13.3b** Mr. and Mrs. White applied to their credit union for a first mortgage of $60 000.00 to buy a house. The mortgage is to be amortized over 25 years and interest on the mortgage is 13.25% compounded semi-annually. What is the size of the monthly payment if payments are made at the end of each month?

Solution

$$A_{nc} = 60\ 000.00; \quad n = 25(12) = 300; \quad c = \frac{2}{12} = \frac{1}{6};$$

$$i = \frac{13.25\%}{2} = 6.625\% = 0.06625$$

The equivalent effective monthly rate of interest

$$f = 1.06625^{\frac{1}{6}} - 1 = 1.0107487 - 1 = 0.0107487 = 1.07487\%$$

$$60\,000.00 = R\left(\frac{1 - 1.0107487^{-300}}{0.0107487}\right) \longleftarrow \text{substituting in Formula 13.2}$$

$$60\,000.00 = R(89.270194)$$

$$R = \frac{60\,000.00}{89.270194}$$

$$R = \$672.12$$

Programmed solution

1.07487	0	60 000	300			
%i	FV	PV	N	CPT	PMT	672.12

The monthly payment is \$672.12.

B. Finding the term n

You can find the term of an ordinary general annuity by substituting the given values in Formula 13.1 when S_{nc} is known or in Formula 13.2 when A_{nc} is known. Since either formula converts the ordinary general annuity into an ordinary simple annuity, the method of solution is exactly the same as used in Section 11.5.

***Example* 13.3c** What period of time is required for \$125.00 deposited at the end of each month at 11% compounded quarterly to grow to \$15 000.00?

Solution

$$S_{nc} = 15\,000.00; \quad R = 125.00; \quad c = \frac{4}{12} = \frac{1}{3};$$

$$i = \frac{11\%}{4} = 2.75\% = 0.0275$$

The equivalent effective monthly rate of interest

$$f = 1.0275^{\frac{1}{3}} - 1 = 1.0090839 - 1 = 0.0090839 = 0.90839\%$$

$$15\,000.00 = 125.00\left(\frac{1.0090839^{n} - 1}{0.0090839}\right) \longleftarrow \text{using Formula 13.1}$$

$$120.00 = \frac{(1.0090839^{n} - 1)}{0.0090839}$$

$$1.0900678 = 1.0090839^{n} - 1$$

$$1.0090839^n = 2.0900678$$

$$n \ln 1.0090839 = \ln 2.0900678$$

$$n(0.0090429) = 0.7371965$$

$$n = \frac{0.7371965}{0.0090429}$$

$$n = 81.522227$$

$$n = 82 \text{ months approximately}$$

With a preprogrammed calculator, the procedure, after finding *f*, is

Key in	Press	Display shows
	%*i*	0.90839
0	PV	0
15 000	FV	15 000
125 (or −125)	PMT	125 (or −125)
CPT	N	81.5222

It will take 6 years and 10 months to accumulate \$15 000.00.

Example **13.3d** A business valued at \$96 000.00 is bought for a down payment of 25% and payments of \$4000.00 at the end of every three months. If interest is 18% compounded monthly, for how long will payments have to be made?

Solution

$$A_{nc} = 96\ 000.00(0.75) = 72\ 000.00; \quad R = 4000.00;$$

$$c = \frac{12}{4} = 3; \quad i = \frac{18\%}{12} = 1.5\% = 0.015$$

The equivalent effective quarterly rate of interest

$$f = 1.015^3 - 1 = 1.0456784 - 1 = 0.0456784 = 4.56784\%$$

$$72\ 000.00 = 4000.00\left(\frac{1 - 1.0456784^{-n}}{0.0456784}\right) \longleftarrow \text{using Formula 13.2}$$

$$0.8222112 = 1 - 1.0456784^{-n}$$

$$1.0456784^{-n} = 0.1777888$$

$$-n \ln 1.0456784 = \ln 0.1777888$$

$$-n(0.0446659) = -1.727159$$

$$n = 38.668403 \text{ (quarters)}$$

Programmed solution

4.56784	0	72 000	4000			
%i	FV	PV	PMT	CPT	N	38.6684

Payments will have to be made for 9 years and 9 months.

C. Finding i *using preprogrammed calculators*

For ordinary general annuities, you can determine the interest per conversion period i by first finding the effective rate per payment period. This is done in the same way as when finding i for ordinary simple annuities explained in Section 11.6. Enter the three unknown values (S_{nc}, R, n or A_{nc}, R, n) and then retrieve the answer by pressing [CPT] [%i]. You can then find the rate per conversion using the relationship $1 + f = (1 + i)^c$ and the nominal rate by multiplying i by the number of compounding periods per year.

Example 13.3e Irina deposited $150 in a savings account at the end of each month for 52 months. If the accumulated value of the deposits was $10 000 and interest is compounded semi-annually, what was the nominal rate of interest?

Solution

$$S_{nc} = 10\ 000; \quad R = 150; \quad n = 52; \quad c = \frac{2}{12} = \frac{1}{6}$$

First, find the effective monthly rate of interest.

Key in	Press	Display shows	
0	PV	0	
10 000	FV	10 000	
150 (or −150)	PMT	150 (or −150)	
52	N	52	
CPT	%i	0.9401521	← wait several seconds for the answer

The effective monthly rate is 0.9401521%.

Second, convert the effective monthly rate into a semi-annual compounding rate.

$$(1 + i)^{\frac{1}{6}} = 1 + 0.009401521$$

$$1 + i = 1.009401521^6$$

$$1 + i = 1.0577517$$

$$i = 0.0577517$$

The semi-annual compounding rate is 5.77517%; the nominal rate of interest is 11.55% approximately.

D. *Finding* i *without a preprogrammed calculator*

You can find the equivalent effective rate per payment period by trial and error. The method is illustrated in the Appendix.

Exercise 13.3

A. For each of the following ordinary general annuities, determine the unknown value.

	Amount S_{nc}	*Present value* A_{nc}	*Periodic payment* R	*Payment interval*	*Term*	*Nom. rate of int.*	*Conversion period*
1.	$45 000.00		?	3 months	10 years	9%	monthly
2.		$35 000.00	?	1 year	15 years	20%	quarterly
3.		$21 400.00	$1660.00	6 months	?	15%	monthly
4.	$13 600.00		$140.00	6 months	?	8%	quarterly
5.	$39 200.00		$1100.00	1 year	12 years	?	monthly
6.		$9 600.00	$1220.00	6 months	5 years	?	monthly
7.		$20 000.00	?	1 month	8 years	7%	semi-annually
8.	$16 500.00		?	3 months	15 years	16%	annually
9.	$7 200.00		$90.00	1 month	?	13%	semi-annually
10.		$11 700.00	$315.00	3 months	?	11%	annually
11.		$62 400.00	$5200.00	6 months	25 years	?	annually
12.	$55 500.00		$75.00	1 month	20 years	?	semi-annually

B. Answer each of the following questions.

1. What payment is required at the end of each month for fifteen years to amortize a $32 000.00 mortgage if interest is 9.5% compounded semi-annually?
2. How much must be deposited at the end of each quarter for ten years to accumulate to $12 000.00 at 6% compounded monthly?
3. What payment made at the end of every three months for twenty years will accumulate to $20 000.00 at 7% compounded semi-annually?
4. Deragh bought a car priced at $9300.00 for 15% down and equal monthly payments for four years. If interest is 18% compounded semi-annually, what is the size of the monthly payment?

5. How long will it take to save \$15 000.00 by making deposits of \$90.00 at the end of every month into an account earning interest at 10% compounded quarterly?

6. For how long will Jack have to make payments of \$350.00 at the end of every three months to repay a loan of \$6000.00 if interest is 15% compounded monthly?

7. A mortgage of \$18 600.00 is to be repaid by making payments of \$260.00 at the end of each month. If interest is 14% compounded semi-annually, what is the term of the mortgage?

8. Mr. Deneau accumulated \$100 000.00 in an RRSP. He converted the RRSP into an RRIF and started to withdraw \$4500.00 at the end of every three months from the fund. If interest is 12% compounded monthly, for how long can Mr. Deneau make withdrawals?

9. Compute the rate of interest compounded monthly at which \$400.00 paid at the end of every three months for eight years accumulates to \$20 000.00.

10. What is the rate of interest compounded quarterly if a loan of \$21 500.00 is repaid in seven years by payments of \$2500.00 made at the end of every six months?

11. A mortgage of \$27 500.00 is repaid by making payments of \$280.00 at the end of each month for fifteen years. What is the rate of interest compounded semi-annually?

12. A property worth \$35 000.00 is purchased for 10% down and semi-annual payments of \$2750.00 for twelve years. What is the effective rate of interest if interest is compounded quarterly?

13.4 *General annuities due*

A. *Amount of a general annuity due*

As with a simple annuity due, the amount of a **general annuity due** is greater than the amount of the corresponding ordinary general annuity by the interest on it for one payment period. Since the interest on a general annuity for one payment period is $(1 + i)^c$, or $(1 + f)$,

$$\text{AMOUNT OF A GENERAL ANNUITY DUE} = (1 + f) \times \text{AMOUNT OF THE CORRESPONDING ORDINARY GENERAL ANNUITY}$$

Thus, the formula for the amount of a general annuity due can be derived directly from Formula 13.1:

$$S_{nc}(\text{due}) = R(1 + f)\left[\frac{(1 + f)^n - 1}{f}\right] \qquad \longleftarrow \textit{Formula } 13.3$$

$$\text{where } f = (1 + i)^c - 1$$

Example **13.4a** What is the accumulated value after five years of payments of \$20 000 made at the beginning of each year if interest is 7% compounded quarterly?

Solution

$$R = 20\ 000.00; \quad n = 5; \quad c = 4; \quad i = \frac{7\%}{4} = 1.75\% = 0.0175$$

The equivalent effective annual rate of interest

$$f = 1.0175^4 - 1 = 1.0718590 - 1 = 0.0718590 = 7.18590\%$$

$$S_{nc}(\text{due}) = 20\ 000.00(1.0718590)\left(\frac{1.0718590^5 - 1}{0.0718590}\right) \longleftarrow \text{substituting in Formula 13.3}$$

$$= 20\ 000.00(1.0718590)(5.7721095)$$

$$= 20\ 000.00(6.1868875)$$

$$= \$123\ 737.75$$

Programmed solution

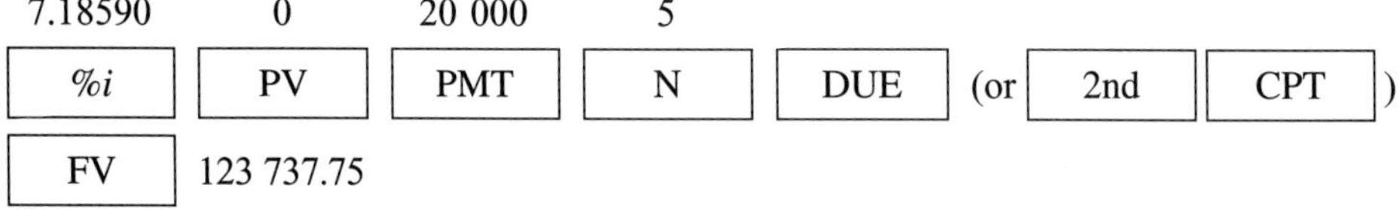

The accumulated value after five years is \$123 737.75.

B. *Present value of a general annuity due*

For a general annuity due, the present value is greater than the present value of the corresponding ordinary general annuity by the interest on it for one payment period.

THE PRESENT VALUE OF A GENERAL ANNUITY DUE = $(1 + f) \times$ THE PRESENT VALUE OF THE CORRESPONDING ORDINARY GENERAL ANNUITY

Thus, the formula for the present value of a general annuity due can be derived directly from Formula 13.2. Using the equivalent effective rate of interest per payment period,

$$A_{nc}(\text{due}) = R(1 + f)\left[\frac{1 - (1 + f)^{-n}}{f}\right]$$
$$\text{where } f = (1 + i)^c - 1$$

$\longleftarrow$ ***Formula*** **13.4**

Example **13.4b** A three-year lease requires payments of \$1600.00 at the beginning of every three months. If money is worth 16.5% compounded monthly, what is the cash value of the lease?

Solution

$$R = 1600.00; \quad n = 3(4) = 12; \quad c = \frac{12}{4} = 3;$$

$$i = \frac{16.5\%}{12} = 1.375\% = 0.01375$$

The equivalent effective quarterly rate of interest

$$f = 1.01375^3 - 1 = 1.0418198 - 1 = 0.0418198 = 4.18198\%$$

$$A_{nc}(\text{due}) = 1600.00(1.0418198)\left(\frac{1 - 1.0418198^{-12}}{0.0418198}\right) \longleftarrow \text{substituting in Formula 13.4}$$

$$= 1600.00(1.0418198)(9.2867522)$$

$$= 1600.00(9.6751223)$$

$$= \$15\,480.20$$

Programmed solution

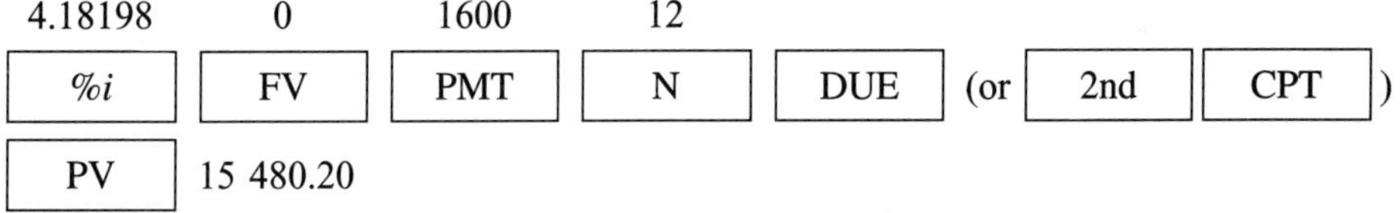

The cash value of the lease is $15 480.20.

C. General annuity due—finding the periodic payment R

If S_{nc}(due), n, and i are known, you can find R by substituting the given values in Formula 13.3. If A_{nc}(due), n, and i are known, you can find R by substituting the given values in Formula 13.4.

Example **13.4c** What deposit made at the beginning of each month will accumulate to $18 000.00 at 5% compounded quarterly at the end of eight years?

Solution

$$S_{nc}(\text{due}) = 18\,000.00; \quad n = 8(12) = 96; \quad c = \frac{4}{12} = \frac{1}{3}$$

$$i = \frac{5\%}{4} = 1.25\% = 0.0125$$

The equivalent effective monthly rate of interest

$$f = 1.0125^{\frac{1}{3}} - 1 = 1.0041494 - 1 = 0.0041494 = 0.41494\%$$

$$18\ 000.00 = R(1.0041494)\left(\frac{1.0041494^{96} - 1}{0.0041494}\right) \longleftarrow \text{substituting in Formula 13.3}$$

$$18\ 000.00 = R(1.0041494)(117.6381049)$$

$$18\ 000.00 = R(118.1262324)$$

$$R = \frac{18\ 000.00}{118.1262324}$$

$$R = \$152.38$$

Programmed solution

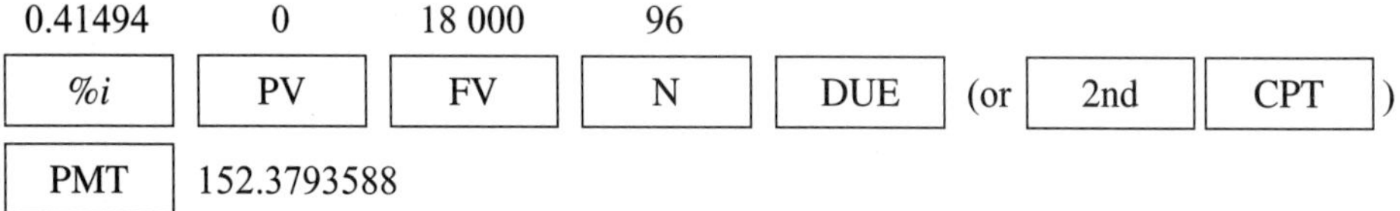

The monthly deposit is $152.38.

***Example* 13.4d** What monthly payment must be made at the beginning of each month on a five-year lease valued at $100 000.00 if interest is 16% compounded semi-annually?

Solution

$$A_{nc}(\text{due}) = 100\ 000.00; \quad n = 5(12) = 60; \quad c = \frac{2}{12} = \frac{1}{6};$$

$$i = \frac{16\%}{2} = 8\% = 0.08$$

The equivalent effective monthly rate of interest

$$f = 1.08^{\frac{1}{6}} - 1 = 1.0129095 - 1 = 0.0129095 = 1.29095\%$$

$$100\ 000.00 = R(1.0129095)\left(\frac{1 - 1.0129095^{-60}}{0.0129095}\right) \longleftarrow \text{substituting in Formula 13.4}$$

$$100\ 000.00 = R(1.0129095)(41.582377)$$

$$100\ 000.00 = R(42.119184)$$

$$R = \frac{100\ 000.00}{42.119184}$$

$$R = \$2374.22$$

Programmed solution

1.29095	0	100 000	60			
%i	FV	PV	N	DUE	(or 2nd	CPT)
PMT	2374.22					

The monthly payment is $2374.22.

D. General annuity due—finding the term n

If S_{nc}(due), R, and i are known, you can find n by substituting the given values in Formula 13.3 and then solving for n using natural logarithms. If A_{nc}(due), R, and i are known, use formula 13.4.

***Example* 13.4e** Ted Davis wants to accumulate $140 000.00 in a RRSP by making annual contributions of $5500.00 at the beginning of each year. If interest on the RRSP is 11% compounded quarterly, for how long will Ted have to make contributions?

Solution

$$S_{nc}(\text{due}) = 140\,000.00; \quad R = 5500.00; \quad c = 4;$$

$$i = \frac{11\%}{4} = 2.75\% = 0.0275$$

The equivalent effective annual rate of interest

$$f = 1.0275^4 - 1 = 1.1146213 - 1 = 0.1146213 = 11.46213\%$$

$$140\,000.00 = 5500.00(1.1146213)\left(\frac{1.1146213^n - 1}{0.1146213}\right) \longleftarrow \text{using Formula 13.3}$$

$$140\,000.00 = 53\,484.101(1.1146213^n - 1)$$

$$2.6176003 = 1.1146213^n - 1$$

$$1.1146213^n = 3.6176003$$

$$n \ln 1.1146213 = \ln 3.6176003$$

$$n(0.1085147) = 1.2858109$$

$$n = \frac{1.2858109}{0.1085147}$$

$$n = 11.849186$$

$$n = 12 \text{ years (approximately)}$$

Programmed solution

11.46213	0	5500	140 000			
%i	PV	PMT	FV	DUE	(or 2nd	CPT)
		(or −5500)				

N	11.849186

Ted will have to contribute for 12 years.

Example **13.4f** Ted Davis, having reached his goal of a $140 000.00 balance in his RRSP, immediately converts it into an RRIF and withdraws from it $1650.00 at the beginning of each month. If interest continues at 11% compounded quarterly, for how long can he make withdrawals?

Solution

$$A_{nc}(\text{due}) = 140\ 000.00; \quad R = 1650.00; \quad c = \frac{4}{12} = \frac{1}{3};$$

$$i = \frac{11\%}{4} = 2.75\% = 0.0275$$

The equivalent effective monthly rate of interest

$$f = 1.0275^{\frac{1}{3}} - 1 = 1.0090839 - 1 = 0.0090839 = 0.90839\%$$

$$140\ 000.00 = 1650.00(1.0090839)\left(\frac{1 - 1.0090839^{-n}}{0.0090839}\right) \longleftarrow \text{using Formula 13.4}$$

$$140\ 000.00 = 183\ 290.04(1 - 1.0090839^{-n})$$

$$0.7638167 = 1 - 1.0090839^{-n}$$

$$1.0090839^{-n} = 0.2361833$$

$$-n \ln 1.0090839 = \ln 0.2361833$$

$$-n(0.0090429) = -1.4431471$$

$$n = 159.58897$$

$$n = 160 \text{ months (approximately)}$$

Programmed solution

0.90839% 0 140 000 1650

[%i] [FV] [PV] [PMT] [DUE] (or [2nd] [DUE])

[N] 159.589

Ted will be able to make withdrawals for 13 years and 4 months.

E. General annuity due—finding i using preprogrammed calculators

For general annuities due, you can determine the interest rate per conversion period i by first finding the effective rate per payment period. Find i as you did for ordinary general annuities, explained in Section 13.3. Enter the three unknown values (S_{nc}(due), R, n or A_{nc}(due), R, n) and then retrieve the answer by pressing [DUE] [%i].

You can then find the rate per conversion using the relationship $1 + f = (1 + i)^c$ and the nominal rate by multiplying i by the number of compounding periods per year.

Example 13.4g Compute the nominal rate of interest compounded monthly at which $500 deposited at the beginning of every three months for ten years will amount to $30 000.

Solution

$$S_{nc}(\text{due}) = 30\ 000; \quad R = 500; \quad n = 40; \quad c = \frac{12}{4} = 3$$

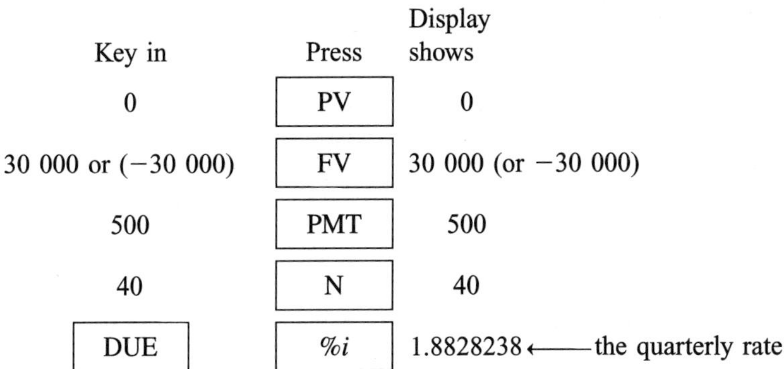

Key in	Press	Display shows
0	[PV]	0
30 000 or (−30 000)	[FV]	30 000 (or −30 000)
500	[PMT]	500
40	[N]	40
[DUE]	[%i]	1.8828238 ←— the quarterly rate

Converting the quarterly rate into a monthly rate,

$$(1 + i)^3 = 1.0188282$$

$$1 + i = 1.0188282^{\frac{1}{3}}$$

$$1 + i = 1.0062371$$

$$i = 0.0062371$$

The monthly compounding rate is 0.62371%; the nominal rate is 7.48% approximately.

Note: For general annuities due, you can compute the conversion rate i without preprogrammed calculators by the trial and error approach shown in the Appendix.

Exercise 13.4

A. For each of the following general annuities due, determine the unknown value as indicated.

	Amount S_{nc}*(due)*	*Present value* A_{nc}*(due)*	*Periodic payment R*	*Payment interval*	*Term*	*Nom. rate of int.*	*Conversion period*
1.	?		$1500.00	6 months	10 years	13%	quarterly
2.	?		$175.00	1 month	7 years	7%	semi-annually
3.		?	$650.00	3 months	6 years	12%	monthly
4.		?	$93.00	1 month	4 years	20%	quarterly
5.	$16 500.00		?	1 year	10 years	14%	quarterly
6.	$9 200.00		?	3 months	5 years	15%	semi-annually
7.		$10 000.00	?	3 months	3 years	6%	monthly
8.		$24 300.00	?	1 month	20 years	9%	semi-annually
9.	$32 000.00		$450.00	6 months	?	15%	monthly
10.	$7 500.00		$150.00	3 months	?	11%	annually
11.		$12 500.00	$860.00	3 months	?	18%	monthly
12.		$45 000.00	$540.00	1 month	?	14%	semi-annually
13.	$6 400.00		$200.00	6 months	9 years	?	monthly
14.	$25 000.00		$790.00	1 year	15 years	?	quarterly
15.		$7 500.00	$420.00	3 months	5 years	?	monthly
16.		$60 000.00	$725.00	1 month	25 years	?	semi-annually

B. Answer each of the following questions.

1. Bomac Steel sets aside $5000.00 at the beginning of every six months in a fund to replace erecting equipment. If interest is 12% compounded quarterly, how much will be in the fund after five years?

2. Jamie Dean contributes $125.00 at the beginning of each month into an RRSP paying interest at 6.5% compounded semi-annually. How much will be the accumulated balance in the RRSP at the end of 25 years?

3. What is the cash value of a lease requiring payments of $750.00 at the beginning of each month for three years if interest is 16% compounded quarterly?

4. Gerald Carter and Marysia Wokawski bought a property by making semi-annual payments of \$2500.00 for seven years. If the first payment is due on the date of purchase and interest is 14% compounded quarterly, what is the purchase price of the property?

5. How much would you have to pay into an account at the beginning of every six months to accumulate \$10 000.00 in eight years if interest is 7% compounded quarterly?

6. Peel Credit Union entered a lease contract valued at \$5400.00. The contract provides for payments at the beginning of each month for three years. If interest is 21% compounded quarterly, what is the size of the monthly payment?

7. Sarah Ling has saved \$85 000.00. If she decides to withdraw \$3000.00 at the beginning of every three months and interest is 11.5% compounded annually, for how long can she make withdrawals?

8. For how long must contributions of \$1600.00 be made at the beginning of each year to accumulate to \$96 000.00 at 10% compounded quarterly?

9. What is the rate of interest compounded annually on a lease valued at \$21 600.00 if payments of \$730.00 are made at the beginning of each month for three years?

10. An insurance policy provides for a lump sum benefit of \$50 000.00 fifteen years from now. Alternatively, payments of \$1700.00 may be received at the beginning of each of the next fifteen years. What is the effective rate of interest if interest is compounded quarterly?

13.5 *Deferred general annuities*

A. Present value of deferred ordinary general annuities

The amount of a deferred general annuity designated by the symbol S_{nc}(defer) is the accumulated value of the periodic payments at the end of the term of the annuity. As with a deferred simple annuity, the period of deferment does not affect the amount. Thus the problem of finding the amount of a deferred general annuity is identical to the problem of finding the amount of a general annuity. No further consideration is given to the problem of finding the amount of a deferred general annuity in this text.

The present value of a deferred general annuity designated by the symbol A_{nc}(defer) is the discounted value of the periodic payments at the beginning of the period of deferment. As with a deferred simple annuity, the problem of finding the present value of a deferred general annuity is divided into two parts. Two approaches may be taken, as illustrated in Example 13.5a.

Example **13.5a** Payments of \$1000.00 are due at the end of each year for five years. If the payments are deferred for three years and interest is 10% compounded quarterly, what is the present value of the deferred payments?

Solution

STEP 1 Find the present value of the ordinary general annuity.

$$R = 1000.00; \quad n = 5; \quad c = 4; \quad i = \frac{10\%}{4} = 2.5\% = 0.025$$

The equivalent effective annual rate of interest

$$f = 1.025^4 - 1 = 1.1038129 - 1 = 0.1038129 = 10.38129\%$$

$$A_{nc} = 1000.00\left(\frac{1 - 1.1038129^{-5}}{0.1038129}\right) \longleftarrow \text{substituting in Formula 13.2}$$

$$= 1000.00(3.7541489)$$

$$= \$3754.15$$

Programmed solution

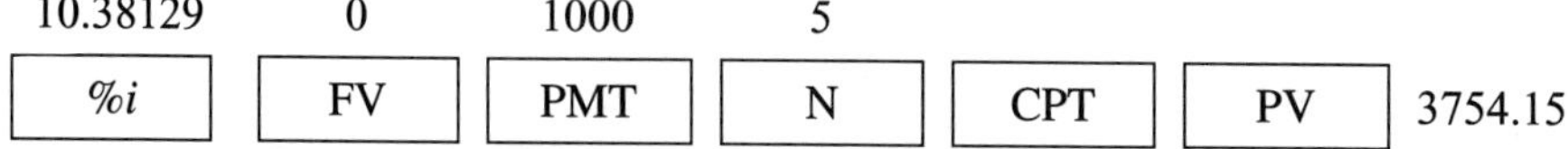

STEP 2 Find the present value of A_{nc} at the beginning of the period of deferment.

$S = 3754.15$ is the present value of the general annuity A_{nc};

$d = 3$ is the number of deferred payment intervals;

$f = 10.38129\%$ is the equivalent effective rate of interest per payment interval.

$$A_{nc}(\text{defer}) = P = 3754.15(1.1038129^{-3}) \longleftarrow \text{substituting in Formula 9.2B}$$

$$= 3754.15(0.7435559)$$

$$= \$2791.42$$

Programmed solution

10.38129 (%i) 3754.15 (FV) 0 (PMT) 3 (N) (CPT) (PV) 2791.42

The present value of the deferred payments is $2791.42.

Alternative

Assume that periodic payments have been made during the period of deferment. Then the number of actual payments is $n = 5$ and the number of assumed payments is $d = 3$.

STEP 1 Find the present value of the annuity in which the number of payments is $d + n = 3 + 5 = 8$.

$$A_{(d+n)c} = 1000.00\left(\frac{1 - 1.1038129^{-8}}{0.1038129}\right)$$

$$= 1000.00(5.2616725)$$

$$= \$5261.67$$

Programmed solution

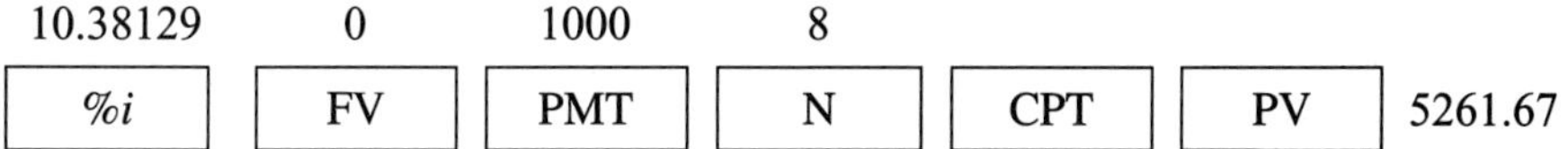
10.38129 (%i) 0 (FV) 1000 (PMT) 8 (N) (CPT) (PV) 5261.67

STEP 2 Find the present value of the annuity consisting of the assumed payments $d = 3$.

$$A_{dc} = 1000.00\left(\frac{1 - 1.1038129^{-3}}{0.1038129}\right)$$

$$= 1000.00(2.4702531)$$

$$= \$2470.25$$

Programmed solution

(10.38129 (%i) 0 (FV) 1000 (PMT)) 3 (N) (CPT) (PV) 2470.25

The first three values need not be programmed (since they are already programmed from Step 1.)

STEP 3 Find the present value of the deferred general annuity by finding the difference.

$$A_{nc}(\text{defer}) = A_{(d+n)c} - A_{dc} = 5261.67 - 2470.25 = \$2791.42$$

B. *Present value of deferred general annuities due*

To determine the present value of a deferred general annuity due, use the approach shown in Example 13.5a but use Formula 13.4 instead of Formula 13.2.

Example **13.5b** Tom Casey wants to withdraw $925.00 at the beginning of each quarter for twelve years. If the withdrawals are to begin ten years from now and interest is 12% compounded monthly, how much must Tom deposit today to be able to make the withdrawals?

Solution

$$R = 925.00; \quad n = 12(4) = 48; \quad d = 10(4) = 40; \quad c = \frac{12}{4} = 3;$$

$$i = \frac{12\%}{12} = 1\% = 0.01$$

The equivalent effective quarterly rate of interest

$$f = 1.01^3 - 1 = 1.030301 - 1 = 0.030301 = 3.0301\%$$

STEP 1 Find the present value of the general annuity due.

$$A_{nc}(\text{due}) = 925.00(1.030301)\left(\frac{1 - 1.030301^{-48}}{0.030301}\right) \longleftarrow \text{substituting in Formula 13.4}$$

$$= 925.00(1.030301)(25.126946)$$

$$= 23\ 946.69$$

Programmed solution

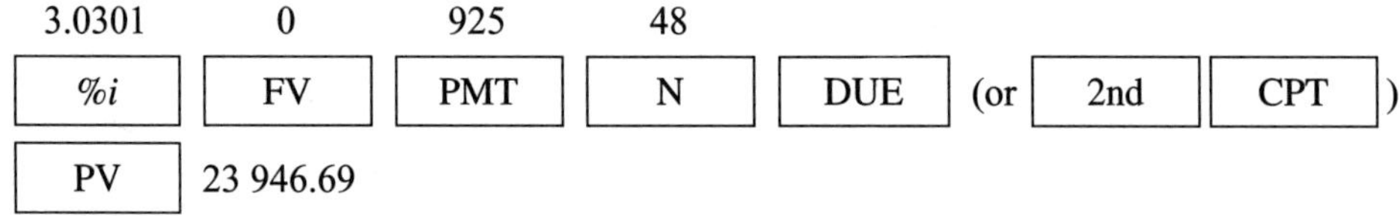

STEP 2 Find the present value of A_{nc} (due) at the beginning of the period of deferment.

S = 23 946.69 is the present value of the general annuity A_{nc}(due)
d = 40 is the number of deferred payment intervals;
f = 3.0301% is the equivalent effective rate of interest per payment interval.

$$A_{nc}(\text{defer}) = P = 23\ 946.69(1.030301)^{-40} \longleftarrow \text{substituting in Formula 9.2B}$$

$$= 23\ 946.69(0.3029948)$$

$$= 7255.72$$

Programmed solution

3.0301	23 946.69	0	40			
%i	FV	PMT	N	CPT	PV	7255.72

Tom must deposit $7255.72 to make the withdrawals.

C. Deferred general annuities—finding the periodic payment R

To find the periodic payment for a deferred general annuity, first determine the accumulated value of the present value at the end of the period of deferment. You can then find the periodic payment for a deferred ordinary general annuity by substituting the known values in Formula 13.2. For deferred general annuities due, you can find R by substituting in Formula 13.4.

Example **13.5c** A contract that has a cash value of \$36 000.00 requires payments at the end of every three months for six years. If the payments are deferred for three years and interest is 17% compounded semi-annually, what is the size of the quarterly payments?

Solution

$$A_{nc}(\text{defer}) = 36\,000.00; \quad n = 6(4) = 24; \quad d = 3(4) = 12;$$

$$c = \frac{2}{4} = 0.5; \quad i = \frac{17\%}{2} = 8.5\% = 0.085$$

The equivalent effective quarterly rate of interest

$$f = 1.085^{0.5} - 1 = 1.0416333 - 1 = 0.0416333 = 4.16333\%$$

First determine the accumulated value of the deposit at the end of the period of deferment.

$$S = 36\,000.00(1.0416333)^{12} \longleftarrow \text{substituting in Formula 9.1}$$
$$= 36\,000.00(1.6314669)$$
$$= 58\,732.82$$

Programmed solution

4.16333	0	36 000	12			
%*i*	PMT	PV	N	CPT	FV	58 732.82

Now determine the periodic payment for the ordinary general annuity whose present value is \$58 732.82.

$$58\,732.82 = R\left(\frac{1 - 1.0416333^{-24}}{0.0416333}\right) \longleftarrow \text{substituting in Formula 13.2}$$

$$58\,732.82 = R(14.995161)$$

$$R = \frac{58\,732.82}{14.995161}$$

$$R = \$3916.79$$

Programmed solution

58 732.82	0	4.16333	24			
PV	FV	%i	N	CPT	PMT	3916.79

The required quarterly payment is $3916.79.

Example **13.5d** A lease contract that has a cash value of $64 000.00 requires payments at the beginning of each month for seven years. If the payments are deferred for two years and interest is 20% compounded quarterly, what is the size of the monthly payment?

Solution

$$A_{nc}(\text{defer}) = 64\,000.00; \quad n = 7(12) = 84; \quad d = 2(12) = 24;$$

$$c = \frac{4}{12} = \frac{1}{3}; \quad i = \frac{20\%}{4} = 5\% = 0.05$$

The equivalent effective monthly rate of interest

$$f = 1.05^{\frac{1}{3}} - 1 = 1.0163964 - 1 = 1.63964\%$$

First determine the accumulated value of the cash value at the end of the period of deferment.

$$\begin{aligned} S &= 64\,000.00(1.0163964)^{24} \\ &= 64\,000.00(1.4774554) \\ &= 94\,557.15 \end{aligned}$$

Programmed solution

1.63964	0	64 000	24			
%i	PMT	PV	N	CPT	FV	94 557.15

Now determine the periodic payment for the general annuity due whose present value is $94 557.15.

$$94\,557.15 = R(1.0163964)\left(\frac{1 - 1.0163964^{-84}}{0.0163964}\right)$$

$$94\,557.15 = R(1.0163964)(45.431148)$$

$$94\,557.15 = R(46.176055)$$

$$R = 2047.75$$

Programmed solution

94 557.15	0	1.63964	84			
PV	FV	%i	N	DUE	(or 2nd	CPT)
PMT	2047.75					

The monthly payment is \$2047.75.

D. Deferred general annuities—finding the term of the annuity n

To find n, use a procedure similar to the one used for finding R.

Example **13.5e** Mr. Kovacs deposited a retirement gratuity of \$21 500.00 in an income averaging annuity paying \$375.00 at the end of each month. If payments are deferred for nine months and interest is 12% compounded quarterly, for what period of time will Mr. Kovacs receive annuity payments?

Solution

$$A_{nc}(\text{defer}) = 21\ 500.00; \quad R = 375.00; \quad d = 9; \quad c = \frac{4}{12} = \frac{1}{3};$$

$$i = \frac{12\%}{4} = 3\% = 0.03$$

The equivalent effective monthly rate of interest

$$f = 1.03^{\frac{1}{3}} - 1 = 1.0099016 - 1 = 0.0099016 = 0.99016\%.$$

First find the accumulated value at the end of the period of deferment.

$$\begin{aligned} S &= 21\ 500.00(1.0099016)^9 \\ &= 21\ 500.00(1.092727) \\ &= 23\ 493.63 \end{aligned}$$

Programmed solution

0.99016	0	21 500	9			
%i	PMT	PV	N	CPT	FV	23 493.63

Then find the number of payments for an ordinary annuity with a present value of \$23 493.63.

$$23\,493.63 = 375.00\left(\frac{1 - 1.0099016^{-n}}{0.0099016}\right)$$

$$23\,493.63 = 37\,872.667(1 - 1.0099016^{-n})$$

$$0.6203321 = 1 - 1.0099016^{-n}$$

$$1.0099016^{-n} = 0.3796679$$

$$-n \ln 1.0099016 = \ln 0.3796679$$

$$-n(0.0098529) = -0.9684583$$

$$n = \frac{0.9684583}{0.0098529}$$

$$n = 98.291701$$

$$n = 99 \text{ months}$$

Programmed solution

23 493.63	0	0.99016	375			
PV	FV	%i	PMT	CPT	N	98.291701

Mr. Kovacs will receive payments for 8 years and 3 months.

***Example* 13.5f** By age 65, Janice Berstein had accumulated $120 000.00 in an RRSP by making yearly contributions over a period of years. At age 70, she converted the existing balance into an RRIF from which she started to withdraw $2000.00 per month. If the first withdrawal was on the date of conversion and interest on the account is 11% compounded quarterly, for how long will Janice Berstein receive annuity payments?

Solution

$$A_{nc}(\text{defer}) = 120\,000.00; \quad R = 2000.00; \quad d = 5(12) = 60;$$

$$c = \frac{4}{12} = \frac{1}{3}; \quad i = \frac{11\%}{4} = 2.75\% = 0.0275$$

The equivalent effective monthly rate of interest

$$f = 1.0275^{\frac{1}{3}} - 1 = 1.0090839 - 1 = 0.0090839 = 0.90839\%$$

Since payments are at the beginning of each month, the problem involves a deferred general annuity due.

First find the accumulated value at the end of the period of deferment.

$$\begin{aligned} S &= 120\,000.00(1.0090839)^{60} \\ &= 120\,000.00(1.7204283) \\ &= 206\,451.39 \end{aligned}$$

Programmed solution

0.90839	0	120 000	60			
%*i*	PMT	PV	N	CPT	FV	206 451.39

Then find the number of payments for an annuity due with a present value of \$206 451.39.

$$206\,451.39 = 2000.00(1.0090839)\left(\frac{1 - 1.0090839^{-n}}{0.0090839}\right)$$

$$206\,451.39 = 222\,169.75(1 - 1.0090839^{-n})$$

$$0.9292507 = 1 - 1.0090839^{-n}$$

$$1.0090839^{-n} = 0.0707493$$

$$-n \ln 1.0090839 = \ln 0.0707493$$

$$-n(0.0090429) = -2.6486123$$

$$n = 292.89447$$

$$n = 293 \text{ months}$$

Programmed solution

206 451.39	0	0.90839	2000			
PV	FV	%*i*	PMT	DUE	(or 2nd	CPT)
N	292.89447					

Janice Berstein will receive payments for 24 years and 5 months.

E. Finding the conversion rate i *for deferred general annuities*

You can determine the periodic rate of interest for deferred general annuities by trial and error using the method shown in the Appendix.

Exercise 13.5

A. For each of the following deferred general annuities, determine the unknown value as shown.

	Present value A_{nc}(defer)	Payment made at	Periodic payment R	Payment period	Period of deferment	Term	Int. rate	Conversion period
1.	?	end	$720.00	3 months	4 years	10 years	12%	monthly
2.	?	beginning	$145.00	6 months	3 years	5 years	14%	quarterly
3.	?	beginning	$225.00	3 months	6 years	8 years	9%	annually
4.	?	end	$1500.00	1 month	2 years	3 years	15%	semi-annually
5.	$9 000.00	end	?	1 month	3 years	7 years	5%	quarterly
6.	$12 650.00	beginning	?	6 months	2 years	4 years	16%	quarterly
7.	$3 740.00	beginning	$4100.00	1 year	10 years	?	18%	monthly
8.	$22 750.00	end	$385.00	1 month	1 year	?	13%	semi-annually

B. Answer each of the following questions.

1. Mrs. Bell expects to retire in seven years and would like to receive $800.00 at the end of each month for ten years following the date of her retirement. How much must Mrs. Bell deposit today in an account paying 7.5% compounded semi-annually to receive the monthly payments?

2. The sale of a property provides for payments of $2000.00 due at the beginning of every three months for five years. If the payments are deferred for two years and interest is 15% compounded monthly, what is the cash value of the property?

3. Dr. Young bought $18 000 worth of equipment from Medical Supply Company. The purchase agreement requires equal payments every six months for eight years. If the first payment is due two years after the date of purchase and interest is 14% compounded quarterly, what is the size of the payments?

4. Ed Ainsley borrowed $10 000.00 from his uncle to finance his post-graduate studies. The loan agreement calls for equal payments at the end of each month for ten years. The payments are deferred for four years and interest is 8% compounded semi-annually. What is the size of the monthly payments?

5. A property development agreement valued at $45 000.00 requires annual lease payments of $15 000.00. The first payment is due five years after the date of the agreement and interest is 15% compounded semi-annually. For how long will payments be made?

6. A retirement gratuity of $23 600.00 is invested in an annuity deferred for twelve years. The annuity provides payments of $4000.00 due at the beginning of every six months. If interest is 10% compounded annually, for how long will annuity payments be made?

13.6 *General perpetuities*

A. Present value of an ordinary general perpetuity

A **general perpetuity** is an annuity in which the payments begin at a fixed date and continue forever but for which the payment interval is not the same length as the interest conversion period. As with any general annuity, the general perpetuity can be converted into a simple perpetuity by replacing the given periodic rate of interest by the equivalent effective rate of interest per payment interval.

As with other annuities, we will use the following symbols in dealing with general perpetuities:

A = the present value of the perpetuity;

R = the periodic payment or perpetuity payment;

i = the rate of interest per conversion period;

f = the effective rate of interest per payment interval equivalent to i;

c = the number of conversion periods per payment period.

For a general perpetuity, the payment R is the interest earned by the present value of the perpetuity in one payment interval. That is,

$$R = fA$$

$$A = \frac{R}{f} \text{ where } f = (1 + i)^c - 1 \quad \longleftarrow \textit{Formula } 13.5$$

Example **13.6a** What sum of money invested today at 12% compounded quarterly will provide a scholarship of $2500.00 at the end of each year?

Solution

Since the payments are to continue indefinitely, the payments form a perpetuity. Furthermore, since the payments are made at the end of each payment interval and the interest conversion period is not the same length as the payment interval, the problem involves an ordinary general perpetuity.

$$R = 2500.00; \quad c = 4; \quad i = \frac{12\%}{4} = 3\% = 0.03$$

The equivalent effective annual rate of interest

$$f = 1.03^4 - 1 = 1.1255088 - 1 = 0.1255088 = 12.55082\%$$

$$A = \frac{2500.00}{0.1255088} = \$19\,918.92 \longleftarrow \text{substituting in Formula 13.5}$$

The required sum of money is $19 918.92.

Example **13.6b** The alumni of Peel College collected \$32 000.00 to provide a fund for bursaries. If the money is invested at 7% compounded annually, what is the size of the bursary that can be paid every six months?

Solution

$$A = 32\ 000.00; \quad c = \frac{1}{2}; \quad i = 7\% = 0.07$$

The equivalent effective semi-annual rate of interest

$$f = 1.07^{0.5} - 1 = 1.0344080 - 1 = 0.0344080 = 3.44080\%$$

$$R = fA = 0.0344080(32\ 000.00) = \$1101.06$$

The size of the bursary is \$1101.06.

B. *Present value of general perpetuities due*

As in the case of the simple perpetuity due, the general perpetuity due can be treated as consisting of an immediate payment R followed by an ordinary general perpetuity. Using the symbol A(due) for the present value,

$$A(\text{due}) = R + \frac{R}{f} \text{ where } f = (1 + i)^c - 1 \quad \longleftarrow \textit{Formula } \mathbf{13.6}$$

Example **13.6c** What is the present value of perpetuity payments of \$750.00 made at the beginning of each month if interest is 14.5% compounded semi-annually?

Solution

$$R = 750.00; \quad c = \frac{2}{12} = \frac{1}{6}; \quad i = \frac{14.5\%}{2} = 7.25\% = 0.0725$$

The equivalent effective monthly rate of interest

$$f = 1.0725^{\frac{1}{6}} - 1 = 1.0117337 - 1 = 0.0117337 = 1.17337\%$$

$$A(\text{due}) = 750.00 + \frac{750.00}{0.0117337} = \$64\ 668.46 \longleftarrow \text{substituting in Formula 13.6}$$

The present value of the perpetuity is \$64 668.46.

Example **13.6d** What sum of money invested today in a fund earning 12% compounded monthly will provide perpetuity payments of \$395.00 every three months starting

(i) immediately?

(ii) three months from now?

(iii) one year from now?

Solution

$$R = 395.00; \quad c = \frac{12}{4} = 3; \quad i = \frac{12\%}{12} = 1\% = 0.01$$

The equivalent effective quarterly rate of interest

$$f = 1.01^3 - 1 = 1.030301 - 1 = 0.030301 = 3.0301\%$$

(i) Because the perpetuity payments are at the beginning of each payment interval, they form a perpetuity due.

$$A(\text{due}) = 395.00 + \frac{395.00}{0.030301} = 395.00 + 13\,035.87 = \$13\,430.87$$

The required sum of money is \$13 430.87.

(ii) Since the first payment is three months from now, the perpetuity payments form an ordinary perpetuity.

$$A = \frac{395.00}{0.030301} = \$13\,035.87$$

The required sum of money is \$13 035.87.

(iii) If you consider that the payments are deferred for one year, they form a deferred perpetuity due.

$$\begin{aligned} A(\text{defer}) &= A(\text{due}) \times (1.01)^{-12} \\ &= 13\,430.87(0.8874492) \\ &= \$11\,919.22 \end{aligned}$$

Alternatively, the period of deferment could be considered to be nine months (3 quarters) in which case the payments would form a deferred ordinary perpetuity.

$$\begin{aligned} A(\text{defer}) &= A \times (1.01)^{-9} \\ &= 13\,035.87(0.9143398) \\ &= \$11\,919.22 \end{aligned}$$

The required sum of money is \$11 919.22.

Exercise 13.6

A. Find the present value of each of the following perpetuities.

	Perpetuity payment	*Payment made at*	*Payment interval*	*Interest rate*	*Conversion period*
1.	\$5600.00	end	6 months	12%	monthly
2.	\$2150.00	beginning	3 months	15%	monthly
3.	\$725.00	beginning	1 month	10%	quarterly
4.	\$380.00	end	3 months	8%	semi-annually

B. Answer each of the following questions.

1. The Xorex Company pays a dividend of $4.25 every three months per preferred share. What is the expected market price per share if money is worth 13% compounded semi-annually?
2. Transcontinental Pipelines is considering a technical process which is expected to reduce annual maintenance costs by $85 000.00. What is the maximum amount of money that could be invested in the process to be economically feasible if interest is 14% compounded quarterly?
3. A rental property provides a net income of $4200.00 at the beginning of every three months. What is the cash value of the property if money is worth 18% compounded monthly?
4. Municipal Hydro offers to acquire a right-of-way from a property owner who receives annual lease payments of $2225.00 due in advance. What is a fair offer if money is worth 21.5% compounded quarterly?
5. What is the size of the scholarship that can be paid at the end of every six months from a fund of $25 000.00 if interest is 11% compounded quarterly?
6. What monthly lease payment due in advance should be charged for a tract of land valued at $35 000 if the agreed interest is 14.5% compounded semi-annually?

Review exercise

1. Payments of $375.00 made every three months are accumulated at 12% compounded monthly. What is their amount after eight years if the payments are made
   (a) at the end of every three months?
   (b) at the beginning of every three months?
2. What is the accumulated value after twelve years of monthly deposits of $145.00 earning interest at 5% compounded semi-annually if the deposits are made
   (a) at the end of each month?
   (b) at the beginning of each month?
3. What single cash payment is equivalent to payments of $3500.00 every six months at 14% compounded quarterly if the payments are made
   (a) at the end of every six months for fifteen years?
   (b) at the beginning of every six months for ten years?
   (c) at the end of every six months for eight years but deferred for four years?
   (d) at the beginning of every six months for nine years but deferred for three years?
   (e) at the end of every six months in perpetuity?
   (f) at the beginning of every six months in perpetuity?

4. What is the principal invested at 12.5% compounded semi-annually from which monthly withdrawals of $240.00 can be made
   (a) at the end of each month for 25 years?
   (b) at the beginning of each month for 15 years?
   (c) at the end of each month for 20 years but deferred for 10 years?
   (d) at the beginning of each month for 15 years but deferred for 12 years?
   (e) at the end of each month in perpetuity?
   (f) at the beginning of each month in perpetuity?
5. What size payment will accumulate to $12 500.00 at 10% compounded quarterly if made
   (a) at the end of each month for twenty years?
   (b) at the beginning of every six months for eight years?
6. How much must be deposited into an account to accumulate to $32 000.00 at 7% compounded semi-annually
   (a) at the beginning of each month for twenty years?
   (b) at the end of each year for fifteen years?
7. What size payment has a present value of $9600.00 at 18% compounded monthly if made
   (a) at the end of every three months for eight years?
   (b) at the beginning of every six months for ten years?
   (c) at the end of each year for ten years but deferred for three years?
   (d) at the beginning of every six months for seven years but deferred for five years?
   (e) at the end of every three months in perpetuity?
   (f) at the beginning of each year in perpetuity?
8. What sum of money can be withdrawn from a fund of $16 750.00 invested at 16.5% compounded semi-annually
   (a) at the end of every three months for twelve years?
   (b) at the beginning of each year for twenty years?
   (c) at the end of each month for fifteen years but deferred for ten years?
   (d) at the beginning of every three months for 12 years but deferred for 20 years?
   (e) at the end of each month in perpetuity?
   (f) at the beginning of each year in perpetuity?
9. If monthly deposits of $15.00 earn interest at 12% compounded quarterly, how long will it take to save $5000.00 if the deposits are made
   (a) at the end of each month?
   (b) at the beginning of each month?

10. In what period of time will payments of $450.00 accumulate to $20 000.00 at 6% compounded monthly if made
   (a) at the end of every three months?
   (b) at the beginning of every six months?

11. For how long can withdrawals of $2000.00 be made from a fund of $10 000.00 invested at 14.5% compounded annually if withdrawals are made
   (a) at the end of every three months?
   (b) at the beginning of every six months?
   (c) at the end of each month but deferred for fifteen years?
   (d) at the beginning of every three months but deferred for five years?

12. A debt of $20 000.00 is repaid by making payments of $3500.00. If interest is 15% compounded monthly, for how long will payments have to be made
   (a) at the end of every six months?
   (b) at the beginning of each year?
   (c) at the end of every three months with payments deferred for five years?
   (d) at the beginning of every six months with payments deferred for three years?

13. What is the rate of interest compounded quarterly at which payments of $400.00 made at the beginning of every six months accumulate to $8400.00 in eight years?

14. A $60 000.00 mortgage with a 25-year term is repaid by making monthly payments of $480.00. What is the rate of interest compounded semi-annually on the mortgage?

15. Contributions of $500.00 are made at the end of every three months into an RRSP. What is the accumulated balance after twenty years if interest is 6% compounded semi-annually?

16. If you save $25.00 at the beginning of each month and interest is 4% compounded quarterly, how much will you accumulate in thirty years?

17. A property was bought for quarterly payments of $1350.00 for ten years. If the first payment was made on the date of purchase and interest is 15.5% compounded annually, what was the purchase price of the property?

18. A 35-year mortgage is amortized by payments of $761.50 made at the end of each month. If interest is 13.5% compounded semi-annually, what is the mortgage principal?

19. What sum of money invested today in a retirement fund will permit withdrawals of $800.00 at the end of each month for twenty years if interest is 12% compounded semi-annually and the payments are deferred for fifteen years?

20. A lease requires semi-annual payments of $6000.00 for five years. If the first payment is due in four years and interest is 21% compounded monthly, what is the cash value of the lease?

21. The semi-annual dividend per preferred share issued by InterCity Trust is $7.50. If comparable investments yield 14% compounded quarterly, what should be the selling price of these shares?

22. A fund to provide an annual scholarship of $4000.00 is to be set up. If the first payment is due in three years and interest is 11% compounded quarterly, what sum of money must be deposited in the scholarship fund today?

23. How much must be contributed into an RRSP at the end of each year for 25 years to accumulate to $100 000.00 if interest is 8% compounded quarterly?

24. Kelly Associates are the makers of a ten-year $75 000.00 promissory note bearing interest at 16% compounded semi-annually. To pay off the note on its due date, the company is making payments at the beginning of every three months into a fund paying 13.5% compounded monthly. What is the size of the monthly payments?

25. A debt of $40 000.00 is to be repaid in instalments due at the end of each month for seven years. If the payments are deferred for three years and interest is 17% compounded quarterly, what is the size of the monthly payments?

26. Redden Ogilvie bought his parents' farm for $200 000.00. The transfer agreement requires Redden to make quarterly payments for twenty years. If the first payment is due in five years and the rate of interest is 10% compounded annually, what is the size of the quarterly payments?

27. Preferred shares of Western Oil paying a quarterly dividend are to be offered at $55.65 per share. If money is worth 9% compounded semi-annually, what is the minimum quarterly dividend to make investment in such shares economically feasible?

28. A church congregation has raised $37 625.00 for future outreach work. If the money is invested in a fund paying 11% compounded quarterly, what annual payment can be made from the fund to its mission if the first payment is to be made four years from the date of investment in the fund?

29. For how long must $75.00 be deposited at the end of each month to accumulate to $8500.00 at 6% compounded quarterly?

30. Over what period of time will RRSP contributions of $1350.00 made at the beginning of each year amount to $125 000.00 if interest is 7% compounded quarterly?

31. A $60 000.00 mortgage is amortized by making monthly payments of $618.19. If interest is 12.5% compounded semi-annually, what is the term of the mortgage?

32. A lease contract valued at $50 000.00 requires semi-annual payments of $5200.00. If the first payment is due at the date of signing the contract and interest is 18% compounded monthly, what is the term of the lease?

33. An annuity provides payments of $3600.00 at the end of every three months. The annuity is bought for $33 500.00 and payments are deferred for twelve years. If interest is 10% compounded monthly, for how long will payments be received?

34. A retirement gratuity of $25 000.00 is invested in an income averaging annuity paying $1400.00 every three months. If the interest is 11.5% compounded semi-annually and the first payment is due in one year, for how long will payments be received?

Self-test

1. Monthly deposits of $480.00 were made at the end of each month for eight years. If interest is 9.5% compounded semi-annually, what amount can be withdrawn five years after the last deposit?

2. A loan was repaid in five years by quarterly payments of $1200.00 at 19.5% compounded semi-annually. How much interest was paid?

3. A mortgage of $95 000.00 is to be amortized by monthly payments over twenty-five years. If the payments are made at the end of each month and interest is 13.5% compounded semi-annually, what is the size of the monthly payments?

4. Sara Engel wants to withdraw $3000.00 at the beginning of every three months for thirty years starting at the date of her retirement. If she retires in twenty years and interest is 10% compounded quarterly, how much must Ms. Engel deposit into an account every month for the next twenty years starting now?

5. A bank pays a quarterly dividend of $0.75 per share. If comparable investments yield 13.5% compounded monthly, what is the sales value of the shares?

6. A lease requires monthly payments of $950.00 due in advance. If interest is 12% compounded quarterly and the cash value of the lease is $43 246.00, what is the term of the lease?

7. A $45 000.00 mortgage is repaid in twenty years by making monthly payments of $486.44. What is the nominal annual rate of interest compounded semi-annually?

8. For how long would you have to deposit $491.00 at the end of every three months to accumulate $20 000.00 at 6.0% compounded monthly?

9. Ken acquired his sister's share of their business by agreeing to make payments of $4000.00 at the end of each year for twelve years. If the payments are deferred for three years and money is worth 13% compounded quarterly, what is the cash value of the sister's share of the business?

10. A retirement annuity providing equal monthly payments for 25 years is purchased for $20 000.00. If the first payment is due twenty years after the date of purchase and interest is 8% compounded quarterly, what is the size of the monthly payments?

CASE STUDY

A house and associated expenses will take up a large percentage of a couple's income. Several options are available for paying these expenses. It is important to calculate all expenses before buying a house. The following examples illustrate typical monthly expenses and available payment options.

1. A house has a list price of \$128 000. A deposit of 5% is required and the balance can be financed with a mortgage of 9% p.a. compounded semi-annually over 25 years.

   (a) Calculate how much money would be saved by paying weekly rather than monthly.

   (b) Why is money saved?

   (c) Calculate how much more each weekly payment would need to be to bring the amortization period to 15 years.

2. Taxes may be paid monthly. The taxes are \$229.17 per month in advance. If the interest charged is 12% p.a. compounded quarterly, how much can be saved by paying the taxes in a lump sum at the beginning of the year?

3. A \$900 water softener can be bought by making monthly payments of \$29.90. The interest rate is 12% compounded semi-annually.

   (a) How many months before the softener is paid for?

   (b) How much interest is charged by using the payment plan?

4. The yearly utility bill will be \$2160.

   (a) Calculate the per-month payment if rates are 10% p.a.

   (b) How much would the couple save by paying cash at the beginning of the year?

5. The couple contributes \$125 at the end of each month into an RRSP paying 9% p.a. compounded semi-annually.

   (a) Calculate the amount in the fund at the end of the year.

   (b) How much will the fund be worth in forty years?

   (c) How much of the retirement fund is interest?

   (d) If house prices are expected to grow at 3% p.a. compounded monthly and car prices will grow at 4% p.a. compounded monthly, how much will a \$128 000 house and a \$26 000 car cost in forty years?

   (e) If the couple wants to buy this house and car, how much will be left in the RRSP fund?

6. The couple has a combined gross yearly income of \$47 000. Taxes and benefits amount to 28% of this total. How much money is left over per month after they pay their monthly expenses and investments?

Summary of formulae used

Formula 9.1

$$S = P(1 + i)^n$$

Finding the compound amount when n is a fractional value using the exact method

Formula 9.2B

$$P = S(1 + i)^{-n}$$

Finding the present value by means of the discount factor (the reciprocal of the compounding factor)

Formula 10.1

$$f = (1 + i)^m - 1$$

Finding the effective rate of interest f for a nominal annual rate compounded m times per year

Formula 11.2

$$A_n = R\left[\frac{1 - (1 + i)^{-n}}{i}\right]$$

Finding the present value (discounted value) of an ordinary annuity

Formula 13.1

$$S_{nc} = R\left[\frac{(1 + f)^n - 1}{f}\right]$$

where $f = (1 + i)^c - 1$

Formula for finding the amount of a general annuity using the equivalent effective rate of interest per payment period

Formula 13.2

$$A_{nc} = R\left[\frac{1 - (1 + f)^{-n}}{f}\right]$$

where $f = (1 + i)^c - 1$

Formula for finding the present value of a general annuity using the equivalent effective rate of interest per payment period

Formula 13.3

$$S_{nc}(\text{due}) = R(1 + f)\left[\frac{(1 + f)^n - 1}{f}\right]$$

where $f = (1 + i)^c - 1$

Formula for finding the amount of a general annuity due using the equivalent effective rate of interest per payment period

Formula 13.4

$$A_{nc}(\text{due}) = R(1 + f)\left[\frac{1 - (1 + f)^{-n}}{f}\right]$$

where $f = (1 + i)^c - 1$

Formula for finding the present value of a general annuity due using the equivalent effective rate of interest per payment period

Formula 13.5

$$A = \frac{R}{f} \text{ where } f = (1 + i)^c - 1$$

Formula for finding the present value of an ordinary general perpetuity

Formula 13.6

$$A = R + \frac{R}{f} \text{ where } f = (1 + i)^c - 1$$

Formula for finding the present value of a general perpetuity due

Glossary of terms

General annuity an annuity in which the length of the interest conversion period is different from the length of the payment period

General annuity due a general annuity in which the payments are made at the beginning of each payment period

General perpetuity a general annuity in which the payments continue forever

Ordinary general annuity a general annuity in which the payments are made at the end of each payment period

14 Amortization and sinking funds

Introduction

Amortization refers to the repayment of interest-bearing debts by a series of payments, usually equal in size, made at equal intervals of time. The periodic payments, when equal in size, form an annuity whose present value is equivalent to the original loan principal. Mortgages and many consumer loans are repaid by this method. An amortization schedule shows the allocation of each payment to first cover the interest due and then to reduce the principal.

In the sinking fund method of providing for the repayment of a future obligation, periodic payments are accumulated in a fund earmarked for this purpose. The payments, when equal in size, form an annuity whose accumulated value is the maturity value of the debt. A prime example of a sinking fund is a fund associated with the issue and redemption of corporate or municipal bonds.

Objectives

Upon completing this chapter, you will be able to

1. perform computations associated with amortization of debts involving simple annuities, including the size of the periodic payments, outstanding balance, interest due, and principal repaid, and construct complete or partial amortization schedules;
2. perform computations as in objective (1) associated with the amortization of debts when the payments form general annuities and construct complete or partial amortization schedules;
3. find the size of the final payment when all payments except the final payment are equal in size;
4. make computations associated with sinking funds when the payments form simple annuities, including the size of the periodic payments, accumulated balance, interest earned, and increase in the fund, and construct complete or partial sinking fund schedules.

14.1 *Amortization (simple annuities)*

A. Finding the periodic payment

An interest-bearing debt is **amortized** if both principal and interest are repaid by a series of equal payments made at equal intervals of time.

Example **14.1a** A debt of \$5000.00 with interest at 12% compounded annually is to be repaid by equal payments at the end of each year for six years. What is the size of the annual payments?

Solution

FIGURE 14.1 ***Graphic representation of method of solution and data***

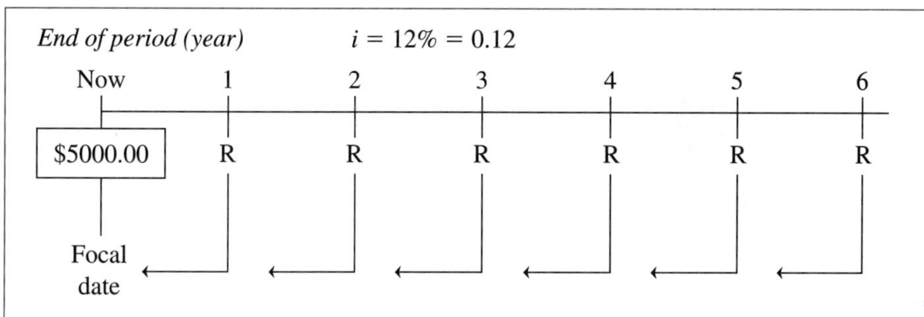

As Figure 14.1 shows, the equal annual payments (designated by R) form an ordinary annuity in which

$$A_n = 5000.00; \quad n = 6; \quad i = 12\% = 0.12$$

Using 'now' as the focal date, you can find the value of the annual payment R using the same method and formulae used in Chapter 11.

$$5000.00 = R\left(\frac{1 - 1.12^{-6}}{0.12}\right) \longleftarrow \text{using Formula 11.2}$$

$$5000.00 = R(4.1114073)$$

$$R = \$1216.13$$

Programmed solution

0	5000	12	6			
FV	PV	%*i*	N	CPT	PMT	1216.13

The annual payment is \$1216.13.

The basic problem in amortizing a debt is finding the size of the periodic payment. If the payment interval and the interest conversion period are equal in length, the problem involves finding the periodic payment for a simple annuity. Since debts are generally repaid by making payments at the end of the payment interval, the method and formulae used in Section 11.4 apply.

$$A_n = R\left[\frac{1-(1+i)^{-n}}{i}\right] \longleftarrow \textit{Formula } \mathbf{11.2}$$

Example **14.1b** A loan of $8000.00 made at 15% compounded monthly is amortized over five years by making equal monthly payments.

(i) What is the size of the monthly payment?

(ii) What is the total amount paid to amortize the loan?

(iii) What is the cost of financing?

Solution

(i) $A_n = 8000.00; \quad n = 5(12) = 60; \quad i = \frac{15\%}{12} = 1.25\%$

$$8000.00 = R\left(\frac{1 - 1.0125^{-60}}{0.0125}\right) \longleftarrow \text{using Formula 11.2}$$

$$8000.00 = R(42.034591)$$

$$R = \$190.32$$

Programmed solution

0	8000	1.25	60			
FV	PV	%i	N	CPT	PMT	190.32

The monthly payment is $190.32.

(ii) The total amount paid is 60(190.32) = $11 419.20

(iii) The cost of financing is 11 419.20 − 8000.00 = $3419.20

B. *Amortization schedules*

As previously discussed in Section 8.6, **amortization schedules** show in detail how a debt is repaid. Such schedules normally show the payment number (or payment date), the amount paid, the interest paid, the principal repaid, and the outstanding debt balance.

1. *Amortization schedule when all payments are equal (blended payments)*
When all payments are equal, you must first determine the size of the periodic payment as shown above.

***Example* 14.1c** A debt of $5000.00 is amortized by making equal payments at the end of every three months for two years. If interest is 15% compounded quarterly, construct an amortization schedule.

Solution

STEP 1 Determine the size of the quarterly payments.

$$A_n = 5000.00; \quad n\ 4(2) = 8; \quad i = \frac{15\%}{4} = 3.75\%$$

$$5000.00 = R\left(\frac{1 - 1.0375^{-8}}{0.0375}\right)$$

$$5000.00 = R(6.8027959)$$

$$R = \$734.99$$

Programmed solution

0	5000	3.75	8			
FV	PV	%i	N	CPT	PMT	743.99

STEP 2 Construct the amortization schedule as shown below.

Payment number	*Amount paid*	*Interest paid* i = *0.0375*	*Principal repaid*	*Outstanding principal balance*
0				5000.00
1	734.99	187.50	547.49	4452.51
2	734.99	166.97	568.02	3884.49
3	734.99	145.67	589.32	3295.17
4	734.99	123.57	611.42	2683.75
5	734.99	100.64	634.35	2049.40
6	734.99	76.85	658.14	1391.26
7	734.99	52.17	682.82	708.44
8	735.01	26.57	708.44	0.00
TOTAL	5879.94	879.94	5000.00	

Explanations regarding the construction of the amortization schedule

1. Payment number 0 is used to introduce the initial balance of the loan.
2. The interest included in the first payment is $0.0375 \times 5000.00 = \$187.50$. Since the amount paid is \$734.99, the amount available for repayment of principal is $734.99 - 187.50 = \$547.49$. The outstanding principal balance after the first payment is $5000.00 - 547.49 = \$4452.51$.
3. The interest included in the second payment is $0.0375 \times 4452.51 = \$166.97$. Since the amount paid is \$734.99, the amount available for repayment of principal is $734.99 - 166.97 = \$568.02$. The outstanding principal is $4452.51 - 568.02 = \$3884.49$.
4. Computation of interest, principal repaid, and outstanding balance for payments 3 to 7 are made in a similar manner.
5. The last payment of \$735.01 is slightly different from the other payments as a result of rounding in the amount paid or the interest paid. To allow for such rounding errors, the last payment is computed by adding the interest due in the last payment ($0.0375 \times 708.44 = \$26.57$) to the outstanding balance: $708.44 + 26.57 = \$735.01$.
6. The three totals provide useful information and can be used as a check on the accuracy of the schedule.

   (a) The total principal repaid must equal the original outstanding balance;

   (b) the total amount paid is the periodic payment times the number of such payments plus/minus any adjustment in the last payment $734.99 \times 8 + 0.02 = 5879.92 + 0.02 = \$5879.94$;

   (c) the total interest paid is the difference between the amount paid and the original principal $5879.94 - 5000.00 = \$879.94$.

2. *Amortization schedule when all payments except the final payment are equal*
When the size of the periodic payment is determined by agreement, usually because it is a convenient round figure rather than a computed blended payment, the size of the final payment will probably be different from the preceding agreed-upon payments. This final payment is obtained in the amortization schedule by adding the interest due on the outstanding balance to the outstanding balance.

This type of loan repayment schedule has been illustrated and explained in Section 8.6. The following example is included for review.

***Example* 14.1d** Sheridan Service borrowed \$15 000.00 from Peel Community Credit Union at 16% compounded quarterly. The loan agreement requires payment of \$2500.00 at the end of every three months. Construct an amortization schedule.

Solution

$$i = \frac{16\%}{4} = 4\% = 0.04$$

Payment number	*Amount paid*	*Interest paid* i = *0.04*	*Principal repaid*	*Outstanding principal balance*
0				15 000.00
1	2 500.00	600.00	1 900.00	13 100.00
2	2 500.00	524.00	1 976.00	11 124.00
3	2 500.00	444.96	2 055.04	9 068.96
4	2 500.00	362.76	2 137.24	6 931.72
5	2 500.00	277.27	2 222.73	4 708.99
6	2 500.00	188.36	2 311.64	2 397.35
7	2 493.24	95.89	2 397.35	0.00
TOTAL	17 493.24	2 493.24	15 000.00	

Note: After payment number 6, the outstanding principal is less than the agreed-upon payment. When this happens, the final payment will be the outstanding balance plus the interest due on the outstanding balance.

$$2397.35 + 2397.35 \times 0.04 = 2397.35 + 95.89 = \$2493.24$$

C. Finding the outstanding principal balance

For various reasons, such as early partial or full repayment or refinancing, either the borrower or the lender needs to know the outstanding balance at a certain time. This can be done by checking the amortization schedule, if available, or by direct mathematical computation. This computation is also useful for checking the accuracy of the schedule as it is developed.

1. *Finding the outstanding principal when all payments are equal*

Example **14.1e** For Example 14.1c, compute the outstanding balance just after the third payment has been made.

Solution

The loan history showing the quarterly payments of \$734.99 can be represented on a time diagram as shown in Figure 14.2.

FIGURE 14.2 ***Graphic representation of loan payments***

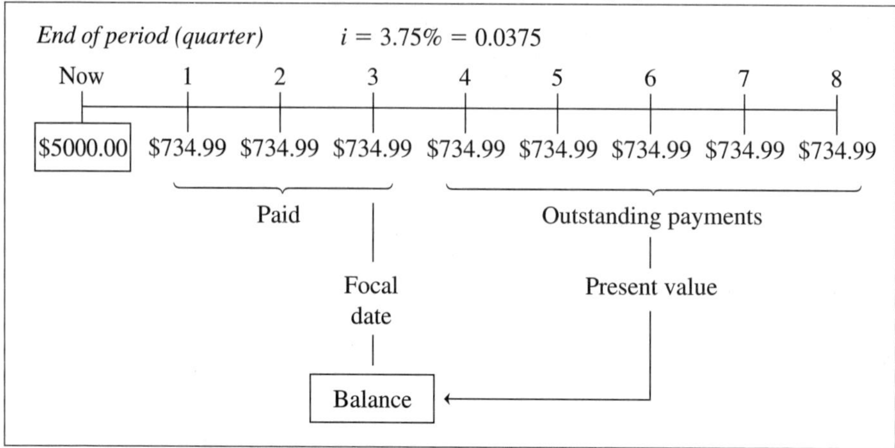

In the same way in which the original loan balance of $5000.00 equals the present value of the number of payments that are necessary to amortize the loan, the outstanding balance at the end of any payment interval just after a payment has been made is the present value of the outstanding payments.

$$\text{OUTSTANDING BALANCE} = \text{PRESENT VALUE OF THE OUTSTANDING PAYMENTS}$$

To answer this problem, use Formula 11.2. Since three of the eight payments have been made, five payments remain outstanding.

$$R = 734.99; \quad n = 5; \quad i = 3.75\%$$

$$A_3 = 734.99\left(\frac{1 - 1.0375^{-5}}{0.0375}\right) \longleftarrow \text{using Formula 11.2}$$

$$= 734.99(4.4832618)$$

$$= \$3295.15$$

Programmed solution

0	734.99	3.75	5			
FV	PMT	%i	N	CPT	PV	3295.15

The outstanding balance after the third payment is $3295.15.

Note: The amortization schedule shows $3295.17; the difference is due to rounding.

Example **14.1f** You borrow $7500.00 from your credit union at 13.5% compounded monthly. If the loan is amortized over five years, what is the loan balance after two years?

Solution

First determine the size of the monthly payment.

$$A_n = 7500.00; \quad n = 5(12) = 60; \quad i = \frac{13.5\%}{12} = 1.125\%$$

$$7500.00 = R\left(\frac{1 - 1.01125^{-60}}{0.01125}\right)$$

$$7500.00 = R(43.459657)$$

$$R = \$172.57$$

0	7500	1.125	60			
FV	PV	%i	N	CPT	PMT	172.57

Now determine the balance after two years.

After two years, 24 of the 60 payments have been made; 36 payments remain outstanding.

$$R = 172.57; \quad n = 36; \quad i = 1.125\%$$

$$A_{24} = 172.57\left(\frac{1 - 1.01125^{-36}}{0.01125}\right)$$

$$= 172.57(29.467851)$$

$$= \$5085.27$$

172.57	0	1.125	36			
PMT	FV	%i	N	CPT	PV	5085.27

The outstanding balance after two years is \$5085.27.

The method used in Examples 14.1e and 14.1f is sometimes called the **prospective method** of finding the outstanding balance because it considers the future prospects of the debt—the payments that remain outstanding.

Alternatively, the outstanding balance can be found by the **retrospective method** which considers the payments that have been made. This method finds the outstanding balance by deducting the accumulated value of the payments that have been made from the accumulated value of the original debt.

OUTSTANDING BALANCE = ACCUMULATED VALUE OF THE ORIGINAL DEBT — ACCUMULATED VALUE OF THE PAYMENTS MADE

For Example 14.1e

The accumulated value of the original debt at the end of three payment intervals

$S = 5000.00(1.0375^3)$ ⟵ using Formula 9.1

$= 5000.00(1.1167715)$

$= \$5583.86$

The accumulated value of the payments made

$$S_3 = 734.99\left(\frac{1.0375^3 - 1}{0.0375}\right) \longleftarrow \text{using Formula 11.1}$$

$$= 734.99(3.1139063)$$

$$= \$2288.69$$

Programmed solution

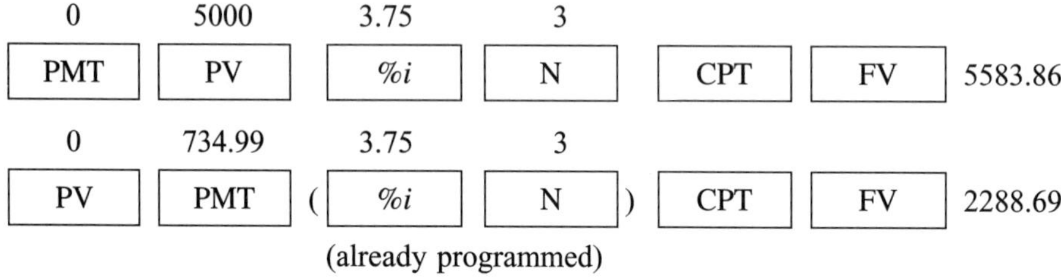

The outstanding balance is 5583.86 − 2288.69 = \$3295.17.

For Example 14.1f
The accumulated value of the debt after two years (24 payments)

$$S = 7500.00(1.01125^{24})$$

$$= 7500.00(1.3079912)$$

$$= \$9809.93$$

The accumulated value of the 24 payments made

$$S_{24} = 172.57\left(\frac{1.01125^{24} - 1}{0.01125}\right)$$

$$= 172.57(27.376998)$$

$$= \$4724.45$$

Programmed solution

0	7500	1.125	24			
PMT	PV	%i	N	CPT	FV	9809.93
0	172.57	1.125	24			
PV	PMT	%i	N	CPT	FV	4724.45

The outstanding balance is 9809.93 − 4724.45 = \$5085.48.

Note: The difference in the two methods—\$5085.48 versus \$5085.27—is due to rounding in the payment.

Because the prospective method is more direct, it is preferred when finding the outstanding balance of loans repaid by instalments that are all equal.

2. *Finding the outstanding balance when all payments except the final payment are equal*

When the last payment is different from the other payments, the retrospective method for finding the outstanding balance is preferable.

Example **14.1g** For Example 14.1d, compute the outstanding balance after four payments.

Solution

The accumulated value of the original debt after four payments

$$S = 15\ 000.00(1.04^4)$$
$$= 15\ 000.00(1.1698586)$$
$$= \$17\ 547.88$$

The accumulated value of the four payments

$$S_4 = 2500.00\left(\frac{1.04^4 - 1}{0.04}\right)$$
$$= 2500.00(4.2464639)$$
$$= \$10\ 616.16$$

Programmed solution

0	15 000	4	4			
PMT	PV	%i	N	CPT	FV	17 547.88
0	2500	4	4			
PV	PMT	%i	N	CPT	FV	10 616.16

The outstanding balance is 17 547.88 − 10 616.16 = \$6931.72.

Example **14.1h** A debt of \$25 000.00 with interest at 14% compounded semi-annually is amortized by making payments of \$2000.00 at the end of every six months. Determine the outstanding balance after five years.

Solution

$$A_n = P = 25\ 000.00; \quad i = \frac{14\%}{2} = 7\%$$

The accumulated value of the original principal after five years

$S = 25\ 000.00(1.07^{10})$

$= 25\ 000.00(1.9671514)$

$= \$49\ 178.78$

The accumulated value of the first ten payments

$S_{10} = 2000.00\left(\frac{1.07^{10} - 1}{0.07}\right)$

$= 2000.00(13.816448)$

$= \$27\ 632.90$

Programmed solution

0	25 000	7	10			
PMT	PV	%*i*	N	CPT	FV	49 178.78

0	2000	7	10			
PV	PMT	%*i*	N	CPT	FV	27 632.90

The outstanding balance after five years is 49 178.78 − 27 532.90 = \$21 545.88.

D. *Finding the interest paid and the principal repaid; constructing partial amortization schedules*

Apart from computing the outstanding balance at any one time, all the other information contained in an amortization schedule such as interest paid and principal repaid can also be computed.

Example **14.1i** For Example 14.1c, compute

(i) the interest paid by the fifth payment;
(ii) the principal repaid by the fifth payment.

Solution

(i) The interest due for any given payment period is based on the outstanding balance at the beginning of the period. This balance is the same as the outstanding balance at the end of the previous payment period.

To find the interest paid by the fifth payment, we need to know the outstanding balance after the fourth payment.

$$A_4 = 734.99\left(\frac{1 - 1.0375^{-4}}{0.0375}\right)$$

$$= 734.99(3.6513841)$$

$$= \$2683.73$$

Programmed solution

0	734.99	3.75	4			
FV	PMT	%i	N	CPT	PV	2683.73

Interest for Payment Period 5 is 2683.73(0.0375) = \$100.64.

(ii) Principal repaid = Amount paid − Interest paid
= 734.99 − 100.64
= \$634.35

Example **14.1j** Jackie Kim borrowed \$6000.00 from her trust company at 15% compounded monthly. The loan is amortized over five years.

(i) What is the interest included in the 20th payment?

(ii) What is the principal repaid by the 36th payment?

(iii) Construct a partial amortization schedule showing the details of the first three payments, the 20th payment, the 36th payment, and the last three payments, and determine the totals of amount paid, interest paid, and principal repaid.

Solution

$$A_n = 6000.00; \quad n = 5(12) = 60; \quad i = \frac{15\%}{12} = 1.25\%$$

$$6000.00 = R\left(\frac{1 - 1.0125^{-60}}{0.0125}\right)$$

$$6000.00 = R(42.034591)$$

$$R = \$142.74$$

Programmed solution

0	6000	1.25	60			
FV	PV	%i	N	CPT	PMT	142.74

(i) The outstanding balance after the 19th payment,

$$A_{19} = 142.74\left(\frac{1 - 1.0125^{-41}}{0.0125}\right)$$

$$= 142.74(31.927835)$$

$$= \$4557.38$$

Programmed solution

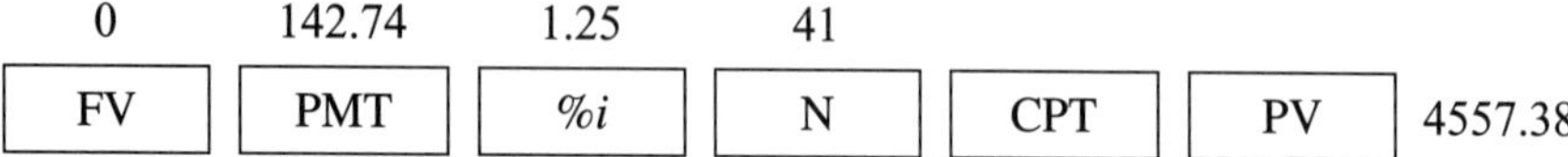

0	142.74	1.25	41			
FV	PMT	%i	N	CPT	PV	4557.38

The interest paid by the 20th payment is 4557.38(0.0125) = \$56.97.

(ii) The outstanding balance after the 35th payment,

$$A_{35} = 142.74\left(\frac{1 - 1.0125^{-25}}{0.0125}\right)$$

$$= 142.74(21.357268)$$

$$= \$3048.54$$

Programmed solution

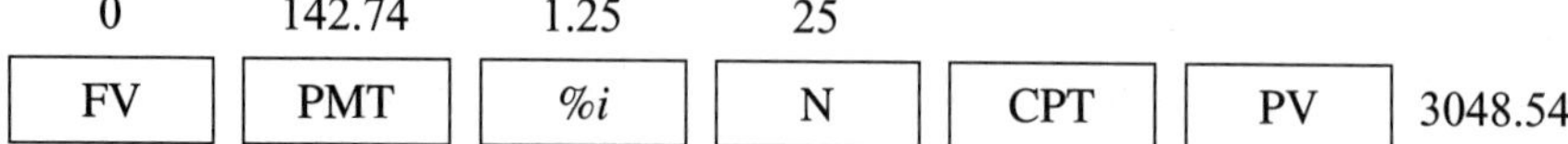

0	142.74	1.25	25			
FV	PMT	%i	N	CPT	PV	3048.54

The interest included in Payment 36 is 3048.54(0.0125) = \$38.11.
The principal repaid by Payment 36 is 142.74 − 38.11 = \$104.63.

(iii) We can develop the first three payments of the amortization schedule in the usual way. To show the details of the 20th payment, we need to know the outstanding balance after 19 payments (computed in part (i)). For the 36th payment, we need to know the outstanding balance after 35 payments (computed in part (ii)). Since there are 60 payments, the last three payments are Payments 58, 59, and 60. To show the details of these payments, we must determine the outstanding balance after Payment 57.

$$A_{57} = 142.74\left(\frac{1 - 1.0125^{-3}}{0.0125}\right)$$

$$= 142.74(2.9265336)$$

$$= \$417.73$$

Programmed solution

0	142.74	1.25	3			
FV	PMT	%i	N	CPT	PV	417.73

Partial amortization schedule

Payment number	*Amount paid*	*Interest paid* i = *0.0125*	*Principal repaid*	*Outstanding principal balance*
0				6000.00
1	142.74	75.00	67.74	5932.26
2	142.74	74.15	68.59	5863.67
3	142.74	73.30	69.44	5794.23
.	.	.	.	.
.	.	.	.	.
19	.	.	.	4557.38
20	142.74	56.97	85.77	4471.61
.	.	.	.	.
.	.	.	.	.
35	.	.	.	3048.54
36	142.74	38.11	104.63	2943.91
.	.	.	.	.
.	.	.	.	.
57	.	.	.	417.73
58	142.74	5.22	137.52	280.21
59	142.74	3.50	139.24	140.97
60	142.74	1.77	140.97	0.00
TOTAL	8564.40	2564.40	6000.00	

Note: The total principal repaid must be \$6000.00; the total amount paid is 142.74(60) = \$8564.40; the total interest paid is 8564.40 − 6000.00 = \$2564.40.

Example **14.1k** The Erin Construction Company borrowed \$75 000.00 at 14% compounded quarterly to buy construction equipment. Payments of \$3500.00 are to be made at the end of every three months.

(i) Determine the principal repaid in the 16th payment.

(ii) Construct a partial amortization schedule showing the details of the first three payments, the 16th payment, the last three payments, and the totals.

Solution

(i) Since the quarterly payments are not computed blended payments, the last payment will probably be different from the preceding equal payments. Use the retrospective method for finding the outstanding balance.

$$P = 75\,000.00; \quad R = 3500.00; \quad i = \frac{14\%}{4} = 3.5\% = 0.035$$

The accumulated value of the original principal after the 15th payment,

$$S = 75\,000.00(1.035^{15})$$
$$= 75\,000.00(1.6753488)$$
$$= \$125\,651.16$$

Programmed solution

0	75 000	3.5	15			
PMT	PV	%i	N	CPT	FV	125 651.16

The accumulated value of the first 15 payments

$$S_{15} = 3500.00\left(\frac{1.035^{15} - 1}{0.035}\right)$$
$$= 3500.00(19.295681)$$
$$= \$67\,534.88$$

Programmed solution

0	3500	3.5	15			
PV	PMT	%i	N	CPT	FV	67 534.88

The outstanding principal after the 15th payment

$$= 125\,651.16 - 67\,534.88$$
$$= \$58\,116.28$$

The interest included in the 16th payment is 58 116.28(0.035) = \$2034.07. The principal repaid by the 16th payment is 3500.00 − 2034.07 = \$1465.93.

(ii) To show details of the last three payments, we need to know the number of payments required to amortize the loan principal.

$$A_n = 75\,000.00; \quad R = 3500.00; \quad i = 3.5\%$$

$$75\,000.00 = 3500.00\left(\frac{1 - 1.035^{-n}}{0.035}\right)$$

$$0.75 = 1 - 1.035^{-n}$$

$$1.035^{-n} = 0.25$$

$$-n \ln 1.035 = \ln 0.25$$

$$-n(0.344014) = -1.3862944$$

$$n = 40.297584$$

Programmed solution

0	75 000	3500	3.5			
FV	PV	PMT	%i	CPT	N	40.297584

41 payments (40 payments of \$3500.00 each plus a final payment) are required. This means the amortization schedule should show details of Payments 39, 40, and 41. To do so, we need to know the outstanding balance after 38 payments. The accumulated value of the original loan principal after 38 payments

$$\begin{aligned} S &= 75\,000.00(1.035^{38}) \\ &= 75\,000.00(3.6960113) \\ &= \$277\,200.85 \end{aligned}$$

Programmed solution

0	75 000	3.5	38			
PMT	PV	%i	N	CPT	FV	277 200.85

The accumulated value of the first 38 payments

$$\begin{aligned} S_{38} &= 3500.00\left(\frac{1.035^{38} - 1}{0.035}\right) \\ &= 3500.00(77.028895) \\ &= \$269\,601.13 \end{aligned}$$

Programmed solution

0	3500	3.5	38			
PV	PMT	%i	N	CPT	FV	269 601.13

The outstanding balance after the 38th payment

$$= 277\,200.85 - 269\,601.13$$

$$= \$7599.72$$

Partial amortization schedule

Payment number	*Amount paid*	*Interest paid* i = *0.035*	*Principal repaid*	*Outstanding principal balance*
0				75 000.00
1	3 500.00	2 625.00	875.00	74 125.00
2	3 500.00	2 594.38	905.62	73 219.38
3	3 500.00	2 562.68	937.32	72 282.06
.	.	.	.	.
.	.	.	.	.
.	.	.	.	.
15	.	.	.	58 116.28
16	3 500.00	2 034.07	1 465.93	56 650.35
.	.	.	.	.
.	.	.	.	.
.	.	.	.	.
38	.	.	.	7 599.72
39	3 500.00	265.99	3 234.01	4 365.71
40	3 500.00	152.80	3 347.20	1 018.51
41	1 054.16	35.65	1 018.51	0.00
TOTAL	141 041.16	66 041.16	75 000.00	

E. Computer application—Amortization schedule

A computer solution for the amortization of loans illustrated in Section 14.1 is provided by Program 4 (see the Solutions Manual).

Exercise 14.1

A. For each of the following debts amortized by equal payments made at the end of each payment interval, compute (a) the size of the periodic payments; (b) the outstanding principal at the time indicated; (c) the interest paid; and (d) the principal repaid by the payment following the time indicated for finding the outstanding principal.

	Debt principal	*Repayment period*	*Payment interval*	*Interest rate*	*Conversion period*	*Outstanding principal required after*
1.	$12 000.00	8 years	3 months	12%	quarterly	20th payment
2.	$8 000.00	5 years	1 month	15%	monthly	30th payment
3.	$15 000.00	10 years	6 months	8%	semi-annually	15th payment
4.	$9 600.00	7 years	3 months	16%	quarterly	12th payment
5.	$5 500.00	4 years	1 month	21%	monthly	14th payment
6.	$24 000.00	12 years	6 months	7%	semi-annually	8th payment

B. For each of the following debts repaid by periodic payments as shown, compute (a) the number of payments required to amortize the debts; (b) the outstanding principal at the time indicated.

	Debt principal	*Debt payment*	*Payment interval*	*Interest rate*	*Conversion period*	*Outstanding principal required after*
1.	\$12 000.00	\$750.00	3 months	8%	quarterly	16th payment
2.	\$7 800.00	\$175.00	1 month	12%	monthly	24th payment
3.	\$21 000.00	\$2000.00	6 months	15%	semi-annually	10th payment
4.	\$15 000.00	\$800.00	3 months	20%	quarterly	12th payment

C. Answer each of the following questions.

1. Mr. and Mrs. Good purchased a ski chalet for \$36 000.00. They paid \$4000.00 down and agreed to make equal payments at the end of every three months for fifteen years. Interest is 14% compounded quarterly.

   (a) What size payment are the Goods making every three months?

   (b) How much will they owe after ten years?

   (c) How much will they have paid in total after fifteen years?

   (d) How much interest will they pay in total?

2. A contractor's price for a new building was \$96 000.00. Slade Inc., the buyers of the building, paid \$12 000.00 down and financed the balance by making equal payments at the end of every six months for twelve years. Interest is 16% compounded semi-annually.

   (a) What is the size of the semi-annual payment?

   (b) How much will Slade Inc. owe after eight years?

   (c) What is the total cost of the building for Slade Inc.?

   (d) What is the total interest included in the payments?

3. A loan of \$10 000.00 with interest at 15% compounded annually is to be amortized by equal payments at the end of each year for seven years. Find the size of the annual payments and construct an amortization schedule showing the total paid and the cost of financing.

4. A loan of \$8000.00 is repaid by equal payments made at the end of every three months for two years. If interest is 14% compounded quarterly, find the size of the quarterly payments and construct an amortization schedule showing the total paid and the total cost of the loan.

5. Hansco borrowed \$9200.00 paying interest at 13% compounded annually. If the loan is repaid by payments of \$2000.00 made at the end of each year, construct an amortization schedule showing the total paid and the total interest paid.

6. Pinto Bros. are repaying a loan of \$14 500.00 by making payments of \$2600.00 at the end of every six months. If interest is 17% compounded semi-annually, construct an amortization schedule showing the total paid and the total cost of the loan.

7. For Question 3, find the interest included in the fourth payment. Verify your answer by checking the amortization schedule.

8. For Question 4, find the principal repaid by the fifth payment. Verify your answer by checking the amortization schedule.

9. For Question 5, find the principal repaid by the fourth payment. Verify your answer by checking the amortization schedule.

10. For Question 6, find the interest included in the fifth payment. Verify your answer by checking the amortization schedule.

11. Amex Corporation borrowed \$85 000.00 at 18% compounded quarterly for eight years to buy a warehouse. Equal payments are made at the end of every three months.

    (a) Determine the size of the quarterly payments.

    (b) Compute the interest included in the 16th payment.

    (c) Determine the principal repaid by the 20th payment.

    (d) Construct a partial amortization schedule showing details of the first three payments, the last three payments, and totals.

12. Mr. Brabham borrowed \$7500.00 at 15% compounded monthly. He agreed to repay the loan in equal monthly payments over five years.

    (a) What is the size of the monthly payment?

    (b) How much of the 25th payment is interest?

    (c) What is the principal repaid by the 40th payment?

    (d) Prepare a partial amortization schedule showing details of the first three payments, the last three payments, and totals.

13. Thornhill Equipment Co. borrowed \$24 000.00 at 17% compounded semi-annually. It is to repay the loan by payments of \$2500.00 at the end of every six months.

    (a) How many payments are required to repay the loan?

    (b) How much of the sixth payment is interest?

    (c) How much of the principal will be repaid by the tenth payment?

    (d) Construct a partial amortization schedule showing details of the first three payments, the last three payments, and totals.

14. Locust Inc. owes \$16 000.00 to be repaid by monthly payments of \$475.00. Interest is 18% compounded monthly.

    (a) How many payments will Locust Inc. have to make?

(b) How much interest is included in the 18th payment?

(c) How much of the principal will be repaid by the 30th payment?

(d) Construct a partial amortization schedule showing details of the first three payments, the last three payments, and totals.

14.2 *Amortization involving general annuities*

A. Finding the periodic payment and constructing amortization schedules

If the length of the payment interval is different from the length of the interest conversion period, the equal debt payments form a general annuity. The amortization of such debts involves the same principles and methods discussed in Section 14.1 except that general annuity formulae are applicable. Provided that the payments are made at the end of the payment intervals, use Formula 13.2.

$$A_{nc} = R\left[\frac{1-(1+f)^{-n}}{f}\right] \quad \text{where } f = (1+i)^c - 1 \qquad \longleftarrow \textit{Formula } \textbf{13.2}$$

Example **14.2a** A debt of \$30 000.00 with interest at 12% compounded quarterly is to be repaid by equal payments at the end of each year for seven years.

(i) Compute the size of the yearly payments.

(ii) Construct an amortization schedule.

Solution

(i) $A_{nc} = 30\,000.00; \quad n = 7; \quad c = 4; \quad i = \frac{12\%}{4} = 3\%$

$$f = 1.03^4 - 1 = 1.1255088 - 1 = 0.1255088 = 12.55088\%$$

$$30\,000.00 = R\left(\frac{1-1.1255088^{-7}}{0.1255088}\right) \longleftarrow \text{using Formula 13.2}$$

$$30\,000.00 = R(4.4851295)$$

$$R = \$6688.77$$

Programmed solution

0	30 000	12.55088	7			
FV	PMT	%*i*	N	CPT	PV	6688.77

(ii) ***Amortization schedule***

Payment number	*Amount paid*	*Interest paid* i = *0.1255088*	*Principal repaid*	*Outstanding principal balance*
0				30 000.00
1	6688.77	3765.26	2923.51	27 076.49
2	6688.77	3398.34	3290.43	23 786.06
3	6688.77	2985.36	3703.41	20 082.65
4	6688.77	2520.55	4168.22	15 914.43
5	6688.77	1997.40	4691.37	11 223.06
6	6688.77	1408.59	5280.18	5 942.88
7	6688.76	745.88	5942.88	0.00
TOTAL	46 821.38	16 821.38	30 000.00	

B. Finding the outstanding principal

1. *Finding the outstanding principal when all payments are equal*
When all payments are equal, the prospective method used in Section 14.1 is the more direct method.

***Example* 14.2b** For Example 14.2a, compute the outstanding balance after three payments.

Solution

The outstanding balance after three payments is the present value of the remaining four payments.

$$R = 6688.77; \quad n = 4; \quad c = 4; \quad i = 3\%; \quad f = 12.55088\%$$

$$A_{nc} = 6688.77\left(\frac{1 - 1.1255088^{-4}}{0.1255088}\right)$$

$$= 6688.77(3.0024432)$$

$$= \$20\,082.65$$

Programmed solution

0	6688.77	12.55088	4			
FV	PMT	%*i*	N	CPT	PV	20 082.65

The outstanding balance after three payments is $20 082.65.

Example 14.2c A $25 000.00 mortgage amortized by monthly payments over twenty years is renewable after five years.

(i) If interest is 14.5% compounded semi-annually, what is the outstanding balance at the end of the five-year term?

(ii) If the mortgage is renewed for a further three-year term at 13% compounded semi-annually, what is the size of the new monthly payment?

(iii) What is the payout figure at the end of the three-year term?

Solution

(i) $A_{nc} = 25\ 000.00; \quad n = 20(12) = 240; \quad c = \frac{2}{12} = \frac{1}{6};$

$$i = \frac{14.5\%}{2} = 7.25\% = 0.0725;$$

$$f = 1.0725^{\frac{1}{6}} - 1 = 1.0117337 - 1 = 0.0117337 = 1.17337\%$$

$$25\ 000.00 = R\left(\frac{1 - 1.0117337^{-240}}{0.0117337}\right)$$

$$25\ 000.00 = R(80.040513)$$

$$R = 312.34$$

The number of outstanding payments after five years is 15(12) = 180.

$$A_{nc} = 312.34\left(\frac{1 - 1.0117337^{-180}}{0.0117337}\right)$$

$$= 312.34(74.785918)$$

$$= \$23\ 358.63$$

Programmed solution

0	25 000	1.17337	240			
FV	PV	%i	N	CPT	PMT	312.34
0	312.34	1.17337	180			
FV	PMT	%i	N	CPT	PV	23 358.63

The outstanding balance after five years is $23 358.63.

(ii) After the five-year term is up, the outstanding balance of \$23 358.63 is to be amortized over the remaining 15 years.

$$A_{nc} = 23\,358.63; \quad n = 15(12) = 180; \quad c = \frac{1}{6};$$

$$i = \frac{13\%}{2} = 6.5\% = 0.065;$$

$$f = 1.065^{\frac{1}{6}} - 1 = 1.0105511 - 1 = 0.0105511 = 1.05511\%$$

$$23\,358.63 = R\left(\frac{1 - 1.0105511^{-180}}{0.0105511}\right)$$

$$23\,358.63 = R(80.447976)$$

$$R = \$290.36$$

Programmed solution

0	23 358.63	1.05511	180			
FV	PV	%i	N	CPT	PMT	290.36

The monthly payment for the three-year term will be \$290.36.

(iii) At the end of the three-year term, the number of outstanding payments is 144.

$$A_{nc} = 290.36\left(\frac{1 - 1.0105511^{-144}}{0.0105511}\right)$$

$$= 290.36(73.868965)$$

$$= \$21\,448.59$$

Programmed solution

0	290.36	1.05511	144			
FV	PMT	%i	N	CPT	PV	21 448.59

The outstanding balance at the end of the three-year term will be \$21 448.59.

2. *Finding the outstanding balance when all payments except the final payment are equal*
When the final payment is different from the preceding payments, use the retrospective method for finding the outstanding balance. Since this method requires finding the amount of an ordinary annuity, Formula 13.1 applies.

$$S_{nc} = R\left[\frac{(1 + f)^n - 1)}{f}\right]$$
where $f = (1 + i)^c - 1$

←——*Formula* **13.1**

***Example* 14.2d** A loan of $12 000.00 with interest at 12% compounded monthly and amortized by payments of $700.00 at the end of every three months is repaid in full after three years. What is the payout figure just after the last regular payment?

Solution

Accumulate the value of the original principal after three years.

$$P = 12\ 000.00; \quad n = 3(12) = 36; \quad i = \frac{12\%}{12} = 1\% = 0.01$$

$$\begin{aligned} S &= 12\ 000.00(1.01^{36}) \\ &= 12\ 000.00(1.4307688) \\ &= \$17\ 169.23 \end{aligned}$$

Programmed solution

0	12 000	1	36			
PMT	PV	%i	N	CPT	FV	17 169.23

Accumulate the value of the twelve payments made.

$$R = 700.00; \quad n = 3(4) = 12; \quad c = \frac{12}{4} = 3; \quad i = 1\%$$

$$f = 1.01^3 - 1 = 1.030301 - 1 = 0.030301 = 3.0301\%$$

$$\begin{aligned} S_{nc} &= 700.00\left(\frac{1.030301^{12} - 1}{0.030301}\right) \\ &= 700.00(14.216322) \\ &= \$9951.43 \end{aligned}$$

Programmed solution

0	700	3.0301	12			
PV	PMT	%i	N	CPT	FV	9951.43

The outstanding balance after three years is 17 169.23 − 9951.43 = $7217.80. The payout figure after three years is $7217.80.

C. Finding the interest paid and the principal repaid; constructing partial amortization schedules

***Example* 14.2e** Mr. and Mrs. Evans took out a $40 000.00, 25-year mortgage renewable after five years. The mortgage bears interest at 12.5% compounded semi-annually and is amortized by equal monthly payments.

(i) What is the interest included in the 13th payment?
(ii) How much of the principal is repaid by the 13th payment?
(iii) What is the total interest cost during the first year?
(iv) What is the total interest cost during the fifth year?
(v) What will be the total interest paid by the Evans during the initial five-year term?

Solution

(i) First find the size of the monthly payment.

$$A_{nc} = 40\ 000.00; \quad n = 300; \quad c = \frac{1}{6}; \quad i = 6.25\%$$

$$f = 1.0625^{\frac{1}{6}} - 1 = 1.0101553 - 1 = 0.0101553 = 1.01553\%$$

$$40\ 000.00 = R\left(\frac{1 - 1.0101553^{-300}}{0.0101553}\right)$$

$$40\ 000.00 = R(93.718894)$$

$$R = \$426.81$$

Programmed solution

0	40 000	1.01553	300			
FV	PV	%*i*	N	CPT	PMT	426.81

Now find the outstanding balance after one year.

$$R = 426.81; \quad f = 1.01553\%$$

The number of outstanding payments after one year $n = 288$.

$$A_{nc} = R\left(\frac{1 - 1.0101553^{-288}}{0.0101553}\right)$$

$$= 426.81(93.106352)$$

$$= \$39\ 738.72$$

Programmed solution

0	426.81	1.01553	288			
FV	PMT	%*i*	N	CPT	PV	39 738.72

The interest in the 13th payment is 39 738.72(0.0101553) = \$403.56.

(ii) The principal repaid in the 13th payment is 426.81 − 403.56 = \$23.25.

(iii) The total amount paid during the first year is 426.81(12) = \$5121.72
The total principal repaid is 40 000.00 − 39 738.72 = 261.28

The total cost of interest for the first year = \$4860.44

(iv) After four years, $n = 300 - 48 = 252$.

$$A_{nc} = 426.81\left(\frac{1 - 1.0101553^{-252}}{0.0101553}\right)$$

$$= 426.81(90.752936)$$

$$= \$38\,734.26$$

Programmed solution

0	426.81	1.01553	252			
FV	PMT	%i	N	CPT	PV	38 734.26

After five years, $n = 300 - 60 = 240$.

$$A_{nc} = 426.81\left(\frac{1 - 1.0101553^{-240}}{0.0101553}\right)$$

$$= 426.81(89.7578064)$$

$$= \$38\,309.64$$

Programmed solution

0	426.81	1.01553	240			
FV	PMT	%i	N	CPT	PV	38 309.64

The total amount paid during the fifth year is 426.81(12) = \$5 121.72
The total principal repaid in Year 5 is 38 734.26 − 38 309.64 = 424.62

The total cost of interest in Year 5 = \$4 697.10

(v) The total amount paid during the first five years is 426.81(60) = \$25 608.60
The total principal repaid is 40 000.00 − 38 309.64 = 1 690.36

The total cost of interest for the first five years = \$23 918.24

Example **14.2f** Confederated Venture Company financed a project by borrowing \$120 000.00 at 17% compounded annually and is repaying the loan at the rate of \$7000.00 due at the end of every three months.

(i) Compute the interest paid and the principal repaid by the tenth payment.

(ii) Construct a partial amortization schedule showing the first three payments, the tenth payment, the last three payments, and the totals.

Solution

(i) Accumulate the value of the original loan after nine payments.

$$P = 120\,000.00; \quad n = 9; \quad c = \frac{1}{4} = 0.25; \quad i = 17\% = 0.17;$$

$$f = 1.17^{0.25} - 1 = 1.0400314 - 1 = 0.0400314 = 4.00314\%$$

$$\begin{aligned} S &= 120\,000.00(1.0400314^9) \\ &= 120\,000.00(1.4236986) \\ &= \$170\,843.85 \end{aligned}$$

Programmed solution

0	120 000	4.00314	9			
PMT	PV	%i	N	CPT	FV	170 843.85

Accumulate the value of the first nine payments.

$$R = 7000.00; \quad n = 9$$

$$\begin{aligned} S_{nc} &= 7000.00\left(\frac{1.0400314^9 - 1}{0.0400314}\right) \\ &= 7000.00(10.584157) \\ &= \$74\,089.10 \end{aligned}$$

Programmed solution

0	7000	4.00314	9			
PV	PMT	%i	N	CPT	FV	74 089.10

The outstanding balance after nine payments is 170 843.85 − 74 089.10 = \$96 754.75.

The interest included in the tenth payment is 96 754.75(0.0400314) = \$3873.23.

The principal repaid by the tenth payment is 7000.00 − 3873.23 = \$3126.77.

(ii) To show the details of the last three payments, we need to know the number of payments required to amortize the loan.

$$A_{nc} = 120\ 000.00; \quad R = 7000.00; \quad f = 4.00314\%$$

$$120\ 000.00 = 7000.00\left(\frac{1 - 1.0400314^{-n}}{0.0400314}\right)$$

$$0.6862526 = 1 - 1.0400314^{-n}$$

$$1.0400314^{-n} = 0.3137474$$

$$-n \ln 1.0400314 = \ln 0.3137474$$

$$-n(0.0392509) = -1.159167$$

$$n = 29.532236$$

Programmed solution

0	120 000	7000	4.00314			
FV	PV	PMT	%*i*	CPT	N	29.532236

30 payments (29 payments of \$7000.00 plus a final payment) are required. This means the amortization schedule needs to show details of Payments 28, 29, and 30. To do so, we need to know the outstanding balance after 27 payments.

Accumulate the value of the original principal after 27 payments.

$$S = 120\ 000.00(1.0400314^{27})$$
$$= 120\ 000.00(2.8857200)$$
$$= \$346\ 286.40$$

Programmed solution

0	120 000	4.00314	27			
PMT	PV	%*i*	N	CPT	FV	346 286.40

Accumulate the value of the first 27 payments.

$$S_{nc} = 7000.00\left(\frac{1.0400314^{27} - 1}{0.0400314}\right)$$
$$= 7000.00(47.106022)$$
$$= \$329\ 742.15$$

Programmed solution

0	7000	4.00314	27			
PV	PMT	%i	N	CPT	FV	329 742.15

The outstanding balance after 27 payments is 346 286.40 − 329 742.15 = $16 544.25.

Partial amortization schedule

Payment number	*Amount paid*	*Interest paid* f = *0.0400314*	*Principal repaid*	*Outstanding principal balance*
0				120 000.00
1	7 000.00	4 803.77	2 196.23	117 803.77
2	7 000.00	4 715.85	2 284.15	115 519.62
3	7 000.00	4 624.41	2 375.59	113 144.03
.	.	.	.	.
.	.	.	.	.
9	.	.	.	96 754.75
10	7 000.00	3 873.23	3 126.77	93 627.98
.	.	.	.	.
.	.	.	.	.
.	.	.	.	.
27	.	.	.	16 544.25
28	7 000.00	662.29	6 337.71	10 206.54
29	7 000.00	408.58	6 591.42	3 615.12
30	3 759.84	144.72	3 615.12	0.00
TOTAL	206 759.84	86 759.84	120 000.00	

D. Computer application—Amortization schedule

A computer solution for the amortization of loans involving a general annuity illustrated in Section 14.2 is provided by Program 4 (see the Solutions Manual).

Exercise 14.2

A. For each of the following debts amortized by equal payments made at the end of each payment interval, compute (a) the size of the periodic payments; (b) the outstanding principal at the time indicated; (c) the interest paid and (d) the principal repaid by the payment following the time indicated for finding the outstanding principal.

	Debt principal	*Repayment period*	*Payment interval*	*Interest rate*	*Conversion period*	*Outstanding principal required after*
1.	$36 000.00	20 years	6 months	8%	quarterly	25th payment
2.	$15 000.00	10 years	3 months	18%	monthly	15th payment
3.	$8 500.00	5 years	1 month	15%	semi-annually	30th payment
4.	$9 600.00	7 years	3 months	9%	semi-annually	10th payment
5.	$45 000.00	15 years	6 months	21%	monthly	12th payment
6.	$60 000.00	25 years	1 month	14%	semi-annually	120th payment

B. For each of the following debts repaid by periodic payments as indicated, compute (a) the number of payments required to amortize the debts; (b) the outstanding principal at the time indicated.

	Debt principal	*Debt payment*	*Payment interval*	*Interest rate*	*Conversion period*	*Outstanding principal required after*
1.	$6 000.00	$400.00	3 months	15%	monthly	10th payment
2.	$8 400.00	$1200.00	6 months	10%	quarterly	5th payment
3.	$23 500.00	$1800.00	3 months	7%	annually	14th payment
4.	$18 200.00	$430.00	1 month	18%	semi-annually	48th payment

C. Answer each of the following questions.

1. A $36 000.00 mortgage amortized by monthly payments over 25 years is renewable after three years.

(a) If interest is 13% compounded semi-annually, what is the size of the monthly payments?

(b) What is the mortgage balance at the end of the three-year term?

(c) How much interest will have been paid during the first three years?

(d) If the mortgage is renewed for a further three-year term at 15% compounded semi-annually, what will be the size of the monthly payments for the renewal period?

2. Fink and Associates bought a property valued at $80 000.00 for $15 000.00 down and a mortgage amortized over fifteen years. The firm makes equal payments due at the end of every three months. Interest on the mortgage is 13.5% compounded annually and the mortgage is renewable after five years.

(a) What is the size of the quarterly payments?

(b) What is the outstanding principal at the end of the five-year term?

(c) What is the cost of the mortgage for the first five years?

(d) If the mortgage is renewed for a further five years at 18% compounded semi-annually, what will be the size of the quarterly payments?

3. A loan of $10 000.00 with interest at 14% compounded quarterly is repaid by payments of $950.00 made at the end of every six months.

(a) How many payments will be required to amortize the loan?

(b) If the loan is repaid in full after six years, what is the payout figure?

(c) If paid out, what is the total cost of the loan?

4. The owner of the Blue Goose Motel borrowed $12 500.00 at 16% compounded semi-annually and agreed to repay the loan by making payments of $700.00 at the end of every three months.

(a) How many payments will be needed to repay the loan?

(b) How much will be owed at the end of five years?

(c) How much of the payments made at the end of five years will be interest?

5. A loan of $16 000.00 with interest at 19% compounded quarterly is repaid in seven years by equal payments made at the end of each year. Find the size of the annual payments and construct an amortization schedule showing the total paid and the total interest.

6. A debt of $12 500.00 with interest at 17% compounded semi-annually is repaid by payments of $1900.00 made at the end of every three months. Construct an amortization schedule showing the total paid and the total cost of the debt.

7. For Question 5, determine the interest included in the fifth payment. Verify your answer by checking the amortization schedule.

8. For Question 6, find the principal repaid by the sixth payment. Verify your answer by checking the amortization schedule.

9. A $40 000.00 mortgage amortized by monthly payments over 25 years is renewable after five years.

(a) If interest is 8.5% compounded semi-annually, what is the size of the monthly payments?

(b) Find the total interest paid during the first year.

(c) Compute the interest included in the 48th payment.

(d) If the mortgage is renewed after five years at 10.5% compounded semi-annually, what is the size of the monthly payment for the renewal period?

(e) Construct a partial amortization schedule showing details of the first three payments for each of the two five-year terms.

10. A debt of $32 000.00 is repaid by payments of $2950.00 made at the end of every six months. Interest is 16% compounded quarterly.

(a) What is the number of payments needed to retire the debt?

(b) What is the cost of the debt for the first five years?

(c) What is the interest paid by the tenth payment?

(d) Construct a partial amortization schedule showing details of the first three payments, the last three payments, and totals.

14.3 *Finding the size of the final payment*

A. *Three methods for computing the final payment*

When all payments except the final payment are equal, three methods are available to compute the size of the final payment.

METHOD 1 Compute the value of n and determine the present value of the outstanding fractional payment. If the final payment is made at the end of the payment interval, add interest for one payment interval to the present value.

METHOD 2 Use the retrospective method to compute the outstanding principal after the last of the equal payments. If the final payment is made at the end of the payment interval, add to the outstanding principal the interest for one payment interval.

METHOD 3 Assume all payments to be equal, compute the overpayment, and subtract the overpayment from the size of the equal payments. This method must not be used when the payments are made at the beginning of the payment interval.

***Example* 14.3a** For Example 14.1d, compute the size of the final payment using each of the three methods. Compare the results with the size of the payment shown in the amortization schedule.

Solution

METHOD 1 $\quad A_n = 15\,000.00; \quad R = 2500.00; \quad i = 4\%$

$$15\,000.00 = 2500.00\left(\frac{1 - 1.04^{-n}}{0.04}\right)$$

$$6.00 = \frac{1 - 1.04^{-n}}{0.04}$$

$$0.24 = 1 - 1.04^{-n}$$

$$1.04^{-n} = 0.76$$

$$-n \ln 1.04 = \ln 0.76$$

$$-n(0.0392207) = -0.2744368$$

$$n = 6.9972427$$

Programmed solution

0	15 000	2500	4			
FV	PV	PMT	%i	CPT	N	6.9972427

$$R = 2500.00; \quad i = 4\%; \quad n = 0.9972427$$

$$A_n = 2500.00\left(\frac{1 - 1.04^{-0.9972427}}{0.04}\right)$$

$$= 2500.00(0.9589387)$$

$$= \$2397.35$$

Programmed solution

0	2500	4	0.9972427			
FV	PMT	%i	N	CPT	PV	2397.35

Interest for one interval is 2397.35(0.04) = \$95.89
Final payment is 2397.35 + 95.89 = \$2493.24

METHOD 2 Compute the value of n as done in Method 1.

Since $n = 6.9972427$, the number of equal payments is 6.

The accumulated value of the original principal after six payments

$$S = 15\,000.00(1.04^6)$$

$$= 15\,000.00(1.2653190)$$

$$= \$18\,979.79$$

Programmed solution

0	15 000	4	6			
PMT	PV	%i	N	CPT	FV	18 979.79

The accumulated value of the first six payments

$$S_6 = 2500.00\left(\frac{1.04^6 - 1}{0.04}\right)$$

$$= 2500.00(6.6329754)$$

$$= \$16\,582.44$$

Programmed solution

0	2500	4	6			
PV	PMT	%i	N	CPT	FV	16 582.44

The outstanding balance after six payments is 18 979.79 − 16 582.44 = \$2397.35.

The final payment = outstanding balance + interest for one period
= the accumulated value of \$2397.35 for one year
= 2397.35(1.04)
= \$2493.24

METHOD 3 Compute the value of n as done in Method 1.

Since n = 6.9972427, the number of assumed full payments is 7.

The accumulated value of the original principal after seven payments

$$S = 15\,000.00(1.04^7)$$
$$= 15\,000.00(1.3159318)$$
$$= \$19\,738.98$$

Programmed solution

0	15 000	4	7			
PMT	PV	%*i*	N	CPT	FV	19 738.98

The accumulated value of seven payments

$$S_7 = 2500.00\left(\frac{1.04^7 - 1}{0.04}\right)$$
$$= 2500.00(7.8982944)$$
$$= \$19\,745.74$$

Programmed solution

0	2500	4	7			
PV	PMT	%*i*	N	CPT	FV	19 745.74

Since the accumulated value of seven payments is greater than the accumulated value of the original principal, there is an overpayment.

19 745.74 − 19 738.98 = \$6.76

The size of the final payment is 2500.00 − 6.76 = \$2493.24.

Note:

1. For all three methods, you must determine n using the methods shown in chapters 11, 12, and 13.
2. When using a calculator, Method 1 is preferable because it is the most direct method. It is the method used in Subsection B below.

B. Applications

***Example* 14.3b** On his retirement, Art received a gratuity of \$8000.00 from his employer. Taking advantage of the existing tax legislation, he invested his money in an income averaging annuity that provides for semi-annual payments of \$1200.00 at the end of every six months. If interest is 11.5% compounded semi-annually, determine the size of the final payment (see Chapter 11, Example 11.5d).

Solution

$$A_n = 8000.00; \quad R = 1200.00; \quad i = \frac{11.5\%}{2} = 5.75\%$$

$$8000.00 = 1200.00\left(\frac{1 - 1.0575^{-n}}{0.0575}\right)$$

$$0.3833333 = 1 - 1.0575^{-n}$$

$$1.0575^{-n} = 0.616667$$

$$-n \ln 1.0575 = \ln 0.616667$$

$$-n(0.0559076) = -0.4834266$$

$$n = 8.6468812$$

$$R = 1200.00; \quad i = 5.75\%; \quad n = 0.6468812$$

$$A_n = 1200.00\left(\frac{1 - 1.0575^{-0.6468812}}{0.0575}\right)$$

$$= 1200.00(0.6177293)$$

$$= \$741.28$$

Programmed solution

0	8000	1200	5.75			
FV	PV	PMT	%i	CPT	N	8.6468812

0	1200	5.75	0.6468812			
FV	PMT	%i	N	CPT	PV	741.28

Final payment including the interest for one payment interval is 741.28(1.0575) = \$783.90.

***Example* 14.3c** A lease contract valued at \$7800.00 is to be fulfilled by rental payments of \$180.00 due at the beginning of each month. If money is worth 21% compounded monthly, determine the size of the final lease payment (see Chapter 12, Example 12.2h).

Solution

$$A_n(\text{due}) = 7800.00; \quad R = 180.00; \quad i = \frac{21\%}{12} = 1.75\%$$

$$n = 78.832271 \text{ (see solution to Example 12.2h)}$$

Present value of the final payment

$$R = 180.00; \quad i = 1.75\%; \quad n = 0.832271$$

$$A_n(\text{due}) = 180.00(1.0175)\left(\frac{1 - 1.0175^{-0.832271}}{0.0175}\right)$$

$$= 180.00(1.0175)(0.8191445)$$

$$= 180.00(0.8334795)$$

$$= \$150.03$$

Programmed solution

0	180	1.75	7800			
FV	PMT	%i	PV	DUE	(or 2nd	CPT)
N	78.832271					

0	180	1.75	0.832271			
FV	PMT	%i	N	DUE	(or 2nd	CPT)
PV	150.03					

Since the payment is made at the beginning of the last payment interval, no interest is added. The final payment is \$150.03.

***Example* 14.3d** Payments of \$500.00 deferred for nine years are received at the end of each month from a fund of \$10 000.00 deposited at 10.5% compounded monthly. Determine the size of the final payment (see Chapter 12, Example 12.4c).

Solution

$$A_n(\text{defer}) = 10\,000.00; \quad R = 500.00; \quad d = 9(12) = 108;$$

$$i = \frac{10.5\%}{12} = 0.875\%$$

$$n = 68.288334 \text{ (see solution to Example 12.4c)}$$

Present value of the final payment:

$$R = 500.00; \quad i = 0.875\%; \quad n = 0.288334$$

$$A_n = 500.00\left(\frac{1 - 1.00875^{-0.288334}}{0.00875}\right)$$

$$= 500.00(0.2867195)$$

$$= \$143.36$$

Programmed solution

0	500	0.875	0.288334			
FV	PMT	%i	N	CPT	PV	143.36

The size of the final payment is 143.36(1.00875) = \$144.61.

Example **14.3e** A business valued at \$96 000.00 is bought for a down payment of 25% and payments of \$4000.00 at the end of every three months. If interest is 18% compounded monthly, what is the size of the final payment? (See Chapter 13, Example 13.3d.)

Solution

$$A_{nc} = 96\,000.00(0.75) = 72\,000.00; \quad R = 4000.00; \quad c = \frac{12}{4} = 3;$$

$$i = \frac{18\%}{12} = 1.5\% = 0.015; \quad f = 1.015^3 - 1 = 4.56784\%;$$

$$n = 38.668403 \text{ (see solution to Example 13.3d)}$$

Present value of the final payment:

$$R = 4000.00; \quad f = 4.56784\%; \quad n = 0.668403$$

$$A_n = 4000.00\left(\frac{1 - 1.0456784^{-0.668403}}{0.0456784}\right)$$

$$= 4000.00(0.6439267)$$

$$= \$2575.71$$

Programmed solution

0	4000	4.56784	0.668403			
FV	PMT	%i	N	CPT	PV	2575.71

The final payment is 2575.71(1.0456784) = \$2693.36.

Example **14.3f** Ted Davis, having reached his goal of a \$140 000.00 balance in his RRSP, converts it into an RRIF and withdraws from it \$1650.00 at the beginning of each month. If interest is 11% compounded quarterly, what is the size of the final withdrawal? (See Chapter 13, Example 13.4f.)

Solution

$$A_{nc}(\text{due}) = 140\ 000.00; \quad R = 1650.00; \quad c = \frac{4}{12} = \frac{1}{3};$$

$$i = \frac{11\%}{4} = 2.75\% = 0.0275;$$

$$f = 1.0275^{\frac{1}{3}} - 1 = 1.0090839 - 1 = 0.90839\%$$

$$n = 159.58897 \text{ (see solution to Example 13.4f)}$$

Present value of final payment:

$$R = 1650.00; \quad f = 0.90839\%; \quad n = 0.58897$$

$$A_n = 1650.00(1.0090839)\left(\frac{1 - 1.0090839^{-0.58897}}{0.0090839}\right)$$

$$= 1650.00(1.0090839)(0.5847524)$$

$$= 1650.00(0.5900642)$$

$$= \$973.61$$

Programmed solution

0	1650	0.90839	0.58897			
PV	PMT	%*i*	N	DUE	PV	973.61

Since the payment is at the beginning of the last payment interval, its size is $973.61.

Exercise 14.3

A. For each of the following, compute the size of the final payment.

	Principal	*Periodic payment*	*Payment interval*	*Payment made at*	*Interest rate*	*Conversion period*
1.	$17 500.00	$1100.00	3 months	end	14%	quarterly
2.	$35 000.00	$925.00	1 month	end	12%	monthly
3.	$7 800.00	$775.00	6 months	beginning	7%	semi-annually
4.	$9 300.00	$580.00	3 months	beginning	17%	quarterly
5.	$15 400.00	$1600.00	6 months	end	8%	quarterly
6.	$29 500.00	$1650.00	3 months	end	18%	monthly
7.	$17 300.00	$425.00	1 month	beginning	20%	quarterly
8.	$10 500.00	$900.00	3 months	beginning	11%	semi-annually

B. Answer each of the following questions.

1. A loan of $7200.00 is repaid by payments of $360.00 at the end of every three months. Interest is 15% compounded quarterly.

(a) How many payments are required to repay the debt?

(b) What is the size of the final payment?

2. Seanna O'Brien receives pension payments of $3200.00 at the end of every six months from a retirement fund of $50 000.00. The fund earns 12% compounded semi-annually.

(a) How many payments will Seanna receive?

(b) What is the size of the final pension payment?

3. Payments of $1200.00 are made out of a fund of $25 000.00 at the end of every three months. If interest is 12% compounded monthly, what is the size of the final payment?

4. A debt of $30 000.00 is repaid in monthly instalments of $550.00. If interest is 16% compounded quarterly, what is the size of the final payment?

5. A lease valued at $20 000.00 requires payments of $1000.00 every three months due in advance. If money is worth 17% compounded quarterly, what is the size of the final lease payment?

6. Eduardo Martinez has saved $125 000.00. If he withdraws $1250.00 at the beginning of every month and interest is 10.5% compounded monthly, what is the size of the last withdrawal?

7. Equipment priced at $42 000.00 was purchased on a contract requiring payments of $5000.00 at the beginning of every six months. If interest is 17% compounded quarterly, what is the size of the final payment?

8. Noreen Leung has agreed to purchase her partner's share in the business by making payments of $1100.00 every three months. The agreed transfer value is $16 500.00 and interest is 10% compounded annually. If the first payment is due at the date of the agreement, what is the size of the final payment?

9. David Jones has paid $16 000.00 for a retirement annuity from which he will receive $1375.00 at the end of every three months. The payments are deferred for ten years and interest is 10% compounded quarterly.

(a) How many payments will David receive?

(b) What is the size of the final payment?

(c) How much will David receive in total?

(d) How much of what he receives will be interest?

10. A contract valued at $27 500.00 requires payments of $6000.00 every six months. The first payment is due in four years and interest is 17% compounded semi-annually.

(a) How many payments are required?

(b) What is the size of the last payment?

(c) How much will be paid in total?

(d) How much of what is paid is interest?

14.4 *Sinking funds*

A. *Finding the size of the periodic payment*

Sinking funds are interest-bearing funds into which payments are made at periodic intervals to provide a desired sum of money at a specified future time. Such funds usually involve large sums of money used by both the private and the public sectors to repay loans, redeem bonds, finance future capital acquisitions, provide for the replacement of depreciable plant and equipment, and recover investments in depletable natural resources.

The basic problem in dealing with sinking funds is to determine the *size of the periodic payments* that will accumulate to a known future amount. These payments form an annuity in which the accumulated value is known.

Depending on whether the periodic payments are made at the end or at the beginning of each payment period, the annuity formed is an ordinary annuity or an annuity due. Depending on whether or not the payment interval is equal in length to the interest conversion period, the annuity formed is a simple annuity or a general annuity. However, since sinking funds are normally set up so that the payment interval and the interest conversion period are equal in length, only the simple annuity cases are considered in this text.

(a) For sinking funds with payments at the end of each payment interval,

$$S_n = R\left[\frac{(1+i)^n - 1}{i}\right]$$

(b) For sinking funds with payments at the beginning of each payment interval,

$$S_n(\text{due}) = R(1+i)\left[\frac{(1+i)^n - 1}{i}\right]$$

***Example* 14.4a** Western Oil plans to create a sinking fund of \$20 000.00 by making equal deposits at the end of every six months for four years. Interest is 12% compounded semi-annually.

(i) What is the size of the semi-annual deposit into the fund?

(ii) What is the total amount deposited into the fund?

(iii) How much of the fund will be interest?

Solution

(i) $S_n = 20\,000.00;\quad n = 4(2) = 8;\quad i = \frac{12\%}{2} = 6\%$

$$20\,000.00 = R\left(\frac{1.06^8 - 1}{0.06}\right)$$

$$20\,000.00 = R(9.8974679)$$

$$R = \$2020.72$$

Programmed solution

0 20 000 6 8

PV FV %i N CPT PMT 2020.72

The size of the semi-annual payment is \$2020.72.

(ii) The total deposited into the sinking fund is 8(2020.72) = \$16 165.76.

(iii) The amount of interest in the fund is 20 000.00 − 16 165.76 = \$3834.24.

Example **14.4b** Ace Machinery wants to provide for replacement of equipment seven years from now estimated to cost \$60 000.00. To do so, the company set up a sinking fund into which it will pay equal sums of money at the beginning of each of the next seven years. Interest paid by the fund is 11.5% compounded annually.

(i) What is the size of annual payment into the fund?

(ii) What is the total paid into the fund by Ace Machinery?

(iii) How much of the fund will be interest?

Solution

(i) S_n(due) = 60 000.00; $n = 7$; $i = 11.5\%$

$$60\,000.00 = R(1.115)\left(\frac{1.115^7 - 1}{0.115}\right)$$

$$60\,000.00 = R(1.115)(9.9349216)$$

$$60\,000.00 = R(11.077438)$$

$$R = \$5416.42$$

Programmed solution

0 60 000 11.5 7

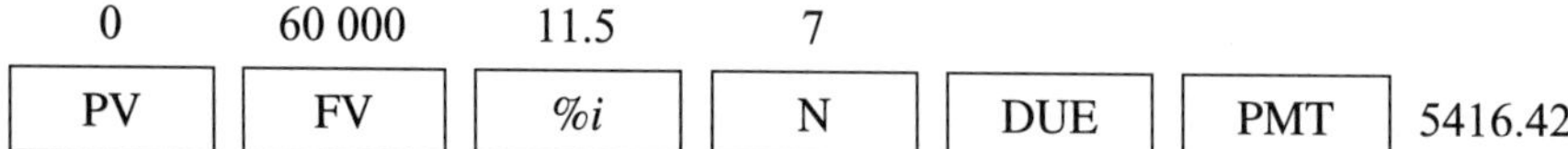

PV FV %i N DUE PMT 5416.42

The size of the annual payment is \$5416.42.

(ii) The total paid into the fund by Ace Machinery will be 7(5416.42) = \$37 914.94.

(iii) The interest earned by the fund will be 60 000.00 − 37 914.94 = \$22 085.06.

B. *Constructing sinking fund schedules*

The details of a sinking fund can be presented in the form of a schedule. Sinking fund schedules normally show the payment number (or payment date), the periodic payment into the fund, the interest earned by the fund, the increase in the fund, and the accumulated balance.

Example 14.4c Construct a sinking fund schedule for Example 14.4a.

Solution

$$R = 2020.72; \quad n = 8; \quad i = 6\% = 0.06$$

Sinking fund schedule

Payment interval number	*Periodic payment*	*Interest for payment interval* i = *0.06*	*Increase in fund*	*Balance in fund at end of payment interval*
0				0.00
1	2 020.72	0.00	2 020.72	2 020.72
2	2 020.72	121.24	2 141.96	4 162.68
3	2 020.72	249.76	2 270.48	6 433.16
4	2 020.72	385.99	2 406.71	8 839.87
5	2 020.72	530.39	2 551.11	11 390.98
6	2 020.72	683.46	2 704.18	14 095.16
7	2 020.72	845.71	2 866.43	16 961.59
8	2 020.72	1017.70	3 038.42	20 000.01
TOTAL	16 165.76	3834.25	20 000.01	

Explanations regarding the construction of the sinking fund schedule

1. The payment number 0 is used to introduce the beginning balance.
2. The first deposit is made at the end of the first payment interval. The interest earned by the fund during the first payment interval is $0, the increase in the fund is $2020.72, and the balance is $2020.72.
3. The second deposit is added at the end of the second payment interval. The interest for the interval is 0.06(2020.72) = $121.24. The increase in the fund is 2020.72 + 121.24 = $2141.96 and the new balance in the fund is 2020.72 + 2141.96 = $4162.68.
4. The third deposit is made at the end of the third payment interval. The interest for the interval is 0.06(4162.68) = $249.76, the increase in the fund is 2020.72 + 249.76 = $2270.48, and the new balance in the fund is 2270.48 + 4162.68 = $6433.16.
5. Calculations for the remaining payment intervals are made in a similar manner.
6. The final balance in the sinking fund will probably be slightly different from the expected value. This difference is a result of rounding. The balance may be left as shown ($20 000.01) or the exact balance of $20 000.00 may be obtained by adjusting the last payment to $2020.71.
7. The three totals shown are useful and should be obtained for each schedule. The total increase in the fund must be the same as the final balance. The total periodic payments are 8(2020.72) = 16 165.76. The total interest is the difference: 20 000.01 − 16 165.76 = $3834.25.

***Example* 14.4d** Construct a sinking fund schedule for Example 14.4b (an annuity due with payments at the beginning of each payment interval).

Solution

R = 5416.42 (made at the beginning); $n = 7$; $i = 11.5\% = 0.115$

Sinking fund schedule

Payment interval number	*Periodic payment*	*Interest for payment interval* i = *0.115*	*Increase in fund*	*Balance in fund at end of payment interval*
0				0.00
1	5 416.42	622.89	6 039.31	6 039.31
2	5 416.42	1 317.41	6 733.83	12 773.14
3	5 416.42	2 091.80	7 508.22	20 281.36
4	5 416.42	2 955.24	8 371.66	28 653.02
5	5 416.42	3 917.99	9 334.41	37 987.43
6	5 416.42	4 991.44	10 407.86	48 395.29
7	5 416.42	6 188.35	11 604.77	60 000.06
TOTAL	37 914.94	22 085.12	60 000.06	

Explanations regarding the construction of the sinking fund schedule

1. The starting balance is $0.00.
2. The first deposit is made at the beginning of the first payment interval and the interest earned by the fund during the first payment interval is 0.115(5416.42) = $622.89. The increase in the fund is 5416.42 + 622.89 = $6039.31 and the balance is $6039.31.
3. The second deposit is made at the beginning of the second payment interval, the interest earned is 0.115(6039.31 + 5416.42) = $1317.41, the increase is 5416.42 + 1317.41 = $6733.83, and the balance is 6039.31 + 6733.83 = $12 773.14.
4. The third deposit is made at the beginning of the third payment interval, the interest earned is 0.115(12 773.14 + 5416.42) = $2091.80, the increase is 5416.42 + 2091.80 = $7508.22, and the balance is 12 773.14 + 7508.22 = $20 281.36.
5. Calculations for the remaining payment intervals are made in a similar manner. Be careful to add the deposit to the previous balance when computing the interest earned.
6. The final balance of $60 000.06 is slightly different from the expected balance of $60 000.00 due to rounding. The exact balance may be obtained by adjusting the last payment to $5416.36.
7. The total increase in the fund must equal the final balance of $60 000.06. The total periodic payments are 7(5416.42) = $37 914.94. The total interest is 60 000.06 − 37 914.94 = $22 085.12.

C. *Finding the accumulated balance and interest earned or increase in a sinking fund for a payment interval; constructing partial sinking fund schedules*

Example **14.4e** For Examples 14.4a and 14.4b, compute

(i) the accumulated value in the fund at the end of the third payment interval;

(ii) the interest earned by the fund in the fifth payment interval;

(iii) the increase in the fund in the fifth interval.

Solution

(i) The balance in a sinking fund at any time is the accumulated value of the payments made into the fund.

For Example 14.4a (when payments are made at the end of each payment interval)

$$R = 2020.72; \quad n = 3; \quad i = 6\%$$

$$S_n = 2020.72\left(\frac{1.06^3 - 1}{0.06}\right)$$

$$= 2020.72(3.1836000)$$

$$= \$6433.16$$ ⟶ see Sinking Fund Schedule, Example 14.4c

Programmed solution

0	2020.72	6	3			
PV	PMT	%i	N	CPT	FV	6433.16

For Example 14.4b (when payments are made at the beginning of each payment interval)

$$R = 5416.42; \quad n = 3; \quad i = 11.5\%$$

$$S_n(\text{due}) = 5416.42(1.115)\left(\frac{1.115^3 - 1}{0.115}\right)$$

$$= 5416.42(1.115)(3.3582250)$$

$$= \$20\,281.36$$ ⟶ see Sinking Fund Schedule, Example 14.4d

Programmed solution

0	5416.42	11.5	3			
PV	PMT	%i	N	DUE	FV	20 281.36

(ii) The interest earned during any given payment interval is based on the balance in the fund at the beginning of the interval. This figure is the same as the balance at the end of the previous payment interval.

For Example 14.4a
The balance at the end of the fourth payment interval

$$S_4 = 2020.72\left(\frac{1.06^4 - 1}{0.06}\right)$$

$$= 2020.72(4.3746160)$$

$$= \$8839.87$$

Programmed solution

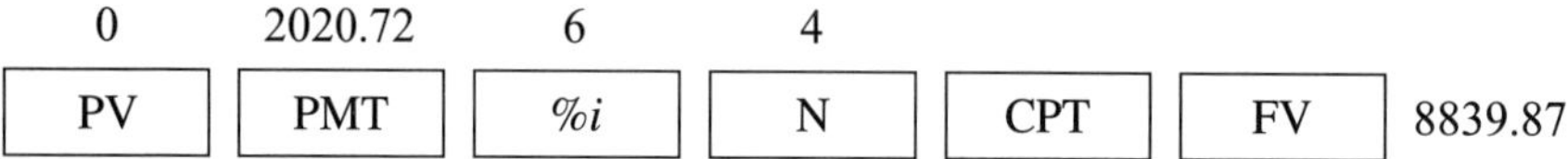

The interest earned by the fund in the fifth payment interval is 0.06(8839.87) = \$530.39.

For Example 14.4b
The balance in the fund at the end of the fourth payment interval

$$S_4 = 5416.42(1.115)\left(\frac{1.115^4 - 1}{0.115}\right)$$

$$= 5416.42(1.115)(4.7444209)$$

$$= \$28\,653.02$$

Programmed solution

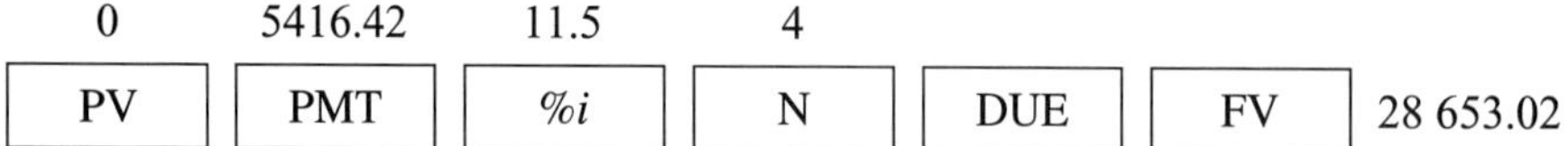

The interest earned by the fund in the fifth payment interval is 0.115(28 653.02 + 5416.42) = 0.115(34 069.44) = \$3917.99.

(iii) The increase in the sinking fund in any given payment interval is the interest earned by the fund during the payment interval plus the periodic payment.

For Example 14.4a
The increase in the fund during the fifth payment interval is 530.39 + 2020.72 = \$2551.11.

For Example 14.4b
The increase in the fund during the fifth payment period is 3917.99 + 5416.42 = \$9334.41.

Example **14.4f** The Board of Directors of Peel Credit Union decided to establish a building fund of \$130 000.00 by making equal deposits into a sinking fund at the end of every three months for seven years. Interest is 12% compounded quarterly.

(i) Compute the increase in the fund during the twelfth payment interval.

(ii) Construct a partial sinking fund schedule showing details of the first three deposits, the twelfth deposit, the last three deposits, and totals.

Solution

Size of the quarterly deposit:

$$S_n = 130\,000.00; \quad n = 7(4) = 28; \quad i = \frac{12\%}{4} = 3\%$$

$$130\,000.00 = R\left(\frac{1.03^{28} - 1}{0.03}\right)$$

$$130\,000.00 = R(42.930922)$$

$$R = 3028.12$$

Programmed solution

0	130 000	3	28			
PV	FV	%i	N	CPT	PMT	3028.12

(i) Balance in the fund at the end of the eleventh payment interval

$$S_{11} = 3028.12\left(\frac{1.03^{11} - 1}{0.03}\right)$$

$$= 3028.12(12.807796)$$

$$= \$38\,783.54$$

Programmed solution

0	3028.12	3	11			
PV	PMT	%i	N	CPT	FV	38 783.54

The interest earned by the fund during the twelfth payment interval is 0.03(38 783.54) = \$1163.51.

The increase in the fund during the twelfth payment interval is 1163.51 + 3028.12 = \$4191.63.

(ii) The last three payments are Payments 26, 27, and 28. To show details of these, we must know the accumulated value after 25 payment intervals.

$$S_{25} = 3028.12\left(\frac{1.03^{25} - 1}{0.03}\right) = 3028.12(36.459264) = \$110\,403.03$$

Programmed solution

0	3028.12	3	25			
PV	PMT	%i	N	CPT	FV	110 403.03

Partial sinking fund schedule

Payment interval number	*Periodic payment made at end*	*Interest for payment interval* i = *0.03*	*Increase in fund*	*Balance in fund at the end of payment interval*
0				0.00
1	3 028.12	0.00	3 028.12	3 028.12
2	3 028.12	90.84	3 118.96	6 147.08
3	3 028.12	184.41	3 212.53	9 359.61
.	.	.	.	.
.	.	.	.	.
11	.	.	.	38 783.54
12	3 028.12	1 163.51	4 191.63	42 975.17
.	.	.	.	.
.	.	.	.	.
25	.	.	.	110 403.03
26	3 028.12	3 312.09	6 340.21	116 743.24
27	3 028.12	3 502.30	6 530.42	123 273.66
28	3 028.12	3 698.21	6 726.33	129 999.99
TOTAL	84 787.36	45 212.63	129 999.99	

***Example* 14.4g** Laurin and Company want to build up a fund of \$75 000.00 by making payments of \$2000.00 at the beginning of every six months into a sinking fund earning 11% compounded semi-annually. Construct a partial sinking fund schedule showing details of the first three payments, the last three payments, and totals.

Solution

To show details of the last three payments, we need to know the number of payments.

$$S_n(\text{due}) = 75\ 000.00; \quad R = 2000.00; \quad i = \frac{11\%}{2} = 5.5\%$$

$$75\ 000.00 = 2000.00(1.055)\left(\frac{1.055^n - 1}{0.055}\right)$$

$$1.055^n = 2.9549763$$

$$n \ln 1.055 = \ln 2.9549763$$

$$n(0.0535408) = 1.0834906$$

$$n = 20.236741$$

Programmed solution

0	75 000	2000	5.5			
PV	FV	PMT	%i	DUE	N	20.236741

Twenty-one payments are needed. The last three payments are Payments 19, 20, and 21. The balance in the fund at the end of the 18th payment interval

$$S_{18}(\text{due}) = 2000.00(1.055)\left(\frac{1.055^{18} - 1}{0.055}\right)$$

$$= 2000.00(1.055)(29.481205)$$

$$= \$62\ 205.34$$

Programmed solution

0	2000	5.5	18			
PV	PMT	%i	N	DUE	FV	62 205.34

Partial sinking fund schedule

Payment interval number	Periodic payment made at beginning	Interest for payment interval i = 0.055	Increase in fund	Balance in fund at the end of payment interval
0				0.00
1	2 000.00	110.00	2 110.00	2 110.00
2	2 000.00	226.05	2 226.05	4 336.05
3	2 000.00	348.48	2 348.48	6 684.53
.	.	.	.	.
.	.	.	.	.
18	.	.	.	62 205.34
19	2 000.00	3 531.29	5 531.29	67 736.63
20	2 000.00	3 835.51	5 835.51	73 572.14
21	1 427.86	0.00	1 427.86	75 000.00
TOTAL	41 427.86	33 572.14	75 000.00	

Note: The desired balance in the sinking fund will be reached at the beginning of the 21st payment interval by depositing $1427.86.

D. Computer application—Sinking fund schedule

A computer solution for the construction of sinking fund schedules is provided by Program 5 (see the Solutions Manual).

E. Debt retirement by the sinking fund method

When a sinking fund is created to retire a debt, the debt principal is repaid in total at the due date from the proceeds of the sinking fund while interest on the principal is paid periodically. The payments into the sinking fund are usually made at the same time as the interest payments are made. The sum of the two payments (debt interest payment plus payment into the sinking fund) is called the **periodic cost of the debt.** The difference between the debt principal and the sinking fund balance at any point is called the **book value of the debt**.

Example **14.4h** The City Board of Education borrowed $750 000.00 for twenty years at 13% compounded annually to finance construction of Hillview Elementary School. The board created a sinking fund to repay the debt at the end of twenty years. Equal payments are made into the sinking fund at the end of each year and interest earned by the fund is 10.5% compounded annually. Rounding all computations to the nearest dollar,

(i) determine the annual cost of the debt;

(ii) compute the book value of the debt at the end of ten years;

(iii) construct a partial sinking fund schedule showing the book value of the debt, the three first payments, the three last payments, and the totals.

Solution

(i) The annual interest cost on the principal:

$$P = 750\ 000; \quad i = 13\% = 0.13;$$

$$I = 750\ 000(0.13) = \$97\ 500$$

The annual payment into the sinking fund:

$$S_n = 750\ 000; \quad n = 20; \quad i = 10.5\%$$

$$750\ 000 = R\left(\frac{1.105^{20} - 1}{0.105}\right)$$

$$750\ 000 = R(60.630808)$$

$$R = \$12\ 370$$

Programmed solution

0	750 000	10.5	20			
PV	FV	%*i*	N	CPT	PMT	12 370

The annual cost of the debt is 97 500 + 12 370 = \$109 870.

(ii) The balance in the sinking fund after the tenth payment

$$S_{10} = 12\ 370\left(\frac{1.105^{10} - 1}{0.105}\right)$$

$$= 12\ 370(16.324579)$$

$$= \$201\ 935$$

Programmed solution

0	12 370	10.5	10			
PV	PMT	%*i*	N	CPT	FV	201 935

The book value of the debt at the end of the tenth year is
750 000 − 201 935 = \$548 065.

(iii) The last three payments are Payments 18, 19, and 20. The balance in the sinking fund at the end of Year 17

$$S_{17} = 12\ 370\left(\frac{1.105^{17} - 1}{0.105}\right) = 12\ 370(42.47213) = \$525\ 380$$

Programmed solution

0	12 370	10.5	17			
PV	PMT	%i	N	CPT	FV	525 380

Partial sinking fund schedule

Payment interval number	Periodic payment made at end	Interest for payment interval i = 0.105	Increase in fund	Balance in fund at the end of the payment interval	Book value of debt
0				0	750 000
1	12 370	0	12 370	12 370	737 630
2	12 370	1 299	13 669	26 039	723 961
3	12 370	2 734	15 104	41 143	708 857
.	.	.	.	.	
.	.	.	.	.	
.	.	.	.	.	
17	.	.	.	525 380	224 620
18	12 370	55 165	67 535	592 915	157 085
19	12 370	62 256	74 626	667 541	82 459
20	12 367	70 092	82 459	750 000	0
TOTAL	247 397	502 603	750 000		

Note: The last payment has been adjusted to create a fund of exactly $750 000.

Exercise 14.4

A. For each of the following sinking funds, compute (a) the size of the periodic payment; (b) the accumulated balance at the time indicated.

	Amount of sinking fund	Payment interval	Payments made at	Term	Int. rate	Conversion period	Accumulated balance required after
1.	$15 000.00	6 months	end	10 years	6%	semi-ann.	10th payment
2.	$9 600.00	1 month	end	8 years	12%	monthly	36th payment
3.	$8 400.00	1 month	beginning	15 years	18%	monthly	96th payment
4.	$21 000.00	3 months	beginning	20 years	8%	quarterly	28th payment
5.	$45 000.00	3 months	end	12 years	10%	quarterly	16th payment
6.	$72 000.00	6 months	beginning	15 years	13%	semi-ann.	20th payment

B. Each of the following debts is retired by the sinking fund method. Interest payments on the debt are made at the end of each payment interval and the payments into the sinking fund are made at the same time. Determine

(a) the size of the periodic interest expense of the debt;

(b) the size of the periodic payment into the sinking fund;

(c) the periodic cost of the debt;

(d) the book value of the debt at the time indicated.

				Interest rate			
	Debt principal	*Term of debt*	*Payment interval*	*On debt*	*On fund*	*Conversion period*	*Book value required after*
1.	\$20 000.00	10 years	3 months	14%	12%	quarterly	6 years
2.	\$14 500.00	8 years	6 months	15%	12.5%	semi-ann.	5 years
3.	\$10 000.00	5 years	1 month	7.5%	6.0%	monthly	4 years
4.	\$40 000.00	15 years	3 months	18%	17%	quarterly	10 years
5.	\$95 000.00	20 years	6 months	9.0%	7.0%	semi-ann.	15 years
6.	\$80 000.00	12 years	1 month	15%	13.5%	monthly	8 years

C. Answer each of the following questions.

1. Hein Engineering expects to expand its plant facilities in six years at an estimated cost of \$75 000.00. To provide for the expansion, a sinking fund has been established into which equal payments are made at the end of every three months. Interest is 5% compounded quarterly.

   (a) What is the size of the quarterly payments?

   (b) How much of the maturity value will be payments?

   (c) How much interest will the fund contain?

2. To redeem a \$100 000.00 promissory note due in ten years, Cobblestone Enterprises has set up a sinking fund earning 7.5% compounded semi-annually. Equal deposits are made at the beginning of every six months.

   (a) What is the size of the semi-annual deposits?

   (b) How much of the maturity value of the fund is deposits?

   (c) How much is interest?

3. Equal deposits are made into a sinking fund at the end of each year for seven years. Interest is 14.5% compounded annually and the maturity value of the fund is \$20 000.00. Find the size of the annual deposits and construct a sinking fund schedule showing totals.

4. A sinking fund amounting to \$15 000.00 is to be created by making payments at the beginning of every six months for four years. Interest earned by the fund is 12.5% compounded semi-annually. Determine the size of the semi-annual payments and prepare a sinking fund schedule showing totals.

5. For Question 3, find the increase in the fund for the fourth year. Verify your answer by checking the sinking fund schedule.

6. For Question 4, compute the interest earned during the fifth payment interval. Verify your answer by checking the sinking fund schedule.

7. Kirk, Klein, & Co. requires \$100 000.00 fifteen years from now to retire a debt. A sinking fund is established into which equal payments are made at the end of every month. Interest is 16.5% compounded monthly.
   (a) What is the size of the monthly payment?
   (b) What is the balance in the sinking fund after five years?
   (c) How much interest will be earned by the fund in the 100th payment interval?
   (d) By how much will the fund increase during the 150th payment interval?
   (e) Construct a partial sinking fund schedule showing details of the first three payments, the last three payments, and totals.

8. The Town of Keewatin issued debentures worth \$120 000.00 maturing in ten years to finance construction of water and sewer facilities. To redeem the debentures, the town council decided to make equal deposits into a sinking fund at the beginning of every three months. Interest earned by the sinking fund is 16% compounded quarterly.
   (a) What is the size of the quarterly payment into the sinking fund?
   (b) What is the balance in the fund after six years?
   (c) How much interest is earned by the fund in the 28th payment interval?
   (d) By how much will the fund increase in the 33rd payment interval?
   (e) Prepare a partial sinking fund schedule showing details of the first three payments, the last three payments, and totals.

9. The Township of Jeffrey Melnick borrowed \$300 000 for road improvements. The debt agreement requires that the township pay the interest on the loan at the end of each year and make equal deposits at the time of the interest payments into a sinking fund until the loan is retired in twenty years. Interest on the loan is 18.25% compounded annually and interest earned by the sinking fund is 15.5% compounded annually (round all answers to the nearest dollar).
   (a) What is the annual interest expense?
   (b) What is the size of the annual deposit into the sinking fund?
   (c) What is the total annual cost of the debt?
   (d) How much is the increase in the sinking fund in the tenth year?
   (e) What is the book value of the debt after fifteen years?
   (f) Construct a partial sinking fund schedule showing details, including the book value of the debt, for the first three years, the last three years, and totals.

10. Sheridan Credit Union borrowed \$225 000 at 13% compounded semi-annually from League Central to build an office complex. The loan agreement requires payment of interest at the end of every six months. In addition, the credit union is to make equal payments into a sinking fund so that the principal can be retired in total after fifteen years. Interest earned by the fund is 11% compounded semi-annually (round all answers to the nearest dollar).

(a) What is the semi-annual interest payment on the debt?

(b) What is the size of the semi-annual deposits into the sinking fund?

(c) What is the total annual cost of the debt?

(d) What is the interest earned by the fund in the 20th payment interval?

(e) What is the book value of the debt after twelve years?

(f) Prepare a partial sinking fund schedule showing details, including the book value of the debt, for the first three years, the last three years, and totals.

Review exercise

1. Sylvie Cardinal bought a business for \$45 000.00. She made a down payment of \$10 000.00 and agreed to repay the balance by equal payments at the end of every three months for eight years. Interest is 16% compounded quarterly.

   (a) What is the size of the quarterly payments?

   (b) What will be the total cost of financing?

   (c) How much will Sylvie owe after five years?

   (d) How much interest will be included in the 20th payment?

   (e) How much of the principal will be repaid by the 24th payment?

   (f) Construct a partial amortization schedule showing details of the first three payments, Payments 10, 11, 12, the last three payments, and totals.

2. Angelo Lemay borrowed \$8000.00 from his credit union. He agreed to repay the loans by making equal monthly payments for five years. Interest is 15% compounded monthly.

   (a) What is the size of the monthly payments?

   (b) How much will the loan cost him?

   (c) How much will Angelo owe after eighteen months?

   (d) How much interest will he pay in his 36th payment?

   (e) How much of the principal will be repaid by the 48th payment?

   (f) Prepare a partial amortization schedule showing details of the first three payments, Payments 24, 25, 26, the last three payments, and totals.

3. Comfort Swim Limited borrowed \$40 000.00 for replacement of equipment. The debt is repaid in instalments of \$2000.00 made at the end of every three months.

   (a) If interest is 15% compounded quarterly, how many payments are needed?

   (b) How much will Comfort Swim owe after two years?

   (c) How much of the 12th payment is interest?

   (d) How much of the principal will be repaid by the 20th payment?

(e) Construct a partial amortization schedule showing details of the first three payments, the last three payments, and totals.

4. A $48 000.00 mortgage amortized by monthly payments over 35 years is renewable after five years. Interest is 14% compounded semi-annually.

 (a) What is the size of the monthly payments?

 (b) How much interest is paid during the first year?

 (c) How much of the principal is repaid during the first five-year term?

 (d) If the mortgage is renewed for a further five-year term at 18% compounded semi-annually, what will be the size of the monthly payments?

 (e) Construct a partial amortization schedule showing details of the first three payments for each of the two five-year terms, the last three payments for the second five-year term, and totals at the end of the second five-year term.

5. Pelican Recreational Services owes $27 500.00 secured by a collateral mortgage. The mortgage is amortized over fifteen years by equal payments made at the end of every three months and is renewable after three years.

 (a) If interest is 15% compounded annually, what is the size of the payments?

 (b) How much of the principal is repaid by the fourth payment?

 (c) What is the balance at the end of the three-year term?

 (d) If the mortgage is renewed for a further four years but amortized over eight years and interest is 17.5% compounded semi-annually, what is the size of the quarterly payments for the renewal period?

 (e) Construct a partial amortization schedule showing details of the first three payments for each of the two terms, the last three payments in the four-year term, and totals at the end of the four-year term.

6. A debt of $17 500.00 is repaid by payments of $2850.00 made at the end of each year. Interest is 14% compounded semi-annually.

 (a) How many payments are needed to repay the debt?

 (b) What is the cost of the debt for the first three years?

 (c) What is the principal repaid in the seventh year?

 (d) Construct an amortization schedule showing details of the first three payments, the last three payments, and totals.

7. A debt of $25 000.00 is repaid by payments of $3500.00 made at the end of every six months. Interest is 11% compounded semi-annually.

 (a) How many payments are needed to repay the debt?

 (b) What is the size of the final payment?

8. Jane Evans receives payments of $900.00 at the beginning of each month from a pension fund of $72 500.00. Interest earned by the fund is 12% compounded monthly.

(a) What is the number of payments Jane will receive?

(b) What is the size of the final payment?

9. A lease agreement valued at $33 000.00 requires payment of $4300.00 every three months in advance. The payments are deferred for three years and money is worth 20% compounded quarterly.

(a) How many lease payments are to be made under the contract?

(b) What is the size of the final lease payment?

10. A contract worth $52 000.00 provides benefits of $20 000.00 at the end of each year. The benefits are deferred for ten years and interest is 11% compounded quarterly.

(a) How many payments are to be made under the contract?

(b) What is the size of the last benefit payment?

11. To provide for the purchase of heavy construction equipment estimated to cost $110 000.00, Valmar Construction is paying equal sums of money at the end of every six months for five years into a sinking fund earning 17.5% compounded semi-annually.

(a) What is the size of the semi-annual payment into the sinking fund?

(b) Compute the balance in the fund after the third payment.

(c) Compute the amount of interest earned during the sixth payment interval.

(d) Construct a sinking fund schedule showing totals. Check your answers to parts (b) and (c) with the values in the schedule.

12. Alpha Corporation is depositing equal sums of money at the beginning of every three months into a sinking fund to redeem a $65 000.00 promissory note due eight years from now. Interest earned by the fund is 12% compounded quarterly.

(a) Determine the size of the quarterly payments into the sinking fund.

(b) Compute the balance in the fund after three years.

(c) Compute the increase in the fund during the 24th payment interval.

(d) Construct a partial sinking fund schedule showing details of the first three deposits, the last three deposits, and totals.

13. The municipality of Kirkfield borrowed $100 000.00 to build a recreation centre. The debt principal is to be repaid in eight years and interest at 13.75% compounded annually is to be paid annually. To provide for the retirement of the debt, the municipal council set up a sinking fund into which equal payments are made at the time of the annual interest payments. Interest earned by the fund is 11.5% compounded annually.

(a) What is the annual interest payment?

(b) What is the size of the annual payment into the sinking fund?

(c) What is the total annual cost of the debt?

(d) Compute the book value of the debt after three years.

(e) Compute the interest earned by the fund in Year 6.

(f) Construct a sinking fund schedule showing the book value of the debt and totals. Verify your computations in parts (d) and (e) against the schedule.

14. The Harrow Board of Education financed the acquisition of a building site through a \$300 000 long-term promissory note due in fifteen years. Interest on the promissory note is 19.25% compounded semi-annually and is payable at the end of every six months. To provide for the redemption of the note, the board agreed to make equal payments at the end of every six months into a sinking fund paying 18% compounded semi-annually. (Round all answers to the nearest dollar.)

(a) What is the semi-annual interest payment?

(b) What is the size of the semi-annual payment into the sinking fund?

(c) What is the annual cost of the debt?

(d) Compute the book value of the debt after five years.

(e) Compute the increase in the sinking fund in the 20th payment interval.

(f) Construct a partial sinking fund schedule showing details, including the book value of the debt, for the first three years, the last three years, and totals.

15. A debt of \$6500.00 is repaid in equal monthly instalments over four years. Interest is 15% compounded monthly.

(a) What is the size of the monthly payments?

(b) What will be the total cost of borrowing?

(c) What is the outstanding balance after one year?

(d) How much of the 30th payment is interest?

(e) Construct a partial amortization schedule showing details of the first three payments, the last three payments, and totals.

16. Milton Investments borrowed \$32 000.00 at 21% compounded semi-annually. The loan is repaid by payments of \$4500.00 due at the end of every six months.

(a) How many payments are needed?

(b) How much of the principal will be repaid by the fifth payment?

(c) Prepare a partial amortization schedule showing the details of the last three payments and totals.

17. Northern Flying Service is preparing to buy an aircraft estimated to cost \$60 000.00 by making equal payments at the end of every three months into a sinking fund for five years. Interest earned by the fund is 16% compounded quarterly.
    (a) What is the size of the quarterly payment into the sinking fund?
    (b) How much of the maturity value of the fund will be interest?
    (c) What is the accumulated value of the fund after two years?
    (d) How much interest will the fund earn in the 15th payment interval?

18. A sinking fund of \$10 000.00 is to be created by equal annual payments at the beginning of each year for seven years. Interest earned by the fund is 17.5% compounded annually.
    (a) Compute the annual deposit into the fund.
    (b) Construct a sinking fund schedule showing totals.

19. A \$28 000.00 mortgage is amortized by quarterly payments over twenty years. The mortgage is renewable after three years and interest is 14% compounded semi-annually.
    (a) What is the size of the quarterly payments?
    (b) How much interest will be paid during the first year?
    (c) What is the balance at the end of the three-year term?
    (d) If the mortgage is renewed for another three years at 15% compounded annually, what will be the size of the quarterly payments for the renewal period?

20. The Superior Tool Company is repaying a debt of \$16 000.00 by payments of \$1000.00 made at the end of every three months. Interest is 16.5% compounded monthly.
    (a) How many payments are needed to repay the debt?
    (b) What is the size of the final payment?

21. Joe Ngosa bought a retirement fund for \$15 000.00. Beginning twenty-five years from the date of purchase, he will receive payments of \$17 500.00 at the beginning of every six months. Interest earned by the fund is 12% compounded semi-annually.
    (a) How many payments will Joe receive?
    (b) What is the size of the last payment?

22. The town of Kildare bought firefighting equipment for \$96 000.00. The financing agreement provides for annual interest payments and equal payments into a sinking fund for ten years. After ten years the proceeds of the sinking fund will be used to retire the principal. Interest on the debt is 14.5% compounded annually and interest earned by the sinking fund is 13% compounded annually.

(a) What is the annual interest payment?

(b) What is the size of the annual payment into the sinking fund?

(c) What is the total annual cost of the debt?

(d) What is the book value of the debt after four years?

(e) Construct a partial sinking fund schedule showing details, including the book value of the debt, for the last three years and totals.

Self-test

1. A $9000.00 loan is repaid by equal monthly payments over five years. What is the outstanding balance after two years if interest is 12% compounded monthly?

2. Cottingham Pies made semi-annual payments into a sinking fund for ten years. If the fund had a balance of $100 000.00 after ten years and interest is 11% compounded semi-annually, what was the accumulated balance in the fund after seven years?

3. A loan of $15 000.00 is repaid by quarterly payments of $700.00 each at 18% compounded quarterly. What is the principal repaid by the twenty-fifth payment?

4. A fund of $165 000.00 is to be accumulated in six years by making equal payments at the beginning of each month. If interest is 13.5% compounded monthly, how much interest is earned by the fund in the twentieth payment interval?

5. A $50 000.00 mortgage is amortized by monthly payments over twenty years. If interest is 14% compounded semi-annually, how much interest will be paid during the first three years?

6. A debt of $24 000.00 is repaid by quarterly payments of $1100.00. If interest is 16% compounded quarterly, what is the size of the final payment?

7. Gillian Armes invested $10 000.00 in an income fund at 13% compounded semi-annually for twenty years. After twenty years, she is to receive semi-annual payments of $10 000.00 at the end of every six-month period until the fund is exhausted. What is the size of the final payment?

8. A company financed a plant expansion of $750 000.00 at 14% compounded annually. The financing agreement requires annual payments of interest and the funding of the debt through equal annual payments for fifteen years into a sinking fund earning 12% compounded annually. What is the book value of the debt after five years?

9. Annual sinking fund payments made at the beginning of every year for six years earning 11.5% compounded annually amount to $25 000.00 at the end of six years. Construct a sinking fund schedule showing totals.

10. A loan of $12 000.00 is amortized over ten years by equal monthly payments at 15% compounded monthly. Construct an amortization schedule showing details of the first three payments, the fortieth payment, the last three payments, and totals.

CASE STUDY

A computer programmer/analyst is responsible for developing computer programs for specific purposes and analyzing them. The computer programmer for the Jamesway Manufacturing Co. is asked to design programs that will allow the company to know the financial status of the company at any given time. The following situations need to be solved manually before the programmer can develop a program.

1. Four years ago, Jamesway took out a \$105 000 mortgage amortized over ten years at 12% p.a. compounded monthly. The term of the mortgage was for five years. The rate has now dropped to 9% p.a. compounded monthly.

(a) Calculate the original monthly payment.

(b) Calculate the total interest that Jamesway will pay over ten years.

(c) Jamesway must pay a three-month interest penalty on the outstanding balance if it breaks the term of the mortgage to renew at a lower rate. Calculate the new payment. Is it advisable to renew at the new rate?

2. The company would like to borrow \$57 000 to invest in new equipment. Payments of \$4000 every quarter will pay off the loan at 9% p.a. compounded annually.

(a) How many payments are needed to pay off the loan?

(b) Calculate the final payment.

3. The company is allowed to deduct the interest on a \$145 000 loan from its income tax. The company will pay back the loan in equal monthly instalments over six years at 6% p.a. compounded monthly.

(a) Calculate the total interest paid in the fourth year.

(b) Construct a partial amortization schedule showing details of the 37th and 38th payments.

4. Jamesway plans to finance a building site with a \$250 000 loan over the next ten years at 7.5% p.a. compounded monthly. It will set up a sinking fund with monthly payments at 6% p.a. compounded monthly.

(a) Determine the monthly cost of the debt.

(b) Calculate the book value of the debt at the end of five years.

(c) Construct a partial sinking fund schedule showing details of the 61st deposit.

5. Jamesway wants to update an existing production line. The \$35 000 loan that is needed will be financed with monthly payments for one year at 9% p.a. compounded semi-annually. This extra cost will be passed on to the consumer by an increase in the price of the item produced.

(a) Calculate the monthly payment.

(b) This item has monthly sales of 8200 units. Its current cost is \$14.78 and has a 40% markup based on selling price. Calculate the selling price.

(c) What will the new selling price per unit be?

Summary of formulae used

No new formulae were introduced in this chapter. However, some of the formulae introduced in Chapters 9 to 13 have been used and are listed below.

Formula 11.1

$$S_n = R\left[\frac{(1+i)^n - 1}{i}\right]$$

Formula 11.2

$$A_n = R\left[\frac{1-(1+i)^{-n}}{i}\right]$$

Formula 12.1

$$S_n(\text{due}) = R(1+i)\left[\frac{(1+i)^n - 1}{i}\right]$$

Formula 13.1

$$S_{nc} = R\left[\frac{(1+f)^n - 1}{f}\right] \text{ where } f = (1+i)^c - 1$$

Formula 13.2

$$A_{nc} = R\left[\frac{1-(1+f)^{-n}}{f}\right] \text{ where } f = (1+i)^c - 1$$

Glossary of terms used

Amortization repayment of both interest and principal of interest-bearing debts by a series of equal payments made at equal intervals of time

Amortization schedule a schedule showing in detail how a debt is repaid

Book value of a debt the difference at any time between the debt principal and the associated sinking fund balance

Periodic cost of a debt the sum of the interest paid and the payment into the sinking fund when a debt is retired by the sinking fund method

Prospective method a method for finding the outstanding debt balance that considers the payments that remain outstanding

Retrospective method a method of finding the outstanding balance of a debt that considers the payments that have been made

Sinking fund a fund into which payments are made to provide a specific sum of money at a future time; usually set up for the purpose of meeting some future obligation

15 *Bond valuation*

Introduction

Bonds are contracts used to borrow sizeable sums of money from a usually large group of investors. The indenture for most bonds provides for the repayment of the principal at a specified future date plus periodic payment of interest at a specified percent of the face value. Bonds are negotiable; that is, they can be freely bought and sold. The mathematical problems arising from the trading of bonds are the topic of this chapter.

Objectives

Upon completing this chapter, you will be able to

1. determine the purchase price of bonds, redeemable at par or otherwise, bought on or between interest dates;
2. determine the premium or discount on the purchase of a bond;
3. construct bond schedules showing the amortization of premiums or accumulation of discounts;
4. calculate the yield rate for bonds bought on the market by the method of averages and, more accurately, by trial and error;
5. deal with special kinds of bonds such as annuity bonds and serial bonds.

15.1 *Purchase price of bonds*

A. *Basic concepts and terminology*

Corporations and governments use bonds to borrow money from a usually large group of lenders (investors). To deal with the expected large number of investors, the borrower prints up written contacts, called bonds or **debentures**, in advance.

The printed bonds specify the terms of the contract including

(a) the **face value** (or **par value** or **denomination**) which is the amount owed to the holder of the bond, usually a multiple of \$100 such as \$100, \$1000, \$5000, \$10 000, \$25 000, \$100 000;

(b) the **bond rate** (or **coupon rate** or **nominal rate**) which is the rate of interest paid, usually semi-annually, based on the face value of the bond;

(c) the **redemption date** (or **maturity date** or **due date**) which is the date on which the principal of the loan is to be repaid;

(d) the **redemption value** which is the money paid by the issuer to the bondholder at the date of surrender of the bonds.

Most bonds are **redeemable at par**; that is, they are redeemable at their *face* value. However, some bonds have a redemption feature either to make the bonds more attractive to the investor or because they are callable, that is, because they can be redeemed *before* maturity. In either case, the bonds will be **redeemed at a premium**, that is, at a value *greater* than their face value. The redemption value in such cases is stated as a percent of the face values. For example, the redemption value of a $5000 bond redeemable at 104 is 104% of $5000, or $5200.

Investors in bonds expect to receive periodic interest payments during the term of the bond from the date of issue to the date of maturity and they expect to receive the principal at the date of maturity.

To facilitate the payment of interest, most bonds have dated interest **coupons** attached that can be cashed on or after the stated interest payment date at any bank. For example, a twenty-year, $1000.00 bond bearing interest at 10% payable semi-annually will have attached to it at the date of issue forty coupons of $50 each. Each coupon represents the semi-annual interest due on each of the forty interest payment dates.

The issuer may or may not offer security such as real estate, plant, or equipment as a guarantee for the repayment of the principal. Bonds for which no security is offered are called debentures.

Bonds are marketable and may be freely bought and sold. When investors acquire bonds, they buy two promises:

1. a promise to be paid the redemption value of the bond at maturity;
2. a promise to be paid the periodic interest payments according to the rate of interest stated on the bond.

Two basic problems arise for investors when buying bonds:

1. What should be the purchase price of a bond to provide the investor with a given rate of return?
2. What is the rate of interest which a bond will yield if bought at a given price?

In this section we will deal with the first of these two problems.

B. *Purchase price of a bond bought on an interest date*

Example **15.1a** A $1000 bond bearing interest at 10% payable semi-annually is due in four years. If money is worth 12% compounded semi-annually, what is the value of the bond if bought today?

Solution

The buyer of the bond acquires two promises:

1. a promise of \$1000.00 four years from now;
2. a promise of \$50.00 interest due at the end of every six months (the annual interest is 10% of 1000.00 = \$100.00, half of which is paid after the first six months, the other half at the end of the year).

The two promises can be represented on a time graph as Figure 15.1 shows.

FIGURE 15.1 ***Graphic representation of method and data***

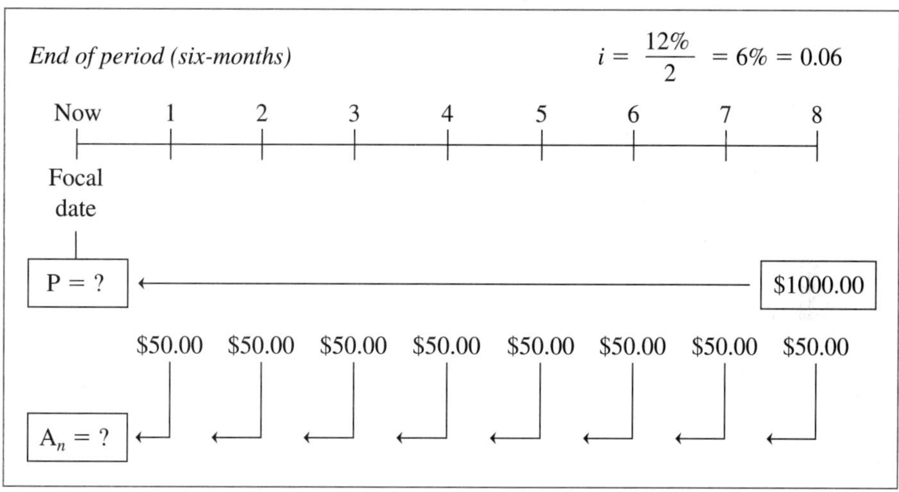

The focal date for evaluating the two promises is 'now' and the rate of interest to be used for the valuation is 12% compounded semi-annually.

The value of the redemption value of \$1000.00 is its present value.

$$S = 1000.00; \quad n = 4(2) = 8; \quad i = \frac{12\%}{2} = 6\% = 0.06$$

$$\begin{aligned} P &= 1000.00(1.06)^{-8} \longleftarrow \text{using Formula 9.2B} \\ &= 1000.00(0.6274124) \\ &= \$627.41 \end{aligned}$$

Programmed solution

0	1000	6	8			
PMT	FV	%i	N	CPT	PV	627.41

The value 'now' of the semi-annual interest payments is the present value of an ordinary annuity.

$$R = \frac{10\% \text{ of } 1000.00}{2} = 50.00; \quad n = 8; \quad i = 6\%;$$

$$A_n = 50.00\left(\frac{1 - 1.06^{-8}}{0.06}\right) \longleftarrow \text{using Formula 11.2}$$

$$= 50.00(6.2097938)$$

$$= \$310.49$$

Programmed solution

0	50	6	8			
FV	PMT	%i	N	CPT	PV	310.49

The purchase price of the bond is the sum of the present values of the two promises

$$= P + A_n$$

$$= 627.41 + 310.49 = \$937.90$$

THE PURCHASE PRICE OF A BOND BOUGHT ON AN INTEREST PAYMENT DATE
= THE PRESENT VALUE OF THE REDEMPTION VALUE
+ THE PRESENT VALUE OF THE INTEREST PAYMENTS

The two steps involved in using the above relationship can be combined.

$$\text{PURCHASE PRICE} = P + A_n$$

$$= S(1 + i)^{-n} + R\left[\frac{1 - (1 + i)^{-n}}{i}\right] \longleftarrow \textit{Formula } \mathbf{15.1}$$

where S = the redemption value of the bond;
R = the periodic interest payment (coupon);
n = the number of outstanding interest payments (or compounding periods);
i = the yield rate per payment interval.

Note: It is important to recognize that two rates of interest are used in determining the purchase price:

1. the bond rate which determines the size of the periodic interest payments (coupons);
2. the **yield rate** which is used to determine the present values of the two promises.

Example **15.1b** A $5000 bond bearing interest at 10.5% payable semi-annually is redeemable at par in ten years. If it is bought to yield 9% compounded semi-annually, what is the purchase price of the bond?

Solution

The redemption value S = 5000.00;

$$\text{the coupon } R = \frac{5000.00(0.105)}{2} = 262.50;$$

$$n = 10(2) = 20; \quad i = \frac{9\%}{2} = 4.5\% = 0.045$$

$$\text{Purchase price} = \begin{matrix}\text{Present value of the}\\ \text{redemption value}\end{matrix} + \begin{matrix}\text{Present value}\\ \text{of the coupons}\end{matrix}$$

$$= \quad P \quad + \quad A_n$$

$$= 5000.00(1.045^{-20}) + 262.50\left(\frac{1 - 1.045^{-20}}{0.045}\right)$$

$$= 5000.00(0.4146429) + 262.50(13.007936)$$

$$= 2073.21 + 3414.58$$

$$= \$5487.79$$

Programmed solution

0	5000	4.5	20			
PMT	FV	%i	N	CPT	PV	2073.21

0	262.50			
FV	PMT	CPT	PV	3414.58

The purchase price is 2073.21 + 3414.58 = \$5487.79.

***Example* 15.1c** A bond with a par value of \$10 000 is redeemable at 106 in 25 years. The coupon rate is 8% payable semi-annually. What is the purchase price of the bond to yield 10% compounded semi-annually?

Solution

The redemption value S = 10 000.00(1.06) = 10 600.00;

$$\text{the coupon } R = \frac{10\,000.00(0.08)}{2} = 400.00;$$

$$n = 25(2) = 50; \quad i = \frac{10\%}{2} = 5\% = 0.05$$

$$\text{Purchase price} = P + A_n$$

$$= 10\,600.00(1.105^{-50}) + 400.00\left(\frac{1 - 1.05^{-50}}{0.05}\right)$$

$$= 10\,600.00(0.0872037) + 400.00(18.255925)$$

$$= 924.36 + 7302.37$$

$$= \$8226.73$$

Programmed solution

0	10 600	5	50			
PMT	FV	%i	N	CPT	PV	924.36

0	400			
FV	PMT	CPT	PV	7302.37

The purchase price is 924.36 + 7302.37 = \$8226.73

***Example* 15.1d** A $25 000 bond bearing interest at 11% payable quarterly is redeemable at 107 in twelve years. Find the purchase price of the bond to yield 10% compounded quarterly.

Solution

$$\text{The redemption value } S = 25\ 000.00(1.07) = 26\ 750.00;$$

$$\text{the coupon } R = \frac{25\ 000.00(0.11)}{4} = 687.50;$$

$$n = 12(4) = 48; \quad i = \frac{10\%}{4} = 2.5\% = 0.025$$

$$\text{Purchase price} = 26\ 750.00(1.025^{-48}) + 687.50\left(\frac{1 - 1.025^{-48}}{0.025}\right)$$

$$= 26\ 750.00(0.3056712) + 687.50(27.773154)$$

$$= 8176.70 + 19\ 094.04$$

$$= \$27\ 270.74$$

Programmed solution

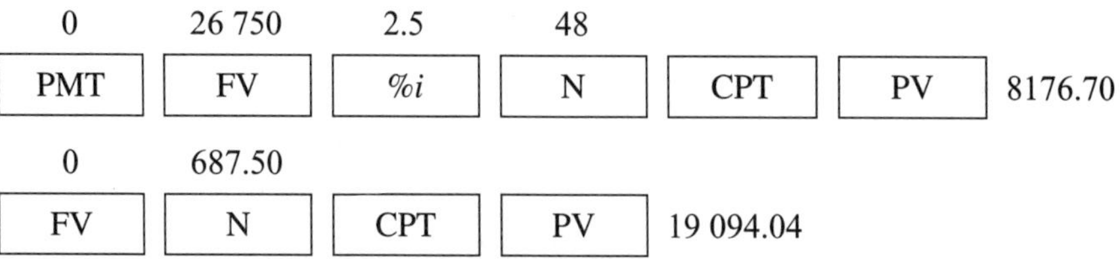

The purchase price is 8186.70 + 19 094.04 = 27 270.74.

In the preceding problems, the bond interest payment period and the yield rate conversion period were equal in length. This permitted the use of simple annuity formulae. However, when the bond interest payment period and the yield rate conversion period are not equal in length, general annuity formulae must be used.

***Example* 15.1e** A municipality issues ten-year bonds in the amount of $1 000 000. Interest on the bonds is 10% payable annually. What is the issue price of the bonds if the bonds are sold to yield 11% compounded quarterly?

Solution

The redemption value of the bonds S = 1 000 000.00;

the annual interest payment R = 1 000 000.00(0.10) = $100 000.00.

Since the interest payment period (annual) is not equal in length to the yield rate conversion period (quarterly), the interest payments form an ordinary general annuity.

$$n = 10; \quad c = \frac{4}{1} = 4; \quad i = \frac{11\%}{4} = 2.75\% = 0.0275;$$

$$f = 1.0275^4 - 1 = 1.1146213 - 1 = 0.1146213$$

The present value of the redemption value

$$\begin{aligned} P &= 1\,000\,000.00(1.1146213^{-10}) \\ &= 1\,000\,000.00(0.3378521) \\ &= \$337\,852.10 \end{aligned}$$

The present value of the annual interest payments

$$A_{nc} = 100\,000.00\left[\frac{(1 - 1.1146213^{-10})}{0.1146213}\right] \longleftarrow \text{using Formula 13.2}$$

$$= 100\,000.00(5.7768312)$$

$$= \$577\,683.12$$

Programmed solution

0	1 000 000	11.46213	10			
PMT	FV	%*i*	N	CPT	PV	337 852.10

0	100 000			
FV	PMT	CPT	PV	577 683.12

The issue price is 337 852.10 + 577 683.12 = \$915 535.22.

We can modify Formula 15.1 to allow for the general annuity case by using Formula 13.2.

$$\text{PURCHASE PRICE} = P + A_{nc} = S(1+f)^{-n} + R\left[\frac{1-(1+f)^{-n}}{f}\right] \longleftarrow \textbf{\textit{Formula} 15.2}$$

$$\text{where } f = (1+i)^c - 1$$

***Example* 15.1f** A \$100 000 bond redeemable at 103 bearing interest at 11.5% payable semi-annually is bought eight years before maturity to yield 10% compounded quarterly. What is the purchase price of the bond?

Solution

$$\text{The redemption value } S = 100\,000.00(1.03) = \$103\,000.00;$$

$$\text{the size of the semi-annual coupon } R = 100\,000.00\left(\frac{0.115}{2}\right) = \$5750.00$$

$$n = 8(2) = 16; \quad c = \frac{4}{2} = 2; \quad i = \frac{10\%}{4} = 2.5\% = 0.025;$$

$$f = 1.025^2 - 1 = 1.050625 - 1 = 0.050625 = 5.0625\%$$

The purchase price of the bond using Formula 15.2

$$= 103\,000.00(1.050625^{-16}) + 5750.00\left(\frac{1 - 1.050625^{-16}}{0.050625}\right)$$

$$= 103\,000.00(0.4537706) + 5750.00(10.789717)$$

$$= 46\,738.37 + 62\,040.87$$

$$= \$108\,779.24$$

Programmed solution

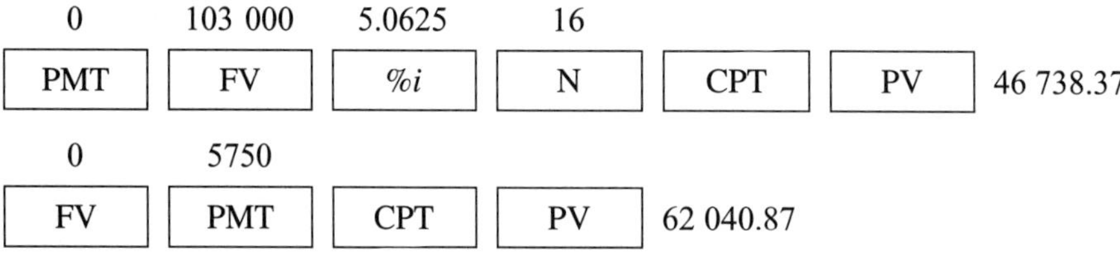

The purchase price is 46 738.37 + 62 040.87 = $108 779.24.

C. *Purchase price of bonds between interest dates*

The trading of bonds is, of course, not restricted to interest dates. In practice, most bonds are bought and sold between interest dates.

In such cases, we can compute the price of the bond on the date of purchase by first finding the purchase price on the interest date immediately preceding the date of purchase. The resulting value can then be accumulated using the amount formula for simple interest at the nominal yield rate for the number of days elapsed between the interest payment date and the purchase date.

Example **15.1g** A bond with a face value of $1000 bearing interest at 10% payable semi-annually matures on August 1, 1997. What is the purchase price of the bond on April 18, 1995, to yield 9% compounded semi-annually?

Solution

STEP 1 Find the purchase price on the preceding interest date.

The redemption value S = $1000.00;

the semi-annual coupon $R = 1000.00\left(\frac{0.10}{2}\right) = \$50.00.$

Since the maturity date is August 1, the semi-annual interest dates are February 1 and August 1. The interest date preceding the date of purchase is February 1, 1995. The time period from February 1, 1995, to the date of maturity is 2.5 years.

$$n = 2.5(2) = 5; \quad i = \frac{9\%}{2} = 4.5\% = 0.045$$

The purchase price of the bond on February 1, 1995,

$$= 1000.00(1.045^{-5}) + 50.00\left(\frac{1 - 1.045^{-5}}{0.045}\right)$$

$$= 1000.00(0.802451) + 50.00(4.3899767)$$

$$= 802.45 + 219.50$$

$$= \$1021.95$$

Programmed solution

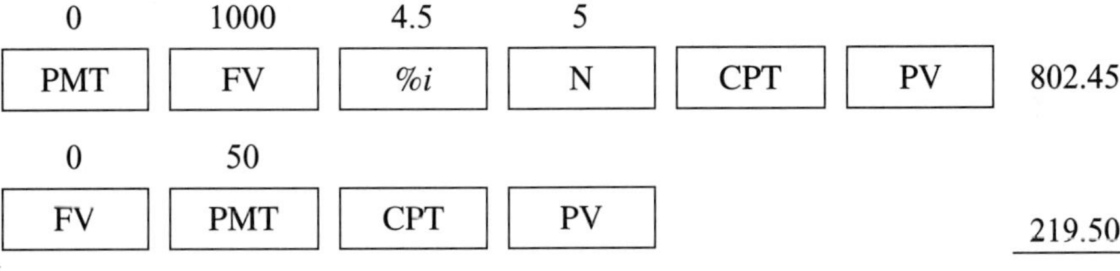

The purchase price is 1021.95

STEP 2 Accumulate the purchase price on February 1, 1995, to the purchase date at simple interest.

The number of days from February 1, 1995, to April 18, 1995, is 76; the number of days in the interest interval February 1, 1995, to August 1, 1995, is 181.

$$P = 1021.95; \quad r = i = 0.045; \quad t = \frac{76}{181}$$

$$S = 1021.95\left[1 + 0.045\left(\frac{76}{181}\right)\right] = 1021.95(1.018895) = \$1041.26.$$

The purchase price of the bond on April 18, 1995, is $1041.26.

D. Flat price and quoted price

In Example 15.1g, the total purchase price of $1041.26 is called the **flat price**. This price includes interest that has accrued from February 1, 1995, to April 18, 1995, but will not be paid until August 1, 1995.

The actual accrued interest is $1000.00(0.05)\left(\frac{76}{181}\right) = \$20.99$.

As far as the seller of the bond is concerned, the net price of the bond is 1041.26 − 20.99 = \$1020.27. This price is called the **quoted price** or market price.

$$\text{QUOTED PRICE} = \text{FLAT PRICE} - \text{ACCRUED INTEREST}$$

$$\text{FLAT PRICE} = \text{QUOTED PRICE} + \text{ACCRUED INTEREST}$$

In a stable market, the flat price of bonds increases as the accrued interest increases and drops suddenly by the amount of the interest paid on the interest date. To avoid this fluctuation in price, which is entirely due to the accrued interest, bonds are offered for sale at the quoted price. The accrued interest is added to obtain the total price or flat price.

***Example* 15.1h** A \$5000 bond redeemable at par in seven years and four months bearing interest at 10.5% payable semi-annually is bought to yield 11.5% compounded semi-annually. Determine

(i) the purchase price (flat price);

(ii) the accrued interest;

(iii) the market price (quoted price).

Solution

(i) The redemption value S = \$5000.00;

the semi-annual coupon $R = 5000.00\left(\frac{0.105}{2}\right) = \$262.50$.

The interest date preceding the purchase date is 7.5 years before maturity.

$$n = 7.5(2) = 15; \quad i = \frac{11.5\%}{2} = 5.75\% = 0.0575$$

The purchase price on the interest date preceding the date of purchase

$$= 5000.00(1.0575^{-15}) + 262.50\left(\frac{1 - 1.0575^{-15}}{0.0575}\right)$$

$$= 5000.00(0.4323091) + 262.50(9.8728855)$$

$$= 2161.55 + 2591.63$$

$$= \$4753.18$$

Programmed solution

0	5000	5.75	15			
PMT	FV	%i	N	CPT	PV	2161.55
0	262.50					
FV	PMT	CPT	PV			2591.63
				The purchase price is		4753.18

The accumulated value two months later

$$P = 4753.18; \quad r = i = 0.0575; \quad t = \frac{2}{6};$$

$$S = 4753.18\left[1 + 0.0575\left(\frac{2}{6}\right)\right]$$
$$= 4753.18(1.0191667)$$
$$= \$4844.28$$

The purchase price (flat price) is \$4844.28.

(ii) The accrued interest is $5000.00(0.0525)\left(\frac{2}{6}\right) = \$87.50$.

(iii) The quoted price (market price) is $4844.28 - 87.50 = \$4756.78$.

***Example* 15.1i** A \$10 000, 11% bond redeemable at 108 matures on May 1, 2010. Interest is payable semi-annually. The bond is purchased on March 21, 1998, to yield 10% compounded semi-annually.

(i) What is the purchase price of the bond?

(ii) What is the accrued interest?

(iii) What is the quoted price?

Solution

(i) The redemption price $S = 10\,000.00(1.08) = \$10\,800.00$;

the semi-annual coupon $R = 10\,000.00\left(\frac{0.11}{2}\right) = \$550.00$.

The interest dates on the bond are May 1 and November 1.
The interest date preceding the date of purchase is November 1, 1997.

The time period November 1, 1997, to May 1, 2010, is 12.5 years.

$$n = 12.5(2) = 25; \quad i = \frac{10\%}{2} = 5\% = 0.05$$

The purchase price on November 1, 1997,

$$= 10\,800.00(1.05^{-25}) + 550.00\left(\frac{1 - 1.05^{-25}}{0.05}\right)$$

$$= 10\,800.00(0.2953028) + 550.00(14.093945)$$

$$= 3189.27 + 7751.67$$

$$= \$10\,940.94$$

Programmed solution

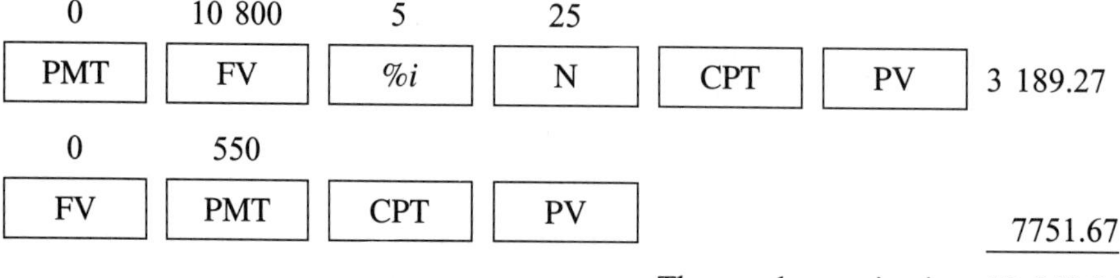

The purchase price is 10 940.94

The time period November 1, 1997, to March 21, 1998, contains 140 days; the number of days in the interest payment interval November 1, 1997, to May 1, 1998, is 181.

$$P = 10\,940.94; \quad r = i = 0.05; \quad t = \frac{140}{181}$$

The accumulated value on March 21, 1998,

$$= 10\,940.94\left[1 + 0.05\left(\frac{140}{181}\right)\right] = 10\,940.94(1.0386740) = \$11\,364.07$$

(ii) The actual accrued interest is $10\,000.00(0.055)\left(\frac{140}{181}\right) = \$425.41$.

(iii) The quoted price is $11\,364.07 - 425.41 = \$10\,938.66$.

Exercise 15.1

A. Determine the purchase price at the indicated time before redemption of each of the following bonds.

	Par value	*Redeemed at*	*Bond rate payable semi-annually*	*Time before redemption*	*Yield rate*	*Conversion period*
1.	$100 000	par	15.5%	5.5 years	13.5%	semi-annually
2.	$5 000	par	10%	12 years	12%	semi-annually
3.	$25 000	103	16%	7 years	14%	semi-annually
4.	$1 000	110	8.5%	12.5 years	13.5%	semi-annually
5.	$50 000	par	14%	10 years	13%	annually
6.	$20 000	par	10.5%	6.5 years	13%	quarterly
7.	$8 000	104	11.5%	18.5 years	9%	monthly
8.	$3 000	107	10%	20 years	12%	quarterly
9.	$15 000	par	9.5%	6 yrs, 4 mo	15%	semi-annually
10.	$5 000	par	11%	12 yrs, 9 mo	12%	semi-annually
11.	$10 000	108	12%	9 yrs, 5 mo	14%	semi-annually
12.	$2 000	105	17.5%	5 yrs, 10 mo	19.5%	semi-annually

B. Answer each of the following questions.

1. A $500 bond is redeemable at par on March 1, 2002. Interest is 11% payable semi-annually. Find the purchase price of the bond on September 1, 1996, to yield 16.5% compounded semi-annually.

2. A $25 000, 13% bond redeemable at par is purchased twelve years before maturity to yield 16% compounded semi-annually. If the bond interest is payable semi-annually, what is the purchase price of the bond?

3. A $1000, 11.5% bond redeemable at 104 is purchased 8.5 years before maturity to yield 13% compounded semi-annually. If the bond interest is payable semi-annually, what is the purchase price of the bond?

4. A $100 000 bond is redeemable at 108 in fifteen years. If interest on the bond is 15.5% payable semi-annually, what is the purchase price to yield 14% compounded semi-annually?

5. A 25-year bond issue of $5 000 000 redeemable at par and bearing interest at 7.25% payable annually is sold to yield 8.5% compounded semi-annually. What is the issue price of the bonds?

6. A $100 000 bond bearing interest at 16% payable semi-annually is bought eight years before maturity to yield 14.5% compounded annually. If the bond is redeemable at par, what is the purchase price?

7. Bonds with a par value of $40 000 redeemable at 103 in 7.5 years bearing interest at 13% payable quarterly are sold to yield 14% compounded semi-annually. Determine the purchase price of the bonds.

8. Six $1000 bonds with 11.5% coupons payable semi-annually are bought to yield 18% compounded monthly. If the bonds are redeemable at 109 in eight years, what is the purchase price?

9. A $25 000, 10% bond redeemable at par on December 1, 2007, is purchased on September 25, 1996, to yield 14.5% compounded semi-annually. Bond interest is payable semi-annually.

   (a) What is the flat price of the bond?

   (b) What is the accrued interest?

   (c) What is the quoted price?

10. A $100 000 bond redeemable at par on October 1, 2017, is purchased on January 15, 1996. Interest is 13% payable semi-annually and the yield is 11.5% compounded semi-annually.

    (a) What is the purchase price of the bond?

    (b) How much interest has accrued?

    (c) What is the market price?

11. A $5000, 15% bond redeemable at 104 matures on August 1, 2004. If the coupons are payable semi-annually, what is the quoted price on May 10, 1995, to yield 13.5% compounded semi-annually?

12. Bonds in denominations of $1000 redeemable at 107 are offered for sale. If the bonds mature in six years and ten months and the coupon rate is 9.5% payable quarterly, what is the market price of the bonds to yield 12% compounded quarterly?

15.2 *Premium and discount*

A. Basic concepts—bond rate versus yield (or market) rate

Comparing the redemption values with the purchase prices obtained in Examples 15.1a to 15.1i (see Table 15.1 below) shows that the purchase price is sometimes less than and sometimes more than the redemption value.

TABLE 15.1 ***Comparison of redemption values with purchase prices for Examples 15.1a to 15.1i***

Example	*Redemption value* S	*Purchase (flat) price* PP	*Comparison of S and PP*	*Premium or discount*	*Amount of premium or discount*	*Bond rate* b	*Yield rate* i	b *versus* i
15.1a	\$1 000.00	\$937.90	S > PP	discount	\$62.10	5%	6%	b < i
15.1b	\$5 000.00	\$5 487.79	PP > S	premium	\$487.79	5.25%	4.5%	b > i
15.1c	\$10 600.00	\$8 226.73	S > PP	discount	\$2 373.27	4%	5%	b < i
15.1d	\$26 750.00	\$27 270.74	PP > S	premium	\$520.74	2.75%	2.5%	b > i
15.1e	\$1 000 000.00	\$915 535.22	S > PP	discount	\$84 464.78	10%	11.46%	b < i
15.1f	\$103 000.00	\$108 779.24	PP > S	premium	\$5 779.24	5.75%	5.06%	b > i
15.1g	\$1 000.00	\$1 041.26	PP > S	premium	\$41.26	5%	4.5%	b > i
15.1h	\$5 000.00	\$4 844.28	S > PP	discount	\$155.72	5.25%	5.75%	b < i
15.1i	\$10 800.00	\$11 364.07	PP > S	premium	\$564.07	5.5%	5%	b > i

If the purchase price of a bond is greater than the redemption value, the bond is said to be bought at a premium and the difference between the purchase price and the redemption value is called the **premium**

PREMIUM = PURCHASE PRICE − REDEMPTION VALUE
where purchase price > redemption value

If the purchase price of a bond is less than the redemption value, the bond is said to be bought at a discount and the difference between the redemption value and the purchase price is called the **discount**.

DISCOUNT = REDEMPTION VALUE − PURCHASE PRICE
where redemption value > purchase price

An examination of the size of the bond rate b relative to the size of the market rate i shows that this relationship determines whether there is a premium or discount.

The bond rate (or coupon rate) stated on the bond is the percent of the *face* value of the bond that will be paid at the end of each interest period to the bondholder. This rate is established at the time of issue of the bonds and remains the same throughout the term of the bond.

On the other hand, the rate at which lenders are willing to provide money fluctuates in response to economic conditions. The combination of factors at work in the capital market at any given time in conjunction with the perceived risk associated with a particular bond determines the yield rate (or market rate) for a bond and thus the price at which a bond will be bought or sold.

The bond rate and the market rate are usually *not* equal. However, if the two rates happen to be equal, then bonds that are redeemable at par will sell at their face value. If the bond rate is *less* than the market rate, the bond will sell at a price less than the face value, that is, at a *discount.* If the bond rate is *greater* than the market rate, the bond will sell at a price above its face value, that is, at a *premium.*

Conversely, if a bond is redeemable at par (that is, at 100), purchasers will realize the bond rate if they pay 100. They will realize less than the bond rate if they buy at a premium and more than the bond rate if they buy at a discount.

At any time, one of three possible situations exists for any given bond:

(1) Bond rate = Market rate ($b = i$) $\longrightarrow$ The bond sells at *par.*
(2) Bond rate < Market rate ($b < i$) $\longrightarrow$ The bond sells at a *discount.*
(3) Bond rate > Market rate ($b > i$) $\longrightarrow$ The bond sells at a *premium.*

Example **15.2a** A $10 000 bond is redeemable at par and bears interest at 10% compounded semi-annually.

(i) What is the purchase price ten years before maturity if the market rate compounded semi-annually is

(a) 10%; **(b)** 12%; **(c)** 8%.

(ii) What is the purchase price five years before maturity if the market rate compounded semi-annually is

(a) 10%; **(b)** 12%; **(c)** 8%.

Solution

(i) S = 10 000.00; R = 10 000.00(0.05) = 500.00; $n = 10(2) = 20$; $b = 5\%$

(a) $i = \dfrac{10\%}{2} = 5\% = 0.05$; $(b = i)$

$$\text{Purchase price} = 10\,000.00(1.05^{-20}) + 500.00\left(\frac{1 - 1.05^{-20}}{0.05}\right)$$

$$= 10\,000.00(0.3768895) + 500.00(12.46221)$$

$$= 3768.90 + 6231.11$$

$$= \$10\,000.01$$

Programmed solution

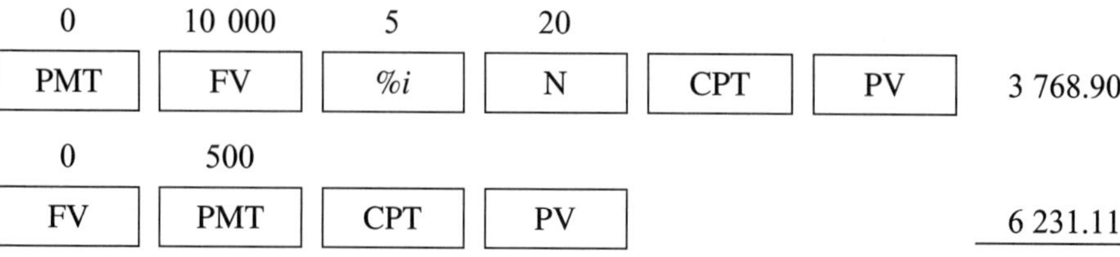

The purchase price is $10 000.01

The bond sells at par.

(b) $i = \dfrac{12\%}{2} = 6\% = 0.06; \quad (b < i)$

$$\text{Purchase price} = 10\,000.00(1.06^{-20}) + 500.00\left(\frac{1 - 1.06^{-20}}{0.06}\right)$$

$$= 10\,000.00(0.3118047) + 500.00(11.469921)$$

$$= 3118.05 + 5734.96$$

$$= \$8853.01$$

Programmed solution

0	10 000	6	20			
PMT	FV	%i	N	CPT	PV	3118.05
0	500					
FV	PMT	CPT	PV			5234.96

The purchase price is $8853.01

The bond sells below par.

The discount is 10 000.00 − 8853.01 = $1146.99.

(c) $i = \dfrac{8\%}{2} = 4\% = 0.04; \ (b > i)$

$$\text{Purchase price} = 10\,000.00(1.04^{-20}) + 500.00\left(\frac{1 - 1.04^{-20}}{0.04}\right)$$

$$= 10\,000.00(0.4563869) + 500.00(13.590326)$$

$$= 4563.87 + 6795.16$$

$$= \$11\,359.03$$

Programmed solution

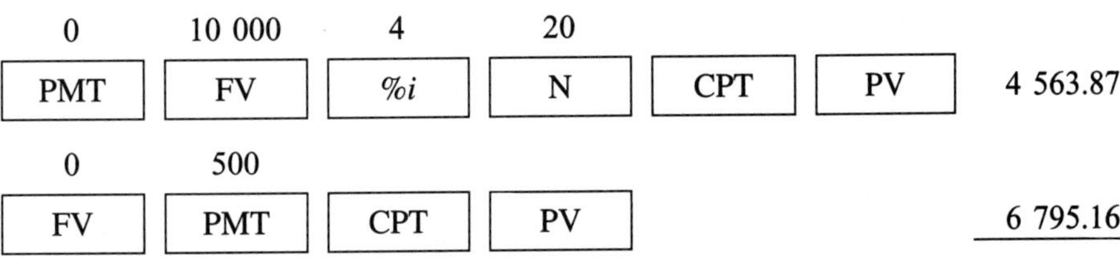

The purchase price is $11 359.03

The bond sells above par.

The premium is 11 359.03 − 10 000.00 = $1359.03.

(ii) S = 10 000.00; R = 500.00; $n = 5(2) = 10$; $b = 5\%$

(a) $i = 5\%$; (see part (b)) $(b = i)$

$$\text{Purchase price} = 10\,000.00(1.05^{-10}) + 500.00\left(\frac{1 - 1.05^{-10}}{0.05}\right)$$

$$= 6139.13 + 3860.87$$

$$= \$10\,000.00$$

Programmed solution

0	10 000	5	10			
PMT	FV	%i	N	CPT	PV	6 139.13
0	500					
FV	PMT	CPT	PV			3 860.87
				The purchase price is		$10 000.00

The bond sells at par.

(b) $i = 6\%$; $(b < i)$

$$\text{Purchase price} = 10\,000.00(1.06^{-10}) + 500.00\left(\frac{1 - 1.06^{-10}}{0.06}\right)$$

$$= 5583.95 + 3680.04$$

$$= \$9263.99$$

Programmed solution

0	10 000	6	10			
PMT	FV	%i	N	CPT	PV	5583.95
0	500					
FV	PMT	CPT	PV			3680.04
				The purchase price is		$9263.99

The bond sells below par.

The discount is 10 000.00 − 9263.99 = $736.01. It is smaller than in part (i) because the time to maturity is shorter.

(c) $i = 4\%$; $(b > i)$

$$\text{Purchase price} = 10\,000.00(1.04^{-10}) + 500.00\left(\frac{1 - 1.04^{-10}}{0.04}\right)$$

$$= 6755.64 + 4055.45$$

$$= \$10\,811.09$$

Programmed solution

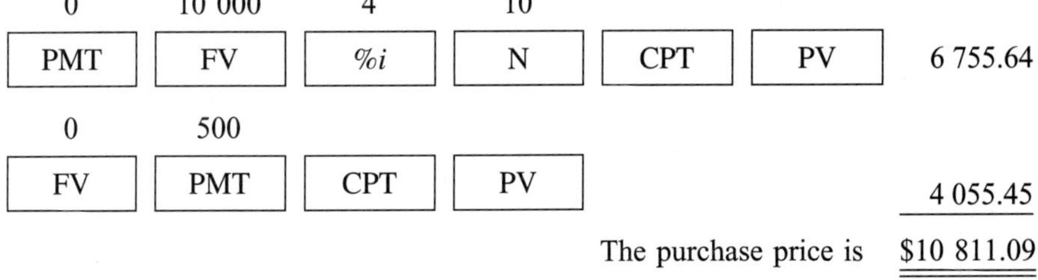

The bond sells above par.

The premium is 10 811.09 − 10 000.00 = \$811.09. It is smaller than in part (i) because the time to maturity is shorter.

B. *Direct method of computing the premium or discount—alternate method for finding the purchase price*

***Example* 15.2b** A \$5000, 12% bond with semi-annual coupons is bought six years before maturity to yield 10% compounded semi-annually. Determine the premium.

Solution

$$S = 5000.00; \quad b = \frac{12\%}{2} = 6\% = 0.06; \quad R = 5000.00(0.06) = 300.00;$$

$$i = \frac{10\%}{2} = 5\% = 0.05; \quad n = 6(2) = 12$$

Since $b > i$, the bond will sell at a premium.

$$\text{Purchase price} = 5000.00(1.05^{-12}) + 300.00\left(\frac{1 - 1.05^{-12}}{0.05}\right)$$

$$= 5000.00(0.5568374) + 300.00(8.8632516)$$

$$= 2784.19 + 2658.97$$

$$= \$5443.16$$

Programmed solution

0	5000	6	12			
PMT	FV	%i	N	CPT	PV	2784.19
0	300					
FV	PMT	CPT	PV			2658.97

The purchase price is $5443.16

The premium is 5443.16 − 5000.00 = $443.16.

While you can always determine the premium by the basic method using Formula 15.1, it is more convenient to determine the premium directly by considering the relationship between the bond rate b and the yield rate i.

As previously discussed, a premium results when $b > i$. When this is the case, the premium is paid because the periodic interest payments received exceed the periodic interest required according to the yield rate.

In Example 15.2b

The semi-annual interest payment	5000.00(0.06) = $300.00
The required semi-annual interest based on the yield rate	5000.00(0.05) = $250.00
The excess of the actual interest received over the required interest to make the yield rate	= $50.00

This excess is received at the end of every payment interval; thus it forms an ordinary annuity whose present value can be computed at the yield rate i.

$$\text{R (the excess interest)} = 50.00; \quad i = 5\%; \quad n = 12$$

$$A_n = 50.00\left(\frac{1 - 1.05^{-12}}{0.05}\right)$$

$$= 50.00(8.8632516)$$

$$= \$443.16$$

Programmed solution

0	50	5	12			
FV	PMT	%i	N	CPT	PV	443.16

The premium is $443.16.

The purchase price is 5000.00 + 443.16 = $5443.16.

The premium is the present value of the ordinary annuity formed by the excess of the actual bond interest over the required interest based on the yield rate. We can obtain the purchase price by adding the premium to the redemption value.

$$\text{PREMIUM} = (\text{PERIODIC BOND INTEREST} - \text{REQUIRED INTEREST})\left[\frac{1-(1+i)^{-n}}{i}\right]$$

$$= (\text{FACE VALUE} \times b - \text{REDEMPTION VALUE} \times i)\left[\frac{1-(1+i)^{-n}}{i}\right]$$

Example **15.2c** A \$5000, 12% bond with semi-annual coupons is bought six years before maturity to yield 14% compounded semi-annually. Determine the discount.

Solution

$$S = 5000.00; \quad b = \frac{12\%}{2} = 6\% = 0.06; \quad R = 5000.00(0.06) = 300.00;$$

$$i = \frac{14\%}{2} = 7\% = 0.07; \quad n = 6(2) = 12$$

Since $b < i$, the bond will sell at a discount.

$$\text{Purchase price} = 5000.00(1.07^{-12}) + 300.00\left(\frac{1-1.07^{-12}}{0.07}\right)$$

$$= 5000.00(0.444012) + 300.00(7.9426863)$$

$$= 2220.06 + 2382.81$$

$$= \$4602.87$$

Programmed solution

0	5000	7	12			
PMT	FV	%i	N	CPT	PV	2220.06
0	300					
FV	PMT	CPT	PV			2382.81

The purchase price is \$4602.87

The discount is 5000.00 − 4602.87 = \$397.13.

As in the case of a premium, while you can always determine the discount by the basic method using Formula 15.1, it is more convenient to determine the discount directly.

When $b < i$, a discount results. The discount on a bond is received because the periodic interest payments are less than the periodic interest required to earn the yield rate.

In Example 15.2c

The semi-annual interest payment	5000.00(0.06) = \$300.00
The required semi-annual interest based on the yield rate	5000.00(0.07) = \$350.00
The shortage of the actual interest received as compared to the required interest based on the yield rate	= \$50.00

This shortage occurs at the end of every interest payment interval; it forms an ordinary annuity whose present value can be computed at the yield rate i.

$$R = 50.00; \quad i = 7\%; \quad n = 12$$

$$A_n = 50.00\left(\frac{1 - 1.07^{-12}}{0.07}\right)$$

$$= 50.00(7.9426863)$$

$$= \$397.13$$

Programmed solution

0	50	7	12			
FV	PMT	%i	N	CPT	PV	397.13

The discount is \$397.13.

The purchase price is 5000.00 − 397.13 = \$4602.87.

The discount is the present value of the ordinary annuity formed by the shortage of the actual bond interest received as compared to the required interest based on the yield rate. We can obtain the purchase price by subtracting the discount from the redemption value.

$$\text{DISCOUNT} = (\text{REQUIRED INTEREST} - \text{PERIODIC BOND INTEREST})\left[\frac{1-(1+i)^{-n}}{i}\right]$$

$$= -(\text{PERIODIC BOND INTEREST} - \text{REQUIRED INTEREST})\left[\frac{1-(1+i)^{-n}}{i}\right]$$

$$= -(\text{FACE VALUE} \times b - \text{REDEMPTION VALUE} \times i)\left[\frac{1-(1+i)^{-n}}{i}\right]$$

Since in both cases the difference between the periodic bond interest and the required interest is involved, the premium or discount on the purchase of a bond can be obtained using the same relationship.

$$\text{PREMIUM or DISCOUNT} = (b \times \text{FACE VALUE} - i \times \text{REDEMPTION VALUE})\left[\frac{1-(1+i)^{-n}}{i}\right] \quad \longleftarrow \textit{Formula } \mathbf{15.3}$$

***Example* 15.2d** A \$1000, 11.5% bond with semi-annual coupons redeemable at par in fifteen years is bought to yield 10% compounded semi-annually. Determine

(i) the premium or discount;

(ii) the purchase price.

Solution

(i) $$S = 1000.00; \quad b = \frac{11.5\%}{2} = 5.75\% = 0.0575;$$

$$R = 1000.00(0.0575) = 57.50;$$

$$i = \frac{10\%}{2} = 5\% = 0.05; \quad n = 15(2) = 30$$

Since $b > i$, the bond will sell at a premium.

The required interest based on the yield rate is 1000.00(0.05) = 50.00; the excess interest is 57.50 − 50.00 = 7.50.

The premium is $7.50\left(\frac{1 - 1.05^{-30}}{0.05}\right) = 7.50(15.372451) = \$115.29$.

Programmed solution

0	57.50	5	30			
FV	PMT	%i	N	CPT	PV	115.29

(ii) The purchase price is 1000.00 + 115.29 = \$1115.29.

***Example* 15.2e** A \$50 000, 10% bond with quarterly coupons redeemable at par in ten years is purchased to yield 11% compounded quarterly.

(i) What is the premium or discount?

(ii) What is the purchase price?

Solution

(i) $$S = 50\ 000.00; \quad b = \frac{10\%}{4} = 2.5\% = 0.025;$$

$$n = 10(4) = 40; \quad i = \frac{11\%}{4} = 2.75\% = 0.0275$$

Since $b < i$, the bond will sell at a discount.

$$\text{Discount} = (0.025 \times 50\ 000.00 - 0.0275 \times 50\ 000.00)\left(\frac{1 - 1.0275^{-40}}{0.0275}\right) \longleftarrow \text{using Formula 15.3}$$

$$= (1250.00 - 1375.00)(24.078101)$$

$$= -(125.00)(24.078101)$$

$= -\$3009.76$ ⟵ the negative sign indicates a discount

Programmed solution

First compute [PMT] $= (0.025 \times 50\,000 - 0.0275 \times 50\,000) = -125.00$

0	125	2.75	40			
FV	PMT	%i	N	CPT	PV	3009.76

(ii) The purchase price is $50\,000.00 - 3009.76 = \$46\,990.24$.

Example **15.2f** Bonds with a face value of \$15 000 redeemable at 108 with interest at 9% payable semi-annually are bought twelve years before maturity to yield 11% compounded semi-annually.

(i) What is the premium or discount?

(ii) What is the purchase price?

Solution

(i) $$S = 15\,000.00(1.08) = 16\,200.00; \quad b = \frac{9\%}{2} = 4.5\% = 0.045;$$

$$n = 12(2) = 24; \quad i = \frac{11\%}{2} = 5.5\% = 0.055$$

Since $b < i$ and the redemption value is greater than par, the bond will sell at a discount.

$$\text{Discount} = (0.045 \times 15\,000.00 - 0.055 \times 16\,200.00)\left(\frac{1 - 1.055^{-24}}{0.055}\right)$$

$$= (675.00 - 891.00)(13.151699)$$

$$= (-216.00)(13.151699)$$

$$= -\$2840.77$$

Programmed solution

PMT = (0.045 × 15 000 − 0.055 × 16 200) = −216.00

0	216	5.5	24			
FV	PMT	%*i*	N	CPT	PV	2840.77

(ii) The purchase price is 16 200.00 − 2840.77 = $13 359.23.

Example **15.2g** A $10 000, 13% bond with quarterly coupons redeemable at 106 in seven years is purchased to yield 11% compounded quarterly.

(i) What is the premium or discount?

(ii) What is the purchase price?

Solution

(i) $S = 10\,000.00(1.06) = 10\,600.00; \quad b = \frac{13\%}{4} = 3.25\% = 0.0325;$

$$n = 7(4) = 28; \quad i = \frac{11\%}{4} = 2.75\% = 0.0275$$

Since $b > i$, the bond is expected to sell at a premium.

$$\text{Premium} = (0.0325 \times 10\,000.00 - 0.0275 \times 10\,600.00)\left(\frac{1 - 1.0275^{-28}}{0.0275}\right)$$

$$= (325.00 - 291.50)(19.350826)$$

$$= (33.50)(19.350826)$$

$$= \$648.25$$

Programmed solution

PMT = (0.0325 × 10 000 − 0.0275 × 10 600) = 33.50

0	33.50	2.75	28			
FV	PMT	%*i*	N	CPT	PV	648.25

(ii) The purchase price is 10 600.00 + 648.25 = $11 248.25.

Example **15.2h** A \$1000, 11.5% bond redeemable at 110 with interest payable annually is bought nine years before maturity to yield 11% compounded annually. Determine

(i) the premium or discount;

(ii) the purchase price.

Solution

(i) $$S = 1000.00(1.10) = 1100.00; \quad b = 11.5\% = 0.115;$$
$$n = 9; \quad i = 11\% = 0.11$$

Since $b > i$, the bond is expected to be sold at a premium. While this is always true for bonds redeemable at par, it does not necessarily follow for bonds redeemable above par.

In this particular case:

the actual bond interest per year	1000.00(0.115) = \$115.00
the interest required to make the yield rate	1100.00(0.11) = \$121.00

Because of the redemption premium, the required interest exceeds the actual interest: the bond will, in fact, sell at a discount. This conclusion is borne out when using Formula 15.3.

$$\text{Premium/Discount} = (0.115 \times 1000.00 - 0.11 \times 1100.00)\left(\frac{1 - 1.11^{-9}}{0.11}\right)$$
$$= (115.00 - 121.00)(5.5370475)$$
$$= (-6.00)(5.5370475)$$
$$= -\$33.22$$

Programmed solution

PMT = (0.115 × 1000 − 0.11 × 1100) = −6.00

0	6	11	9			
FV	PMT	%i	N	CPT	PV	33.22

(ii) Since the answer (PMT) is negative, the bond sells at a discount of \$33.22. The purchase price is 1100.00 − 33.22 = \$1066.78.

Example **15.2i** A \$25 000 bond, redeemable at 104 on July 1, 2006, with 11% coupons payable quarterly, is bought on May 20, 1997, to yield 10% compounded quarterly. What is

(i) the premium or discount?

(ii) the purchase price?

(iii) the quoted price?

Solution

$$S = 25\ 000.00(1.04) = 26\ 000.00; \quad b = \frac{11\%}{4} = 2.75\% = 0.0275;$$

$$i = \frac{10\%}{4} = 2.5\% = 0.025$$

The interest payment dates are October 1, January 1, April 1, and July 1. The interest payment date preceding the date of purchase is April 1, 1997. The time period April 1, 1997, to July 1, 2006, contains 9 years and 3 months; $n = 9.25(4) = 37$.

The premium on April 1, 1997,

$$= (25\ 000.00 \times 0.0275 - 26\ 000.00 \times 0.025)\left(\frac{1 - 1.025^{-37}}{0.025}\right)$$

$$= (687.50 - 650.00)(23.957318)$$

$$= (37.50)(23.957318)$$

$$= \$898.40$$

Programmed solution

$\text{PMT} = (25\ 000 \times 0.0275 - 26\ 000 \times 0.025) = 37.50$

0	37.50	2.5	37			
FV	PMT	%*i*	N	CPT	PV	898.40

The purchase price on April 1, 1997, is 26 000.00 + 898.40 = \$26 898.40.

The time period April 1 to May 20 contains 49 days; the number of days in the interest payment interval April 1 to July 1 is 91.

$$P = 26\ 898.40; \quad r = i = 0.025; \quad t = \frac{49}{91}$$

The accumulated value on May 20, 1997,

$$= 26\ 898.40\left[1 + 0.025\left(\frac{49}{91}\right)\right]$$

$$= 26\ 898.40(1.0134615)$$

$$= \$27\ 260.49$$

The accrued interest to May 20 is $25\ 000.00(0.0275)\left(\frac{49}{91}\right) = \$370.19$.

The quoted price is 27 260.49 − 370.19 = \$26 890.30.

Thus, on May 20, 1997,

(i) the premium is 26 890.30 − 26 000.00 = $890.30;

(ii) the purchase price is $27 260.49;

(iii) the quoted price is $26 890.30.

Example **15.2j** A $2 000 000.00 issue of twenty-year municipal bonds redeemable at 104 is offered for sale to yield 11% compounded quarterly. If the bond interest is 12% payable annually, what is the issue price of the bonds?

Solution

$$S = 2\ 000\ 000.00(1.04) = 2\ 080\ 000.00; \quad n = 20; \quad c = 4;$$

$$b = 12\% = 0.12; \quad i = \frac{11\%}{4} = 2.75\% = 0.0275;$$

$$f = 1.0275^4 - 1 = 1.1146213 - 1 = 0.1146213 = 11.46213\%$$

Since $b > f$, the issue is expected to sell at a premium.

$$\text{Premium} = (0.12 \times 2\ 000\ 000.00 - 0.1146213 \times 2\ 080\ 000.00)\left(\frac{1 - 1.1146213^{-20}}{0.1146213}\right)$$

$$= (240\ 000.00 - 238\ 412.30)(7.7284570)$$

$$= (1587.70)(7.7284570)$$

$$= \$12\ 270.47$$

Programmed solution

PMT = (0.12 × 2 000 000 − 0.1146213 × 2 080 000) = 1587.70

0	1587.70	11.46213	20			
FV	PMT	%i	N	CPT	PV	12 270.47

The issue price is 2 080 000.00 + 12 270.47 = $2 092 270.47.

Exercise 15.2

A. For each of the following bonds, use Formula 15.3 to determine

(a) the premium or discount;

(b) the purchase price.

	Par value	Redeemed at	*Bond rate payable semi-annually*	*Time before redemption*	*Yield rate compounded semi-annually*
1.	$25 000	par	12%	10 years	15%
2.	$5 000	par	16.5%	8 years	14%
3.	$10 000	104	9%	15 years	11%
4.	$3 000	107	13.5%	9 years	10.5%
5.	$60 000	108	7%	7 years	9.5%
6.	$7 000	110	9%	5 years	8.5%
7.	$1 000	105	13%	6 years, 10 months	17%
8.	$50 000	108	12%	4 years, 5 months	11.5%

B. Answer each of the following questions.

1. A $100 000, 11% bond redeemable at par with quarterly coupons is purchased to yield 16.5% compounded quarterly. Find the premium or discount and the purchase price if the bond is purchased

   (a) fifteen years before maturity; **(b)** five years before maturity.

2. A $25 000, 9% bond redeemable at par with interest payable annually is bought six years before maturity. Determine the premium or discount and the purchase price if the bond is purchased to yield

   (a) 13.5% compounded annually; **(b)** 6% compounded annually.

3. A $5000, 14.5% bond redeemable at 104 with semi-annual coupons is purchased to yield 13% compounded semi-annually. What is the premium or discount and the purchase price if the bond is bought

   (a) ten years before maturity; **(b)** six years before maturity.

4. A $1000, 14% bond redeemable at 108 in seven years bears coupons payable annually. Compute the premium or discount and the purchase price if the yield, compounded annually, is

   (a) 12.5%; **(b)** 13.5% **(c)** 15.5%.

5. Twelve $1000 bonds redeemable at par bearing interest at 10% payable semi-annually and maturing on September 1, 2002, are bought on June 18, 1997, to yield 17.5% compounded semi-annually. Determine

   (a) the premium or discount on the preceding interest payment date;

   (b) the purchase price;

   (c) the quoted price.

6. Bonds with a face value of \$30 000 redeemable at 107 on June 1, 2003, are offered for sale to yield 15.5% compounded quarterly. If interest is 17% payable quarterly and the bonds are bought on January 24, 1994, what is
   - **(a)** the premium or discount on the interest payment date preceding the date of sale?
   - **(b)** the purchase price?
   - **(c)** the quoted price?
7. A \$5 000 000 issue of ten-year bonds redeemable at par offers 14% coupons payable semi-annually. What is the issue price of the bonds to yield 15% compounded monthly?
8. Twenty \$5000 bonds redeemable at 110 bearing 12% coupons payable quarterly are sold eight years before maturity to yield 11.5% compounded annually. What is the purchase price of the bonds?

15.3 *Bond schedules*

A. Amortization of premium

If a bond is bought at more than the redemption value, the resulting premium is not recovered when the bond is redeemed at maturity and becomes a capital *loss*. To avoid the capital loss at maturity, the premium is written down gradually over the period from the date of purchase to the maturity date. The writing down of the premium gradually reduces the bond's book value until it equals the redemption value at the date of maturity.

The process of writing down the premium is called **amortization of the premium**. The most direct method of amortizing a premium assigns the difference between the interest received (coupon) and the interest required according to the yield rate to write down the premium. The details of writing down the premium are often shown in a tabulation referred to as a schedule of amortization of premium.

Example **15.3a** A \$1000, 12% bond redeemable at par matures in three years. The coupons are payable semi-annually and the bond is bought to yield 10% compounded semi-annually.

(i) Compute the purchase price.

(ii) Construct a schedule of amortization of premium.

Solution

(i)

$$\mathrm{S} = 1000.00; \quad n = 3(2) = 6;$$

$$b = \frac{12\%}{2} = 6\% = 0.06; \quad i = \frac{10\%}{2} = 5\% = 0.05$$

Since $b > i$, the bond sells at a premium.

$$\text{Premium} = (0.06 \times 1000.00 - 0.05 \times 1000.00)\left(\frac{1 - 1.05^{-6}}{0.05}\right)$$

$$= (60.00 - 50.00)(5.075692)$$

$$= (10.00)(5.075692)$$

$$= \$50.76$$

Programmed solution

PMT = (0.06 × 1000 − 0.05 × 1000) = 10.00

0	10	5	6			
FV	PMT	%i	N	CPT	PV	50.76

The purchase price is 1000.00 + 50.76 = $1050.76.

(ii) ***Schedule of amortization of premium***

End of interest payment interval	*Bond interest received (coupon) b = 6%*	*Interest on book value at yield rate i = 5%*	*Amount of premium amortized*	*Book value of bond*	*Remaining premium*
0				1050.76	50.76
1	60.00	52.54	7.46	1043.30	43.30
2	60.00	52.17	7.83	1035.47	35.47
3	60.00	51.77	8.23	1027.24	27.24
4	60.00	51.36	8.64	1018.60	18.60
5	60.00	50.93	9.07	1009.53	9.53
6	60.00	50.47	9.53	1000.00	0.00
TOTAL	360.00	309.24	50.76		

Explanations of schedule

1. The original book value shown is the purchase price of $1050.76.
2. At the end of the first interest payment interval, the interest received (coupon) is 1000.00(0.06) = $60.00; the interest required according to the yield rate is 1050.76(0.05) = $52.54; the difference 60.00 − 52.54 = 7.46 is used to write down the premium to $43.30 and reduces the book value from $1050.76 to $1043.30.

3. The coupon at the end of the second interest payment interval is again \$60.00. The interest required according to the yield rate is 1043.30(0.05) = \$52.17; the difference 60.00 − 52.17 = 7.83 reduces the premium to \$35.47 and the book value of the bond to \$1035.47.
4. Continue in a similar manner until the maturity date when the redemption value is reached. If a rounding error becomes apparent at the end of the final interest payment interval, adjust the final interest on the book value at the yield rate to make the premium zero and to obtain the exact redemption price as the book value.
5. The totals provide useful accounting information showing the total interest received (\$360.00) and the net income realized (\$309.24).

Example **15.3b** A \$25 000, 12.5% bond redeemable at 106 with coupons payable annually matures in seven years. The bond is bought to yield 11% compounded annually.

(i) Compute the premium and the purchase price.

(ii) Construct a schedule of amortization of premium.

Solution

(i) $$S = 25\,000.00(1.06) = 26\,500.00; \quad n = 7;$$

$$b = 12.5\% = 0.125; \quad i = 11\% = 0.11$$

Since $b > i$, the bond is expected to sell at a premium.

$$\begin{aligned}\text{Premium} &= (0.125 \times 25\,000.00 - 0.11 \times 26\,500.00)\left(\frac{1 - 1.11^{-7}}{0.11}\right)\\ &= (3125.00 - 2915.00)(4.7121963)\\ &= (210.00)(4.7121963)\\ &= \$989.56\end{aligned}$$

Programmed solution

PMT = (0.125 × 25 000 − 0.11 × 26 500) = 210

0	210	11	7			
FV	PMT	%i	N	CPT	PV	989.56

The purchase price is 26 500.00 + 989.56 = \$27 489.56.

(ii) ***Schedule of amortization of premium***

End of interest payment interval	*Coupon* b = *12.5%*	*Interest on book value at yield rate* i = *11%*	*Amount of premium amortized*	*Book value of bond*	*Remaining premium*
0				27 489.56	989.56
1	3 125.00	3 023.85	101.15	27 388.41	888.41
2	3 125.00	3 012.73	112.27	27 276.14	776.14
3	3 125.00	3 000.38	124.62	27 151.52	651.52
4	3 125.00	2 986.67	138.33	27 013.19	513.19
5	3 125.00	2 971.45	153.55	26 859.64	359.64
6	3 125.00	2 954.56	170.44	26 689.20	189.20
7	3 125.00	2 935.80	189.20	26 500.00	0.00
TOTAL	21 875.00	20 885.44	989.56		

B. *Accumulation of discount*

If a bond is bought at less than the redemption value, there will be a gain at the time of redemption equal to the amount of discount. It is generally accepted accounting practice that this gain does not accrue in total to the accounting period in which the bond is redeemed. Instead, some of the gain accrues to each of the accounting periods from the date of purchase to the date of redemption.

To adhere to this practice, the discount is decreased gradually so that the book value of the bond increases gradually until, at the date of redemption, the discount is reduced to zero while the book value equals the redemption price. The process of reducing the discount so as to increase the book value is called **accumulation of discount**.

In the case of discount, the interest required according to the yield rate is greater than the actual interest received (the coupon). Similar to amortization of a premium, the most direct method of accumulating a discount assigns the difference between the interest required by the yield rate and the coupon to reduce the discount. The details of decreasing the discount while increasing the book value of a bond are often shown in a tabulation called a schedule of accumulation of discount.

Example **15.3c** A $10 000 bond, redeemable at par in four years with 11.5% coupons payable semi-annually, is bought to yield 13% compounded semi-annually.

(i) Determine the discount and the purchase price.

(ii) Construct a schedule of accumulation of discount.

Solution

(i) $$S = 10\,000.00; \quad n = 4(2) = 8;$$

$$b = \frac{11.5\%}{2} = 5.75\% = 0.0575; \quad i = \frac{13\%}{2} = 6.5\% = 0.065$$

Since $b < i$, the bond sells at a discount.

$$\text{Discount} = (0.0575 \times 10\,000.00 - 0.065 \times 10\,000.00)\left(\frac{1 - 1.065^{-8}}{0.065}\right)$$

$$= (575.00 - 650.00)(6.088751)$$

$$= (-75.00)(6.088751)$$

$$= -\$456.66$$

Programmed solution

PMT = (0.0575 × 10 000 − 0.065 × 10 000) = −75.00

0	75	6.5	8			
FV	PMT	%i	N	CPT	PV	456.66

The purchase price is 10 000.00 − 456.66 = $9543.34.

(ii) ***Schedule of accumulation of discount***

End of interest payment interval	*Coupon* b = *5.75%*	*Interest on book value at yield rate* i = *6.5%*	*Amount of discount accumulated*	*Book value of bond*	*Remaining discount*
0				9 543.34	456.66
1	575.00	620.32	45.32	9 588.66	411.34
2	575.00	623.26	48.26	9 636.92	363.08
3	575.00	626.40	51.40	9 688.32	311.68
4	575.00	629.74	54.74	9 743.06	256.94
5	575.00	633.30	58.30	9 801.36	198.64
6	575.00	637.09	62.09	9 863.45	136.55
7	575.00	641.12	66.12	9 929.57	70.43
8	575.00	645.43	70.43	10 000.00	0.00
TOTAL	4 600.00	5056.66	456.66		

Explanations of schedule

1. The original book value shown is the purchase price of \$9543.34.
2. At the end of the first interest payment interval, the coupon is 10 000.00(0.0575) = \$575.00; the interest required according to the yield rate is 9543.34(0.065) = \$620.32; the difference used to reduce the discount and to increase the book value is 620.32 − 575.00 = \$45.32; the book value is 9543.34 + 45.32 = \$9588.66, and the remaining discount is 456.66 − 45.32 = \$411.34.
3. The coupon at the end of the second interest payment interval is again \$575.00; the interest required on the book value is 9588.66(0.065) = \$623.26; the difference is 623.26 − 575.00 = \$48.26; the book value is 9588.66 + 46.26 = \$9636.92; and the remaining discount is 411.34 − 46.26 = \$363.08.
4. Continue in a similar manner until the maturity date when the redemption value is reached. If a rounding error becomes apparent at the end of the final interest payment interval, adjust the final interest on the book value at the yield rate to make the remaining discount equal to zero and obtain the exact redemption price as the book value.
5. The totals provide useful accounting information showing the total interest received (\$4600.00) and the net income realized (\$5056.66).

***Example* 15.3d** A \$5000, 10% bond redeemable at 102 on April 1, 1996, with coupons payable quarterly is bought on October 1, 1994, to yield 13% compounded quarterly.

(i) Compute the discount and the purchase price.

(ii) Construct a schedule showing the accumulation of the discount.

Solution

(i)
$$S = 5000.00(1.02) = 5100.00;$$

the time period October 1, 1994, to April 1, 1996, contains 18 months.

$$n = \frac{18}{3} = 6 \text{ (quarters)};$$

$$b = \frac{10\%}{4} = 2.5\% = 0.025; \quad i = \frac{13\%}{4} = 3.25\% = 0.0325$$

Since $b < i$, the bond sells at a discount.

$$\text{Discount} = (0.025 \times 5000.00 - 0.0325 \times 5100.00)\left(\frac{1 - 1.0325^{-6}}{0.0325}\right)$$

$$= (125.00 - 165.75)(5.3725899)$$

$$= (-40.75)(5.3725899)$$

$$= -\$218.93$$

Programmed solution

PMT = (0.025 × 5000 − 0.0325 × 5100) = −40.75

0	40.75	3.25	6			
FV	PMT	%i	N	CPT	PV	218.93

The purchase price is 5100.00 − 218.93 = $4881.07.

(ii) ***Schedule of accumulation of discount***

End of interest payment interval	*Coupon* b = *2.5%*	*Interest on book value at yield rate* i = *3.25%*	*Amount of discount accumulated*	*Book value of bond*	*Remaining discount*
Oct. 1, 1994				4881.07	218.93
Jan. 1, 1995	125.00	158.63	33.63	4914.70	185.30
Apr. 1, 1995	125.00	159.73	34.73	4949.43	150.57
July 1, 1995	125.00	160.86	35.86	4985.29	114.71
Oct. 1, 1995	125.00	162.02	37.02	5022.31	77.69
Jan. 1, 1996	125.00	163.23	38.23	5060.54	39.46
Apr. 1, 1996	125.00	164.46	39.46	5100.00	0.00
TOTAL	750.00	968.93	218.93		

C. Book value of a bond—finding the gain or loss on the sale of a bond

Example **15.3e** A $10 000, 12% bond redeemable at par with semi-annual coupons was purchased fifteen years before maturity to yield 10% compounded semi-annually. The bond was sold three years later at $101\frac{1}{4}$. Find the gain or loss on the sale of the bond.

Solution

The market quotation of $101\frac{1}{4}$ indicates that the bond was sold at 101.25% of its face value. The proceeds from the sale of the bond are 10 000.00(1.0125) = $10 125.00. To find the gain or loss on the sale of the bond, we need to know the book value of the bond at the date of sale. This we can do by determining the original purchase price, constructing a bond schedule, and reading the book value at the time of sale from the schedule.

$$S = 10\,000.00; \quad n = 15(2) = 30$$

$$b = \frac{12\%}{2} = 6\% = 0.06; \quad i = \frac{10\%}{2} = 5\% = 0.05$$

Since $b > i$, the bond was bought at a premium.

$$\text{Premium} = (0.06 \times 10\,000.00 - 0.05 \times 10\,000.00)\left(\frac{1 - 1.05^{-30}}{0.05}\right)$$

$$= (600.00 - 500.00)(15.372451)$$

$$= (100.00)(15.372451)$$

$$= \$1537.25$$

Programmed solution

PMT = (0.06 × 10 000 − 0.05 × 10 000) = 100.00

0	100	5	30			
FV	PMT	%i	N	CPT	PV	1537.25

The purchase price is 10 000.00 + 1537.25 = \$11 537.25.

Schedule of amortization of premium

End of interest payment interval	*Coupon* b = *6%*	*Interest on book value at yield rate* i = *5%*	*Amount of premium amortized*	*Book value of bond*	*Remaining premium*
0				11 537.25	1 537.25
1	600.00	576.86	23.14	11 514.11	1 514.11
2	600.00	575.71	24.29	11 489.82	1 489.82
3	600.00	574.49	25.51	11 464.31	1 464.31
4	600.00	573.22	26.78	11 437.53	1 437.53
5	600.00	571.88	28.12	11 409.41	1 409.41
6	600.00	570.47	29.53	11 379.88	1 379.88
	etc				

The book value after three years (six semi-annual periods) is \$11 379.88. Since the book value is greater than the proceeds, the loss on the sale of the bond is 11 379.88 − 10 125.00 = \$1254.88.

We can solve this problem more quickly by computing the book value directly. The book value of a bond at a given time is the purchase price of the bond on that date. We can determine the book value of a bond without constructing a bond schedule by using Formula 15.1 or 15.3. This approach can also be used to verify book values in a bond schedule.

$$S = 10\,000.00; \quad n = (15 - 3)(2) = 24; \quad b = 6\%; \quad i = 5\%$$

$$\text{Premium} = (0.06 \times 10\,000.00 - 0.05 \times 10\,000.00)\left(\frac{1 - 1.05^{-24}}{0.05}\right)$$
$$= (100.00)(13.798642)$$
$$= \$1379.86$$

Programmed solution

PMT = (0.06 × 10 000 − 0.05 × 10 000) = 100.00

0	100	5	24	
FV	PMT	%i	N	1379.86

The purchase price is 10 000.00 + 1379.86 = \$11 379.86.

The loss on the sale is 11 379.86 − 10 125.00 = \$1254.86. (The difference in the loss is due to rounding.)

***Example* 15.3f** A \$5000, 11% bond redeemable at 106 with semi-annual coupons was purchased twelve years before maturity to yield 10.5% compounded semi-annually. The bond is sold five years later at $98\frac{7}{8}$. Find the gain or loss on the sale of the bond.

Solution

Proceeds from the sale of the bond are 5000.00(0.98875) = \$4943.75.

$$S = 5000.00(1.06) = 5300.00; \quad n = (12 - 5)(2) = 14;$$
$$b = \frac{11\%}{2} = 5.5\% = 0.055; \quad i = \frac{10.5\%}{2} = 5.25\% = 0.0525$$

$$\text{Premium/Discount} = (0.055 \times 5000.00 - 0.0525 \times 5300.00)\left(\frac{1 - 1.0525^{-14}}{0.0525}\right)$$
$$= (275.00 - 278.25)(9.7423008)$$
$$= (-3.25)(9.7423008)$$
$$= -\$31.66 \longleftarrow \text{discount}$$

Programmed solution

PMT = (0.055 × 5000 − 0.0525 × 5300) = −3.25

0	3.25	5.25	14			
FV	PMT	%i	N	CPT	PV	31.66

The purchase price or book value is 5300.00 − 31.66 = \$5268.34.

The loss on the sale is 5268.34 − 4943.75 = \$324.59.

***Example* 15.3g** A \$1000, 10% bond with quarterly coupons redeemable at 104 on May 1, 2004, was purchased on August 1, 1994, to yield 12% compounded quarterly. If the bond is sold at $95\frac{1}{2}$ on December 11, 1997, what is the gain or loss on the sale of the bond?

Solution

The interest payment dates are August 1, November 1, February 1, and May 1. The interest date preceding the date of sale is November 1, 1997. The proceeds from the sale of the bond on December 11, 1977

= 1000.00(0.955) + accrued interest from November 1 to December 11

$$= 955.00 + 1000.00(0.025)\left(\frac{40}{92}\right)$$

$$= 955.00 + 10.87$$

$$= \$965.87$$

$$S = 1000.00(1.04) = 1040.00;$$

$$b = \frac{10\%}{4} = 2.5\% = 0.025; \quad i = \frac{12\%}{4} = 3\% = 0.03$$

The time interval November 1, 1997 to May 1, 2004, contains six years and six months: $n = 6.5(4) = 26$.

Since $b < i$, the bond will sell at a discount.

$$\text{Discount} = (0.025 \times 1000.00 - 0.03 \times 1040.00)\left(\frac{1 - 1.03^{-26}}{0.03}\right)$$

$$= (25.00 - 31.20)(17.876842)$$

$$= (-6.20)(17.876842)$$

$$= -\$110.84$$

Programmed solution

PMT = (0.025 × 1000 − 0.03 × 1040) = −6.20

0	6.20	3	26			
FV	PMT	%i	N	CPT	PV	110.84

The purchase price on November 1, 1997, is 1040.00 − 110.84 = \$929.16.

The accumulated value on December 11, 1997

$$= 929.16\left[1 + 0.03\left(\frac{40}{92}\right)\right]$$

$$= 929.16(1.0130435)$$

$$= \$941.28$$

The gain from the sale of the bond is $965.87 - 941.28 = \$24.59$.

Exercise 15.3

A. For each of the following bonds, compute the premium or discount and the purchase price, and construct the appropriate bond schedule.

1. A $5000, 9% bond redeemable at par in three-and-a-half years with semi-annual coupons is purchased to yield 16.5% compounded semi-annually.
2. A $25 000 bond with interest at 12.5% payable quarterly redeemable at par is bought two years before maturity to yield 11% compounded quarterly.
3. A $1000, 12% bond with semi-annual coupons redeemable at 103 on September 1, 1998, is bought on March 1, 1995, to yield 10% compounded semi-annually.
4. A $10 000, 14.75% bond with annual coupons redeemable at 110 in seven years is bought to yield 14.25% compounded annually.

B. Find the gain or loss on the sale of each of the following bonds without constructing a bond schedule.

1. A $25 000, 10.5% bond redeemable at par with semi-annual coupons bought ten years before maturity to yield 12% compounded semi-annually is sold four years before maturity at $99\frac{1}{4}$.
2. Four $5000, 14.5% bonds with interest payable semi-annually redeemable at par were bought twenty years before maturity to yield 13.5% compounded semi-annually. The bonds were sold three years later at $103\frac{5}{8}$.
3. Seven $1000, 9.25% bonds with annual coupons redeemable at 107 were bought nine years before maturity to yield 13.25% compounded annually. The bonds are sold three years before maturity at $94\frac{1}{2}$.
4. A $100 000, 13% bond with semi-annual coupons redeemable at 102 was purchased eleven-and-a-half years before maturity to yield 12% compounded semi-annually. The bond was sold five years later at $99\frac{1}{8}$.
5. A $5000 bond with 15% interest payable semi-annually redeemable at par on June 1, 2008, was bought on December 1, 1994, to yield 16% compounded semi-annually. The bond was sold on September 22, 1998, at $101\frac{3}{8}$.
6. Three $10 000, 10.5% bonds with quarterly coupons redeemable at 109 on August 1, 2002, were bought on May 1, 1988, to yield 12% compounded quarterly. The bonds were sold on January 16, 1996, at $93\frac{1}{2}$.

15.4 *Finding the yield rate*

A. Quoted price of a bond—buying bonds on the market

Bonds are usually bought or sold through a bond exchange where agents trade bonds on behalf of their clients. To allow for the different denominations, bonds are offered at a quoted price stated as a percent of their face value.

It is understood that, if the bond is bought between interest dates, such a quoted price does not include any accrued interest. As explained in Section 15.1, the seller of a bond is entitled to the interest earned by the bond to the date of sale and the interest is added to the quoted price to obtain the purchase price (flat price).

Example **15.4a** A \$5000, 12% bond with semi-annual coupons payable April 1 and October 1 is purchased on August 25 at $104\frac{3}{4}$. What is the purchase price of the bond?

Solution

The quoted price is 5000.00(1.0475) = \$5237.50.

The time period April 1 to August 25 contains 146 days; the number of days in the interest payment interval April 1 to October 1 is 183.

$$P = 5000.00; \quad r = i = \frac{12\%}{2} = 6\% = 0.06; \quad t = \frac{146}{183}$$

The accrued interest is $5000.00(0.06)\left(\frac{146}{183}\right) = \$239.34$.

The purchase price (flat price) is 5237.50 + 239.34 = \$5476.84.

B. Finding the yield rate—the average investment method

When bonds are bought on the market, the yield rate is not directly available; it needs to be determined. The simplest method in use is the so-called **method of averages** which gives a reasonable approximation of the yield rate as the ratio of the average income per interest payment interval to the average book value.

$$\text{APPROXIMATE VALUE OF } i = \frac{\text{AVERAGE INCOME PER INTEREST PAYMENT INTERVAL}}{\text{AVERAGE BOOK VALUE}}$$

where

$$\text{AVERAGE BOOK VALUE} = \frac{1}{2}(\text{QUOTED PRICE} + \text{REDEMPTION PRICE})$$

and

$$\text{AVERAGE INCOME PER INTEREST PAYMENT INTERVAL} = \frac{\text{TOTAL INTEREST PAYMENTS} \begin{array}{l} -\text{PREMIUM} \\ +\text{DISCOUNT} \end{array}}{\text{NUMBER OF INTEREST PAYMENT INTERVALS}}$$

***Example* 15.4b** A \$25 000, 11.5% bond with semi-annual coupons redeemable at par in ten years is purchased at $103\frac{1}{2}$. What is the approximate yield rate?

Solution

The quoted price (initial book value) is 25 000.00(1.035) = \$25 875.00; the redemption price is \$25 000.00.

The average book value is $\frac{1}{2}(25\,875.00 + 25\,000.00) = \$25\,437.50$.

The semi-annual interest payment is $25\,000.00\left(\frac{0.115}{2}\right) = \$1437.50$;

the number of interest payments to maturity is 10(2) = 20;
the total interest payments are 20(1437.50) = \$28 750.00;
the premium is 25 875.00 − 25 000.00 = \$875.00.

$$\text{Average income per interest payment interval} = \frac{(28\,750 - 875.00)}{20}$$

$$= \$1393.75$$

$$\text{Approximate value of } i = \frac{1393.75}{25\,437.50} = 0.0547912 = 5.48\%$$

The yield rate is 2(5.48) = 10.96%.

***Example* 15.4c** Eight \$1000, 10% bonds with semi-annual coupons redeemable at 105 in seventeen years are purchased at $97\frac{3}{8}$. What is the approximate yield rate?

Solution

The quoted price is 8000.00(0.97375) = \$7790.00;

the redemption value is 8000.00(1.05) = \$8400.00;

the average book value is $\frac{(7790.00 + 8400.00)}{2} = \$8095.00$.

The semi-annual interest payment is $8000.00\left(\frac{0.10}{2}\right) = \$400.00$;

the number of interest payments to maturity is 17(2) = 34;
the total interest payments are 34(400.00) = \$13 600.00;
the bond discount is 8400.00 − 7790.00 = \$610.00.

$$\text{Average income per interest payment interval} = \frac{(13\,600.00 + 610.00)}{34}$$

$$= \$417.94$$

The approximate value of i is $\frac{417.94}{8095.00} = 0.0516295 = 5.16\%$.

The approximate yield rate is $2(5.16\%) = 10.32\%$.

***Example* 15.4d** A \$5000, 10% bond with semi-annual coupons redeemable at par on July 15, 2008, is quoted on December 2, 1996, at $103\frac{3}{4}$. What is the approximate yield rate?

Solution

To find the approximate yield rate for a bond purchased between interest dates, assume that the price was quoted on the nearest interest date. Since the interest dates are January 15 and July 15, the nearest interest date is January 15, 1997, which is 11.5 years before maturity.

The quoted price is $5000.00(1.0375) = \$5187.50$;

the redemption value is 5000.00;

the average book value is $\frac{(5187.50 + 5000.00)}{2} = \$5093.75$.

The semi-annual interest is $5000.00\left(\frac{0.10}{2}\right) = \$250.00$;

the number of interest payments to maturity is $11.5(2) = 23$;

the total interest payments are $23(250.00) = \$5750.00$;

the premium is $5187.50 - 5000.00 = \$187.50$.

$$\text{The average income per interest payment interval} = \frac{(5750.00 - 187.50)}{23} = \$241.85$$

The approximate value of i is $\frac{241.85}{5093.75} = 0.047479 = 4.75\%$.

The approximate yield rate is $2(4.75\%) = 9.50\%$.

C. Finding the accurate yield rate by trial and error

A method of trial and error similar to the one used to find the nominal rate of interest may be used to obtain as precise an approximation to the yield rate as desired. The method is illustrated in the Appendix.

Exercise 15.4

Use the method of averages to find the approximate yield rate for each of the following bonds.

	Face value	Bond rate payable semi-annually	Time before redemption	Redeemed at	Market quotation
1.	\$10 000	12%	15 years	par	$101\frac{3}{8}$
2.	\$5 000	10.5%	7 years	par	$94\frac{3}{4}$
3.	\$25 000	11.5%	10 years	104	$97\frac{1}{8}$
4.	\$1 000	15.5%	8 years	109	101
5.	\$50 000	13%	5 years, 4 months	par	$98\frac{7}{8}$
6.	\$20 000	17%	9 years, 8 months	106	$109\frac{1}{4}$

15.5 *Other types of bonds*

A. *Annuity bonds*

The bonds considered in the previous sections have all been bonds redeemed in one payment at maturity. However, some bonds are redeemed in such a way that the repayment of the face value plus interest payments form an ordinary annuity. Such bonds are called **annuity bonds** and may be dealt with by the methods shown in Chapter 14 to amortize debts.

Example **15.5a** A 12% annuity bond of \$40 000 is to be redeemed by equal semi-annual payments, including principal and interest, over ten years.

(i) What is the purchase price to yield 11% compounded semi-annually?

(ii) If the bond is sold four years later to yield 13% compounded semi-annually, what is the selling price of the bond?

(iii) What is the gain or loss on the sale of the bond?

Solution

(i) STEP 1 Determine the size of the semi-annual payment.

$$A_n = 40\ 000.00; \quad i = \frac{12\%}{2} = 6\% = 0.06; \quad n = 10(2) = 20$$

$$40\ 000.00 = R\left(\frac{1 - 1.06^{-20}}{0.06}\right)$$

$$40\ 000.00 = R(11.469921)$$

$$R = \$3487.38$$

Programmed solution

0	40 000	20	6			
FV	PV	N	%i	CPT	PMT	3487.38

The semi-annual bond redemption payment is $3487.38.

STEP 2 Since the buyer of the bond receives semi-annual payments of $3487.38, the purchase price is the present value of the payments discounted at the yield rate.

$$R = 3487.38; \quad i = \frac{11\%}{2} = 5.5\%; \quad n = 20$$

$$A_n = 3487.38\left(\frac{1 - 1.055^{-20}}{0.055}\right)$$

$$= 3487.38(11.950382)$$

$$= \$41\,675.52$$

Programmed solution

0	3487.38	20	5.5			
FV	PMT	N	%i	CPT	PV	41 675.52

The purchase price of the bond to yield 11% is $41 675.52.

(ii) The selling price four years later is the present value of the outstanding semi-annual payments at the new yield rate.

$$R = 3487.38; \quad i = \frac{13\%}{2} = 6.5\%; \quad n = 6(2) = 12$$

$$A_n = 3487.38\left(\frac{1 - 1.065^{-12}}{0.065}\right)$$

$$= 3487.38(8.1587253)$$

$$= \$28\,452.58$$

Programmed solution

0	3487.38	12	6.5			
FV	PMT	N	%i	CPT	PV	28 452.58

The selling price four years later to yield 13% is $28 452.58.

(iii) The gain or loss on the sale of the bond is the difference between the selling price and the book value.

The book value is the present value of the outstanding semi-annual payments at the time of the sale discounted at the original yield rate.

$$R = 3487.38; \quad i = 5.5\%; \quad n = 12$$

$$\begin{aligned} A_n &= 3487.38\left(\frac{1 - 1.055^{-12}}{0.055}\right) \\ &= 3487.38(8.6185178) \\ &= \$30\,056.05 \end{aligned}$$

Programmed solution

0	3487.38	12	5.5			
FV	PMT	N	%i	CPT	PV	30 056.05

The loss on the sale of the bond is 30 056.05 − 28 452.58 = $1603.47.

B. *Serial bonds*

When a bond issue is redeemed at staggered dates rather than on a common maturity date, the bond is called a **serial bond**. For computational purposes, treat such serial bonds as separate bonds according to their redemption dates.

***Example* 15.5b** A serial bond issue of $20 million with interest at 10% payable semi-annually is to be redeemed by a payment of $12 million in twelve years and $8 million in fifteen years. What is the purchase price of the bond issue to yield 12% compounded semi-annually?

Solution

The purchase price of the serial bond issue is equivalent to the combined purchase price of two separate bond issues: the purchase price of the $12 million bond issue due in twelve years and the purchase price of the $8 million bond issue due in fifteen years.

Purchase price (PP) of the $12 million bond issue

$$S = 12 \text{ million}; \quad R = 12\,000\,000\left(\frac{0.10}{2}\right) = 600\,000;$$

$$n = 12(2) = 24; \quad i = \frac{12\%}{2} = 6\% = 0.06$$

$$PP = 12\,000\,000(1.06^{-24}) + 600\,000\left(\frac{1 - 1.06^{-24}}{0.06}\right)$$

$$= 12\,000\,000(0.2469785) + 600\,000(12.550358)$$

$$= 2\,963\,742.60 + 7\,530\,214.80$$

$$= \$10\,493\,957.40$$

Programmed solution

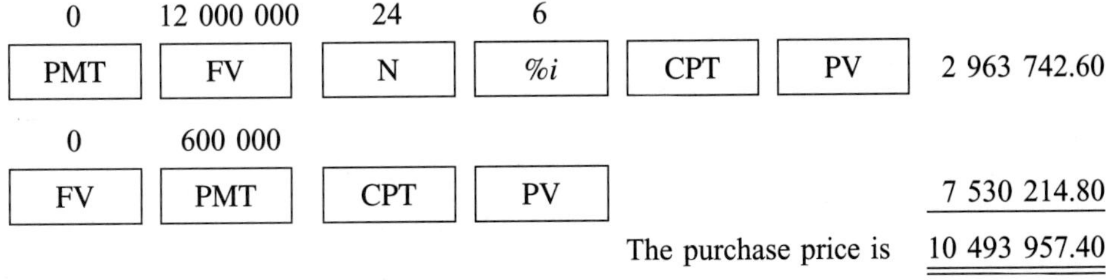

Purchase price of the $8 million bond issue

$$S = 8 \text{ million}; \quad R = 8\,000\,000(0.05) = 400\,000;$$

$$n = 30; \quad i = 6\%$$

$$PP = 8\,000\,000(1.06^{-30}) + 400\,000\left(\frac{1 - 1.06^{-30}}{0.06}\right)$$

$$= 8\,000\,000(0.1741101) + 400\,000(13.764831)$$

$$= 1\,392\,881.00 + 5\,505\,932.40$$

$$= \$6\,898\,813.40$$

Programmed solution

0	8 000 000	30	6			
PMT	FV	N	%i	CPT	PV	1 392 881.00
0	400 000					
FV	PMT	CPT	PV			5 505 932.40
					The purchase price is	6 898 813.40

The total purchase price is 10 493 957.40 + 6 898 813.40 = $17 392 770.80.

Exercise 15.5

A. Answer each of the following questions.

1. A $75 000, 14.5% annuity bond with interest payable semi-annually is to be repaid by equal semi-annual payments in fifteen years.
   (a) What is the purchase price to yield 12.5% compounded semi-annually?
   (b) What is the book value after five years?
   (c) What is the gain or loss if the bond is sold to yield 12% compounded semi-annually after five years?

2. A 14% annuity bond contracts to repay the principal of $35 000 in equal quarterly payments over eight years. The bond interest is payable quarterly.
   (a) What is the purchase price to yield 16% compounded quarterly?
   (b) For how much will the bond sell in three years to yield 15% compounded quarterly?
   (c) What is the gain or loss on the sale of the bond?

3. A $600 000, 14% serial bond with interest payable semi-annually is to be redeemed in three instalments of $200 000 each in six, eight, and ten years respectively. What is the purchase price to yield 12% compounded semi-annually?

4. A $120 000, 13% serial bond issued June 1, 1980, with interest payable annually is to be redeemed by four instalments of $30 000 each due June 1, 1994, 1996, 1998, and 2000 respectively. What is the purchase price to yield 15.75% annually?

Review exercise

1. A $5000, 11.5% bond with interest payable semi-annually is redeemable at par in twelve years. What is the purchase price to yield
   (a) 10.5% compounded semi-annually? **(b)** 13% compounded semi-annually?

2. A $10 000, 6% bond with semi-annual coupons is redeemable at 108. What is the purchase price to yield 7.5% compounded semi-annually
   (a) nine years before maturity? **(b)** fifteen years before maturity?

3. A $25 000, 13% bond with interest payable quarterly is redeemable at 104 in six years. What is the purchase price to yield 14.25% compounded annually?

4. A $1000, 9.5% bond with semi-annual coupons redeemable at par on March 1, 2004, is purchased on September 19, 1995, to yield 15% compounded semi-annually. What is the purchase price?

5. Four $5000, 13% bonds with semi-annual coupons are bought seven years before maturity to yield 12% compounded semi-annually. Find the premium or discount and the purchase price if the bonds are redeemable
   (a) at par; **(b)** at 107.

6. Nine \$1000, 14% bonds with interest payable semi-annually and redeemable at par are purchased ten years before maturity. Find the premium or discount and the purchase price if the bonds are bought to yield

(a) 10%; **(b)** 14%; **(c)** 16%.

7. A \$100 000, 15% bond with interest payable semi-annually redeemable at par on July 15, 2007, is bought on April 18, 1996, to yield 17% compounded semi-annually. Determine

(a) the premium or discount;

(b) the purchase price;

(c) the quoted price.

8. Four \$10 000 bonds bearing interest at 16% payable quarterly and redeemable at 106 on September 1, 2008, are bought on January 23, 1996, to yield 15% compounded quarterly. Determine

(a) the premium or discount;

(b) the purchase price;

(c) the quoted price.

9. A \$5000, 8% bond with semi-annual coupons redeemable at 108 in ten years is purchased to yield 10% compounded semi-annually. What is the purchase price?

10. A \$1000 bond bearing interest at 16% payable semi-annually redeemable at par on February 1, 2002, is purchased on October 12, 1995, to yield 15% compounded semi-annually. Determine the purchase price.

11. A \$25 000, 13% bond with semi-annual coupons redeemable at 107 on June 15, 2008, is purchased on May 9, 1997, to yield 14.5% compounded semi-annually. Determine

(a) the premium or discount;

(b) the purchase price;

(c) the quoted price.

12. A \$50 000, 11% bond with semi-annual coupons redeemable at par on April 15, 2003, is purchased on June 25, 1996, at $92\frac{3}{8}$. What is the approximate yield rate?

13. A \$80 000, 13% serial bond with interest payable semi-annually is redeemable by a payment of \$30 000 in seven years and a payment of \$50 000 in ten years. What is the purchase price to yield 15% compounded semi-annually?

14. A \$1000, 14.5% bond with interest payable annually is bought six years before maturity to yield 16.5% compounded annually. Compute the premium or discount and the purchase price and construct the appropriate bond schedule.

15. A \$5000, 12.25% bond with interest payable annually redeemable at par in seven years is purchased to yield 13.5% compounded annually. Find the premium or discount and the purchase price and construct the appropriate bond schedule.

16. A \$20 000, 15.5% bond with semi-annual coupons redeemable at 105 in three years is purchased to yield 14% compounded semi-annually. Find the premium or discount and purchase price and construct the appropriate bond schedule.

17. Three \$25 000, 11% bonds with semi-annual coupons redeemable at par were bought eight years before maturity to yield 12% compounded semi-annually. Determine the gain or loss if the bonds are sold at $89\frac{3}{8}$ five years later.

18. A \$10 000 bond with 13% interest payable quarterly redeemable at 106 on November 15, 2006, was bought on July 2, 1990, to yield 17% compounded quarterly. If the bond was sold at $92\frac{3}{4}$ on September 10, 1996, what was the gain or loss on the sale?

19. A \$25 000, 9.5% bond with semi-annual coupons redeemable at par is bought sixteen years before maturity at $78\frac{1}{4}$. What is the approximate yield rate?

20. A \$10 000, 15% bond with quarterly coupons redeemable at 102 on October 15, 2003, is bought on May 5, 1991, at $98\frac{3}{4}$. What is the approximate yield rate?

21. If the bond in Question 13 was sold at 97 two years before maturity, what approximate yield rate was realized?

22. What is the approximate yield realized if the bond in Question 14 is sold on August 7, 1996, at 92?

23. A 14.5% annuity bond of \$50 000 with interest payable quarterly is to be redeemed by equal quarterly payments over twelve years.

(a) What is the purchase price to yield 16% compounded quarterly?

(b) What is the book value after nine years?

(c) What is the gain or loss if the bond is sold nine years after the date of purchase to yield 17% compounded quarterly?

24. A \$250 000, 15% serial bond with interest payable semi-annually is to be redeemed by two payments, the first for \$100 000 in nine years and the remaining \$150 000 in twelve years. What is the purchase price to yield 14.5% compounded semi-annually?

25. A \$100 000, 10.75% bond with interest payable annually is redeemable at 103 in eight years. What is the purchase price to yield 12% compounded quarterly?

26. A \$5000, 14.5% bond with semi-annual coupons redeemable at par on August 1, 2004, is purchased on March 5, 1993, at $95\frac{1}{2}$. What is the approximate yield rate?

27. A \$25 000, 18% bond with semi-annual coupons, redeemable at 104 in fifteen years, is purchased to yield 16% compounded semi-annually. Determine the gain or loss if the bond is sold three years later at $107\frac{1}{4}$.

28. A \$10 000, 12% annuity bond with interest payable quarterly is redeemed by equal quarterly payments over twenty years.

(a) What is the purchase price to yield 14% compounded quarterly?

(b) What is the book value after seven years?

(c) What is the gain or loss if the bond is sold after seven years to yield 15% compounded quarterly?

Self-test

1. A $10 000, 10% bond with quarterly coupons redeemable at par in fifteen years is purchased to yield 11% compounded quarterly. Determine the purchase price of the bond.

2. What is the purchase price of a $1000, 13.5% bond with semi-annual coupons redeemable at 108 in ten years if the bond is bought to yield 12% compounded semi-annually?

3. A $5000, 8% bond with semi-annual coupons redeemable at 104 is bought six years before maturity to yield 6.5% compounded semi-annually. Determine the premium or discount.

4. A $50 000, 9% annuity bond with interest payable monthly is redeemed by equal monthly payments over fifteen years. What is the purchase price of the bond to yield 8.4% compounded monthly?

5. A $20 000, 16% bond with semi-annual coupons redeemable at par March 1, 2003, is bought on November 15, 1996, to yield 15% compounded semi-annually. What is the purchase price of the bond?

6. A $5000, 13% bond with semi-annual coupons redeemable at 102 on December 15, 2006, is purchased on November 9, 1995, to yield 14.5% compounded semi-annually. Determine the quoted price.

7. A $5000, 11.5% bond with semi-annual coupons redeemable at 105 is bought four years before maturity to yield 13% compounded semi-annually. Construct a bond schedule.

8. A $100 000, 13% bond with semi-annual interest payments redeemable at par on July 15, 2003, is bought on September 10, 1996, at $102\frac{5}{8}$. What is the approximate yield rate?

9. A $1 000 000, 12% serial bond with interest payable semi-annually is redeemable by payments of $400 000 and $600 000 due six years and ten years from now respectively. What is the purchase price of the bond to yield 10% compounded semi-annually?

10. A $25 000, 14% bond with semi-annual coupons redeemable at 106 in twenty years is purchased to yield 16% compounded semi-annually. Determine the gain or loss if the bond is sold seven years after the date of purchase at $98\frac{1}{4}$.

11. A $75 000, twenty-year, 13% annuity bond with interest payable annually is redeemable by equal annual payments. The bond was bought to yield 12% compounded annually. If the bond is sold eight years before maturity to yield 14% compounded annually, what is the gain or loss?

12. A $10 000, 12% bond with semi-annual coupons redeemable at par on December 1, 2007, is purchased on July 20, 1996, at $93\frac{7}{8}$. Compute the approximate yield rate.

Summary of formulae used

Formula 9.2B

$$P = S(1 + i)^{-n}$$

Finding the present value by means of the discount factor (the reciprocal of the compounding factor)

Formula 11.2

$$A_n = R\left[\frac{1 - (1 + i)^{-n}}{i}\right]$$

Finding the present value of an annuity

Formula 13.2

$$A_{nc} = R\left[\frac{1 - (1 + f)^{-n}}{f}\right]$$

where $f = (1 + i)^c - 1$

Preferred formula for finding the present value using the equivalent effective rate of interest per payment period

Formula 15.1

$$PP = S(1 + i)^{-n} + R\left[\frac{1 - (1 + i)^{-n}}{i}\right]$$

Basic formula for finding the purchase price of a bond when the interest payment interval and the yield rate conversion period are equal

Formula 15.2

$$PP = S(1 + f)^{-n} + R\left[\frac{1 - (1 + f)^{-n}}{f}\right]$$

where $f = (1 + i)^c - 1$

Basic formula for finding the purchase price of a bond when the interest payment interval and the yield rate conversion period are different

Formula 15.3

$$\text{PREMIUM or DISCOUNT} = (b \times \text{FACE VALUE} - i \times \text{REDEMPTION VALUE})\left[\frac{1 - (1 + i)^{-n}}{i}\right]$$

Direct formula for finding the premium or discount of a bond (a negative answer indicates a discount)

Glossary of terms used

Accumulation of discount the process of reducing a bond discount

Amortization of premium the process of writing down a bond premium

Annuity bond a bond redeemed by equal periodic payments

Bond rate the rate of interest paid by a bond, stated as a percent of the face value

Coupon a voucher attached to a bond to facilitate the collection of interest by the bondholder

Coupon rate see *Bond rate*

Debentures bonds for which no security is offered

Denomination see *Face value*

Discount the difference between the purchase price of a bond and its redemption value when the purchase price is less than the redemption price

Due date see *Redemption date*

Face value amount owed by the issuer of the bond to the bondholder

$$R = \frac{C - T(1+i)^{-n}}{\left[\frac{1-(1+i)^{-n}}{i}\right]}$$

The annual depreciation charge

$$= \frac{\text{Original cost} - \text{Present value of residual value}}{\left[\frac{1-(1+i)^{-n}}{i}\right]}$$

B. The sinking-fund method of depreciation

The sinking-fund method, like the annuity method, provides for an annual depreciation charge that is composed of a provision for a yearly loss in value plus interest. However, in this case, the annual depreciation charge involves an *assumed* payment into a sinking fund. These payments into a sinking fund would accumulate to the wearing value at the end of the useful life of the asset at a rate of interest which the payments could earn. The mathematical aspects of this method involve the techniques used in Section 14.4 for dealing with sinking funds involving ordinary annuities.

Example **16.1b** Assume that money is worth 14% compounded annually and that the machine in Example 16.1a is depreciated by the sinking-fund method.

(i) Determine the assumed annual sinking-fund payment.

(ii) Construct a depreciation schedule.

Solution

(i) Original cost = 20 000.00; residual value = 3200.00;

wearing value = 16 800.00; $n = 5$; $i = 14\%$.

Since the wearing value is the final amount in the sinking fund, S_n = 16 800.00.

$$16\,800.00 = R\left(\frac{1.14^5 - 1}{0.14}\right)$$

$$16\,800.00 = R(6.610104)$$

$$R = \$2541.56$$

Programmed solution

0	16 800	5	14			
PV	FV	N	%i	CPT	PMT	2541.56

(ii) ***Depreciation schedule (sinking-fund method)***

End of year	*Assumed annual payment into sinking fund*	*Provision for interest* i = *14%*	*Annual depreciation charge*	*Accumulated depreciation*	*Book value*
0					20 000.00
1	2 541.56	0.00	2 541.56	2 541.56	17 458.44
2	2 541.56	355.82	2 897.38	5 438.94	14 561.06
3	2 541.56	761.45	3 303.01	8 741.95	11 258.05
4	2 541.56	1 223.87	3 765.43	12 507.38	7 492.62
5	2 541.59	1 751.03	4 292.62	16 800.00	3 200.00
TOTAL	12 707.83	4 092.17	16 800.00		

C. *Finding the book value and yearly depreciation without depreciation schedules*

We can determine the book value after a given number of years or the depreciation in any particular year without constructing a depreciation schedule for any of the methods illustrated.

Example **16.1c** Equipment costing \$35 720.00 has an estimated trade-in value of \$1400.00 after fifteen years. Find **(a)** the book value after nine years and **(b)** the depreciation charge in Year 10 for

(i) the annuity method if interest is 16% compounded annually;

(ii) the sinking-fund method if interest is 12% compounded annually.

Solution

Original cost = 35 720.00; residual value = 1400.00;
wearing value is 35 720.00 − 1400.00 = 34 320.00; $n = 15$

(i) *Annuity method*

At 16%, the present value of the depreciation charges

$= 35\ 720.00 - 1400.00(1.16^{-15})$

$= 35\ 720.00 - 1400.00(0.107927)$

$= 35\ 720.00 - 151.10$

$= \$35\ 568.90$

The annual depreciation charge

$$R = \frac{35\ 568.90}{\left(\frac{1 - 1.16^{-15}}{0.16}\right)} = \frac{35\ 568.90}{5.5754562} = \$6379.55$$

Programmed solution

0	1400	15	16			
PMT	FV	N	%i	CPT	PV	151.10

$$PV = 35\ 720.00 - 151.10 = 35\ 568.90$$

0	35 568.90			
FV	PV	CPT	PMT	6379.55

(a) Since the Present value of the depreciation charges =
Original book value − Present value of the residual value,
Original book value = Present value of the depreciation charges
+ Present value of the residual value.

Similarly, the Book value at the end of a particular year
= Present value of the outstanding annual depreciation charges + Present value of the residual value at that time.

Therefore, after nine years, the depreciation charges for the remaining six years in the life of the asset are outstanding and the Book value after nine years

$$= 6379.55\left(\frac{1 - 1.16^{-6}}{0.16}\right) + 1400.00(1.16^{-6})$$

$$= 6379.55(3.6847359) + 1400.00(0.4104423)$$

$$= 23\ 506.96 + 574.62$$

$$= \$24\ 081.58$$

Programmed solution

0	6379.55	6	16			
FV	PMT	N	%i	CPT	PV	23 506.96
0	1400					
PMT	FV	CPT	PV			574.62

The book value after nine years is $24 081.58.

(b) The depreciation charge for Year 10 is $6379.55 and consists of provision for interest at 24 081.58(0.16) = $3853.05 and provision for loss in value at 6379.55 − 3853.05 = $2526.50.

(ii) *Sinking-fund method*

The assumed annual sinking-fund payment at 12%

$$= \frac{34\,320.00}{\left(\frac{1.12^{15} - 1}{0.12}\right)} = \frac{34\,320.00}{37.279714} = \$920.61$$

The accumulated value of the sinking-fund payments after nine years

$$= 920.61\left(\frac{1.12^{9} - 1}{0.12}\right) = 920.61(14.775656) = \$13\,602.62$$

Programmed solution

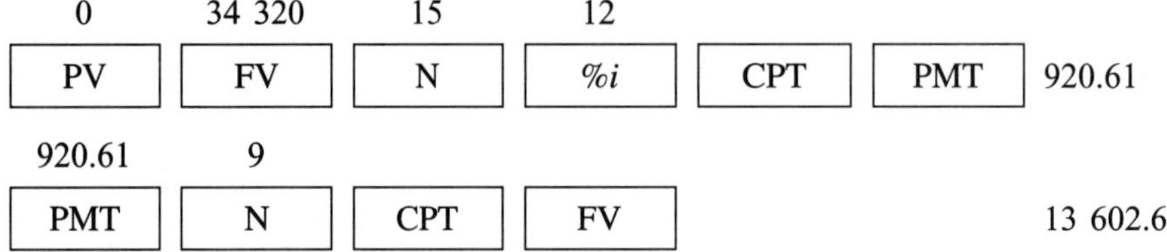

(a) The book value after nine years is 35 720.00 − 13 602.62 = $22 117.38.

(b) The depreciation charge in Year 10
= 920.61 + 13 602.62(0.12) = 920.61 + 1632.31 = $2552.92

Exercise 16.1

A. For each of the following, construct a depreciation schedule using the methods of depreciation shown.

1. Equipment with an original book value of $40 000 is estimated to have a scrap value of $5000 after ten years. Interest is 15%. Construct a depreciation schedule using
   (a) the annuity method;
   (b) the sinking-fund method.
2. A combine costing $32 000 has a trade-in value of $5000 after eight years. Construct a depreciation schedule using
   (a) the annuity method (assume interest to be 13%);
   (b) the sinking-fund method (assume interest to be 11.5%).

B. Answer each of the following questions.

1. A building costing \$560 000 is estimated to have a life of 40 years and a salvage value of \$68 000. Compute the book value after 15 years and the depreciation charge in Year 16 for
   (a) the annuity method at 12%;
   (b) the sinking-fund method at 12%.

2. Heavy machinery costing \$150 000 with a scrap value of \$13 500 is estimated to have a life of 25 years. Compute the book value after 10 years and the depreciation charge in Year 11 for
   (a) the annuity method at 14%;
   (b) the sinking-fund method at 17%.

16.2 *Depletion*

A. Basic concepts

Many natural resources such as mines, oil wells, natural gas fields, gravel pits, and peat moss bogs are nonrenewable, while other resources such as timber cannot be replaced in the short term. Such resources are called **wasting assets**.

In contrast to depreciable assets which usually retain their physical characteristics during their useful life, wasting assets are in essence long-term inventories of raw materials that will be removed from the property during the production process.

The value of such wasting assets diminishes as they are used up. The loss in value is called **depletion**. When the resources are exhausted, there will be little or no residual value in some cases, while the residual value will be considerable in other cases. As with depreciable assets, the loss in value will be the difference between the original capital investment and the residual value.

Since investors expect the return of their capital, the net annual income from investment in wasting assets must provide not only interest on the capital but must also be sufficient to restore the amount of capital invested over the estimated life of the assets.

This restoration of capital is usually accomplished by an annual deposit into a sinking fund. This fund, called a **depletion reserve**, must over the life of a wasting asset accumulate to the amount of capital originally invested less any residual value. Interest earned on the depletion reserve is normally lower than the yield required on the capital investment.

ANNUAL NET INCOME FROM OPERATIONS	=	ANNUAL INTEREST ON CAPITAL INVESTMENT	+	ANNUAL DEPOSIT INTO DEPLETION RESERVE

← *Formula* **16.2**

Two basic computational problems are encountered when dealing with depletion:

1. What value of a property will produce a given yield rate?
2. What is the yield rate for a given investment?

B. Finding the value of the investment

Example **16.2a** A gravel pit is estimated to provide an annual net income of \$80 000 for the next fifteen years. If the property is worthless when the gravel pit is exhausted and the depletion reserve earns 8% compounded annually, what is the value of the investment to yield 14% compounded annually?

Solution

Let the value of the property be represented by X;

the annual net income = 80 000.00;

the annual interest on the capital investment = 0.14X;

the annual deposit into the depletion reserve

$$= \frac{X}{\left(\frac{1.08^{15} - 1}{0.08}\right)} = \frac{X}{27.152114} = 0.0368295X$$

Programmed determination of $\left(\frac{1.08^{15} - 1}{0.08}\right)$

0	1	15	8			
PV	PMT	N	%i	CPT	FV	27.152114

$80\ 000.00 = 0.14X + 0.0368295X \longleftarrow$ using Formula 16.2

$80\ 000.00 = 0.1768295X$

$X = \$452\ 413.09$

The value of the property is \$452 413.

Example **16.2b** Assuming that the gravel pit in Example 16.2a can be sold for \$100 000 when operations cease, what is the value of the property?

Solution

Let the value of the property be Y;

then the annual deposit into the depletion reserve

$$= \frac{(Y - 100\,000.00)}{\left(\frac{1.08^{15} - 1}{0.08}\right)}$$

$$= \frac{(Y - 100\,000.00)}{27.152114}$$

$$= 0.0368295Y - 3682.95$$

$$80\,000.00 = 0.14Y + 0.0368295Y - 3682.95$$

$$83\,682.95 = 0.1768295Y$$

$$Y = \$473\,240.92$$

The value of the property is $473 241.

C. *Finding the yield rate*

***Example* 16.2c** A mining property yields an estimated annual net income of $200 000 for 25 years. The property can be bought for $600 000 and an immediate investment of $800 000 is needed to bring the mine into production. The depletion reserve can be invested at 10% compounded annually. Find the yield rate

(i) if there is no residual value after 25 years;

(ii) if the property can be sold after 25 years for $1 000 000 and other mining assets have a salvage value of $200 000.

Solution

(i) Let the yield rate be represented by i;

the total investment is 600 000.00 + 800 000.00 = 1 400 000.00;

the annual net income is 200 000.00;

the annual yield from the investment is 1 400 000.00i;

the annual deposit into the depletion reserve

$$= \frac{1\,400\,000.00}{\left(\frac{1.10^{25} - 1}{0.10}\right)} = \frac{1\,400\,000.00}{98.347059} = \$14\,235.30$$

Programmed determination of $\left(\frac{1.10^{25} - 1}{0.10}\right)$

0	1	25	10			
PV	PMT	N	%i	CPT	FV	98.347059

$$200\,000.00 = 1\,400\,000.00i + 14\,235.30$$
$$185\,764.70 = 1\,400\,000.00i$$
$$i = 0.1326891$$

The yield rate is approximately 13.27%.

(ii) The total residual value after 25 years is \$1 200 000.00; the annual deposit into the depletion reserve

$$= \frac{(1\,400\,000.00 - 1\,200\,000.00)}{\left(\frac{1.10^{25} - 1}{0.10}\right)}$$

$$= \frac{200\,000.00}{98.347059}$$

$$= 2033.61$$

$$200\,000.00 = 1\,400\,000.00i + 2033.61$$
$$197\,966.39 = 1\,400\,000.00i$$
$$i = 0.1414046$$

The yield is approximately 14.14%.

D. *Finding the depletion for a particular year*

The depletion for a particular year is the increase in the depletion reserve for that year. It can be obtained from a sinking fund schedule or computed directly.

Example **16.2d** Estimates show that an oil well will generate an annual net income of \$150 000 for twenty years. After this time, the well will have no value. If the oil well is purchased to yield 18% p.a. and a sinking fund earning 11% per annum is set up for the recovery of the capital invested, determine the depletion in Year 10.

Solution

STEP 1 Find the purchase price.

Let the purchase price of the oil well be represented by X;

the annual net income is 150 000.00;

the annual yield on the capital invested is 0.18X;

the annual deposit into the sinking fund

$$= \frac{X}{\left(\frac{1.11^{20} - 1}{0.11}\right)} = \frac{X}{64.202832} = 0.0155756X$$

Programmed determination of $\left(\frac{1.11^{20} - 1}{0.11}\right)$

0	1	20	11			
PV	PMT	N	%*i*	CPT	FV	64.202832

$$150\,000.00 = 0.18X + 0.0155756X$$

$$150\,000.00 = 0.1955756X$$

$$X = \$766\,966.70$$

STEP 2 Find the size of the annual deposit R into the sinking fund.

$$R = 0.0155756(766\,966.70) = \$11\,945.97$$

STEP 3 Find the balance in the fund after nine years and determine the increase in the fund in Year 10.

$$S_9 = 11\,945.97\left(\frac{1.11^9 - 1}{0.11}\right) = 11\,945.97(14.163972) = \$169\,202.38$$

Programmed determination of $\left(\frac{1.11^{9} - 1}{0.11}\right)$

0	1	9	11			
PV	PMT	N	%*i*	CPT	FV	14.163972

$$\begin{aligned} \text{Increase} &= \text{Interest earned in Year 10} + \text{Annual deposit} \\ &= 0.11(169\,202.38) + 11\,945.97 \\ &= 18\,612.26 + 11\,945.97 \\ &= \$30\,558.23 \end{aligned}$$

The depletion in Year 10 is $30 558.23.

Exercise 16.2

A. For each of the following problems involving depletion of a natural resource, find the purchase price or the annual yield rate as indicated.

	Annual net income before depletion	*Number of years*	*Annual yield rate*	*Sinking fund rate*	*Residual value*	*Purchase price*
1.	$15 000	15	16%	10%	nil	?
2.	28 500	10	14%	8%	nil	?
3.	36 000	20	15%	11%	$ 4 000	?
4.	54 000	12	18%	12%	9 600	?
5.	8 400	8	?	9%	nil	$32 000
6.	13 500	10	?	10%	nil	62 000
7.	86 000	25	?	11%	45 000	440 000
8.	54 000	18	?	8%	20 000	335 000

B. Answer each of the following questions.

1. A mine is estimated to yield an annual net income before depletion of $45 000 for the next twelve years. When the mine is exhausted after twelve years, the estimated value of the property is $20 000. If a prospective buyer can set up a sinking fund earning 9%, how much can the buyer offer to realize a yield of 14%?

2. A piece of property containing an oil well is offered for sale. If the total reserve of crude oil is removed over twenty years at a constant rate, annual net income before depletion is estimated to be $75 000 and the value of the property after twenty years is estimated to be $200 000. If a buyer expects a yield of 18% and can make deposits into a sinking fund earning 10.5%, what should the offer be to purchase the property?

3. A paper mill acquired timber rights for ten years at a cost of $500 000. If the estimated annual income before depletion is $100 000 and a depletion reserve earning 11.5% can be set up, what is the yield rate on the investment?

4. A peat bog can be purchased for $44 000. The annual net income before depletion is estimated to be $12 000 and the property is estimated to have a value of $5000 when all useable peat has been extracted after eight years. Determine the yield assuming that a replacement fund earning 10% can be set up.

5. A gravel pit is for sale at $85 000. Estimated annual net income before depletion is $22 000. The gravel pit will be exhausted after seven years and the property will then have a value of $30 000. What is the yield rate if deposits into a depletion reserve earn 12%?

6. A dump truck costing $35 000 has an estimated trade-in value of $7000 after five years. The owner of a fleet of such trucks set up a sinking fund earning 11% to replace the trucks. If the net annual income before depreciation is $10 600, what is the yield rate on the investment?

7. An orchard was purchased to yield 22%. The trees are expected to be productive for fifteen years after which the property will have an estimated value of \$35 000. If annual net income is \$20 000 and a replacement fund earning 10% is set up for the recovery of the capital invested, determine the depletion in Year 6.

8. A property that contains removable natural resources is estimated to yield an annual net income of \$17 500 before depletion. The property is bought to yield 17.5% and has an expected value of \$25 000 after twenty years. If a sinking fund earning 12% is set up for the recovery of the capital invested, what is the depletion in Year 15?

16.3 *Capitalization*

A. *Basic concept—valuation of assets and liabilities*

Capitalization is the process of finding the present value of an indefinite number of periodic payments. This process is useful in determining the value of income-producing assets and liabilities.

To capitalize an indefinite number of periodic payments (whether income or outgo) involves finding the present value of a perpetuity. This is done by the methods explained in Sections 12.5 and 13.6 and is facilitated by using Formula 12.3, $A = \frac{R}{i}$, and Formula 13.5, $A = \frac{R}{f}$ where $f = (1 + i)^c - 1$.

Example **16.3a** A revenue-producing property yields a quarterly net income of \$3600.00. What is the value of the property to yield

(i) 18% compounded quarterly?

(ii) 18% effective?

Solution

(i) $$R = 3600.00; \quad i = \frac{18\%}{4} = 4.5\% = 0.045;$$

$$A = \frac{R}{i} = \frac{3600.00}{0.045} \longleftarrow \text{using Formula 12.3}$$

$$= \$80\ 000.00$$

The value of the property is \$80 000.00.

(ii) $$R = 3600.00; \quad i = 18\% = 0.18; \quad c = \frac{1}{4} = 0.25;$$

$$f = 1.18^{0.25} - 1 = 1.0422466 - 1 = 0.0422466 = 4.22466\%$$

$$A = \frac{R}{f} = \frac{3600.00}{0.0422466} \longleftarrow \text{using Formula 13.5}$$

$$= \$85\ 213.89$$

The value of the property is \$85 213.89.

***Example* 16.3b** A utility is required to make annual right-of-way payments of $1950.00 to a landowner. What is the value of the obligation

(i) at 15% effective?

(ii) at 15% compounded monthly?

Solution

(i) $\quad R = 1950.00; \quad i = 15\% = 0.15$

$$A = \frac{1950.00}{0.15} = \$13\,000.00$$

At 15% effective, the utility has an obligation of $13 000.00.

(ii) $\quad R = 1950.00; \quad i = \frac{15\%}{12} = 1.25\% = 0.0125; \quad c = 12;$

$$f = 1.0125^{12} - 1 = 1.1607545 - 1 = 0.1607545$$

$$A = \frac{1950.00}{0.1607545}$$
$$= \$12\,130.30$$

At 15% compounded monthly, the utility's obligation is $12 130.30.

B. *Capitalized cost of an asset*

The concept of **capitalized cost** takes account of the necessity to periodically replace income-producing assets such as plant and equipment. The capitalized cost of an asset is defined as the original cost plus the present value of an unlimited number of periodic replacements. Since the periodic replacements form a perpetuity, the formulae for finding the present value of perpetuities are useful.

$$\text{CAPITALIZED COST} = \text{ORIGINAL COST} + \frac{\text{PERIODIC REPLACEMENT COST}}{f}$$ ⟵ ***Formula* 16.3**

where $f = (1 + i)^c - 1$

i = rate of interest per compounding period

$$c = \frac{\text{number of compounding periods per year}}{\text{number of replacement periods per year}}$$

or

c = the number of compounding periods per replacement period

Note: In the special case when the compounding interval coincides with the replacement interval, $c = 1$ and $f = i$.

Example **16.3c** A machine costing \$40 000 needs to be replaced every six years. If the trade-in value of the machine is \$5000, what is the capitalized cost of the machine at 15% effective?

Solution

Original cost = 40 000.00;

replacement cost = 40 000.00 − 5000.00 = 35 000.00;

$$i = 15\% = 0.15; \quad c = \frac{1}{\frac{1}{6}} = 6;$$

$$f = 1.15^6 - 1 = 2.3130608 - 1 = 1.3130608$$

$$\text{Capitalized cost} = 40\ 000.00 + \frac{35\ 000.00}{1.313068} \longleftarrow \text{using Formula 16.3}$$

$$= 40\ 000.00 + 26\ 655.28$$

$$= \$66\ 655.28$$

Interpretation

The present value of the investment in the machine and its future replacement is \$66 655.28. Deducting the original cost of \$40 000.00 leaves \$26 655.28 which invested at 15% compounded annually for six years amounts to 26 655.28(1.15^6) = 26 655.28(2.3130608) = \$61 655.28. After six years, \$35 000.00 is needed to replace the original machine leaving \$26 655.28 to be invested for the next six years, and so on in perpetuity.

Example **16.3d** Jack Snow bought a licence to operate a taxi for \$25 000 and acquired a taxicab for \$10 000. He plans to replace the taxicab every year and expects to pay \$3000 for each trade-in. If money is worth 12%, what is the capitalized cost of his business?

Solution

The original cost is 25 000.00 + 10 000.00 = 35 000.00;

the annual replacement cost is \$3000.00;

$$i = 12\% = 0.12; \quad c = 1; \quad f = i = 12\% = 0.12$$

$$\text{Capitalized cost} = 35\ 000.00 + \frac{3000.00}{0.12} = 35\ 000.00 + 25\ 000.00 = \$60\ 000.00$$

Example **16.3e** Lyman Corporation is considering buying a plant that consists of land valued at \$200 000, a building costing \$600 000 with an estimated life of 40 years and a salvage value of \$100 000, and equipment worth \$400 000 with an estimated life of 15 years and a scrap value of \$20 000. If money is worth 13% compounded semi-annually, what is the capitalized cost of the plant?

Solution

The original cost of the land is its capitalized cost = 200 000.00.

The original cost of the building is 600 000.00;

the replacement value is 600 000.00 − 100 000.00 = 500 000.00;

$$i = \frac{13\%}{2} = 6.5\% = 0.065; \quad c = \frac{2}{\left(\frac{1}{40}\right)} = 80;$$

$$f = 1.065^{80} - 1 = 153.15891 - 1 = 153.15891$$

$$\text{Capitalized cost of building} = 600\,000.00 + \frac{500\,000.00}{153.15891}$$

$$= 600\,000.00 + 3264.59 \longleftarrow \text{rounded upward to prevent shortfall}$$

$$= \$603\,264.59$$

The original cost of the equipment is 400 000.00;

the replacement value is 400 000.00 − 20 000.00 = 380 000.00;

$$i = \frac{13\%}{2} = 6.5\% = 0.065; \quad c = \frac{2}{\left(\frac{1}{15}\right)} = 30;$$

$$f = 1.065^{30} - 1 = 6.6143662 - 1 = 5.6143662$$

$$\text{Capitalized cost of equipment} = 400\,000.00 + \frac{380\,000.00}{5.6143662}$$

$$= 400\,000.00 + 67\,683.51$$

$$= \$467\,683.51$$

$$\text{Capitalized cost of plant} = 200\,000.00 + 603.264.59 + 467\,683.51$$

$$= \$1\,270\,948.10$$

Alternative

We can obtain the same result by adding the present value of the annual deposit required to finance the replacement of the building and equipment to the original acquisition cost.

$$i = \frac{13\%}{2} = 6.5\% = 0.065; \quad c = 2;$$

$$f = 1.065^2 - 1 = 1.134225 - 1 = 0.134225 = 13.4225\%$$

The annual payment into a sinking fund to replace the building

$$R_1 = \frac{500\,000.00}{\left(\frac{1.134225^{40} - 1}{0.134225}\right)} = \frac{500\,000.00}{1141.0609} = \$438.19$$

Programmed determination of $\left(\frac{1.134225^{40} - 1}{0.134225}\right)$

0	1	40	13.4225			
PV	PMT	N	%i	CPT	FV	1141.0610

The annual payment into a sinking fund to replace the equipment

$$R_2 = \frac{380\,000.00}{\left(\frac{1.134225^{15} - 1}{0.134225}\right)} = \frac{380\,000.00}{41.828021} = \$9084.82$$

The total annual payment is $438.19 + 9084.82 = \$9523.01$.

The present value of these deposits is $\frac{9523.01}{0.134225} = \$70\,948.10$.

$$\begin{aligned}\text{The capitalized cost} &= 200\,000.00 + 600\,000.00 + 40\,000.00 + 70\,948.10 \\ &= \$1\,270\,948.10\end{aligned}$$

***Example* 16.3f** The Beaver Valley Ski Club installed a chairlift at an initial cost of \$225 000. The lift will need to be replaced every ten years at a cost of \$175 000. Seven years after the original installation, it became apparent that a major overhaul would extend the useful life of the lift by two years. If money is worth 12% compounded annually, what is the maximum cost that the club can economically afford for the overhaul?

Solution

The original cost is 225 000.00; the replacement cost is 175 000.00;

$i = 12\% = 0.12; \quad c = \frac{1}{\left(\frac{1}{10}\right)} = 10;$

$f = 1.12^{10} - 1 = 3.1058482 - 1 = 2.1058482.$

$$\begin{aligned}\text{Capitalized cost} &= 225\,000.00 + \frac{175\,000.00}{2.1058482} \\ &= 225\,000.00 + 83\,101.91 \\ &= \$308\,101.91\end{aligned}$$

Of the capitalized cost of \$308 101.91, the original cost of \$225 000.00 is required initially leaving \$83 101.91 to accumulate and finance the replacement. After seven years, the accumulated balance

$$= 83\ 101.91(1.12)^7 = 83\ 101.91(2.2106814) = \$183\ 711.85$$

The required balance to finance the replacement

$$= 175\ 000.00 + 83\ 101.91 = \$258\ 101.91$$

Since the replacement will take place twelve years after the original installation, we need to find the principal that will accumulate to \$258 101.91 from the end of Year 7 to the end of Year 12.

$$P = 258\ 101.91(1.12^{-5}) = 258\ 101.91(0.5674269) = \$146\ 453.96$$

The difference between the capitalized cost after seven years and the required principal is 183 711.85 − 146 453.96 = \$37 257.89.

This difference is the maximum amount that the ski club has economically available for the overhaul. That is, the maximum amount that the ski club should be prepared to pay for the overhaul is \$37 257.89.

C. *Periodic investment cost*

The capitalized cost of an asset represents the investment needed to acquire an asset and replace it indefinitely. The interest that could be earned by that investment is foregone interest revenue; it is the periodic investment cost of the asset. Thus, the **periodic investment cost** is defined as the interest on the capitalized cost of the asset.

$$\text{PERIODIC INVESTMENT COST} = \text{CAPITALIZED COST} \times i$$ ← *Formula* **16.4A**

$$\text{PERIODIC INVESTMENT COST} = \text{ORIGINAL COST} \times i + \text{PERIODIC DEPOSIT NEEDED TO FINANCE THE SINKING FUND}$$

$$= \text{ORIGINAL COST} \times i + \frac{\text{REPLACEMENT COST}}{\left[\frac{(1+i)^c - 1}{i}\right]}$$ ← *Formula* **16.4B**

where i = rate per compounding period

c = the number of compounding periods per replacement period

Programmed determination of $\left[\dfrac{(1+i)^c - 1}{i}\right]$ ***in Formula 16.4B***

0	1	Value of n	Value of i		
PV	PMT	N	%i	CPT	FV

Example **16.3g** Susan Chen initially spent \$3000.00 for tools for her machine shop. After that, she estimates that the shop will need to spend \$500.00 every three months to replace worn or broken tools. If money is worth 14% effective, determine the annual investment cost.

Solution

Original cost is 3000.00; replacement cost is 500.00;

$i = 14\% = 0.14; \quad c = \dfrac{1}{4} = 0.25;$

$f = 1.14^{0.25} - 1 = 1.0332995 - 1 = 0.0332995 = 3.32995\%$

$$\text{Capitalized cost} = 3000.00 + \frac{500.00}{0.0332995}$$

$$= 3000.00 + 15\,015.25$$

$$= \$18\,015.25$$

Annual investment cost $= 18\,015.25(0.14)$ ⟵ using Formula 16.4A

$= \$2522.13$

Alternative

$$\text{Annual investment cost} = 3000.00(0.14) + \frac{500.00}{\left(\dfrac{1.14^{0.25} - 1}{0.25}\right)} \longleftarrow \text{using Formula 16.4B}$$

$$= 420.00 + \frac{500.00}{0.2378535}$$

$$= \$2522.13$$

D. Comparison of buying costs—investment cost basis

Decisions concerning investments in plant and equipment usually involve choosing from a number of similar assets. All are capable of doing the same job but they differ in price, life span, wear and tear, and residual value. After a company has acquired such assets, decisions regarding whether to repair or replace them periodically confront management. A rational approach to making such decisions involves cost comparisons that can be made based on capitalized cost or periodic investment cost.

***Example* 16.3h** Albi Textiles needs to choose between two machines. Machine A costs $4000, has a life of 15 years, and has no salvage value. Machine B costs $3500, has a life of ten years, and has a scrap value of $400. Which machine is more economical in the long run if money is worth

(a) 10%? **(b)** 16%?

Solution

Machine A	**Machine B**
Original cost = 4000.00 Replacement cost = 4000.00	Original cost = 3500.00 Replacement cost = 3100.00
$c = \dfrac{1}{\left(\frac{1}{15}\right)} = 15$	$c = \dfrac{1}{\left(\frac{1}{10}\right)} = 10$

(a) At 10%

$f = 1.10^{15} - 1$ $= 4.1772482 - 1$ $= 3.1772482$	$f = 1.10^{10} - 1$ $= 2.5937425 - 1$ $= 1.5937425$
Capitalized cost $= 4000.00 + \dfrac{4000.00}{3.1772482}$ $= 4000.00 + 1258.95$ $= \$5258.95$	Capitalized cost $= 3500.00 + \dfrac{3100.00}{1.5937425}$ $= 3500.00 + 1945.11$ $= \$5445.11$
Annual investment cost $= 5258.95(0.10) = \$525.90$	Annual investment cost $= 5445.11(0.10) = \$544.51$

Since the capitalized cost of Machine A is smaller than the capitalized cost of Machine B, Machine A is more economical at 10%. The annual investment cost advantage for Machine A is 544.51 − 525.90 = $18.61.

(b) At 16%

Machine A

$f = 1.16^{15} - 1$

$= 9.2655209 - 1$

$= 8.2655209$

Capitalized cost

$= 4000.00 + \dfrac{4000.00}{8.2655209}$

$= 4000.00 + 483.94$

$= \$4483.94$

Annual investment cost

$= 4483.94(0.16) = \$717.43$

Machine B

$f = 1.16^{10} - 1$

$= 4.4114351 - 1$

$= 3.4114351$

Capitalized cost

$= 3500.00 + \dfrac{3100.00}{3.411351}$

$= 3500.00 + 908.71$

$= \$4408.71$

Annual investment cost

$= \$4408.71(0.16) = \$705.39$

Since the capitalized cost of Machine A is greater than the capitalized cost of Machine B, Machine B is more economical at 16%. The annual investment cost advantage for Machine B is 717.43 − 705.39 = \$12.04.

***Example* 16.3i** A machine costing \$8000 with a life of eight years and a salvage value of \$800 can be replaced by a new model lasting twelve years and a residual value of 10% of the original cost. If money is worth 14%, how much can the buyer afford to pay for the new model?

Solution

Old model

Original cost = 8000.00
Replacement cost = 800.00

$c = \dfrac{1}{\left(\frac{1}{8}\right)} = 8$

$i = 14\% = 0.14$

$f = 1.14^{8} - 1$

$= 2.8525864 - 1$

$= 1.8525864$

New model

Let the original cost be C.
Replacement cost = 0.90C.

$c = \dfrac{1}{\left(\frac{1}{12}\right)} = 12$

$i = 14\% = 0.14$

$f = 1.14^{12} - 1$

$= 4.8179048 - 1$

$= 3.8179048$

Capitalized cost

$$= 8000.00 + \frac{7200.00}{1.8525864}$$

$$= 8000.00 + 3886.46$$

$$= \$11\,886.46$$

Capitalized cost

$$= C + \frac{0.90C}{3.8179048}$$

$$= C + 0.2357314C$$

$$= \$1.2357314C$$

The capitalized costs of the two models are to be equal.

$$1.2357314C = 11\,886.46$$

$$C = 9618.97$$

A buyer can afford to pay up to \$9618.97 for the new model.

We would have obtained the same result using the periodic investment cost.

Annual investment cost for the old model

$$8000(0.14) + \frac{7200.00}{\left(\frac{1.14^8 - 1}{0.14}\right)} = 1120.00 + \frac{7200.00}{13.232760} = \$1664.10$$

Annual investment cost for the new model

$$0.14C + \frac{0.90C}{\left(\frac{1.14^{12} - 1}{0.14}\right)} = 0.14C + \frac{0.90C}{27.270749} = 0.1730024C$$

The annual investment costs for the two models are to be equal.

$$0.1730024C = 1664.10$$

$$C = \$9618.94$$

***Example* 16.3j** Equipment that protects against salt corrosion needs to be replaced every four years at a cost of \$12 000. Additional processing can extend the life of the equipment to seven years. At 13%, what is the maximum cost of the additional processing to make it economically feasible?

Solution

Old process

Original cost = 12 000.00
Replacement cost = 12 000.00

$$c = \frac{1}{\left(\frac{1}{4}\right)} = 4$$

$i = 13\% = 0.13$

$$f = 1.13^4 - 1$$
$$= 1.6304736 - 1$$
$$= 0.6304736$$

Capitalized cost

$$= 12\,000.00 + \frac{12\,000.00}{0.6304736}$$
$$= 12\,000.00 + 19\,033.31$$
$$= \$31\,033.31$$

Including additional processing

Original cost = C
Replacement cost = C

$$c = \frac{1}{\left(\frac{1}{7}\right)} = 7$$

$i = 13\% = 0.13$

$$f = 1.13^7 - 1$$
$$= 2.3526055 - 1$$
$$= 1.3526055$$

Capitalized cost

$$= C + \frac{C}{1.3526055}$$
$$= C + 0.7393139C$$
$$= 1.7393139C$$

$$1.7393139C = 31\,033.31$$
$$C = \$17\,842.27$$

The maximum cost including additional processing is \$17 842.27.

The maximum cost of additional processing is 17 842.27 − 12 000.00 = \$5842.27.

E. Comparison of buying costs—production cost basis

The method of comparing assets based on investment cost makes the underlying assumption that the periodic maintenance cost (operating cost plus repair cost) as well as the productive capacity of the assets compared are the same. Since this is often not the case, it is useful to extend the concept of capitalization to allow for differences in capacity and maintenance cost.

To allow for differences in maintenance cost, it is necessary to capitalize the periodic operating expenses and repair costs. Since the capitalized value of periodic payments is the present value of a perpetuity, the periodic maintenance cost is capitalized by dividing by the periodic rate of interest.

$$\text{CAPITALIZED COST INCLUDING MAINTENANCE} = \text{ORIGINAL COST} + \frac{\text{REPLACEMENT COST}}{f} + \frac{\text{MAINTENANCE COST}}{i} \quad \longleftarrow \textit{Formula } \textbf{16.5}$$

To allow for differences in capacity, it is necessary only to determine the capitalized cost per unit of production by dividing the capitalized cost by the number of units of production.

***Example* 16.3k** Equipment costing \$15 000 has a life of ten years with a salvage value of \$2000. Its annual production capacity is 2400 units. Modification of the equipment can increase production by 25%. If interest is 15% and if the life and salvage value remain the same, how much can economically be spent to increase production?

Solution

Regular capacity

Original cost = 15 000.00
Replacement cost = 13 000.00
Production = 2400(10) = 24 000

$$c = \frac{1}{\left(\frac{1}{10}\right)} = 10$$

$i = 15\% = 0.15$

$f = 1.15^{10} - 1$

$= 4.0455577 - 1$

$= 3.0455577$

Increased capacity

Original cost = C
Replacement cost = C − 2000.00
Production = (2400 + 25% of 2400)(10)

= (2400 + 600)(10)

= 3000(10)

= 30 000

$c = 10$

$i = 0.15$

$f = 3.0455577$

Capitalized cost

$$= 15\,000.00 + \frac{13\,000.00}{3.0455577}$$

$$= 15\,000.00 + 4268.51$$

$$= 19\,268.51$$

Capitalized cost per unit of production

$$= \frac{19\,268.51}{24\,000} = 0.8028547$$

Capitalized cost

$$= C + \frac{C - 2000.00}{3.0455577}$$

$$= C + 0.3283471C - 656.69$$

$$= 1.3283471C - 656.69$$

Capitalized cost per unit of production

$$= \frac{1.3283471C - 656.69}{30\,000}$$

$$\frac{1.3283471C - 656.69}{30\,000} = 0.8028547$$

$$1.3283471C - 656.69 = 24\,085.64$$

$$1.3283471C = 24\,742.33$$

$$C = 18\,626.40$$

The original cost including modifications to increase capacity is \$18 626.40. The maximum cost of modification is 18 626.40 − 15 000.00 = \$3626.40.

***Example* 16.3l** Marshall Printing is considering buying new lithographing presses. Research of available equipment has narrowed down the choices to two alternatives.

Alternative A: Buy two presses at a cost of \$60 000 each. The trade-in value of the presses after eight years is \$10 000 per machine. Total operating expenses for the two presses are \$6000 per month and annual repair costs are \$5000.

Alternative B: Buy one machine costing \$250 000 having a life of ten years and a trade-in value of \$45 000. Operating expenses are \$4000 per month and the annual repair cost is \$3000.

If money is worth 12%,

(i) find the capitalized costs of the alternatives;

(ii) determine which alternative is preferable;

(iii) determine the annual costs of the two alternatives.

Solution

(i) **Alternative A**

Original cost = 120 000.00
Replacement cost = 100 000.00

$$c = \frac{1}{\left(\frac{1}{8}\right)} = 8$$

$i = 12\% = 0.12$

$f = 1.12^8 - 1$

$= 2.4759632 - 1$

$= 1.4759632$

Operating expenses per month = 6000.00

$$c = \frac{1}{12}$$

$f = 1.12^{\frac{1}{12}} - 1$

$= 1.0094888 - 1$

$= 0.0094888$

Annual repair cost = 5000.00

Alternative B

Original cost = 250 000.00
Replacement cost = 205 000.00

$$c = \frac{1}{\left(\frac{1}{10}\right)} = 10$$

$i = 12\% = 0.12$

$f = 1.12^{10} - 1$

$= 3.1058482 - 1$

$= 2.1058482$

Operating expenses per month = 4000.00

$$c = \frac{1}{12}$$

$f = 1.12^{\frac{1}{12}} - 1$

$= 1.0094888 - 1$

$= 0.0094888$

Annual repair cost = 3000.00

Capitalized cost for Alternative A

$$= 120\,000.00 + \frac{100\,000.00}{1.4759632} + \frac{6000.00}{0.0094888} + \frac{5000.00}{0.12} \longleftarrow \text{using Formula 16.5}$$

$= 120\,000.00 + 67\,752.37 + 632\,324.42 + 41\,666.67$

$= \$861\,743.46$

Capitalized cost for Alternative B

$$= 250\,000.00 + \frac{205\,000.00}{2.1058482} + \frac{4000.00}{0.0094888} + \frac{3000.00}{0.12}$$

$= 250\,000.00 + 97\,347.95 + 421\,549.62 + 25\,000.00$

$= \$793\,897.57$

(ii) Since the capitalized cost of Alternative B is smaller than the capitalized cost of Alternative A, Alternative B is preferable.

(iii) The total annual cost for Alternative A is 861 743.46(0.12) = \$103 409.22.

The total annual cost for Alternative B is 793 897.57(0.12) = \$95 267.71.

F. Total periodic cost of an asset

The **total periodic cost** of an asset is defined as the interest on the capitalized cost including maintenance.

$$\text{TOTAL PERIODIC COST} = \text{CAPITALIZED COST} \times i$$

We can find the total periodic cost by extending Formula 16.5.

$$\text{TOTAL PERIODIC COST} = \text{ORIGINAL COST} \times i + \frac{\text{REPLACEMENT COST}}{\left[\frac{(1+i)^c - 1}{i}\right]} + \text{PERIODIC OPERATING EXPENSE} + \text{PERIODIC REPAIR COST} \quad \longleftarrow \textit{Formula 16.6}$$

For Example 16.31, we can find the total annual cost (also called the **annual charge**) directly.

Annual charge for Alternative A

$$= 120\,000.00(0.12) + \frac{100\,000.00}{\left(\frac{1.12^8 - 1}{0.12}\right)} + 6000.00\left(\frac{1.0094888^{12} - 1}{.0094888}\right) + 5000.00$$

$$= 120\,000.00(0.12) + \frac{100\,000.00}{12.299693} + 6000.00(12.646498) + 5000.00$$

$$= 14\,400.00 + 8130.28 + 75\,878.99 + 5000.00$$

$$= \$103\,409.27$$

Annual charge for Alternative B

$$= 250\,000.00(0.12) + \frac{205\,000.00}{\left(\frac{1.12^{10} - 1}{0.12}\right)} + 4000.00\left(\frac{1.0094888^{12} - 1}{0.0094888}\right) + 3000.00$$

$$= 250\,000.00(0.12) + \frac{205\,000.00}{17.548735} + 4000.00(12.646498) + 3000.00$$

$$= 30\,000.00 + 11\,681.75 + 50\,585.99 + 3000.00$$

$$= \$95\,267.74$$

Formula 16.6 shows that the periodic charge of owning an asset consists of

1. the periodic interest lost on the investment (Original cost × i)
   plus
2. the periodic depreciation charge $\left(\dfrac{\text{Wearing value}}{\left[\frac{(1+i)^c - 1}{i}\right]}\right)$
   plus
3. the periodic operating expense
   plus
4. the periodic repair cost.

***Example* 16.3m** To keep producing, a machine requires major renovation or it can be sold for \$2500. If renovated, it will have a life of five years with a scrap value of \$500. Monthly operating expenses amount to \$1800 and annual repair cost is \$600. Annual production is 2000 units. A new machine can be bought for \$30 000. The life of the new machine is ten years with a salvage value of \$4000. Monthly operating costs of the new machine are \$2100 and annual repair cost is \$400. Annual production is 2400 units. Assuming interest at 11% and using the periodic cost method, determine the maximum economically feasible cost of renovation.

Solution

Annual charge for the old machine

Let the maximum cost of renovation be X.

Interest on investment $= 0.11(\text{X} + 2500.00) = 0.11\text{X} + 275.00$

$$\text{Depreciation charge} = \frac{\text{X} + 2500.00 - 500.00}{\left(\frac{1.11^5 - 1}{0.11}\right)}$$

$$= \frac{\text{X} + 2000.00}{6.2278014}$$

$$= 0.1605703\text{X} + 321.14$$

$$\text{Operating expense} = 1800.00\left[\frac{(1+f)^{12} - 1}{f}\right] \longleftarrow f = 1.11^{\frac{1}{12}} - 1 = 0.0087346$$

$$= 1800.00\left(\frac{1.0087346^{12} - 1}{0.0087346}\right)$$

$$= 1800.00(12.593602)$$

$$= 22\,668.48$$

Repair cost $= 600.00$

Total annual charge

$= 0.11X + 275.00 + 0.1605703X + 321.14 + 22\,668.48 + 600.00$

$= 0.2705703X + 23\,864.62$

$$\text{Annual charge per unit of production} = \frac{0.2705703X + 23\,864.62}{2000}$$

Annual charge for the new machine

Interest on investment $= 0.11(30\,000.00)$	$=$	3 300.00
Depreciation charge $= \dfrac{26\,000.00}{\left(\dfrac{1.11^{10} - 1}{0.11}\right)} = \dfrac{26\,000.00}{16.722009}$	$=$	1 554.84
Operating expense $= 2100.00\left(\dfrac{1.0087346^{12} - 1}{0.0087346}\right)$ $= 2100.00(12.593602)$	$=$	26 446.56
Repair cost	$=$	400.00
Total annual charge		31 701.40

$$\text{Annual charge per unit of production} = \frac{31\,701.40}{2400} = 13.208918$$

$$\frac{0.2705703X + 23\,864.62}{2000} = 13.208918$$

$$0.2705703X + 23\,864.62 = 26\,417.84$$

$$0.2705703X = 2553.22$$

$$X = 9436.42$$

The maximum economically feasible cost of renovation is $9436.42.

Exercise 16.3

A. Find the capitalized cost for each of the following.

	Original cost	*Residual value*	*Annual maintenance cost*	*Replacement period in years*	*Annual rate of interest*
1.	$ 8 000	nil	—	15	13%
2.	12 500	nil	—	20	15%
3.	26 000	$4000	—	10	14%
4.	18 000	3200	—	8	22%
5.	9 400	900	$15 000	12	16%
6.	16 500	3000	12 400	7	18%

B. Answer each of the following questions.

1. Determine the annual investment cost for Part A, Problems 1 to 4.

2. Determine the annual charge for Part A, Problems 5 and 6.

3. An income property yields a monthly net income of \$1600. What is the value of the property to yield

   (a) 16.5% compounded monthly? **(b)** 16.5% effective?

4. An obligation is met by making quarterly payments of \$2625. What is the value of the obligation at

   (a) 13.5% compounded monthly? **(b)** 15% effective?

5. A delivery service bought a van for \$8600. The van is to be traded in every two years at a cost of \$4000. If interest is 13%, what is the capitalized cost of the van?

6. A swimming pool installed in an apartment building at a cost of \$18 000 is to be renovated every seven years at an estimated cost of \$9000. If money is worth 14%, what is the capitalized cost of the pool?

7. A machine costing \$12 000 has a trade-in value of \$1500 after fifteen years. If the machine is overhauled after ten years, its useful life can be extended by three years. If the trade-in value then is \$1100 and assuming interest at 11%, what is the maximum cost of the overhaul that can economically be justified?

8. A service building costing \$25 000 must be totally renovated every twenty years. Major repairs after fifteen years will extend the service life of the building to 24 years. If interest is 15%, what is the maximum amount of money that should be spent on the repair job?

9. A transformer costing \$30 000 must be replaced every four years. If its scrap value is \$2800 and interest is 16%, what is the annual investment cost?

10. A farmer buys a tractor for \$13 000 and intends to trade in the tractor every four years at an estimated cost of \$7600. What is the annual investment cost at 12%?

11. The manager of Widgits Inc. needs to choose between two machines. Machine A costs \$9000 and has a life of twelve years and a salvage value of \$200. Machine B costs \$8000 and has a life of nine years and a salvage value of \$300. Compute the capitalized cost and the annual investment cost to determine which machine is more economical in the long run. Assume that money is worth

    (a) 12%; **(b)** 18%.

12. Word processing equipment priced at \$1450 has to be replaced every five years at a cost of \$1300. A similar model priced at \$1250 has to be replaced every four years at a cost of \$1100. Compare the annual investment costs to determine which model is the more economical buy at

    (a) 10%; **(b)** 16%.

13. Equipment costing \$15 000 with a life of twelve years and a residual value of \$1000 can be replaced by a different model with a life of nine years and a residual

value of 15% of the original cost. If money is worth 13%, how much can a user afford to pay if she decides to switch to the second model?

14. Equipment costing $150 000 with a life of ten years has a salvage value of $18 000. Protective covering can extend the life of the equipment to fifteen years. If interest is 16% and the salvage value after fifteen years is $6000, what is the maximum cost that can be paid for the protective equipment?

15. Machine A, costing $36 000, has a life of fifteen years with a salvage value of $1500 and a productive capacity of 1600 units per year. Machine B, costing $28 000, has a life of twelve years, a salvage value of $1000, and a productive capacity of 1400 per year. At 17%, what is the difference in the annual investment cost per unit?

16. Equipment costing $55 000 has a life of twelve years with a salvage value of $4000. Annual service hours are 1200. Modification of the equipment would increase the number of service hours to 1600 but the life of the equipment would be reduced to ten years; salvage value would then be $6000. If interest is 16%, how much is the maximum amount that should be spent on the modification?

17. A farmer can buy an MF tractor for $15 000. The tractor has an estimated life of eight years with a trade-in value of $2500. Annual operating expenses are $3000 and annual repair cost is estimated to be $600. An IH tractor which can do the same job costs $13 500 and has a life of six years and a trade-in value of $2800. Annual operating expenses are expected to be $2300 and annual repair cost is estimated at $500. At 15%, which tractor is the more economical buy and what is the difference in the annual cost?

18. The floors of a school building can be finished at a cost of $50 000. The finish will last twenty years and must then be redone totally. Annual costs are $9000 for servicing and $500 for repairs. Alternatively, the school can be carpeted at a cost of $30 000 every five years. Annual costs are $4000 for servicing and $1000 for repairs. If interest is 13%, which method is more economical and what is the difference in the annual costs?

19. A manufacturer requires a drilling machine. Model A costs $16 000 and has an estimated life of fifteen years. Monthly operating expenses are $2450 and annual repair costs are $800. Model B costs $14 000 and has a life of twelve years. Monthly operating expenses are $2550 and annual repair costs are $750. Both machines have a scrap value of $900. If money is worth 18%, which is the more economical model and what is the difference in annual costs?

20. A credit union uses a posting machine to maintain member accounts. The machine costs $12 000, lasts ten years, and has a scrap value of $1000. Monthly operating expenses are $1600 and annual service cost is $500. Alternatively, the credit union can buy a suitable computer for $40 000. The computer has a life of eight years and a salvage value of $3000. Monthly operating expenses are $900 and annual servicing is $1000. As a third choice, the credit union can buy the services of the Credit Union League at a cost of $2000 per month. If interest is 14%, which of the three alternatives is the most economical? What is the annual cost of each alternative?

Review exercise

1. A machine costing $12 000 has a trade-in value of $2460 after eight years. Construct a depreciation schedule using
   (a) the annuity method (assume interest to be 16%);
   (b) the sinking-fund method (assume interest to be 16%).
2. Equipment with an original cost of $32 000 has an estimated life of 25 years and a scrap value of $480. Compute the book value after 20 years and the depreciation charge in Year 21 using
   (a) the annuity method (assume interest to be 20%);
   (b) the sinking-fund method (assume interest to be 20%).
3. A property containing oil wells is estimated to yield a net annual income of $200 000 for fifteen years before depletion. When the oil has been removed, the property value is estimated to be $500 000. If an investor can set up a depletion reserve earning 11%, what should the investor be prepared to pay to realize a yield of 20%?
4. A machine with an original cost of $9160 has a trade-in value of $2230 after ten years. Compute the book value after six years using the sinking-fund method if interest is 10%.
5. A building has an original cost of $80 000, a life of 25 years, and a salvage value of $8500. Find the book value of the building after fifteen years by the annuity method. Assume interest at 18%.
6. A turbine costing $75 000 has a life of twenty years and a scrap value of $3500. Determine the depreciation in Year 12 by the sinking-fund method. Interest is 21%.
7. A saw mill buys timber rights to a tract of land. Useable trees are expected to last for twenty years and yield an annual net income of $75 000 before depletion. After twenty years, the timber rights have no value. The owners of the saw mill can set up a replacement fund earning 9.5%. For how much were the timber rights acquired if purchased to yield 16%?
8. Tires for a crane last four years with a salvage value of $75.00. They can be bought at a cost of $875.00 each. How much should be the price of a tire lasting seven years with a salvage value of 10% of the original cost if money is worth 13%?
9. Artificial turf for a playing field can be installed for $125 000. If the covering needs to be replaced every six years at a cost of $95 000 and interest is 15%,
   (a) what is the capitalized cost of the turf?
   (b) what is the annual investment cost?
10. A property containing natural resources yields an estimated annual net income of $55 000 for eight years before depletion. After the natural resources are removed, the property has an estimated value of $150 000. A prospective buyer has offered $270 000 for the property. If the buyer can earn 10% on a sinking fund set up for the recovery of the capital, what is the yield rate on the investment?

11. A mine is offered for sale for $600 000. A prospective buyer has determined the following: net annual income before depletion is expected to be $90 000 for eighteen years; the value of the property when the ore has been removed is expected to be $75 000; the depletion reserve can be set up to earn 12%.

(a) What is the yield rate on the mine if it is bought for $600 000?

(b) How much should the buyer offer if the investment is to realize 16%?

12. A delivery service bought a van for $12 600 and expects to trade it in every two years at a cost of $5200. Interest is 13% compounded semi-annually.

(a) What is the capitalized cost?

(b) What is the annual investment cost?

13. A pool heating and filtration system costs $2300. If exposed to weather, the system needs to be replaced every five years. If an enclosure is provided, the life of the system including the enclosure is seven years. Scrap value in either case is $400. If money is worth 13%, what is the maximum amount that should be spent on the enclosure?

14. A machine costs $25 000 when new and has a scrap value of $1700 after twelve years. A second machine which can do the same job costs $22 000 and has a life of nine years and a scrap value of $1800. Compute the capitalized cost and the annual investment cost to determine which machine is more economical. Assume that interest is

(a) 13%; **(b)** 20%.

15. Painters can paint a building at a cost of $1350 every three years if using Brand A. If they use longer lasting Brand B, the paint job needs to be done every five years. If interest is 12%, what is the maximum cost at which it is economical to switch to Brand B?

16. A machine costing $18 000 has a life of six years, a trade-in value of $2500 after six years, and an annual productive capacity of 3600 units. A competitor's model costs $21 000 and has a life of eight years, a trade-in value of $2200 after eight years, and an annual productive capacity of 4000 units. At 16%,

(a) which machine is a better buy?

(b) what is the difference in their annual investment cost per unit?

17. A machine that can be disposed of for $3000 must be renovated if it is to be kept in production. If renovated, the machine will have a life of seven years with a scrap value of $500. Annual operating expenses amount to $4000 and annual repair cost is $1500. A new machine will cost $34 000 and has a life of ten years and a scrap value of $3500. Annual operating expenses amount to $3600 and annual repair cost is $1200. If money is worth 15%, what is the maximum amount that can economically be spent on renovating the old machine?

18. Bomac Steel uses two fabricating machines that cost $60 000 each. The machines have a life of twelve years with a trade-in value of $8000 each after twelve years. Monthly operating expenses are $7000 and annual repair costs amount to $2000. A larger machine capable of doing the job of the two machines costs $270 000 and has a life of fifteen years and a trade-in value of $30 000 after fifteen years. Monthly operating expenses are $4000 and annual repair costs amount to $4000. At 17%,
    (a) is it economical to replace the two machines by the larger machine?
    (b) what is the difference in the annual costs?

Self-test

1. A machine with an original book value of $60 000 has a scrap value of $3000 after six years. If interest is 12%, construct a depreciation schedule using the sinking-fund method.
2. Mining equipment with an original book value of $150 000 and an estimated scrap value of $15 000 after eight years is depreciated by the annuity method. If the rate of interest is 13%, what is the accumulated depreciation after five years?
3. A gold mine is estimated to yield an annual net income of $250 000 for the next eight years before depletion. After eight years, the gold mine has no value. If the depletion reserve earns 10%, what is the value of the gold mine to yield 15%?
4. A natural resources property yields an annual net income of $42 000 for ten years before depletion. The residual value of the property after ten years is estimated to be $30 000. If a sinking fund for the recovery of the capital investment can be set up to earn 9% and an offer to purchase of $260 000 is made, what is the yield rate on the investment?
5. Timber rights on a tract of land are expected to yield an annual net income of $100 000 for ten years before depletion. After ten years, the timber rights have a value of $50 000. The depletion reserve fund earns 11%. If the rights were purchased to yield 16%, what is the amount of depletion in Year 5?
6. An asset has an original book value of $40 000. The asset is to be replaced after six years and has a residual value of $3000 at that time. Annual maintenance cost is $4800. What is the capitalized cost of the asset at 15%?
7. Equipment costing $70 000 with an expected life of six years has a salvage value of $10 000. Modification of the equipment can extend the life of the equipment to nine years with a salvage value of $6000 after nine years. If interest is 14%, what is the maximum outlay that can be justified to modify the equipment?
8. A machine costing $4800 has a life of twelve years and a trade-in value of $500 after twelve years. The maximum annual usage is 1250 hours. A competitive model costing $5200 has a life of fifteen years and a trade-in value of $400 after 15 years. The maximum annual usage is 1300 hours. If interest is 18%, what is the difference in the annual investment cost per hour?

9. A manufacturer uses a machine costing \$150 000 that has a life of ten years and a scrap value of \$3000. Monthly operating expenses amount to \$6000 and the annual repair cost is \$4000. A new smaller model with one-third of the productive capacity of the old model can be purchased for \$70 000. The new model has a life of fifteen years with a scrap value of \$2000. Monthly operating expenses are \$1500 and the annual repair cost is \$800. If interest is 16% and the same annual production is maintained, what is the difference in the total annual cost of using the old model as compared to the new?

Summary of formulae used

Formula 12.3

$$A = \frac{R}{i}$$

Finding the present value of an ordinary perpetuity

Formula 13.5

$$A = \frac{R}{f} \text{ where } f = (1 + i)^c - 1$$

Finding the present value of an ordinary general perpetuity

Formula 16.1

$$\text{ANNUAL DEPRECIATION CHARGE, } R = \frac{\left(\text{ORIGINAL COST} - \text{RESIDUAL VALUE}\right) \times (1 + i)^{-n}}{\left[\frac{1 - (1 + i)^{-n}}{i}\right]}$$

where n = the number of years in the life of the asset

i = the applicable rate of interest

Formula for finding the annual depreciation charge when using the annuity method

Formula 16.2

$$\text{ANNUAL NET INCOME FROM OPERATIONS} = \text{ANNUAL INTEREST ON CAPITAL INVESTMENT} + \text{ANNUAL DEPOSIT INTO DEPLETION RESERVE}$$

Basic relationship between net income before depletion and investment in wasting assets

Formula 16.3

$$\text{CAPITALIZED COST} = \text{ORIGINAL COST} + \frac{\text{PERIODIC REPLACEMENT COST}}{f}$$

where $f = (1 + i)^c - 1$

i = rate of interest per compounding period

$$c = \frac{\text{number of compounding periods per year}}{\text{number of replacement periods per year}}$$

Formula for finding the capitalized cost of an asset

Formula 16.4A

$$\text{PERIODIC INVESTMENT COST} = \text{CAPITALIZED COST} \times i$$

Formula for finding the periodic investment cost

Formula 16.4B

$$\text{PERIODIC INVESTMENT COST} = \text{ORIGINAL COST} \times i + \frac{\text{REPLACEMENT COST}}{\left[\frac{(1+i)^c - 1}{i}\right]}$$

where i = rate per compounding period
c = the number of compounding periods per replacement period

Alternative formula for finding the periodic investment cost

Formula 16.5

$$\text{CAPITALIZED COST INCLUDING MAINTENANCE} = \text{ORIGINAL COST} + \frac{\text{REPLACEMENT COST}}{f} + \frac{\text{MAINTENANCE COST}}{i}$$

Formula for finding the capitalized cost including operating expenses and repair costs

Formula 16.6

$$\text{TOTAL PERIODIC COST} = \text{ORIGINAL COST} \times i + \frac{\text{REPLACEMENT COST}}{\left[\frac{(1+i)^c - 1}{i}\right]} + \text{PERIODIC OPERATING COST}$$

Alternative formula for finding the capitalized cost including operating expenses and repair costs

Glossary of terms used

Annual charge the annual interest on the capitalized cost of an asset including operating expenses and repair costs

Capitalization the process of finding the present value of an infinite number of periodic payments

Capitalized cost the original cost of an asset plus the present value of an unlimited number of periodic replacements of the asset

Depletion loss in value of wasting assets due to their removal in the process of operations

Methods of depreciation systematic ways of allocating depreciation to accounting periods

Periodic investment cost the interest on the capitalized cost of an asset including operating expenses and repair costs

Total periodic cost the periodic interest on the capitalized cost of an asset including operating expenses and repair costs

17 Investment decision applications

Introduction

When making investment decisions, all decision makers must consider the comparative effects of alternative courses of action on the cash flows of the business. Since cash flow analysis needs to take into account the time value of money (interest), present-value concepts are useful.

When only cash inflows are considered, the value of the discounted cash flows is helpful in guiding management toward a rational decision. If outlays as well as inflows are considered, the net present value concept is applicable in evaluating projects.

While the net present value method indicates whether or not a project will yield a specified rate of return, knowing the actual rate of return provides useful information to the decision maker. The rate of return may be computed using the net present value concept.

Objectives

Upon completing this chapter, you will be able to

1. determine the discounted value of cash flows and choose between alternative investments based on the discounted cash-flow criterion;
2. determine the net present value of a capital investment project and infer from the net present value whether a project is feasible or not;
3. compute the rate of return on investment.

17.1 *Discounted cash flow*

A. *Evaluation of capital expenditures—basic concepts*

Capital investment projects are projects involving cash outlays that are expected to generate a continuous flow of future benefits. Benefits may be non-monetary but the methods of analysis considered in this chapter will deal only with investment projects generating an inflow of monetary benefits.

While capital expenditures normally result in the acquisition of assets, the primary purpose of capital expenditures is the acquisition of a future stream of benefits in the form of an inflow of cash. In considering investments involving the acquisition of assets and in making decisions about replacing assets or whether to buy or lease, the decision maker needs to analyze the effects of alternative courses of action on the future cash flow.

While factors other than financial concerns often enter into the decision-making process, the analysis techniques considered here are concerned only with the amount and the timing of cash receipts and cash payments under the assumption that the amount and timing of the cash flow is certain.

From the mathematical point of view, the major problem in evaluating capital expenditure projects is the time value of money. This value prevents direct comparison of cash received and cash payments made at different times. The concept of present value, as introduced in Chapter 9 and used in the following chapters, provides the vehicle for making sums of money received or paid at different times comparable at a chosen time.

B. Discounted cash flow

When using the discounting technique to evaluate alternatives, two fundamental principles serve as decision criteria.

1. The bird-in-the-hand principle—Given that all other factors are equal, earlier benefits are preferable to later benefits.
2. The bigger-the-better principle—Given that all other factors are equal, bigger benefits are preferable to smaller benefits.

***Example* 17.1a** Suppose you are offered a choice of receiving $1000.00 today or receiving $1000.00 three years from now. What is the preferred choice?

Solution

Accepting the bird-in-the-hand principle, you should prefer to receive $1000.00 today rather than three years from now. The rationale is that $1000.00 can be invested to earn interest and will accumulate in three years to a sum of money greater than $1000.00. Stated another way, the present value of $1000.00 to be received in three years is less than $1000.00 today.

***Example* 17.1b** Consider a choice of $2000.00 today or $3221.00 five years from now. Which alternative is preferable?

Solution

No definite answer is possible without considering interest. A rational choice must consider the time value of money; that is, we need to know the rate of interest. Once a rate of interest is established, we can make the proper choice by considering the present value of the two sums of money and applying the bigger-the-better principle.

If you choose 'now' as the focal date, three outcomes are possible.

1. The present value of \$3221.00 is greater than \$2000.00. In this case, the preferred choice is \$3221.00 five years from now.
2. The present value of \$3221.00 is less than \$2000.00. In this case, the preferred choice is \$2000.00 now.
3. The present value of \$3221.00 equals \$2000.00. In this case, either choice is equally acceptable.

(a) *Suppose the rate of interest is 8%.*

$S = 3221.00; \quad i = 8\% = 0.08; \quad n = 5$
$P = 3221.00(1.08^{-5}) = 3221.00(0.6805832) = \$2192.16$
Since at 8% the discounted value of \$3221.00 is greater than \$2000.00, the preferred choice at 8% is \$3221.00 five years from now.

(b) *Suppose the rate of interest is 12%.*

$S = 3221.00; \quad i = 12\% = 0.12; \quad n = 5$
$P = 3221.00(1.12^{-5}) = 3221.00(0.5674269) = \$1827.68$
Since at 12% the discounted value is less than \$2000.00, the preferred choice is \$2000.00 now.

(c) *Suppose the rate of interest is 10%.*

$S = 3221.00; \quad i = 10\% = 0.10; \quad n = 5$
$P = 3221.00(1.10^{-5}) = 3221.00(0.6209213) = \$1999.99$
Since at 10% the discounted value is equal to \$2000.00, the two choices are equally acceptable.

Programmed solution

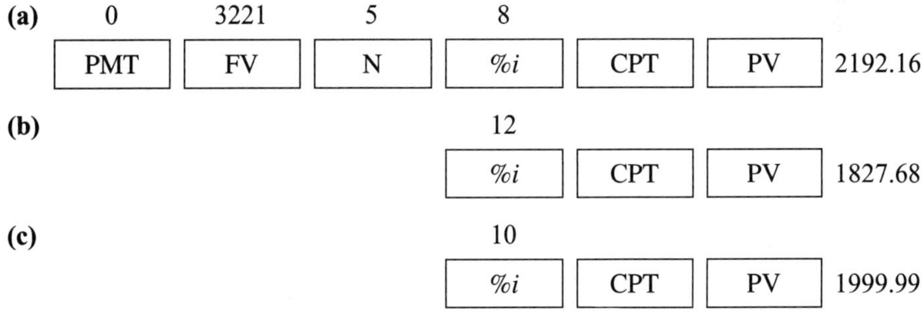

***Example* 17.1c** Two investments are available. Alternative A yields a return of \$6000 in two years and \$10 000 in five years. Alternative B yields a return of \$7000 now and \$7000 in seven years. Which alternative is preferable if money is worth

(i) 11%? (ii) 15%?

Solution

To determine which alternative is preferable, we need to compute the present value of each alternative and choose the alternative with the higher present value.

Let the focal point be 'now.'

(i) For $i = 11\%$

Alternative A

The present value of Alternative A is the sum of the present values of \$6000 in two years and \$10 000 in five years.

Present value of \$6000 in two years $= 6000(1.11^{-2}) = 6000(0.8116224)$	=	\$ 4 870
Present value of \$10 000 in five years $= 10\,000(1.11^{-5}) = 10\,000(0.5934513)$	=	5 935
The present value of Alternative A	=	\$10 805

Alternative B

The present value of Alternative B is the sum of the present values of \$7000 now and \$7000 in seven years.

Present value of \$7000 now	=	\$ 7 000
Present value of \$7000 in seven years $= 7000(1.11^{-7}) = 7000(0.4816584)$	=	3 372
The present value of Alternative B	=	\$10 372

Programmed solution

Alternative A

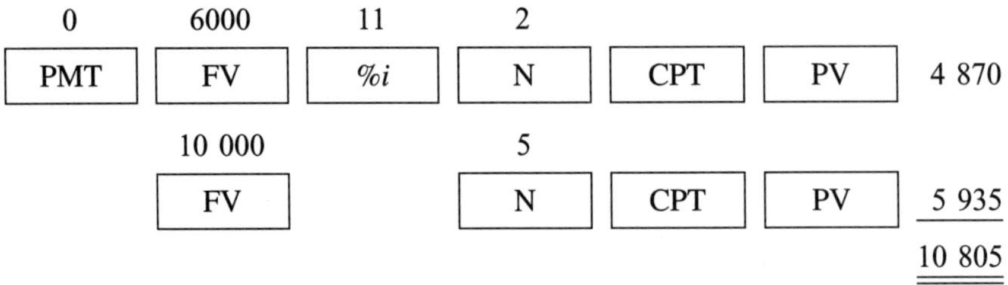

Alternative B

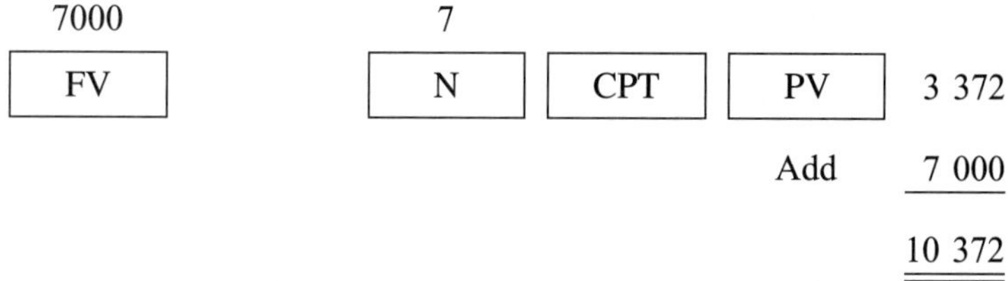

Since at 11% the present value of Alternative A is greater than the present value of Alternative B, Alternative A is preferable.

(ii) For $i = 15\%$

Alternative A

Present value of \$6000 in two years $= 6000(1.15^{-2}) = 6000(0.7561437)$	=	\$4537
Present value of \$10 000 in five years $= 10\,000(1.15^{-5}) = 10\,000(0.4971767)$	=	4972
The present value of Alternative A	=	\$9509

Alternative B

Present value of \$7000 now	=	\$7000
Present value of \$7000 in seven years $= 7000(1.15^{-7}) = 7000(0.3759370)$	=	2632
The present value of Alternative B	=	\$9632

Programmed solution

Alternative A

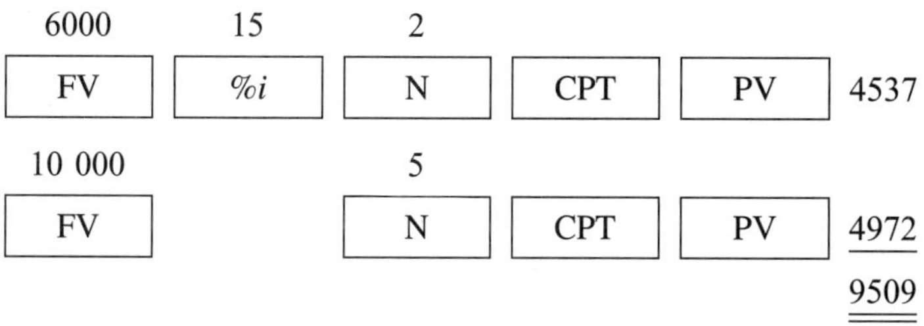

Alternative B

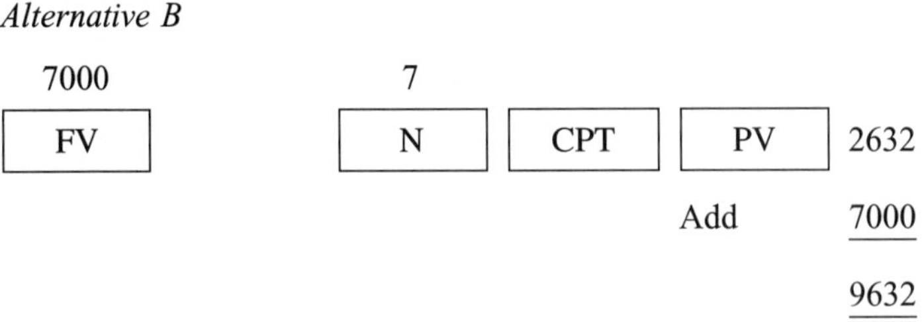

Since at 15% the present value of Alternative B is greater than the present value of Alternative A, Alternative B is preferable.

Note: Applying present value techniques to capital investment problems usually involves estimates. For this reason, dollar amounts in the preceding example and all following examples are rounded to the nearest dollar. We suggest that you do the same when working on problems of this nature.

***Example* 17.1d** An insurance company offers to settle a claim either by making a payment of $50 000 immediately or by making payments of $8000 at the end of each year for ten years. What offer is preferable if interest is 12% compounded annually?

Solution

Present value of $8000 at the end of each year for ten years is the present value of an ordinary annuity in which R = 8000, n = 10, and i = 12%.

$$A_n = 8000\left(\frac{1 - 1.12^{-10}}{0.12}\right) = 8000(5.650223) = \$45\ 202$$

Programmed solution

0	8000	10	12			
FV	PMT	N	%i	CPT	PV	45 202

Since the immediate payment is larger than the present value of the annual payments of $8000, the immediate payment of $50 000 is preferable.

***Example* 17.1e** Sheridan Credit Union needs to decide whether to buy a duplicating machine for $6000 and enter a service contract requiring the payment of $45 at the end of every three months for five years, or to enter a five-year lease requiring the payment of $435 at the beginning of every three months. If leased, the machine can be bought after five years for $600. At 13% compounded quarterly, should the credit union buy or lease?

Solution

To make a rational decision, the credit union should compare the present value of the cash outlays if buying the machine with the present value of the cash outlays if leasing the machine.

Present value of the decision to buy

Present value of cash payment for the machine	=	\$6000
Present value of the service contract involves an ordinary annuity in which R = 45, n = 20, i = 3.25%		
$= 45\left(\dfrac{1 - 1.0325^{-20}}{0.0325}\right) = 45(14.539346)$	=	654
Present value of decision to buy	=	\$6654

Present value of the decision to lease

Present value of the quarterly lease payments involves an annuity due: R = 435, n = 20, i = 3.25%		
$= 435(1.0325)\left(\dfrac{1 - 1.0325^{-20}}{0.0325}\right) = 435(1.0325)(14.539346)$	=	\$6530
Present value of purchase price after five years		
$= 600(1.0325^{-20}) = 600(0.5274712)$	=	316
Present value of decision to lease	=	\$6846

Programmed solution

Present value of the decision to buy

Present value of cash payment for the machine	=	\$6000
Present value of the service contract		

0	45	20	3.25				
FV	PMT	N	%i	CPT	PV	=	654

Present value of decision to buy	=	\$6654

Present value of the decision to lease

Present value of the quarterly lease payments

= \$6530

Present value of purchase price after five years

0	600					
PMT	FV	CPT	PV		=	316

Present value of the decision to lease = $6846

In the case of costs, the selection criterion follows the smaller-the-better principle. Since the present value of the decision to buy is smaller than the present value of the decision to lease, the credit union should buy the duplicating machine.

***Example* 17.1f** Sheridan Service needs a brake machine. The machine can be bought for $4600 and after five years will have a salvage value of $490, or the machine can be leased for five years by making monthly payments of $111 at the beginning of each month. If money is worth 14%, should Sheridan Service buy or lease?

Solution

Alternative 1: Buy machine

Present value of cash price	=	$4600
less: Present value of salvage value		
$= 490(1.14^{-5}) = 490(0.5193687)$	=	255
Present value of decision to buy	=	$4345

Alternative 2: Lease machine

The monthly lease payments form a general annuity due in which

$$R = 111; \quad c = \frac{1}{12}; \quad n = 60; \quad i = 14\%;$$

$$f = 1.14^{\frac{1}{12}} - 1$$
$$= 1.0109789 - 1 = 1.09789\%$$

Present value of the monthly lease payments

$$= 111(1.0109789)\left(\frac{1 - 1.0109789^{-60}}{0.0109789}\right)$$

$$= 111(1.0109789)(43.777866)$$

$$= \$4913$$

The present value of the decision to lease is $4913.

Programmed solution

Alternative 1: Buy machine

Present value of cash price	= \$4600
less: Present value of salvage value	

0	490	5	14			
PMT	FV	N	%*i*	CPT	PV	= 255

Present value of decision to buy	= \$4345

Alternative 2: Lease machine

Present value of the monthly lease payments

0	111	60	1.09789			
FV	PMT	N	%*i*	DUE	PV	= \$4913

Since the present value of the decision to buy is smaller than the present value of the decision to lease, Sheridan Service should buy the machine.

Exercise 17.1

A. For each of the following, compute the present value of each alternative and determine the preferred alternative according to the discounted cash flow criterion.

1. The A company must make a choice between two investment alternatives. Alternative 1 will return the company \$20 000 at the end of three years and \$60 000 at the end of six years. Alternative 2 will return the company \$13 000 at the end of each of the next six years. The A company normally expects to earn a rate of return of 12% on funds invested.

2. An obligation can be settled by making a payment of \$10 000 now and a final payment of \$20 000 in five years. Alternatively, the obligation can be settled by payments of \$1500 at the end of every three months for five years. Interest is 18% compounded quarterly.

3. The B Company has a policy of requiring a rate of return on investment of 16%. Two investment alternatives are available but the company may choose only one. Alternative 1 offers a return of \$50 000 after four years, \$40 000 after seven years, and \$30 000 after ten years. Alternative 2 will return the company \$750 at the end of each month for ten years.

4. An unavoidable cost may be met by outlays of \$10 000 now and \$2000 at the end of every six months for seven years or by making monthly payments of \$500 in advance for seven years. Interest is 17% compounded annually.

B. Answer each of the following questions.

1. A contract offers \$25 000 immediately and \$50 000 in five years or \$10 000 at the end of each year for ten years. If money is worth 13%, which offer is preferable?

2. Bruce and Carol want to sell their business. They have received two offers. If they accept Offer A they will receive \$15 000 immediately and \$20 000 in three years. If they accept Offer B they will receive \$3000 now and \$3000 at the end of every six months for six years. If interest is 20%, which offer is preferable?

3. A warehouse can be bought for \$90 000. After twenty years the property will have a residual value of \$30 000. Alternatively, the warehouse can be leased for twenty years at an annual rent of \$12 000 payable in advance. If money is worth 15%, should the warehouse be purchased or leased?

4. A car costs \$9500. Alternatively, the car can be leased for three years by making payments of \$240 at the beginning of each month and can be bought at the end of the lease for \$4750. If interest is 15% compounded semi-annually, which alternative is preferable?

17.2 *Net present value method*

A. *Introductory examples*

***Example* 17.2a** Net cash inflows from two ventures are as follows:

End of Year	*1*	*2*	*3*	*4*	*5*	*Total*
Venture A	12 000	14 400	17 280	20 736	24 883	89 299
Venture B	17 000	17 000	17 000	17 000	17 000	85 000

Which venture is preferable if the required yield is 20%?

Solution

Present value of Venture A

$$= 12\,000(1.20^{-1}) + 14\,400(1.20^{-2}) + 17\,280(1.20^{-3}) + 20\,736(1.20^{-4}) + 24\,883(1.20^{-5})$$

$$= 12\,000(0.8333333) + 14\,400(0.6944444) + 17\,280(0.5787037) + 20\,736(0.4822531) + 24\,883(0.4018776)$$

$$= 10\,000 + 10\,000 + 10\,000 + 10\,000 + 10\,000$$
$$= \$50\,000$$

Present value of Venture B

$$= 17\,000\left(\frac{1 - 1.20^{-5}}{0.20}\right) = 17\,000(2.9906121) = \$50\,840$$

Programmed solution

Present value of Venture A

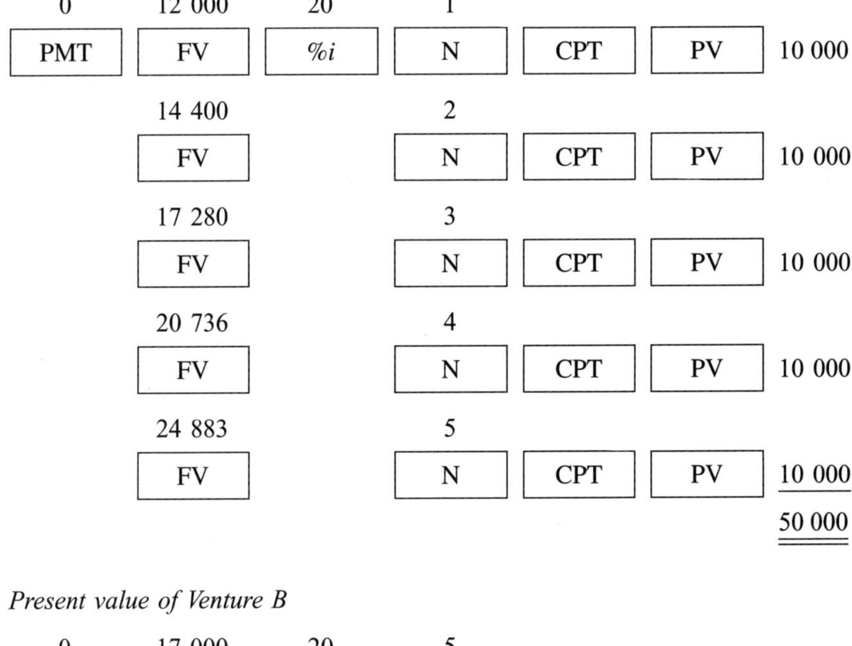

Present value of Venture B

0 17 000 20 5

FV PMT %i N CPT PV 50 840

Since at 20% the present value of Venture B is greater than the present value of Venture A, Venture B is preferable to Venture A.

***Example* 17.2b** Assume for Example 17.2a that Venture A requires a non-recoverable outlay of $9000 while Venture B requires a non-recoverable outlay of $11 000. At 20%, which venture is preferable?

Solution

	Venture A	*Venture B*
Present value of cash inflows	$50 000	$50 840
Present value of immediate outlay	9 000	11 000
Net present value	$41 000	$39 840

Since the net present value of Venture A is greater than the net present value of Venture B, Venture A is preferable.

B. The net present value concept

When only cash inflows were considered in Example 17.2a, Venture B was preferable. However, when outlays are different, as in Example 17.2b, the present value of the outlays as well as the present value of the cash inflows must be considered. The resulting difference is called the **net present value**.

NET PRESENT VALUE (NPV)	=	PRESENT VALUE OF INFLOWS	−	PRESENT VALUE OF OUTLAYS

← ***Formula* 17.1**

Since the net present value involves the difference between the present value of the inflows and the present value of the outlays, three outcomes are possible:

1. If the present value of the inflows is greater than the present value of the outlays, then the net present value is greater than zero.
2. If the present value of the inflows is smaller than the present value of the outlays, then the net present value is smaller than zero.
3. If the present value of the inflows equals the present value of the outlays, then the net present value is zero.

$$PV_{IN} > PV_{OUT} \longrightarrow NPV > 0 \text{ (positive)}$$
$$PV_{IN} = PV_{OUT} \longrightarrow NPV = 0$$
$$PV_{IN} < PV_{OUT} \longrightarrow NPV < 0 \text{ (negative)}$$

Criterion rule

At the organization's required rate of return, accept those capital investment projects that have a positive or zero net present value and reject those projects that have a negative net present value.

For a given rate of return:
ACCEPT if NPV > 0 or NPV $= 0$;
REJECT if NPV < 0.

To distinguish between a negative and a positive net present value, use
$NPV = PV_{IN} - PV_{OUT}$.

If a company is considering more than one project but can choose only one, the project with the greatest positive net present value is preferable.

Assumptions about the timing of inflows and outlays

The net present value method of evaluating capital investment projects is particularly useful when cash outlays are made and cash inflows received at various times. Since the *timing* of the cash flows is of prime importance, follow these assumptions regarding the timing of cash inflows and cash outlays.

Unless otherwise stated,

1. all cash inflows (benefits) are assumed to be received at the end of a period;
2. all cash outlays (costs) are assumed to be made at the beginning of a period.

C. Applications

***Example* 17.2c** A company is offered a contract promising annual net returns of \$36 000 for seven years. If it accepts the contract, the company must spend \$150 000 immediately to expand its plant. After seven years, no further benefits are available from the contract and the plant expansion undertaken will have no residual value. Should the company accept the contract if the required rate of return is

(i) 12%? (ii) 18%? (iii) 15%?

Solution

The net inflows and outlays can be represented on a time graph.

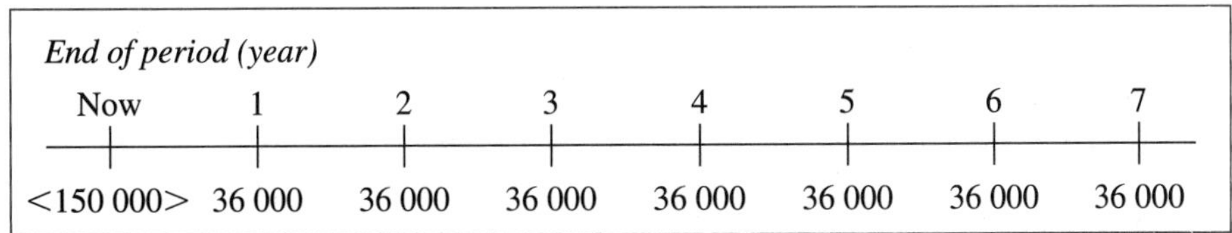

Note: Cash outlays (costs) are identified in such diagrams by a minus sign or by using accounting brackets.

(i) For $i = 12\%$

Since we assume the annual net returns (benefits) are received at the end of a period unless otherwise stated, they form an ordinary annuity in which $R = 36\ 000$; $n = 7$; $i = 12\%$.

$$PV_{IN} = 36\ 000\left(\frac{1 - 1.12^{-7}}{0.12}\right) = 36\ 000(4.5637565) = \$164\ 295$$

$$PV_{OUT} = \text{Present value of } 150\ 000 \text{ now} = \$150\ 000$$

The net present value (NPV)

$$= 164\ 295 - 150\ 000 = \$\ 14\ 295$$

Since at 12% the net present value is greater than zero, the contract should be accepted. The fact that the net present value at 12% is positive means that the contract offers a return on investment of more than 12%.

(ii) For $i = 18\%$

$$PV_{IN} = 36\ 000\left(\frac{1 - 1.18^{-7}}{0.18}\right) = 36\ 000(3.8115276) = \$137\ 215$$

$$PV_{OUT} = \$150\ 000$$

$$NPV = 137\ 215 - 150\ 000 = -\$12\ 785$$

Since at 18% the net present value is less than zero, the contract should not be accepted. The contract does not offer the required rate of return on investment of 18%.

(iii) For $i = 15\%$

$$PV_{IN} = 36\,000\left(\frac{1 - 1.15^{-7}}{0.15}\right) = 36\,000(4.1604197) \qquad = \$149\,775$$

$$PV_{OUT} \qquad = \$150\,000$$

$$NPV = 149\,775 - 150\,000 \qquad = -\$225$$

The net present value is slightly negative which means that the net present value method does not provide a clear signal as to whether to accept or reject the contract. The rate of return offered by the contract is almost 15%.

Programmed solution

(i) For $i = 12\%$

PV_{IN} — 0 [FV] 36 000 [PMT] 7 [N] 12 [%i] [CPT] [PV] = $164 295

PV_{OUT} = Present value of 150 000 now = $150 000

The net present value (NPV) = $ 14 295

(ii) For $i = 18\%$

PV_{IN} — 18 [%i] [CPT] [PV] = $137 215

PV_{OUT} = $150 000

NPV = −$12 785

(iii) For $i = 15\%$

PV_{IN} — 15 [%i] [CPT] [PV] = $149 775

PV_{OUT} = $150 000

NPV = −$225

***Example* 17.2d** A project requires an initial investment of $80 000 with a residual value of $15 000 after six years. It is estimated to yield annual net returns of $21 000 for six years. Should the project be undertaken at 16%?

Solution

The cash flows are represented in the diagram below.

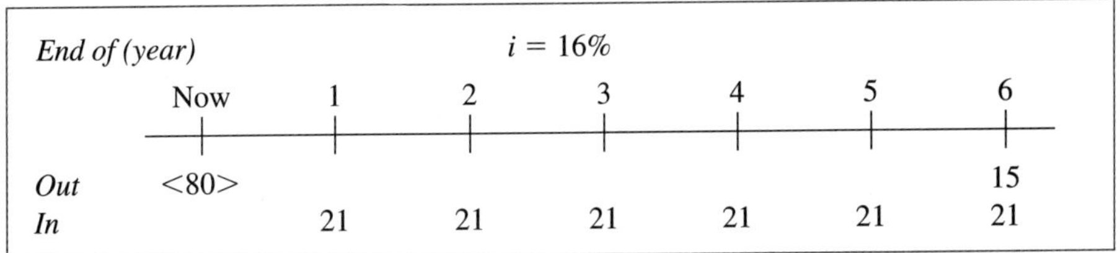

Note: The residual value of $15 000 is considered to be a reduction in outlays. Its present value should be subtracted from the present value of other outlays.

$$PV_{IN} = 21\ 000\left(\frac{1 - 1.16^{-6}}{0.16}\right) = 21\ 000(3.6847359) = \$77\ 379$$

$$PV_{OUT} = 80\ 000 - 15\ 000(1.16^{-6})$$

$$= 80\ 000 - 15\ 000(0.4104423) = 80\ 000 - 6157 = \$73\ 843$$

Net present value (NPV) = $ 3 536

Programmed solution

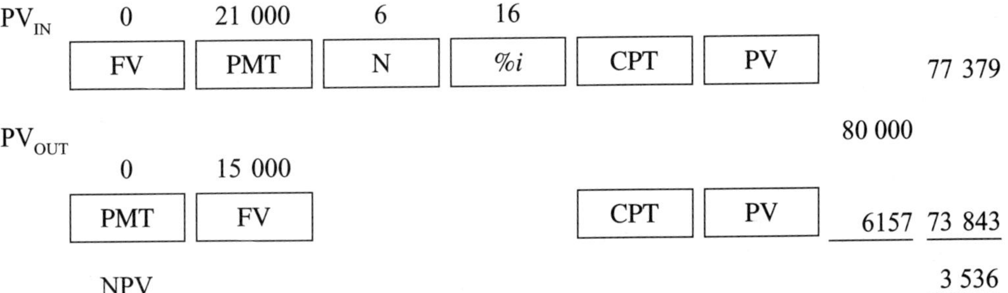

Since the net present value is positive (the present value of the benefits is greater than the present value of the costs), the rate of return on the investment is greater than 16%. The project should be undertaken.

***Example* 17.2e** The IRA Corporation is considering developing a new product. If undertaken, the project requires the outlay of $100 000 per year for three years. Net returns beginning in Year 4 are estimated at $65 000 per year for twelve years. The residual value of the outlays after fifteen years is $30 000. If the corporation requires a return on investment of 14%, should it develop the new product?

Solution

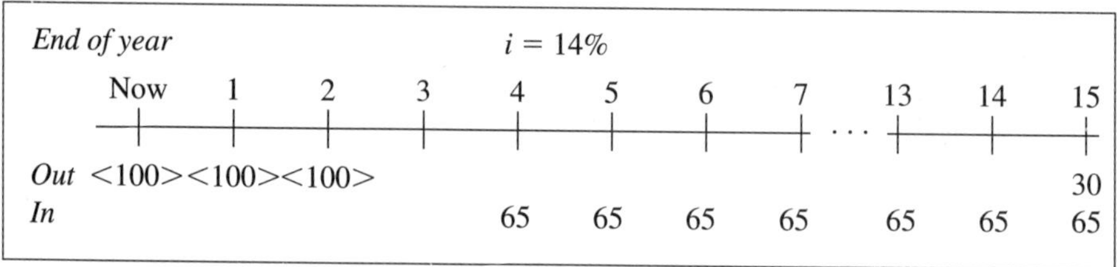

The net returns, due at the end of Year 4 to Year 15 respectively, form an ordinary annuity deferred for *three* years in which R = 65 000, n = 12, d = 3, i = 14%.

$$\begin{aligned}PV_{IN} &= 65\,000\left(\frac{1 - 1.14^{-12}}{0.14}\right)(1.14^{-3})\\ &= 65\,000(5.6602921)(0.6749715)\\ &= \$248\,335\end{aligned}$$

The outlays, assumed to be made at the beginning of each year, form an annuity due in which R = 100 000, n = 3, i = 14%.

$$\begin{aligned}PV_{OUT} &= 100\,000(1.14)\left(\frac{1 - 1.14^{-3}}{0.14}\right) - 30\,000(1.14^{-15})\\ &= 100\,000(1.14)(2.3216320) - 30\,000(0.1400965)\\ &= 264\,666 - 4203\\ &= \$260\,463\end{aligned}$$

$$NPV = 248\,335 - 260\,463 = \text{<\$12 128>}$$

Programmed solution

PV_{IN}	0	65 000	12	14			
	FV	PMT	N	%i	CPT	PV	367 919
	0	367 919	3				
	PMT	FV	N		CPT	PV	248 335
PV_{OUT}	0	100 000	3				
	FV	PMT	N		DUE	PV	264 666
	0	30 000	15				
	PMT	FV	N		CPT	PV	4 203
							260 463
	NPV = 248 335 − 260 463						−12 128

Since the net present value is negative, the investment does not offer a 14% return. The corporation should not develop the product.

***Example* 17.2f** A feasibility study concerning a contemplated venture yielded the following estimates:

initial cost outlay: \$1 300 000;
further outlays in Years 2 to 5: \$225 000 per year;
residual value after 20 years: \$625 000;
net returns: Year 5 to 10: \$600 000 per year;
Year 11 to 20: \$500 000 per year.

Should the venture be undertaken if the required return on investment is 15%?

Solution

End of year $i = 15\%$

	Now	1	2	3	4	5	6	9	10	11	12	19	20
Out	<1300>	<225>	<225>	<225>	<225>								625
In						600	600 . . .	600	600	500	500 . . .	500	500

$$PV_{IN} = 600\,000\left(\frac{1-1.15^{-6}}{0.15}\right)(1.15^{-4}) + 500\,000\left(\frac{1-1.15^{-10}}{0.15}\right)(1.15^{-10})$$

$$= 600\,000(3.7844827)(0.5717532) + 500\,000(5.0187686)(0.2471847)$$

$$= 1\,298\,274 + 620\,281$$

$$= \$1\,918\,555$$

$$PV_{OUT} = 1\,300\,000 + 225\,000\left(\frac{1-1.15^{-4}}{0.15}\right) - 625\,000(1.15^{-20})$$

$$= 1\,300\,000 + 225\,000(2.8549784) - 625\,000(0.0611003)$$

$$= 1\,300\,000 + 642\,370 - 38\,188$$

$$= \$1\,904\,182$$

$$NPV = 1\,918\,555 - 1\,904\,182 = \$14\,373$$

Programmed solution

PV_{IN}

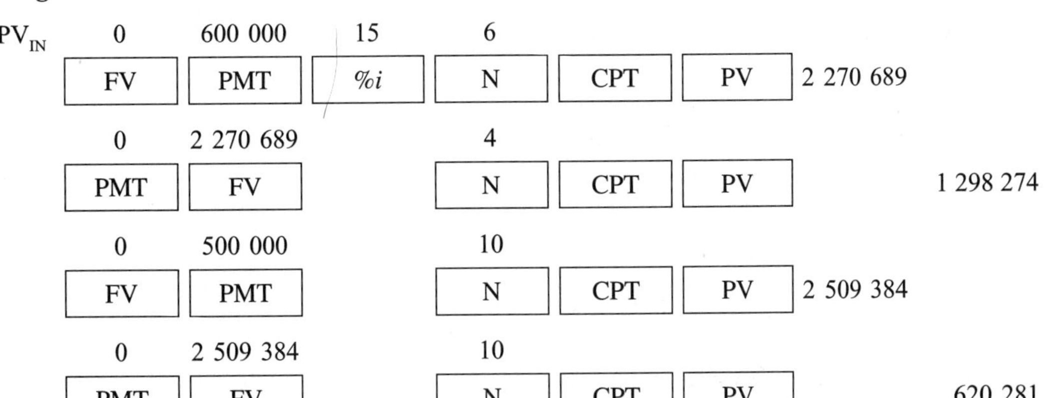

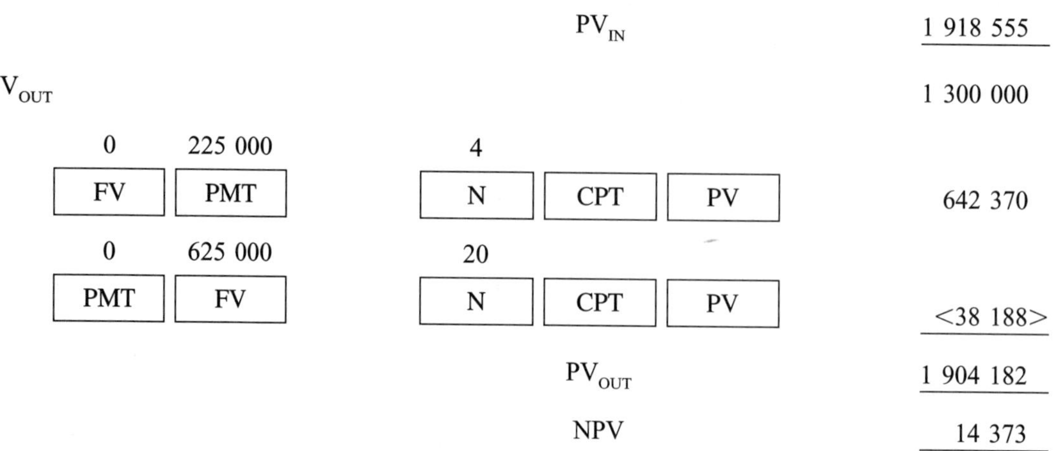

Since the net present value is positive, the rate of return on investment is greater than 15%. The venture should be undertaken.

Exercise 17.2

A. For each of the following investment choices, compute the net present value. Determine which investment should be accepted or rejected according to the net present value criterion.

1. A contract is estimated to yield net returns of \$3500 quarterly for seven years. To secure the contract, an immediate outlay of \$50 000 and a further outlay of \$30 000 three years from now are required. Interest is 12% compounded quarterly.

2. Replacing old equipment at an immediate cost of \$50 000 and an additional outlay of \$30 000 six years from now will result in savings of \$3000 per quarter for twelve years. The required rate of return is 16% compounded annually.

3. A business has two investment choices. Alternative 1 requires an immediate outlay of \$2000 and offers a return of \$7000 after seven years. Alternative 2 requires an immediate outlay of \$1800 in return for which \$250 will be received at the end of every six months for the next seven years. The required rate of return on investment is 17% compounded semi-annually.

4. Suppose you are offered two investment alternatives. If you choose Alternative 1, you will have to make an immediate outlay of \$9000. In return, you will receive \$500 at the end of every three months for the next ten years. If you choose Alternative 2, you will have to make an outlay of \$4000 now and \$5000 in two years. In return, you will receive \$30 000 ten years from now. Interest is 12% compounded semi-annually.

B. Answer each of the following questions.

1. Teck Engineering normally expects a rate of return of 12% on investments. Two projects are available but only one can be chosen. Project A requires an immediate investment of $4000. In return, revenue payments of $4000 will be received in four years and payments of $9000 in nine years. Project B requires an investment of $4000 now and another $2000 in three years. In return, revenue payments will be received in the amount of $1500 per year for nine years. Which project is preferable?

2. The owner of a business is presented with two alternative projects. The first project involves the investment of $5000 now. In return the business will receive a payment of $8000 in four years and a payment of $8000 in ten years. The second project involves an investment of $5000 now and another $5000 three years from now. The returns will be semi-annual payments of $950 for ten years. Which project is preferable if the required rate of return is 14% compounded annually?

3. Northern Teck is developing a special vehicle for Arctic exploration. The development requires an investment of $60 000, $50 000, and $40 000 for the next three years respectively. Net returns beginning in Year 4 are expected to be $33 000 per year for twelve years. If the company requires a rate of return of 14%, compute the net present value of the project and determine whether the company should undertake the project.

4. The Kellog Company has to make a decision about expanding its production facilities. Research indicates that the desired expansion would require an immediate outlay of $60 000 and an outlay of a further $60 000 in five years. Net returns are estimated to be $15 000 per year for the first five years and $10 000 per year for the following ten years. Find the net present value of the project. Should the expansion project be undertaken if the required rate of return is 12%?

5. Agate Marketing Inc. intends to distribute a new product. It is expected to produce net returns of $15 000 per year for the first four years and $10 000 per year for the following three years. The facilities required to distribute the product will cost $36 000 with a disposal value of $9000 after seven years. The facilities will require a major facelift costing $10 000 each after three and after five years respectively. If Agate requires a return on investment of 20%, should the company distribute the new product?

6. A company is considering a project that will require a cost outlay of $15 000 per year for four years. At the end of the project the salvage value will be $10 000. The project will yield returns of $60 000 in Year 4 and $20 000 in Year 5. There are no returns after Year 5. Alternative investments are available that will yield a return of 16%. Should the company undertake the project?

7. Demand for a product manufactured by the Eagle Company is expected to be 15 000 units per year during the next ten years. The net return per unit is \$2. The manufacturing process requires the purchase of a machine costing \$140 000. The machine has an economic life of ten years and a salvage value of \$20 000 after ten years. Major overhauls of the machine require outlays of \$20 000 after four years and \$40 000 after seven years. Should Eagle invest in the machine if it requires a return of 12% on its investments?

8. Magna Electronics Company expects a demand of 20 000 units per year for a special purpose component during the next six years. Net return per unit is \$4.00. To produce the component, Magna must buy a machine costing \$250 000 with a life of six years and a salvage value of \$40 000 after six years. The company estimates that repair costs will be \$20 000 per year during Years 2 to 6. If Magna requires a return on investment of 18%, should it market the component?

17.3 *Finding the rate of return on investment*

A. Net present value, profitability index, rate of return

The **rate of return** on investment (R.O.I.) is widely used to measure the value of an investment. Since it takes interest into account, knowing the rate of return that results from a capital investment project provides useful information when evaluating a project.

The method of finding the rate of return that is explained and illustrated in this section uses the net present value concept introduced in Section 17.2. However, instead of being primarily concerned with a specific discount rate and with comparing the present value of the cash inflows and the present value of the cash outlays, this method is designed to determine the rate of return on the investment.

As explained in Section 17.2, three outcomes are possible when using Formula 17.1. These three outcomes indicate whether the rate of return is greater than, less than, or equal to the discount rate used in finding the net present value.

1. If the net present value is greater than zero (positive), then the rate of return is greater than the discount rate used to determine the net present value.
2. If the net present value is less than zero (negative), then the rate of return is less than the discount rate used.
3. If the net present value is equal to zero, then the rate of return is equal to the rate of discount used.

If NPV > 0 (POSITIVE) ⟶	R.O.I. $> i$
If NPV < 0 (NEGATIVE) ⟶	R.O.I. $< i$
If NPV $= 0$ ⟶	R.O.I. $= i$

It follows, then, that the rate of return on investment (R.O.I.) is that rate of discount for which the NPV $= 0$, that is, for which $PV_{IN} = PV_{OUT}$.

The above definition of the rate of return and the relationship between the net present value, the rate of discount used to compute the net present value, and the rate of return are useful in developing a method of finding the rate of return.

However, before computing the rate of return, it is useful to consider a ratio known as the **profitability index** or **discounted benefit-cost ratio**. It is defined as the ratio that results when comparing the present value of the cash inflows with the present value of the cash outlays.

$$\text{PROFITABILITY INDEX (or DISCOUNTED BENEFIT-COST RATIO)} = \frac{PV_{IN}}{PV_{OUT}} \qquad \longleftarrow \textit{Formula } \mathbf{17.2}$$

Since a division is involved, three outcomes are possible when computing this ratio.

1. If the numerator (PV_{IN}) is greater than the denominator (PV_{OUT}), then the profitability index is greater than one.
2. If the numerator (PV_{IN}) is less than the denominator (PV_{OUT}), then the profitability index is less than one.
3. If the numerator (PV_{IN}) is equal to the denominator (PV_{OUT}), then the profitability index is equal to one.

The three outcomes give an indication of the rate of return.

1. If the profitability index is greater than 1, then the rate of return is greater than the discount rate used.
2. If the profitability index is less than 1, then the rate of return is less than the discount rate used.
3. If the profitability index is equal to 1, then the rate of return equals the discount rate used.

The relationship between the present value of the inflows, the present value of the outlays, the net present value, the profitability index, and the rate of return at a given rate of discount i is summarized below.

PV_{IN} *versus* PV_{OUT}	*Net present value (NPV)*	*Profitability index*	*Rate of return (R.O.I.)*
$PV_{IN} > PV_{OUT}$	$NPV > 0$	> 1	$> i$
$PV_{IN} = PV_{OUT}$	$NPV = 0$	$= 1$	$= i$
$PV_{IN} < PV_{OUT}$	$NPV < 0$	< 1	$< i$

B. Procedure for finding the rate of return by trial and error

From the relationships noted above, the rate of return on investment can be defined as the rate of discount for which the present value of the inflows (benefits) equals the present value of the outlays (costs). This definition implies that the rate of return is the rate of discount for which the net present value equals zero or for which the profitability index (benefit-cost ratio) equals 1. This conclusion permits us to determine the rate of return by trial and error.

STEP 1 Arbitrarily select a discount rate and compute the net present value at that rate.

STEP 2 From the outcome of Step 1, draw one of the three conclusions.

(a) If NPV $= 0$, infer that the R.O.I. $= i$.

(b) If NPV > 0, infer that the R.O.I. $> i$.

(c) If NPV < 0, infer that the R.O.I. $< i$.

STEP 3

(a) If, in Step 1, NPV $= 0$, then R.O.I. $= i$ and the problem is solved.

(b) If, in Step 1, NPV > 0 (positive), then we know that R.O.I. $> i$. A second attempt is needed. This second try requires choosing a discount rate greater than the rate used in Step 1 and computing the net present value using the higher rate.

If the resulting net present value is still positive, choose a still higher rate of discount and compute the net present value for that rate. Repeat this procedure until the selected rate of discount yields a negative net present value.

(c) If, in Step 1, NPV < 0 (negative), then we know that R.O.I. $< i$. The second try requires choosing a discount rate less than the rate used in Step 1 and computing the net present value using the lower rate.

If the resulting net present value is still negative, choose a still lower rate of discount and compute the net present value for that rate. Repeat this procedure until the selected rate of discount yields a positive net present value.

STEP 4 The basic aim of Step 3 is to find one rate of discount for which the net present value is positive and a second rate for which the net present value is negative. Once this has been accomplished, the rate of return must be a rate between the two rates used to generate a positive and a negative net present value.

You can now obtain a reasonably accurate value of the rate of return by using linear interpolation. To ensure sufficient accuracy in the answer, we recommend that the two rates of discount used when interpolating be no more than two percentage points apart. The worked examples in this section have been solved using successive even rates of discounts when interpolating.

STEP 5 (Optional) You can check the accuracy of the method of interpolation when using an electronic calculator by computing the net present value. Use as the discount rate the rate of return determined in Step 4. Expect the rate in Step 4 to be slightly too high. You can obtain a still more precise answer by further trials.

C. *Selecting the rate of discount—using the profitability index*

While the selection of a discount rate in Step 1 of the procedure is arbitrary, a sensible choice is one that is neither too high nor too low. Since the negative net present value immediately establishes a range between zero and the rate used, it is preferable to be on the high side. Choosing a rate of discount within the range 12% to 24% usually leads to quick solutions.

While the initial choice of rate is a shot in the dark, the resulting knowledge about the size of the rate of return combined with the use of the profitability index should ensure the selection of a second rate that is fairly close to the actual rate of return.

In making the second choice, use the profitability index.

1. Compute the index for the first rate chosen and convert the index into a percent.
2. Deduct 100% from the index and divide the difference by 4.
3. If the index is greater than 1, add the above result to obtain the rate that you should use for the second attempt. If, however, the index is smaller than 1, deduct the above result from the rate of discount initially used.

Assume that the rate of discount initially selected is 16%. The resulting $PV_{IN} = 150$ and the $PV_{OUT} = 120$.

1. The profitability index is $\frac{150}{120} = 1.25 = 125\%$.
2. The difference (125% − 100%) divided by 4 = 6.25%.
3. Since the index is greater than 1, add 6.25% to the initial rate of 16%; the recommended choice is 22%.

Assume that the rate of discount initially selected is 20%. The resulting $PV_{IN} = 200$ and the $PV_{OUT} = 250$.

1. The profitability index is $\frac{200}{250} = 0.80 = 80\%$.
2. The difference (80% − 100%) divided by 4 = −5%.
3. Since the index is less than 1, subtract 5% from the initial rate of 20%; the recommended choice is 15%. (If, as in this text, you are using only even rates, try either 14% or 16%.)

D. Using linear interpolation

The method of linear interpolation used in Step 4 of the suggested procedure is illustrated in Example 17.3a below.

***Example* 17.3a** Assume that the net present value of a project is \$420 at 14% and −\$280 at 16%. Use linear interpolation to compute the rate of return correct to the nearest tenth of a percent.

Solution

The data can be represented on a line diagram.

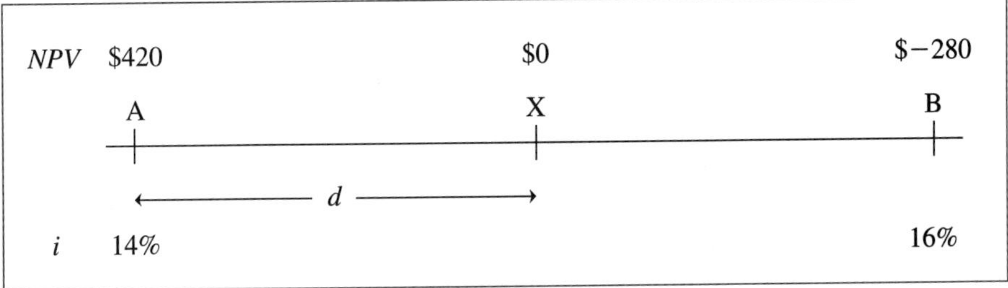

The line segment AB represents the distance between the two rates of discount that are associated with a positive and a negative net present value respectively.

At Point A, where $i = 14\%$, the NPV = 420;
at Point B, where $i = 16\%$, the NPV = −280;
at Point X, where i is unknown, the NPV = 0.

By definition, the rate of return is that rate of discount for which the net present value is zero. Since 0 is a number between 420 and −280, the NPV = 0 is located at a point on AB. This point is marked X.

We can obtain two useful ratios by considering the line segment from the two points of view shown in the diagram.

(i) In terms of the discount rate i,

AB = 2% ←——— 16% − 14%
AX = d% ←——— the unknown percent that must be added to 14% to obtain the rate of discount at which the NPV = 0

$$\frac{AX}{AB} = \frac{d\%}{2\%}$$

(ii) In terms of the net present value figures,

AB = 700 ←——— 420 + 280
AX = 420

$$\frac{AX}{AB} = \frac{420}{700}$$

Since the ratio AX:AB is written twice, we can derive a proportion statement.

$$\frac{d\%}{2\%} = \frac{420}{700}$$

$$d\% = \frac{420}{700} \times 2\%$$

$$d\% = 1.2\%$$

Therefore, the rate at which the net present value is equal to zero is 14% + 1.2% = 15.2%. The rate of return on investment is 15.2%.

E. *Computing the rate of return*

***Example* 17.3b** A project requires an initial outlay of \$25 000. The estimated returns are \$7000 per year for seven years. Compute the rate of return (correct to the nearest tenth of a percent).

Solution

The cash flows (in thousands) are represented in the diagram below.

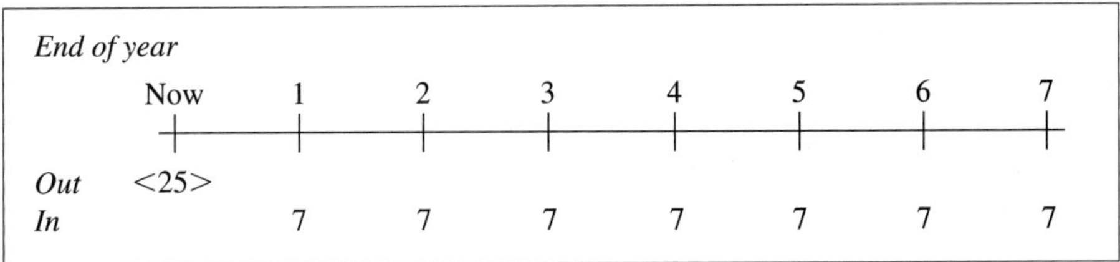

The inflows form an ordinary annuity since inflows are assumed to be received at the end of each year.

$$PV_{IN} = 7000\left[\frac{1-(1+i)^{-7}}{i}\right]$$

The outlays consist of an immediate payment.

$$PV_{OUT} = 25\ 000$$

To determine the rate of return, we will choose a rate of discount, compute the net present value, and try further rates until we find two successive even rates. For one, the NPV $>$ 0 (positive) and, for the other, NPV $<$ 0 (negative).

STEP 1 Try $i = 12\%$.

$$PV_{IN} = 7000\left(\frac{1-1.12^{-7}}{0.12}\right) = 7000(4.5637565) \qquad = \$31\ 946$$

$$PV_{OUT} = \qquad \underline{25\ 000}$$

$$\text{NPV at } 12\% \qquad = \underline{\underline{\$6\ 946}}$$

Since the NPV $>$ 0, R.O.I. $>$ 12%.

STEP 2 Compute the profitability index to estimate what rate should be used next.

$$\text{INDEX} = \frac{PV_{IN}}{PV_{OUT}} = \frac{31\ 946}{25\ 000} = 1.278 = 127.8\%$$

Since at $i = 12\%$, the profitability index is 27.8% more than 100%, the rate of discount should be increased by $\frac{27.8\%}{4} = 7\%$ approximately. To obtain another even rate, the increase should be either 6% or 8%. In line with the suggestion that it is better to go too high, increase the previous rate by 8% and try $i = 20\%$.

STEP 3 Try $i = 20\%$.

$$PV_{IN} = 7000\left(\frac{1 - 1.20^{-7}}{0.20}\right) = 7000(3.6045918) \qquad = \$25\ 232$$

$$PV_{OUT} = \qquad \underline{25\ 000}$$

$$\text{NPV at } 20\% \qquad = \$232$$

Since the NPV > 0, R.O.I. > 20%.

STEP 4 Since the net present value is still positive, a rate higher than 20% is needed. The profitability index at 20% is $\frac{25\ 232}{25\ 000} = 1.009 = 100.9\%$. The index exceeds 100% by 0.9%; division by 4 suggests an increase of 0.2%. For interpolation, the recommended minimum increase or decrease is 2%. The next try should use $i = 22\%$.

STEP 5 Try $i = 22\%$.

$$PV_{IN} = 7000\left(\frac{1 - 1.22^{-7}}{0.22}\right) = 7000(3.4155064) \qquad = \$23\ 908$$

$$PV_{OUT} = \qquad \underline{25\ 000}$$

$$\text{NPV at } 22\% \qquad = \$-1\ 092$$

Since the NPV < 0, R.O.I. < 22%.

Therefore, 20% < NPV < 22%.

STEP 6 Now that the rate of return has been located between two sufficiently close rates of discount, linear interpolation can be used as illustrated in Example 17.3a.

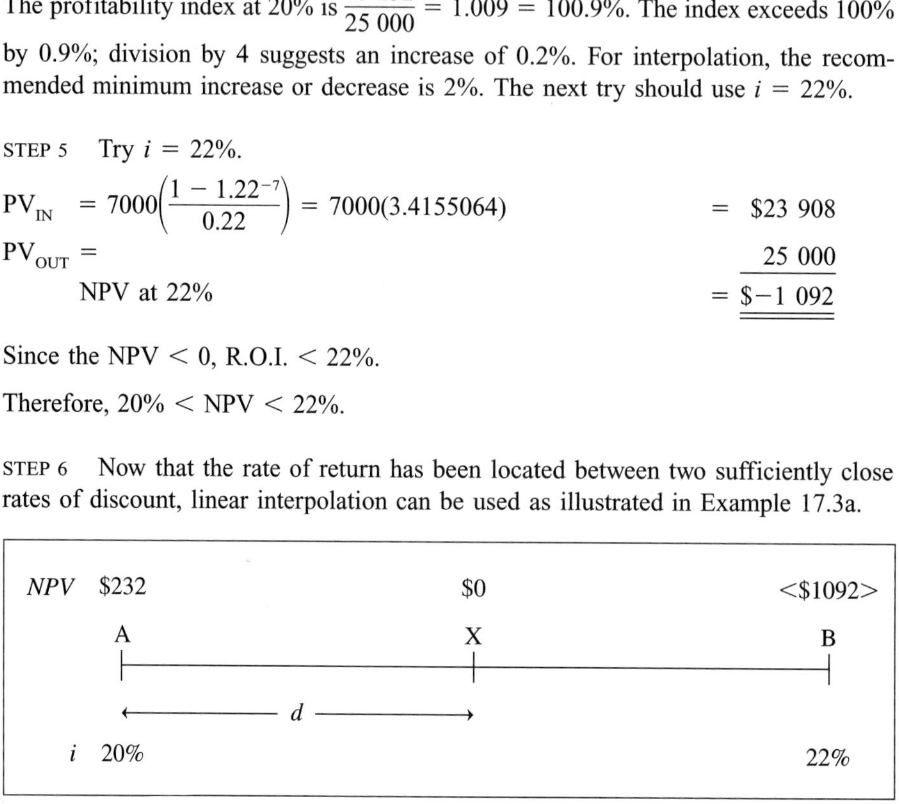

NPV	$232	$0	<$1092>
	A	X	B
	← *d* →		
i	20%		22%

$$\frac{d}{2} = \frac{232}{232 + 1092}$$

$$d = \frac{232(2)}{1324} = 0.35$$

The rate of discount for which the NPV = 0 is approximately 20% + 0.35% = 20.35%. The rate of return is approximately 20.3%. (A more precisely computed value is 20.3382%.)

Note: Three attempts were needed to locate the R.O.I. between 20% and 22%. Three is the usual number of tries necessary. The minimum number is two attempts. Occasionally four attempts may be needed. To produce a more concise solution, organize the computation as shown below.

Present value of amounts in general form	Attempts					
	$i = 12\%$		$i = 20\%$		$i = 22\%$	
PV_{IN}	Factor	$	Factor	$	Factor	$
$7000\left[\frac{1-(1+i)^{-7}}{i}\right]$	4.5637565	31 946	3.6045918	25 232	3.4155064	23 908
PV_{OUT} 25 000 now		25 000		25 000		25 000
NPV		6 946		232		<1 092>

Since estimates are involved, it is sufficient to use present value factors with only three decimal positions. In the following examples, all factors are rounded to three decimals.

Programmed solution

Present value of amounts in general form	Attempts					
	$i = 12\%$	$i = 20\%$	$i = 22\%$	$i = 20.5\%$	$i = 20.3\%$	$i = 20.34\%$
PV_{IN}	0 [FV]					
$7000\left[\frac{1-(1+i)^{-7}}{i}\right]$	7000 [PMT]					
	7 [N]					
	12 [% i]	20 [% i]	22 [% i]	20.5 [% i]	20.3 [% i]	20.34 [% i]
	[CPT]	[CPT]	[CPT]	[CPT]	[CPT]	[CPT]
	[PV]	[PV]	[PV]	[PV]	[PV]	[PV]
PV_{IN}	31 946	25 232	23 908	24 890	25 026	24 999
PV_{OUT} 25 000 now	25 000	25 000	25 000	25 000	25 000	25 000
NPV	6 946	232	−1 092	−110	26	−1
R.O.I.	>12%	>20%	<22%	<20.5%	>20.3%	= 20.34%

***Example* 17.3c** A venture that requires an immediate outlay of $320 000 and an outlay of $96 000 after five years has a residual value of $70 000 after ten years. Net returns are estimated to be $64 000 per year for ten years. Compute the rate of return.

Solution

The cash flow is represented in the diagram below (in thousands).

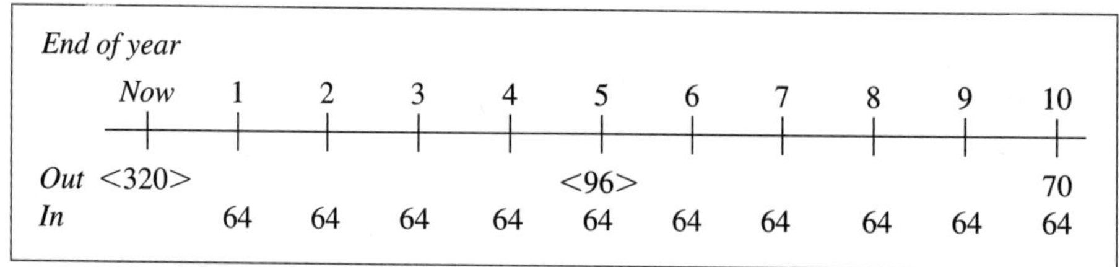

The computations are organized in a chart; explanations regarding the computations follow.

Present value of amounts in general form	Attempts					
	$i = 20\%$		$i = 14\%$		$i = 12\%$	
PV of benefits	Factor	$	Factor	$	Factor	$
$64\,000\left[\frac{1-(1+i)^{-10}}{i}\right]$	4.192	268 288	5.216	333 824	5.650	361 600
PV of costs						
320 000 now		320 000		320 000		320 000
$96\,000(1+i)^{-5}$	0.402	38 592	0.519	49 824	0.567	54 432
<$70\,000(1+i)^{-10}$>	0.162	<11 340>	0.270	<18 900>	0.322	<22 540>
TOTAL		347 252		350 924		351 892
NPV		<78 964>		<17 100>		9 708

Explanations for computations

STEP 1 Try $i = 20\%$.

Since NPV < 0, R.O.I. < 20%.

$$\text{Index at } 20\% = \frac{268\,288}{347\,252} = 0.773 = 77.3\%$$

$$\text{Reduction in rate} = \frac{22.7\%}{4} = 5.7\% \Rightarrow 6\%$$

STEP 2 Try $i = 14\%$.

NPV < 0; R.O.I. < 14%

$$\text{Index} = \frac{333\,824}{350\,924} = 0.951 = 95.1\%$$

$$\text{Reduction in rate} = \frac{4.9\%}{4} = 1.2\% \Rightarrow 2\%$$

STEP 3 Try $i = 12\%$.

NPV > 0; R.O.I. $> 12\%$
$12\% <$ R.O.I. $< 14\%$

STEP 4 $$\frac{d}{2} = \frac{9708}{9708 + 17\,100} = \frac{9708}{26\,808} = 0.362131$$

$d = 2(0.362131) = 0.724$

The rate of discount at which the net present value is zero is 12% + 0.72% = 12.72%. The rate of return is 12.7%.

Programmed solution

Present value of amounts in general form	Attempts				
	$i = 20\%$	$i = 14\%$	$i = 12\%$	$i = 12.7\%$	$i = 12.68\%$
PV of benefits $64\,000\left[\frac{1-(1+i)^{-10}}{i}\right]$	0 FV 64 000 PMT 10 N 20 % i CPT PV	0 FV 64 000 PMT 10 N 14 % i CPT PV	0 FV 64 000 PMT 10 N 12 % i CPT PV	0 FV 64 000 PMT 10 N 12.7 % i CPT PV	0 FV 64 000 PMT 10 N 12.68 % i CPT PV
PV_{IN}	268 318	333 831	361 614	351 484	351 767
PV of costs 320 000 now $96\,000(1+i)^{-5}$	320 000 0 PMT 96 000 FV 5 N CPT PV 38 580	320 000 0 PMT 96 000 FV 5 N CPT PV 49 859	320 000 0 PMT 96 000 FV 5 N CPT PV 54 473	320 000 0 PMT 96 000 FV 5 N CPT PV 52 802	320 000 0 PMT 96 000 FV 5 N CPT PV 52 849
<$70\,000(1+i)^{-10}$>	70 000 FV 10 N CPT PV <11 305>	70 000 FV 10 N CPT PV <18 882>	70 000 FV 10 N CPT PV <22 538>	70 000 FV 10 N CPT PV <21 177>	70 000 FV 10 N CPT PV <21 214>
PV_{OUT}	347 275	350 977	351 935	351 625	351 635
NPV	<78 957>	<17 146>	9 679	<141>	132
R.O.I.	<20%	<14%>	>12%	<12.7%	>12.68%

***Example* 17.3d** A project requires an immediate investment of \$33 000 with a residual value of \$7000 at the end of the project. It is expected to yield a net return of \$7000 in Year 1, \$8000 in Year 2, \$11 000 per year for the following six years, and \$9000 per year for the remaining four years. Find the rate of return.

Solution

The cash flows for the project (in thousands) are represented in the diagram below.

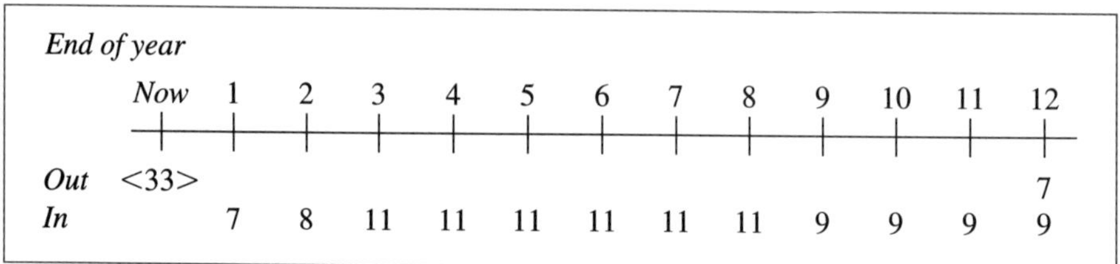

The computations are organized in the chart that follows.

Present value of amounts in general form	Attempts					
	$i = 20\%$		$i = 28\%$		$i = 26\%$	
PV of returns	Factor	\$	Factor	\$	Factor	\$
$7000(1+i)^{-1}$	0.833	5 831	0.781	5 467	0.794	5 558
$8000(1+i)^{-2}$	0.694	5 552	0.610	4 880	0.630	5 040
$11\,000\left[\frac{1-(1+i)^{-6}}{i}\right]$	3.326		2.759		2.885	
	×	25 391	×	18 513	×	19 993
$\times (1+i)^{-2}$	0.694		0.610		0.630	
$9000\left[\frac{1-(1+i)^{-4}}{i}\right]$	2.589		2.241		2.320	
	×	5 429	×	2 803	×	3 278
$\times (1+i)^{-8}$	0.233		0.139		0.157	
TOTAL PV_{IN}		42 203		31 663		33 869
PV of costs						
33 000 now		33 000		33 000		33 000
$<7000(1+i)^{-12}>$	0.112	<784>	0.052	<364>	0.062	<434>
TOTAL PV_{OUT}		32 216		32 636		32 566
NPV		9 987		<973>		1 303

Explanations for computations

STEP 1 The present value of the returns consists of \$7000 discounted for one year, \$8000 discounted for two years, the present value of an ordinary annuity of six payments of \$11 000 deferred for two years, and the present value of an ordinary annuity of four payments of \$9000 deferred for eight years. The present value of the costs consists of the lump sum of \$33 000 less the salvage value of \$7000 discounted for twelve years.

STEP 2 The rate of discount chosen for the first attempt is 20%.

For $i = 20\%$, NPV > 0; R.O.I. $> 20\%$

$$\text{Index} = \frac{42\ 203}{32\ 216} = 1.310 = 131.0\%$$

$$\text{Increase in rate} = \frac{31.0\%}{4} = 7.75\% \text{ or } 8\%$$

STEP 3 For $i = 28\%$, NPV < 0; R.O.I. $< 28\%$

$$\text{Index} = \frac{31\ 663}{32\ 636} = 0.970 = 97.0\%$$

$$\text{Decrease in rate} = \frac{3\%}{4} = 0.75\% \text{ or } 2\%$$

STEP 4 For $i = 26\%$, NPV > 0; R.O.I. $> 26\%$

$26\% <$ R.O.I. $< 28\%$

STEP 5 $$d = \frac{1303}{1303 + 973} \times 2 = \frac{2606}{2276} = 1.14499$$

The rate of discount for which the net present value is zero is approximately 26% + 1.14% = 27.14%. The rate of return, correct to the nearest tenth of a percent, is 27.1%.

Exercise 17.3

A. Use linear interpolation to determine the approximate value of the rate of return for each of the following. State your answer correct to the nearest tenth of a percent.

	Positive NPV at i	*Negative NPV at* i
1.	\$2350 at 24%	−\$1270 at 26%
2.	\$850 at 8%	−\$370 at 10%
3.	\$135 at 20%	−\$240 at 22%
4.	\$56 at 16%	−\$70 at 18%

B. Find the rate of return for each of the following (correct to the nearest tenth of a percent).

1. The proposed expansion of CIV Electronics' plant facilities requires the immediate outlay of \$100 000. Expected net returns are

   Year 1: Nil Year 2: \$30 000 Year 3: \$40 000
   Year 4: \$60 000 Year 5: \$50 000 Year 6: \$20 000

2. The introduction of a new product requires an initial outlay of $60 000. The anticipated net returns from the marketing of the product are expected to be $12 000 per year for ten years.

3. Your firm is considering introducing a new product for which net returns are expected to be

   Year 1 to Year 3 inclusive: $2000 per year;
   Year 4 to Year 8 inclusive: $5000 per year;
   Year 9 to Year 12 inclusive: $3000 per year.

   The introduction of the product requires an immediate outlay of $15 000 for equipment estimated to have a salvage value of $2000 after twelve years.

4. A project requiring an immediate investment of $150 000 and a further outlay of $40 000 after four years has a residual value of $30 000 after nine years. The project yields a negative net return of $10 000 in Year 1, a zero net return in Year 2, $50 000 per year for the following four years, and $70 000 per year for the last three years.

5. You are thinking of starting a hot dog business that requires an initial investment of $16 000 and a major replacement of equipment after ten years amounting to $8000. From competitive experience, you expect to have a net loss of $2000 the first year, a net profit of $2000 the second year, and, for the remaining years of the first fifteen years of operations, net returns of $6000 per year. After fifteen years, the net returns will gradually decline and will be zero at the end of 25 years (assume returns of $3000 per year for that period). After 25 years, your lease will expire. The salvage value of equipment at that time is expected to be just sufficient to cover the cost of closing the business.

6. The Blue Sky Ski Resort plans to install a new chair lift to serve a new ski area. Construction of the lift is estimated to require an immediate outlay of $220 000. The life of the lift is estimated to be fifteen years with a salvage value of $80 000. Cost of clearing and grooming the new area is expected to be $30 000 for each of the first three years of operation. Net cash inflows from the lift are expected to be $40 000 for each of the first five years and $70 000 for each of the following ten years.

Review exercise

1. Wells Inc. has to choose between two investment alternatives. Alternative A will return the company $20 000 after three years, $60 000 after six years, and $40 000 after ten years. Alternative B will bring returns of $10 000 per year for ten years. If the company expects a return of 14% on investments, which alternative should it choose?

2. A piece of property may be acquired by making an immediate payment of $25 000 and payments of $37 500 and $50 000 three and five years from now respectively. Alternatively, the property may be purchased by making quarterly payments of $5150 in advance for five years. Which alternative is preferable if money is worth 15% compounded semi-annually?

3. An investor has two investment alternatives. If he chooses Alternative 1, he will have to make an immediate outlay of $7000 and will receive $500 every three months for the next nine years. If he chooses Alternative 2, he will have to make an immediate outlay of $6500 and will receive $26 000 after eight years. If interest is 12% compounded quarterly, which alternative should the investor choose based on the net present value criterion?

4. Replacing old equipment at an immediate cost of $65 000 and $40 000 five years from now will result in a savings of $8000 semi-annually for ten years. At 14% compounded annually, should the old equipment be replaced?

5. A real estate development project requires annual outlays of $75 000 for eight years. Net cash inflows beginning in Year 9 are expected to be $250 000 per year for fifteen years. If the developer requires a rate of return of 18%, compute the net present value of the project.

6. A company is considering a project that will require a cost outlay of $30 000 per year for four years. At the end of the project, the company expects to salvage the physical assets for $30 000. The project is estimated to yield net returns of $60 000 in Year 4, $40 000 in Year 5, and $20 000 for each of the following five years. Alternative investments are available yielding a rate of return of 14%. Compute the net present value of the project.

7. An investment requires an initial outlay of $45 000. Net returns are estimated to be $14 000 per year for eight years. Determine the rate of return.

8. A project requires an initial outlay of $10 000 and promises net returns of $2000 per year over a twelve-year period. If the project has a residual value of $4000 after twelve years, what is the rate of return?

9. Compute the rate of return for Question 5.

10. Compute the rate of return for Question 6.

11. The Superior Jig Company has developed a new jig for which it expects net returns as follows.

    Year 1: $8000
    Year 2 to 6 inclusive: $12 000 per year
    Year 7 to 10 inclusive: $6000 per year

    The initial investment of $36 000 has a residual value of $9000 after ten years. Compute the rate of return.

12. The owner of a sporting goods store is considering remodelling the store in order to carry a larger inventory. The cost of remodelling and additional inventory is $60 000. The expected increase in net profit is $8000 per year for the next four years and $10 000 each year for the following six years. After ten years, the owner plans to retire and sell the business. She expects to recover the additional $40 000 invested in inventory but not the $20 000 invested in remodelling. Compute the rate of return.

13. Outway Ventures evaluates potential investment projects at 20%. Two alternative projects are available. Project A will return the company $5800 per year for eight years. Alternative B will return the company $13 600 after one year, $17 000 after five years, and $20 400 after eight years. Which alternative should the company choose according to the discounted cash flow criterion?

14. Project A requires an immediate investment of $8000 and another $6000 in three years. Net returns are $4000 after two years, $12 000 after four years, and $8000 after six years. Project B requires an immediate investment of $4000, another $6000 after two years, and $4000 after four years. Net returns are $3400 per year for seven years. Determine the net present value at 10%. Which project is preferable according to the net present value criterion?

15. Net returns from an investment are estimated to be $13 000 per year for twelve years. The investment involves an immediate outlay of $50 000 and a further outlay of $30 000 after six years. The investments are estimated to have a residual value of $10 000 after twelve years. Find the net present value at 20%.

16. The introduction of a new product requires an immediate outlay of $45 000. Anticipated net returns from the marketing of the product are expected to be $12 500 per year for ten years. What is the rate of return on the investment (correct to the nearest tenth of a percent)?

17. Games Inc. has developed a new electronic game and compiled the following product information.

	Production cost	*Promotion cost*	*Sales revenue*
Year 1	$32 000	—	—
Year 2	32 000	$64 000	$ 64 000
Year 3	32 000	96 000	256 000
Year 4	32 000	32 000	128 000
Year 5	32 000		32 000

Should the product be marketed if the company requires a return of 16%?

18. Farmer Jones wants to convert his farm into a golf course. He asked you to determine his rate of return based on the following estimates.

    Development cost for each of the first three years, $80 000.

    Construction of a clubhouse in Year 4, $240 000.

    Upon his retirement in fifteen years, improvements in the property will yield him $200 000.

    Net returns from the operation of the golf course will be nil for the first three years and $100 000 per year afterwards until his retirement.

Self-test

1. Opportunities Inc. requires a minimum rate of return of 15% on investment proposals. Two proposals are under consideration but only one may be chosen. Alternative A offers a net return of $2500 per year for twelve years. Alternative B offers a net return of $10 000 each year after four, eight, and twelve years respectively. Determine the preferred alternative according to the discounted cash flow criterion.

2. A natural resources development project requires an immediate outlay of $10 000 and $50 000 at the end of each year for four years. Net returns are nil for the first two years and $60 000 per year thereafter for fourteen years. What is the net present value of the project at 16%?

3. An investment of $100 000 yields annual net returns of $20 000 for ten years. If the residual value of the investment after ten years is $30 000, what is the rate of return on the investment (correct to the nearest tenth of a percent)?

4. A telephone system with a disposable value of $1200 after five years can be purchased for $6600. Alternatively, a leasing agreement is available that requires an immediate payment of $1500 plus payments of $100.00 at the beginning of each month for five years. If money is worth 12% compounded monthly, should the telephone system be leased or purchased?

5. A choice has to be made between two investment proposals. Proposal A requires an immediate outlay of $60 000 and a further outlay of $40 000 after three years. Net returns are $20 000 per year for ten years. The investment has no residual value after ten years. Proposal B requires outlays of $29 000 in each of the first four years. Net returns starting in Year 4 are $40 000 per year. The residual value of the investment after ten years is $50 000. Which proposal is preferable at 20%?

6. Introducing a new product requires an immediate investment in plant facilities of $180 000 with a disposal value of $45 000 after seven years. The facilities will require additional capital outlays of $50 000 each after three and five years respectively. Net returns on the investment are estimated to be $75 000 per year for each of the first four years and $50 000 per year for the remaining three years. Determine the rate of return on investment (correct to the nearest tenth of a percent).

Summary of formulae used

Formula 17.1

$$\text{NET PRESENT VALUE (NPV)} = \text{PRESENT VALUE OF INFLOWS} - \text{PRESENT VALUE OF OUTLAYS}$$

Formula 17.2

$$\text{PROFITABILITY INDEX} = \frac{\text{PRESENT VALUE OF INFLOWS}}{\text{PRESENT VALUE OF OUTLAYS}}$$

In addition, the present value formulae introduced in chapters 9, 11, 12, and 13 are needed.

Formula 9.2A and 9.2B
Formula 11.2
Formula 12.2
Formula 12.3
Formula 13.2
Formula 13.4
Formula 13.5

Glossary of terms used

Discounted benefit-cost ratio see *Profitability index*
Discounted cash flow the present value of cash payments
Net present value the difference between the present value of the inflows (benefits) and the present value of the outlays (costs) of a capital investment project
Profitability index the ratio of the present value of the inflows (benefits) to the present value of the outlays (costs) of a capital investment project
Rate of return the rate of discount for which the net present value of a capital investment project is equal to zero

Appendix I

Review of basic algebra

I.1 *Basic laws, rules, and definitions*

A. The fundamental operations

The fundamental operations of algebra are *addition*, *subtraction*, *multiplication*, and *division*. The symbols used to show these operations are the same as used in arithmetic.

For any two numbers 'a' and 'b,' the fundamental operations are as follows.

1. *Addition* is denoted by '$a + b$' and referred to as the sum of 'a' and 'b.'
   If $a = 7$ and $b = 4$,
   then $a + b = 7 + 4 = 11$.

2. *Subtraction* is denoted by '$a - b$' and referred to as the difference between 'a' and 'b.'
   If $a = 7$ and $b = 4$,
   then $a - b = 7 - 4 = 3$.

3. *Multiplication* is denoted by '$a \times b$' '$(a)(b)$' or 'ab.' 'a' and 'b' are called **factors** and 'ab' is referred to as the product of 'a' and 'b.'
   If $a = 7$ and $b = 4$,
   then $ab = (7)(4) = 28$.

4. *Division* is denoted by 'a:b' or $\frac{\text{'}a\text{'}}{b}$ or 'a/b.' 'a' is the dividend, 'b' is the divisor, and $\frac{\text{'}a\text{'}}{b}$ is referred to as the quotient.
   If $a = 7$ and $b = 4$,
   then $\frac{a}{b} = \frac{7}{4}$.

B. Basic laws

The basic laws governing algebraic operations are the same as those used for arithmetic operations.

1. *The Commutative Laws for Addition and Multiplication*

(a) When adding two numbers, the two numbers (addends) may be interchanged.

$$\boxed{a + b = b + a} \longleftarrow \textbf{\textit{Formula}} \textbf{ I.1}$$

If $a = 7$ and $b = 4$,
then $7 + 4 = 4 + 7 = 11$.

(b) When multiplying two numbers, the two factors may be interchanged.

$$\boxed{ab = ba} \longleftarrow \textbf{\textit{Formula}} \textbf{ I.2}$$

If $a = 7$ and $b = 4$,
then $(7)(4) = (4)(7) = 28$.

2. *The Associative Laws for Addition and Multiplication*

(a) When adding three or more numbers, the numbers (addends) may be combined in any order.

$$\boxed{a + b + c = (a + b) + c = a + (b + c) = b + (a + c)} \longleftarrow \textbf{\textit{Formula}} \textbf{ I.3}$$

If $a = 7$, $b = 4$, and $c = 2$,
then $7 + 4 + 2 = (7 + 4) + 2 = 7 + (4 + 2) = 4 + (7 + 2) = 13$.

(b) When multiplying three or more numbers, the numbers (factors) may be combined in any order.

$$\boxed{abc = (ab)c = a(bc) = b(ac)} \longleftarrow \textbf{\textit{Formula}} \textbf{ I.4}$$

If $a = 7$, $b = 4$, and $c = 2$,
then $7 \times 4 \times 2 = (7 \times 4) \times 2 = 7 \times (4 \times 2) = 4 \times (7 \times 2) = 56$.

3. *The Distributive Law of Multiplication over Addition*

The product of 'a' times the sum of 'b' and 'c' is equal to the sum of the products 'ab' and 'ac.'

$$\boxed{a(b + c) = ab + ac} \longleftarrow \textbf{\textit{Formula}} \textbf{ I.5}$$

If $a = 7$, $b = 4$, and $c = 2$,
then $7(4 + 2) = 7 \times 4 + 7 \times 2 = 42$.

4. *Special Properties of '1'*

(a) $a \times 1 = 1 \times a = a$ — When any number '*a*' is multiplied by '1,' the product is the number '*a*.'

If $a = 5$, then $5 \times 1 = 1 \times 5 = 5$.

(b) $\frac{a}{1} = a$ — When any number '*a*' is divided by '1,' the quotient is the number '*a*.'

If $a = 5$, then $\frac{5}{1} = 5$.

(c) $\frac{a}{a} = 1$ — When any number '*a*' is divided by itself, the quotient is '1.'

If $a = 5$, then $\frac{5}{5} = 1$.

5. *Special Properties of '0'*

(a) *Addition with '0'*

$a + 0 = 0 + a = a$ — When '0' is added to any number '*a*,' the sum is the number '*a*.'

If $a = 5$, then $5 + 0 = 0 + 5 = 5$.

(b) *Subtraction with '0'*

(i) $a - 0 = a$ — When '0' is subtracted from any number '*a*,' the difference is the number '*a*.'

If $a = 5$, then $5 - 0 = 5$.

(ii) $0 - a = -a$ — When any number '*a*' is subtracted from '0,' the difference is the inverse value of '*a*,' that is, '*a*' with the sign changed.

If $a = 5$, then $0 - 5 = -5$.

(c) *Multiplication with '0'*

$a \times 0 = 0 \times a = 0$ — When '0' is multiplied by any number '*a*,' the product is '0.'

If $a = 5$, then $5 \times 0 = 0 \times 5 = 0$.

(d) *Division with '0'*

(i) $\boxed{\dfrac{0}{a} = 0}$ — When '0' is divided by any number 'a' other than '0,' the quotient is '0.'

If $a = 5$, then $\dfrac{0}{5} = 0$.

(ii) $\boxed{\dfrac{a}{0} = \text{undefined}}$ — Division by '0' has no meaning.

If $a = 5$, then $\dfrac{5}{0} = \text{undefined}$.

C. *Definitions*

1. An **algebraic expression** is a combination of numbers, variables representing numbers, and symbols indicating an algebraic operation.

$$7ab,\ 3a - 5b,\ x^2 - 3x + 4,\ \frac{3}{4}x - \frac{1}{5}y$$

2. A **term** is a part of an algebraic expression separated from other parts by a positive (+) sign or by a negative (−) sign. The preceding (+) sign or (−) sign is part of the term.

The terms for the algebraic expressions listed in part (1) are

$$7ab;\ 3a \text{ and } -5b;\ x^2,\ -3x, \text{ and } +4;\ \frac{3}{4}x \text{ and } -\frac{1}{5}y$$

3. A **monomial** is an algebraic expression consisting of *one* term, such as $7ab$.

A **binomial** is an algebraic expression consisting of *two* terms, such as $3a - 5b$ or $\frac{3}{4}x - \frac{1}{5}y$.

A **trinomial** is an algebraic expression consisting of *three* terms, such as $x^2 - 3x + 4$.

A **polynomial** is an algebraic expression consisting of *more than one* term.

4. A **factor** is one of the numbers that when multiplied by another number or numbers yields a given product.

The factors of the term $7ab$ are 7, a, and b.

5. A *factor of a term* is called the *coefficient* of the rest of the term.

In the term $7ab$, 7 is the coefficient of ab,
$7a$ is the coefficient of b,
$7b$ is the coefficient of a.

6. The **numerical coefficient** is the part of a term formed by *numerals.*

In the term $7ab$, the numerical coefficient is 7;
in the term x^2, the numerical coefficient is *understood* to be 1 (1 is usually not written);
in the term $-\frac{1}{5}y$, the numerical coefficient is $-\frac{1}{5}$ (the sign is considered to be part of the numerical coefficient).

7. The **literal coefficient** of a term is the part of the term formed with *letter* symbols.

In the term $7ab$, ab is the literal coefficient;
in the term $3x^2$, x^2 is the literal coefficient.

8. **Like terms** are terms having the *same* literal coefficients.

$7a, \; -3a, \; a, \; -\frac{1}{3}a$ are like terms;

$x^2, \; -2x^2, \; -\frac{1}{2}x^2, \; 5x^2$ are like terms.

9. **Combining like terms** or **collecting like terms** means *adding* like terms. Only like terms can be added.

10. **Signed numbers** are numbers preceded by a positive (+) or a negative (−) sign. Numbers preceded by a positive (+) sign are called **positive numbers**, while numbers preceded by a negative (−) sign are called **negative numbers**.

11. **Like signed numbers** are numbers that have the *same* sign while numbers with *different* signs are called **unlike signed numbers**.

$+7$ and $+8$ are like signed numbers;
-7 and -8 are like signed numbers;
$+7$ and -8 are unlike signed numbers;
-7 and 8 are unlike signed numbers.

Note: If no sign is written in front of a number, a plus (+) sign is understood to precede the number.

'6' means '+6.'

12. The **absolute value** of a signed number is the value of the number *without* the sign and is denoted by the symbol $| \; |$.

The absolute value of $+5 = |+5| = 5$;

the absolute value of $-5 = |-5| = 5$.

Exercise I.1

A. Answer each of the following questions.

1. List the terms contained in each of the following expressions.

   (a) $-3xy$

   (b) $4a - 5c - 2d$

   (c) $x^2 - \frac{1}{2}x - 2$

   (d) $1.2x - 0.5xy + 0.9y - 0.3$

2. Name the numerical coefficient of each of the following terms.

   (a) $-3b$ **(b)** $7c$ **(c)** $-a$ **(d)** x

   (e) $12a^2b$ **(f)** $-3ax$ **(g)** $-\frac{1}{2}x^2$ **(h)** $\frac{x}{5}$

3. Name the literal coefficient of each of the following.

   (a) $3x$ **(b)** ab **(c)** $-4y$ **(d)** $-xy$

   (e) $-15x^2y^2$ **(f)** $3.5abx$ **(g)** $\frac{4}{3}x^3$ **(h)** $\frac{by}{6}$

I.2 *Fundamental operations with signed numbers*

A. Addition with signed numbers

1. *Addition of Like Signed Numbers*

To add liked signed numbers,

(i) add their absolute values, and

(ii) prefix the common sign.

Example **I.2a** Add each of the following.

(i) -6 and -8

Solution

The absolute values are 6 and 8;
the sum of 6 and 8 is 14;
the common sign is $(-)$.

$$(-6) + (-8) = -6 - 8 = -14$$

(ii) $+6$, $+5$, and $+12$

Solution

The absolute values are 6, 5, and 12;
the sum of 6, 5, and 12 is 23;
the common sign is $(+)$.

$$(+6) + (+5) + (+12) = +6 + 5 + 12 = +23 \text{ or } 23$$

(iii) -9, -3, -1, and -15

Solution

The absolute values are 9, 3, 1, 15;
the sum of the four numbers is 28;
the common sign is $(-)$.

$$(-9) + (-3) + (-1) + (-15) = -9 - 3 - 1 - 15 = -28$$

2. *Addition of Unlike Signed Numbers*

To add unlike signed numbers,

(i) subtract the smaller absolute value from the larger absolute value, and
(ii) prefix the sign of the *larger* absolute value.

***Example* I.2b** Add each of the following.

(i) 8 and -5

Solution

The absolute values are 8 and 5;
the difference between the absolute values is 3;
the sign of the larger absolute value is $(+)$.

$$(+8) + (-5) = +8 - 5 = +3 \text{ or } 3$$

(ii) 4 and -9

Solution

The absolute values are 4 and 9;
the difference between the absolute values is 5;
the sign of the larger absolute value is $(-)$.

$$(+4) + (-9) = 4 - 9 = -5$$

(iii) -6, $+8$, $+3$, -4, and -5

Solution

When more than two numbers are involved and unlike signs appear, two approaches are available.

METHOD 1 Add the first two numbers and then add the sum to the next number and so on.

$$
\begin{aligned}
&(-6) + (+8) + (+3) + (-4) + (-5) \\
&= -6 + 8 + 3 - 4 - 5 \\
&= +2 + 3 - 4 - 5 \longleftarrow \text{add } -6 \text{ and } +8 \text{ which equals } +2 \\
&= +5 - 4 - 5 \longleftarrow \text{add } +2 \text{ and } +3 \text{ which equals } +5 \\
&= +1 - 5 \longleftarrow \text{add } +5 \text{ and } -4 \text{ which equals } +1 \\
&= -4 \longleftarrow \text{add } +1 \text{ and } -5 \text{ which equals } -4
\end{aligned}
$$

METHOD 2 First add the numbers having like signs and then add the two resulting unlike signed numbers.

$$
\begin{aligned}
&(-6) + (+8) + (+3) + (-4) + (-5) \\
&= -6 + 8 + 3 - 4 - 5 \\
&= (-6 - 4 - 5) + (+8 + 3) \\
&= (-15) + (+11) \\
&= -15 + 11 \\
&= -4
\end{aligned}
$$

B. *Subtraction with signed numbers*

The subtraction of signed numbers is changed to addition by using the inverse of the *subtrahend.* Thus, to subtract with signed numbers, change the sign of the subtrahend and add.

***Example* I.2c** Perform each of the following subtractions.

(i) $(+6)$ from (4)

Solution

$$
\begin{aligned}
&(+4) - (+6) \\
&= (+4) + (-6) \longleftarrow \text{change the subtrahend } (+6) \text{ to } (-6) \text{ and change the subtraction to an addition} \\
&= +4 - 6 \longleftarrow \text{use the rules of addition to add } +4 \text{ and } -6 \\
&= -2
\end{aligned}
$$

(ii) (-12) from $(+7)$

Solution

$(+7) - (-12)$
$= (+7) + (+12)$ ⟵ change the subtrahend (-12) to $(+12)$
$= +7 + 12$ ⟵ and add
$= 19$

(iii) $(+9)$ from (-6)

Solution

$(-6) - (+9)$
$= (-6) + (-9)$
$= -6 - 9$
$= -15$

C. Multiplication with signed numbers

The product of two signed numbers is positive or negative according to the following rules.

(a) If the signs of the two numbers are *like*, the product is *positive*.

$(+)(+) = (+)$
$(-)(-) = (+)$

(b) If the signs of the two numbers are *unlike*, the product is *negative*.

$(+)(-) = (-)$
$(-)(+) = (-)$

Example **I.2d**

(i) $(+7)(+4) = 28$ ⟵ both signs are like (both positive); the product is positive

(ii) $(-9)(-3) = 27$ ⟵ the two signs are like (both negative); the product is positive

(iii) $(-8)(3) = -24$ ⟵ the signs are unlike; the product is negative

(iv) $(7)(-1) = -7$ ⟵ the signs are unlike; the product is negative

(v) $(-8)(0) = 0$ ⟵ the product of any number and 0 is 0

(vi) $(-7)(3)(-4) = (-21)(-4)$ ⟵ (-7) times (3) is (-21)
$= 84$

(vii) $(-2)(-1)(-4)(3) = (2)(-4)(3) = (-8)(3) = -24$

Note: Brackets around one or both numbers indicate multiplication.

D. *Division with signed numbers*

The quotient of two signed numbers is positive or negative according to the following rules.

(a) If the signs are *like*, the quotient is *positive.*

$(+) \div (+) = (+)$

$(-) \div (-) = (+)$

(b) If the signs are *unlike*, the quotient is *negative.*

$(+) \div (-) = (-)$

$(-) \div (+) = (-)$

Example I.2e

(i) $15 \div (+5) = 3$ ⟵ the two signs are like; the quotient is positive

(ii) $(-24) \div (-4) = 6$ ⟵ the two signs are like; the quotient is positive

(iii) $(-18) \div 2 = -9$ ⟵ the two signs are unlike; the quotient is negative

(iv) $(12) \div (-1) = -12$ ⟵ the two signs are unlike; the quotient is negative

(v) $0 \div (-10) = 0$ ⟵ 0 divided by any number is 0

(vi) $(-16) \div 0$ = undefined ⟵ division by 0 has no meaning

E. *Absolute value of signed numbers*

The absolute value of signed numbers, denoted by $|\ |$, is the value of the numbers without the signs.

Example I.2f

(i) $|-7| = 7$

(ii) $|-3 + 8| = |+5| = 5$

(iii) $|4 - 9| = |-5| = 5$

(iv) $|-9 - 4| = |-13| = 13$

(v) $|4(-7)| = |-28| = 28$

(vi) $|(-9)(-3)| = |27| = 27$

(vii) $|(-12) \div (4)| = |-3| = 3$

(viii) $|(-30) \div (-5)| = |+6| = 6$

Exercise I.2

A. Simplify.

1. $(+3) + (+7)$ **2.** $(+12) + (+6)$ **3.** $(-5) + (-9)$

4. $(-15) + (-12)$ **5.** $4 + (+5)$ **6.** $(+6) + 8$

7. $-8 + (-7)$ **8.** $(-18) - 7$ **9.** $+3 + 14$

10. $+12 + 1$ **11.** $-6 - 9$ **12.** $-14 - 3$

13. $-8 + 3$ **14.** $-12 + 16$ **15.** $8 - 12$

16. $0 - 9$ **17.** $1 - 0.6$ **18.** $1 - 0.02$

19. $(-4) + (6) + (-3) + (+2)$ **20.** $12 + (-15) + (+8) + (-10)$

21. $-3 - 7 + 9 + 6 - 5$ **22.** $10 - 8 - 12 + 3 - 7$

B. Simplify.

1. $(+9) - (+8)$ **2.** $(+11) - (+14)$ **3.** $(+6) - (-6)$

4. $(+11) - (-12)$ **5.** $(-8) - (-7)$ **6.** $(-9) - (-13)$

7. $(-4) - (+6)$ **8.** $(-15) - (+3)$ **9.** $0 - (-9)$

10. $1 - (-0.4)$ **11.** $1 - (-0.03)$ **12.** $0 - (+15)$

13. $6 - (-5) + (-8) - (+3) + (-2)$

14. $-12 - (-6) - (+9) + (-4) - 7$

C. Simplify.

1. $(+5)(+4)$ **2.** $11(+3)$ **3.** $(-4)(-6)$ **4.** $-7(-3)$

5. $(+7)(-1)$ **6.** $10(-5)$ **7.** $-3(12)$ **8.** $-9(1)$

9. $0(-6)$ **10.** $-12(0)$ **11.** $6(-4)(-3)(2)$ **12.** $-3(5)(-2)(-1)$

D. Simplify.

1. $(+18) \div (+3)$ **2.** $(32) \div (+4)$ **3.** $(+45) \div (-9)$ **4.** $(63) \div (-3)$

5. $(-28) \div (+7)$ **6.** $(-36) \div (+12)$ **7.** $(-16) \div (-1)$ **8.** $(-48) \div (-8)$

9. $0 \div (-5)$ **10.** $0 \div 10$ **11.** $(+4) \div 0$ **12.** $(-12) \div 0$

E. Simplify.

1. $|-9|$ **2.** $|+4|$ **3.** $|6 - 10|$ **4.** $|-5 + 12|$

5. $|-7 - 8|$ **6.** $|0 - 3|$ **7.** $|(-3) \times 3|$ **8.** $|4 \times (-5)|$

9. $|20 \div (-5)|$ **10.** $|(-35) \div (7)|$

I.3 *Common factoring*

A. Basic concept

In arithmetic, certain computations, such as multiplication and division involving common fractions, are helped by factoring. Similarly, algebraic manipulation can be made easier by the process of finding the factors that make up an algebraic expression.

Factoring an algebraic expression means writing the expression as a product in component form. Depending on the type of factors contained in the expression, the process of factoring takes a variety of forms. Only the simplest type of factoring applies to the subject matter dealt with in this text. Accordingly only this type, called *common factoring*, is explained in this section.

A **common factor** is one that is divisible without remainder into each term of an algebraic expression. The factor which is common to each term is usually found by inspection; the remaining factor is then obtained by dividing the expression by the common factor.

B. Examples

Example **I.3a** Factor $14a + 21b$.

Solution

By inspection, recognize that the two terms $14a$ and $21b$ are both divisible by 7.

The common factor is 7.

The second factor is now found by dividing the expression by 7.

$$\frac{14a + 21b}{7} = \frac{14a}{7} + \frac{21b}{7} = 2a + 3b$$

Thus the factors of $14a + 21b$ are 7 and $2a + 3b$.

$$14a + 21b = 7(2a + 3b)$$

Example **I.3b** Factor $18a - 45$.

Solution

By inspection, the highest common factor is 9;

the second factor is $\dfrac{18a - 45}{9} = 2a - 5$.

$$18a - 45 = 9(2a - 5)$$

Note: If 3 is used as the common factor, the second factor, $6a - 15$, contains a common factor 3 and can be factored into $3(2a - 5)$.

Thus, $18a - 45 = 3[6a - 15]$
$= 3[3(2a - 5)]$
$= 9(2a - 5)$

When factoring, the accepted procedure is to always take out the *highest* common factor.

***Example* I.3c** Factor $mx - my$.

Solution

The common factor is m;

the second factor is $\dfrac{mx - my}{m} = x - y$.

$$mx - my = m(x - y)$$

***Example* I.3d** Factor $15x^3 - 25x^2 - 20x$.

Solution

The common factor is $5x$.

The second factor is $\dfrac{15x^3 - 25x^2 - 20x}{5x} = 3x^2 - 5x - 4$.

$$15x^3 - 25x^2 - 20x = 5x\,(3x^2 - 5x - 4)$$

***Example* I.3e** Factor P + Prt.

Solution

The common factor is P.

The second factor is $\dfrac{\mathrm{P} + \mathrm{Prt}}{\mathrm{P}} = \dfrac{\mathrm{P}}{\mathrm{P}} + \dfrac{\mathrm{Prt}}{\mathrm{P}} = 1 + \mathrm{rt}$.

$$\mathrm{P} + \mathrm{Prt} = \mathrm{P}(1 + \mathrm{rt})$$

***Example* I.3f** Factor $a(x + y) - b(x + y)$.

Solution

The common factor is $(x + y)$.

The second factor is $\dfrac{a(x + y) - b(x + y)}{x + y} = \dfrac{a(x + y)}{x + y} - \dfrac{b(x + y)}{x + y} = a - b$.

$$a(x + y) - b(x + y) = (x + y)(a - b)$$

***Example* I.3g** Factor $(1 + i) + (1 + i)^2 + (1 + i)^3$.

Solution

The common factor is $(1 + i)$.

The second factor is $$\frac{(1 + i) + (1 + i)^2 + (1 + i)^3}{(1 + i)}$$

$$= \frac{(1 + i)}{(1 + i)} + \frac{(1 + i)^2}{(1 + i)} + \frac{(1 + i)^3}{(1 + i)}$$

$$= 1 + (1 + i) + (1 + i)^2$$

$$(1 + i) + (1 + i)^2 + (1 + i)^3 = (1 + i)\,[1 + (1 + i) + (1 + i)^2]$$

Exercise I.3

A. Factor each of the following.

1. $8x - 12$
2. $27 - 36a$
3. $4n^2 - 8n$
4. $9x^2 - 21x$
5. $5ax - 10ay - 20a$
6. $4ma - 12mb + 24mab$

B. Factor each of the following.

1. $mx + my$
2. $xa - xb$
3. $m(a - b) + n(a - b)$
4. $k(x - 1) - 3(x - 1)$
5. $\mathrm{P} + \mathrm{P}i$
6. $\mathrm{A} - \mathrm{A}dt$
7. $r - r^2 - r^3$
8. $(1 + i)^4 + (1 + i)^3 + (1 + i)^2$

Summary of formulae (laws) used

Formula I.1

$$a + b = b + a$$

The commutative law for addition that permits the addition of two numbers in any order

Formula I.2

$$ab = ba$$

The commutative law for multiplication that permits the multiplication of two numbers in any order

Formula I.3

$$\begin{aligned} a + b + c &= (a + b) + c \\ &= a + (b + c) \\ &= b + (a + c) \end{aligned}$$

The associative law for addition that permits the addition of three or more numbers in any order

Formula I.4

$$\begin{aligned} abc &= (ab)c \\ &= a(bc) \\ &= b(ac) \end{aligned}$$

The associative law for multiplication that permits the multiplication of three or more numbers in any order

Formula I.5

$a(b + c) = ab + ac$ — The distributive law of multiplication over addition that provides the basis for the multiplication of algebraic expressions

Glossary of terms used

Absolute value the value of a number without its sign

Algebraic expression a combination of numbers, variables representing numbers, and symbols indicating an algebraic operation

Binomial an algebraic expression consisting of two terms

Collecting like terms adding like terms

Combining like terms see *Collecting like terms*

Common factor a factor that is divisible without remainder into each term of an algebraic expression

Factor one of the numbers that when multiplied with the other number or numbers yields a given product

Like signed numbers numbers having the same sign

Like terms terms having the same literal coefficient

Literal coefficient the part of a term formed with letter symbols

Monomial an algebraic expression consisting of one term

Negative number a signed number preceded by a minus (−) sign

Numerical coefficient the part of a term formed with numerals

Polynomial an algebraic expression consisting of more than one term

Positive number a signed number preceded by a plus (+) sign

Signed number a number preceded by a plus (+) or by a minus (−) sign

Term a part of an algebraic expression separated from other parts by a plus (+) sign or by a minus (−) sign

Trinomial an algebraic expression consisting of three terms

Unlike signed numbers numbers having different signs

Appendix II

Linear applications

II.1 *Cost-volume-profit analysis*

A. Cost-volume-profit relationships

A primary function of accounting is the collection of cost and revenue data which may then be used to examine the existing relationships between cost behaviour and revenue behaviour.

Any analysis, whether graphic or algebraic, makes certain assumptions about the behaviour of costs and revenue. In its simplest form, cost-volume-profit analysis makes the following assumptions.

1. Revenue per unit of output is constant. Thus, total revenue varies directly with volume.
2. Costs can be classified as either fixed or variable.
3. **Fixed costs** are those costs that remain constant over the time period considered for all levels of output. Examples of costs in this category are depreciation, rent, property taxes, supervision, and management salaries. Since fixed costs are constant in total, they vary per unit of output. They decrease per unit of output as volume increases and increase per unit of output as volume decreases.
4. **Variable costs** are costs that are constant per unit of output regardless of volume. They fluctuate in total amount as volume fluctuates. Examples of costs in this category are direct material costs, direct labour costs, and sales commissions.

The above assumptions present a simplified view of the real world. Fixed costs are not constant across all levels of output but tend to change in a step-like manner. Per unit variable costs are not always constant but are influenced by economies of scale. There is no black and white classification of costs into fixed costs and variable costs; rather, many costs are semi-variable. That is, they contain a fixed component as well as a variable component. However, for purposes of an uncomplicated introductory analysis, these assumptions serve a useful purpose.

Using these simplifying assumptions, the behaviour of revenue and the behaviour of costs can be represented graphically by straight-line diagrams as shown in Figures II.1 and II.2.

FIGURE II.1 ***Revenue behaviour***

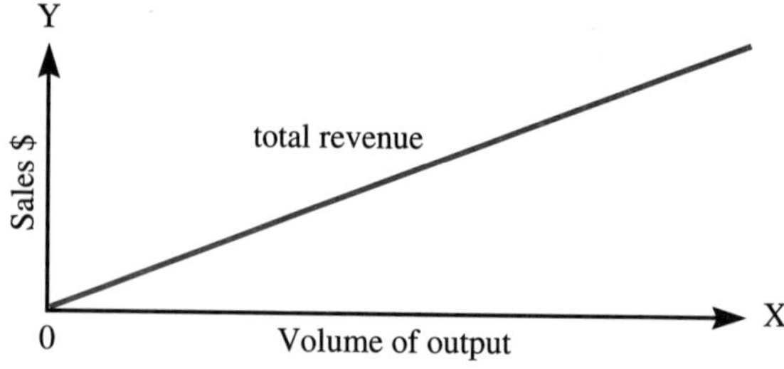

FIGURE II.2 ***Cost behaviour***

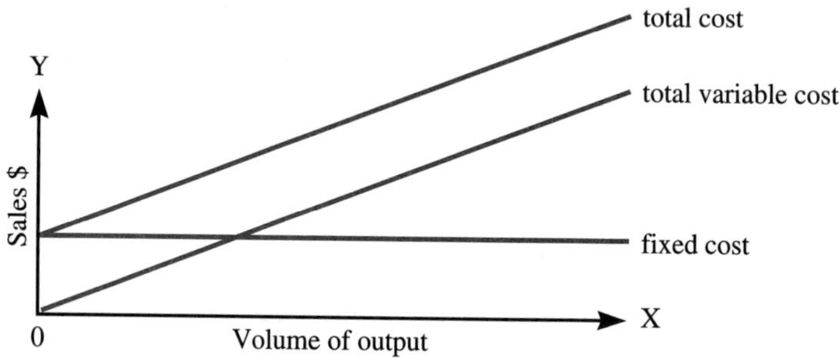

The following components are basic to cost-volume-profit relationships. The mathematical notations as shown will be used for these components.

X = Volume of output
P = Selling price (revenue) per unit of output
TR = Total revenue
TC = Total cost
FC = Fixed cost
TVC = Total variable cost
VC = Variable cost per unit of output
NI = Net income (profit)

The accounting relationship (income statement equation)

TOTAL REVENUE = TOTAL COST + NET INCOME

TR = TC + NI	⟵ ***Formula* II.1**

is basic to cost-volume-profit analysis. The following relationships are also useful.

TOTAL REVENUE = VOLUME × UNIT REVENUE

TR = (X)(P)	⟵ ***Formula* II.2**

TOTAL COST = FIXED COST + TOTAL VARIABLE COST

TC = FC + TVC	⟵ ***Formula* II.3**

TOTAL VARIABLE COST = VOLUME × VARIABLE COST PER UNIT

TVC = (X)(VC)	⟵ ***Formula* II.4**

TOTAL REVENUE = FIXED COST + TOTAL VARIABLE COST + NET INCOME

TR = FC + TVC + NI	⟵ ***Formula* II.5**

B. Break-even analysis

The most popular approach to cost-volume-profit analysis is called **break-even analysis**. The break-even approach focuses on the profitability of the business and is specifically concerned with identifying the level of output at which the business neither makes a profit nor sustains a loss, that is, the level of output at which

NET INCOME = 0

The level of output at which NI = 0 is called the **break-even point** and is obtainable from Formula II.1 (or Formula II.5). Since NI = 0, the break-even point is the level of output at which

TOTAL REVENUE = TOTAL COST

The relationship between revenue and costs at different levels of output may be portrayed graphically by showing revenue behaviour (Figure II.1) and cost behaviour (Figure II.2) on the same graph. The resulting graph shows the break-even point and is known as a **break-even chart** (see Figure II.3).

FIGURE II.3 ***Break-even chart***

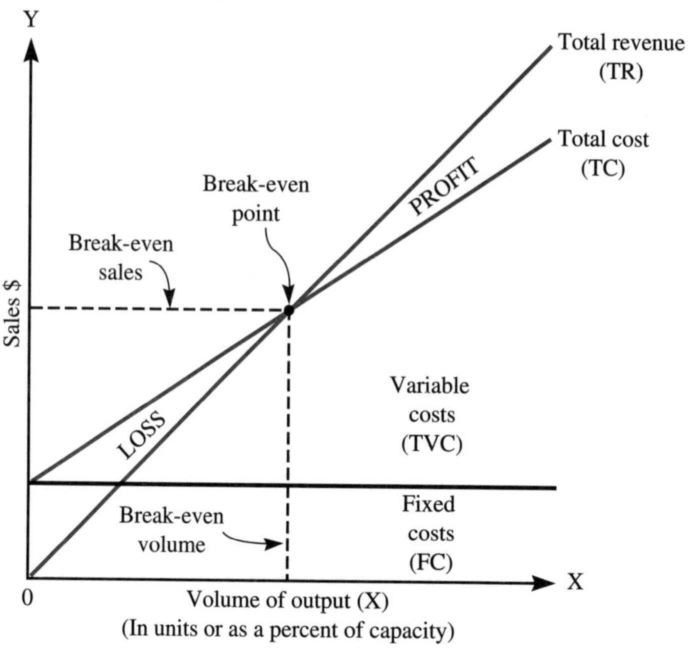

Notes on the charts:

1. The horizontal axis is used to represent volume of output either as a number of units or as a percentage of capacity. The vertical axis represents dollar values (sales revenue). The origin is at zero—representing zero volume and zero dollars.
2. The total revenue line is drawn by plotting two or more total revenue points (one of which is always the origin) and joining them.
3. The fixed cost line is drawn parallel to the horizontal axis from the point on the vertical axis that represents total fixed cost dollars.
4. The total cost line is drawn by plotting two or more total cost points (one of which is always the point where the fixed cost line starts on the vertical axis) and joining them.
5. The point where the total revenue line and the total cost line intersect is the break-even point.
6. The point of intersection on the horizontal axis of the perpendicular drawn from the break-even point to the horizontal axis indicates the break-even volume in units or as a percentage of capacity.
7. The point of intersection on the vertical axis of the perpendicular drawn from the break-even point to the vertical axis indicates the break-even volume in dollars ($Sales).
8. The area between the horizontal axis and the fixed cost line represents the fixed cost in dollars.

9. The area between the fixed cost line and the total cost line represents the total variable cost in dollars for the various levels of operation.
10. The area between the total revenue line and the total cost line to the left of the break-even point represents the loss area where total revenue is less than total cost.
11. The area between the total cost line and the total revenue line to the right of the break-even point represents the profit area where total revenue is greater than total cost.

The graphic approach that results in a break-even chart is complemented by an algebraic approach that uses Formulas II.1 and II.5.

Both approaches are illustrated in the examples that follow. They show the two distinct situations that may be encountered depending on the accounting data that is available. In the first situation, illustrated in Section C, the accounting information is in terms of units. In the second situation, illustrated in Section D, the accounting information is in terms of total dollars.

C. Break-even analysis—Case 1

The available accounting data is in terms of units.

***Example* II.1a** Market research for a new product indicates that the product can be sold at $50.00 per unit. Cost analysis provides the following information.

Fixed cost per period = $8640.00
Variable cost per unit = $30.00
Production capacity per period = 900 units

Perform a break-even analysis providing

(i) an algebraic statement of
  (a) the **revenue function**,
  (b) the **cost function**;

(ii) a detailed break-even chart;

(iii) computation of the break-even point
  (a) in units,
  (b) as a percentage of capacity,
  (c) in dollars.

Solution

(i) Let the volume in units be X.

(a) TR = (X)(P) ⟵ using Formula II.2
= (X)(50.00)
= 50.00X

The revenue function is TR = 50X.

(b) $TVC = (X)(VC) \longleftarrow$ using Formula II.4
$= (X)(30.00)$
$= 30.00X$
$TC = FC + TVC \longleftarrow$ using Formula II.3
$= 8640.00 + 30.00X$

The cost function is $TC = 8640 + 30X$.

(ii) *Break-even chart*
We can draw the break-even chart by graphing the revenue function, $TR = 50X$, and the cost function, $TC = 8640 + 30X$.

Since capacity is 900 units, the horizontal scale needs to allow for X values up to 900. The vertical scale must allow for maximum sales dollars of $(900)(50) = 45\ 000$

Graphing the revenue function, TR = 50X
To graph the revenue function, assume at least two values of X and compute the corresponding value of TR.

For $X = 0$, $TR = (50)(0) = 0 \longrightarrow$ Graph point (0, 0)

For $X = 900$, $TR = (50)(900) = 45\ 000 \longrightarrow$ Graph point (900, 45 000)

While we can use any value of X, the two values selected are the preferred values because they represent the two extreme values (minimum and maximum volume) for the situation.

Graphing the cost function, TC = 8640 + 30X
Assume two values of X and compute the corresponding value of TC.

For $X = 0$, $TC = 8640 + 30(0) = 8640 \longleftarrow$ Graph point (0, 8640)
For $X = 900$, $TC = 8640 + 30(900)$
$= 8640 + 27\ 000 = 35\ 640 \longleftarrow$ Graph (900, 35 640)

FIGURE II.4 ***Break-even chart for example II.1a***

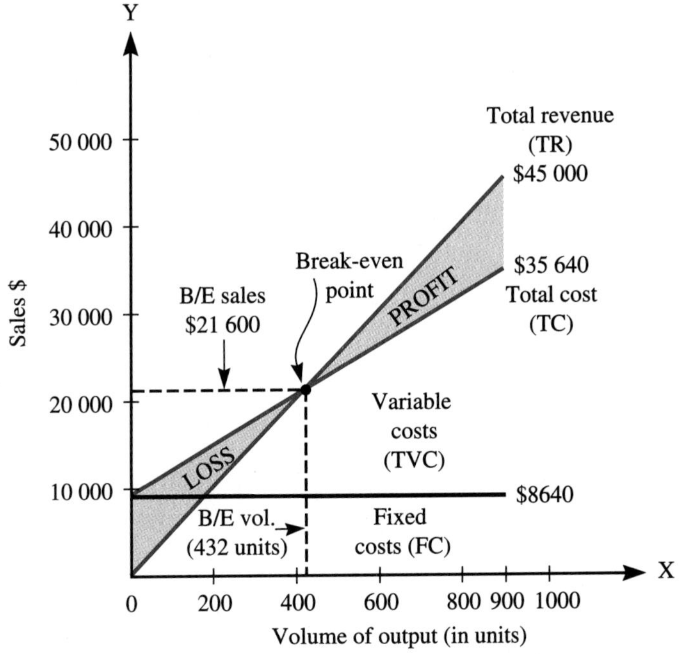

(iii) To determine the break-even point, the basic relationship between revenue and total cost is useful.

$$TR = FC + TVC + NI \longleftarrow \text{Formula II.5}$$

To break even, NI = 0.

$$TR = FC + TVC$$
$$50X = 8640 + 30X$$
$$20X = 8640$$
$$X = 432$$

(a) The break-even volume in units is 432.

(b) As a percentage of capacity, the break-even volume is $\frac{432}{900} = 0.48 = 48\%$.

(c) The break-even volume in dollars $= (432)(50) = \$21\ 600$.

D. *Break-even analysis—Case 2*

The available accounting data is in terms of total dollars.

***Example* II.1b** The following information is available about the operations of the King Corp. for the current year.

Sales		$40 000
Fixed costs	$12 600	
Variable costs	16 000	
Total cost		28 600
Net income		$11 400

Capacity is a sales volume of $60 000.

Perform a break-even analysis providing

(i) an algebraic statement of
  (a) the revenue function,
  (b) the cost function;

(ii) a detailed break-even chart;

(iii) computation of the break-even point
  (a) in sales dollars.
  (b) as a percentage of capacity.

Solution

(i) When the data is in terms of dollars rather than units, express the functions in terms of sales volume.

Let X represent the sales volume in dollars.

(a) The revenue function is TR = X.

(b) Since variable costs are directly related to sales volume, they can be expressed as a percentage of sales volume.

In this example, total variable costs are $16 000 for a sales volume of $40 000.

$$\frac{\text{TVC}}{\text{TR}} = \frac{16\ 000}{40\ 000} = 0.40 = 40\%$$

$$\text{TVC} = 0.40\ \text{TR} = 40\%\ \text{of TR}$$

The cost function is $\text{TC} = 12\ 600 + 0.40\ \text{TR}$

or $\text{TC} = 12\ 600 + 0.40\ \text{X}$

(ii) When the accounting data is in terms of total dollars, use the horizontal axis to represent output in terms of percentage of sales capacity. Subdivide the horizontal scale to allow percentage sales levels up to 100%. The vertical scale must allow for the maximum sales level of $60 000.

Graphing the revenue function, TR = X
To graph the revenue function, assume at least two sales volume levels expressed as a percent of capacity.

For X = 0, TR = 0 $\longrightarrow$ Graph point (0, 0)
For X = 60 000, TR = 60 000 $\longrightarrow$ Graph point (60 000, 60 000)

The revenue function is represented by the line joining the two points.

Graphing the cost function, TC = 12 600 + 0.40X
Assume two sales volume levels and compute TC.

For X = 0, TC = 12 600 + 0.40(0)
= 12 600 $\longrightarrow$ Graph point (0, 12 600)

For X = 60 000, TC = 12 600 + 0.40(60 000)
= 12 600 + 24 000
= 36 600 $\longrightarrow$ Graph point (60 000, 36 600)

FIGURE II.5 ***Break-even chart for example II.1b***

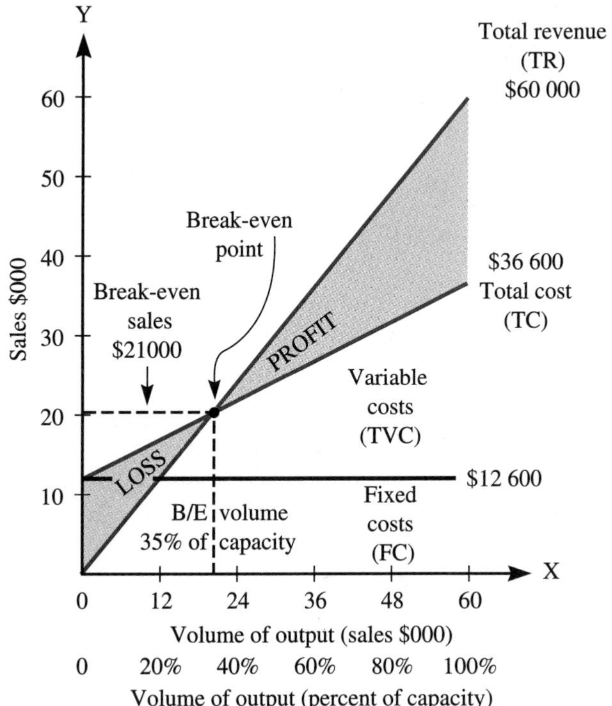

(iii) Using the basic relationship

$$TR = FC + TVC + NI \longleftarrow \text{Formula II.5}$$

and letting NI = 0,
the break-even point is given by

$$X = 12\,600 + 0.40X$$

$$0.60\,X = 12\,600$$

$$X = 21\,000$$

(a) The break-even volume in dollars is \$21 000.

(b) The break-even point is $\frac{21\,000}{60\,000} = 35\%$ of sales capacity.

E. *Algebraic analysis*

Break-even analysis focuses on one particular level of operations. However, the accounting relationship

$$TR = FC + TVC + NI \longleftarrow \text{Formula II.5}$$

can be used to extend cost-volume-profit analysis to any desired level of operations. It is possible to determine the net income at any level of operations and to analyze what effect changes in selling price, fixed cost, or variable costs have on profitability at any level of operations.

***Example* II.1c** Use the information in Example II.1a to answer each of the following questions.

(i) What is the net income at a volume of
(a) 385 units? **(b)** 780 units?

Solution

$$TR = 50X$$

$$TC = 8640 + 30X$$

The basic accounting relationship (using Formula II.5) is
50X = 8640 + 30X + NI.

(a) For X = 385,

$$50(385) = 8640 + 30(385) + NI$$

$$19\,250 = 8640 + 11\,550 + NI$$

$$NI = -940 \text{ (a loss)}$$

The net income (loss) at a volume of 385 units is (\$940).

(b) For X = 780,

$$50(780) = 8640 + 30(780) + NI$$
$$39\,000 = 8640 + 23\,400 + NI$$
$$NI = 6960$$

The net income at a volume of 780 units is \$6960.

(ii) What is the net income at a sales volume of
(a) \$17 500? **(b)** \$40 000?

Solution

(a) At a sales volume of \$17 500,

$$50X = 17\,500$$
$$X = 350 \text{ (units)}$$
$$50(350) = 8640 + 30(350) + NI$$
$$17\,500 = 8640 + 10\,500 + NI$$
$$NI = -1640$$

The net income (loss) at a volume of \$17 500 is (\$1640).

(b) At a sales volume of \$40 000,

$$50X = 40\,000$$
$$X = 800 \text{ (units)}$$
$$50(800) = 8640 + 30(800) + NI$$
$$40\,000 = 8640 + 24\,000 + NI$$
$$NI = 7360$$

The net income at a sales volume of \$40 000 is \$7360.

(iii) What is the net income at a sales volume of

(a) 36% of capacity? **(b)** 95% of capacity?

Solution

(a) Sales volume is 36% of 900 = 324 units.

$$50(324) = 8640 + 30(324) + NI$$
$$16\,200 = 8640 + 9720 + NI$$
$$NI = -2160$$

The net income at 36% of capacity is (\$2160).

(b) Sales volume is 95% of 900 = 855 units.

$$50(855) = 8640 + 30(855) + NI$$
$$42\,750 = 8640 + 25\,650 + NI$$
$$NI = 8460$$

The net income at 95% capacity is \$8460.

(iv) What is the number of units that must be sold to generate a net income of

(a) (\$1000)? **(b)** \$3000?

Solution

(a) $50X = 8640 + 30X - 1000$

$20X = 7640$

$X = 382$

To generate a net income of (\$1000), the sales volume must be 382 units.

(b) $50X = 8640 + 30X + 3000$

$20X = 11\,640$

$X = 582$

To generate a net income of \$3000, the sales volume must be 582 units.

(v) What is the sales volume in dollars that generates a net income of

(a) (\$1600)? **(b)** \$7200?

Solution

(a) $50X = 8640 + 30X - 1600$

$20X = 7040$

$X = 352$ (units)

The sales volume is $(352)(50) = \$17\,600$.

(b) $50X = 8640 + 30X + 7200$

$20X = 15\,840$

$X = 792$ (units)

The sales volume is $(792)(50) = \$39\,600$.

(vi) What is the output required, as a percentage of capacity, to generate a net income of

(a) \$360? **(b)** \$5760?

Solution

(a) $50X = 8640 + 30X + 360$

$20X = 9000$

$X = 450$ (units)

The required output is $\frac{450}{900} = 0.50 = 50\%$ of capacity.

(b) $50X = 8640 + 30X + 5760$

$20X = 14\,400$

$X = 720$ (units)

The required output is $\frac{720}{900} = 0.80 = 80\%$ of capacity.

(vii) What is the break-even point if fixed costs are increased to \$10 400

(a) in units? **(b)** in dollars? **(c)** as a percent of capacity?

Solution

If fixed costs are increased to \$10 400, the basic relationship (Formula II.5) becomes

$$50X = 10\,400 + 30X + NI$$

To break even, NI = 0.

$$50X = 10\,400 + 30X$$

$$20X = 10\,400$$

$$X = 520 \text{ (units)}$$

(a) The break-even point in units is 520.

(b) The break-even point in dollars is 520(50) = \$26 000.

(c) The break-even point as a percent of capacity is

$$\frac{520}{900} = 0.57777778 = 57.8\%$$

(viii) What is the break-even point in dollars if fixed costs are reduced by \$990 and variable cost per unit is increased by \$2?

Solution

The new fixed cost is 8640 − 990 = \$7650 and the new variable cost per unit is 30 + 2 = \$32. The basic relationship (Formula II.5) becomes

$$50X = 7650 + 32X + NI$$

To break even, NI = 0.

$$50X = 7650 + 32X$$

$$18X = 7650$$

$$X = 425 \text{ (units)}$$

The break-even point is (425)(50) = \$21 250.

(ix) What is the break-even point as a percent of capacity if the selling price is reduced by 10%?

Solution

The new selling price = 90% of \$50 = \$45.
The basic relationship becomes

$$45X = 8640 + 30X + NI$$

To break even, NI = 0.

$$45X = 8640 + 30X$$

$$15X = 8640$$

$$X = 576 \text{ (units)}$$

The break-even point is $\frac{576}{900} = 0.64 = 64\%$ of capacity.

(x) To generate a profit of \$4860, what dollar sales must be attained if the selling price per unit is

(a) reduced to \$48? **(b)** increased to \$55?

Solution

(a) $48X = 8640 + 30X + 4860$

$18X = 13\ 500$

$X = 750$ (units)

Sales volume must be $(750)(48) = \$36\ 000$.

(b) $55X = 8640 + 30X + 4860$

$25X = 13\ 500$

$X = 540$ (units)

Sales volume must be $(540)(55) = \$29\ 700$.

(xi) What is the output as a percentage of capacity that must be achieved to generate a profit of \$7830 if the production setup is modified so that fixed costs increase by 25% while variable costs are reduced by 10%?

Solution

The new fixed costs $= 1.25(8640) = \$10\ 800$; the new variable cost per unit $= (0.90)(30) = \$27$.

$$50X = 10\ 800 + 27X + 7830$$

$$23X = 18\ 630$$

$$X = 810 \text{ (units)}$$

The required output is $\frac{810}{900} = 0.90 = 90\%$ of capacity.

***Example* II.1d** Use the information in Example II.1b to answer each of the following questions.

(i) What is the net income at a sales volume of \$34 500?

Solution

Let X represent the sales volume.

$$TR = X$$

$$TC = 12\ 600 + 40\% \text{ of } TR = 12\ 600 + 0.40\ X$$

The basic relationship (Formula II.5) is

$$X = 12\ 600 + 0.40\ X + NI$$

At a sales volume of 34 500, X = 34 500.

$$34\ 500 = 12\ 600 + 0.40(34\ 500) + NI$$
$$34\ 500 = 12\ 600 + 13\ 800 + NI$$
$$NI = 8100$$

The net income at a volume of \$34 500 is \$8100.

(ii) What is the net income at a volume of 95% of capacity?

Solution

At 95% of capacity, X = 0.95(60 000) = 57 000.

$$57\ 000 = 12\ 600 + 0.40(57\ 000) + NI$$
$$57\ 000 = 12\ 600 + 22\ 800 + NI$$
$$NI = 21\ 600$$

The net income at 95% of capacity is \$21 600.

(iii) What volume of output as a percentage of capacity is required to produce a net income of \$13 320?

Solution

$$X = 12\ 600 + 0.40\ X + 13\ 320$$
$$0.60\ X = 25\ 920$$
$$X = 43\ 200$$

The volume of output required is $\frac{43\ 200}{60\ 000} = 72\%$ of capacity.

(iv) What sales volume is required to generate a net income of \$3240?

Solution

$$X = 12\ 600 + 0.40\ X + 3240$$
$$0.60\ X = 15\ 840$$
$$X = 26\ 400$$

The sales volume required is \$26 400.

(v) If fixed costs are increased by 25%, what is the break-even point

(a) in sales dollars? **(b)** as a percentage of capacity?

Solution

New fixed cost is 12 600(1.25) = \$15 750.

$$X = 15\,750 + 0.40\,X + NI$$

To break even, NI = 0.

$$X = 15\,750 + 0.40\,X$$
$$0.60\,X = 15\,750$$
$$X = 26\,250$$

(a) The break-even point is \$26 250.

(b) The break-even point is $\frac{26\,250}{60\,000} = 43.75\%$ of capacity.

(vi) What is the break-even point in sales dollars if fixed costs are increased to \$14 880 while variable costs are decreased to 38% of sales?

Solution

The basic relationship becomes

$$X = 14\,880 + 38\%\text{ of }X + NI$$
$$X = 14\,880 + 0.38\,X + NI$$

To break even, NI = 0.

$$X = 14\,880 + 0.38\,X$$
$$0.62\,X = 14\,880$$
$$X = 24\,000$$

The break-even point is \$24 000.

(vii) To generate a profit of \$5250, what output, as a percentage of capacity, must be attained if fixed costs are increased by 5% and variable costs by 10%?

Solution

$$FC = 12\,600(1.05) = \$13\,230$$

$$TVC = 1.10(40\%\text{ of }TR)$$
$$= 1.10(0.40\,X)$$
$$= 0.44\,X$$

The basic relationship becomes

$$X = 13\,230 + 0.44\,X + 5250$$
$$0.56\,X = 18\,480$$
$$X = 33\,000$$

The required volume is $\frac{33\,000}{60\,000} = 55\%$ of capacity.

F. Computer application—Break-even analysis

Program 1—Break-even analysis—provides a numerical computer solution for Case 1 illustrated in this section (see the Solutions Manual).

Exercise II.1

A. For each of the following, perform a break-even analysis showing

(a) an algebraic statement of
(i) the revenue function,
(ii) the cost function;

(b) a detailed break-even chart;

(c) computation of the break-even point
(i) in units (if applicable),
(ii) as a percentage of capacity,
(iii) in sales dollars.

1. Engineering estimates indicate the variable cost of manufacturing a new product will be \$35 per unit. Based on market research, the selling price of the product is to be \$120 per unit and variable selling expense is expected to be \$15 per unit. The fixed costs applicable to the new product are estimated to be \$2800 per period and capacity per period is 100 units.

2. A firm manufactures a product that sells for \$12.00 per unit. Variable cost per unit is \$8.00 and fixed cost per period is \$1200. Capacity per period is 1000 units.

3. The following data pertains to the operating budget of Matt Mfg.

Sales			\$720 000
	Fixed costs	\$220 000	
	Total variable costs	324 000	544 000
Net Income			\$176 000

Capacity is a sales volume of \$800 000 per period.

4. A company has compiled the following estimates regarding operations.

Sales			\$120 000
	Fixed costs	\$43 200	
	Variable costs	48 000	91 200
Net Income			\$ 28 800

Capacity is a sales volume of \$150 000.

B. Answer each of the following questions.

1. For question 1 in Part A of this exercise, determine

(a) the net income at a volume of 70 units;

(b) the net income at a volume of 30% of capacity;

(c) the net income at a sales volume of \$10 200;

(d) the level of operations as a percentage of capacity to generate a net income of \$2240;

(e) the number of units that must be sold to make a net income of \$1050;

(f) the sales volume in dollars to suffer a loss of no more than \$350;

(g) the break-even point in units if fixed costs are increased to \$3150;

(h) the break-even point as a percentage of capacity if fixed costs are reduced by \$160 and the variable cost of manufacturing is increased to \$39 per unit;

(i) the break-even point in dollars if the selling price is reduced to \$100 per unit.

2. For question 3 in Part A of this exercise, determine

(a) the net income at 85% of capacity;

(b) the net income at 30% of capacity;

(c) the level of operations as a percentage of capacity to realize a net income of \$66 000;

(d) the level of operations in dollars to sustain a loss of no more than \$6600;

(e) the break-even point in dollars if fixed costs are increased by 15%;

(f) the break-even point as a percentage of capacity if fixed costs are decreased by \$18 400 and variable costs are increased to 52% of sales.

3. The lighting division of Universal Electric Company plans to introduce a new streetlight based on the following accounting information.

Fixed costs per period are \$3136; variable cost per unit is \$157; selling price per unit is \$185; and capacity per period is 320 units.

(a) Draw a detailed break-even chart.

(b) Compute the break-even point
(i) in units; (ii) as a percentage of capacity;
(iii) in dollars.

(c) Determine the net income at a sales volume of
(i) 25% of capacity; (ii) \$24 975.

(d) Determine the level of operations as a percentage of capacity to generate a net income of
(i) \$2240; (ii) \$6720.

(e) Determine the break-even point as a percentage of capacity
(i) if fixed costs are reduced to \$2688;
(ii) if fixed costs increase to \$4588 and variable costs are reduced to 80% of the selling price;
(iii) if the selling price is reduced to \$171.

4. The following information is available from the accounting records of Eva Corporation.

Fixed costs per period are \$4800; sales volume for the last period was \$19 360 and variable costs were \$13 552. Capacity per period is a sales volume of \$32 000.

(a) Draw a detailed break-even chart.

(b) Compute the break-even point
(i) in dollars; (ii) as a percentage of capacity.

(c) Determine the net income at a sales volume of
(i) \$24 000; (ii) 30% of capacity.

(d) Determine the level of operations as a percentage of capacity to generate a net income of \$3264.

(e) Determine the break-even point
(i) if fixed costs are decreased by \$600;
(ii) if fixed costs are increased to \$5670 and variable costs are changed to 55% of sales.

5. The operating budget of the Bea Company contains the following information.

Sales at 80% of capacity		\$400 000
Fixed costs	\$105 000	
Variable costs	260 000	365 000
Net Income		\$ 35 000

(a) Draw a detailed break-even chart.

(b) Compute the break-even point
(i) as a percentage of capacity; (ii) in dollars.

(c) Determine the net income at 40% of capacity.

(d) Determine the sales volume as a percentage of capacity to generate a net income of \$61 250.

(e) Determine the break-even point in dollars if fixed costs are reduced by \$11 200 while variable costs are changed to 72% of sales.

6. A manufacturer of major appliances provides the following information about the operations of the refrigeration division.

Fixed costs per period are \$26 880; variable costs per unit are \$360; selling price per unit is \$640; and capacity is 150 units.

(a) Compute the break-even point
(i) in units; (ii) as a percentage of capacity; (iii) in dollars.

(b) Determine the net income at a sales volume of
(i) \$78 080; (ii) 48% of capacity.

(c) Determine the volume of output as a percentage of capacity to generate a net income of \$4200.

(d) Determine the break-even point in dollars if fixed costs are increased to \$32 200.

(e) Determine the break-even point as a percentage of capacity if fixed costs are reduced to \$23 808 while variable costs are increased to 60% of sales.

7. The Superior Records Company sells albums for \$10 each. Manufacturing cost is \$2.60 per album; marketing costs are \$2.40 per album; and royalty payments are 20% of selling price. The fixed cost of preparing the albums is \$18 000. Capacity is 15 000 albums.

(a) Draw a detailed break-even chart.

(b) Compute the break-even point
(i) in units; (ii) in dollars; (iii) as a percentage of capacity.

(c) Determine the net income at a sales volume of 55% of capacity.

(d) Determine the sales volume in dollars to generate a net income of \$13 800.

(e) Determine the break-even point in units if fixed costs are increased by \$1600 while manufacturing cost is reduced \$0.50 per album.

(f) Determine the break-even point in units if the selling price is increased by 10% while fixed costs are increased by \$2900.

8. The management of Lambda Corporation has received the following forecast for the next year.

Sales Revenue		\$600 000
Fixed costs	\$275 000	
Variable costs	270 000	545 000
Net Income		\$ 55 000

Capacity is a sales volume of \$800 000.

(a) Compute the break-even point
(i) in dollars; (ii) as a percentage of capacity.

(b) Determine the net income at 50% of capacity.

(c) Determine the sales volume in dollars to generate a net income of \$82 500.

(d) Determine the break-even volume in dollars if fixed costs are increased by \$40 000 while variables costs are held to 40% of sales.

9. The Peel Credit Union is organizing a charter flight to Bermuda for the March break. A package deal requires a fixed payment of \$9900 plus \$325 per person. The credit union intends to price the one-week package at \$550 per person to cover the cost of flight, accommodation, meals, and tips. With a charge of \$550 per person, the credit union estimates that the smallest number of participants would be 30 and the greatest number would be 70. If the price of the package is reduced to \$475 per person, the minimum number of participants is expected to be 50 and the maximum number 120.

(a) How many participants are needed to break even
(i) at \$550 per person? (ii) at \$475 per person?

(b) What is the variation between the maximum and the minimum expected profit
(i) at \$550 per person? (ii) at \$457 per person?

10. The student senate of the college is planning the annual convocation dinner dance. Rental of facilities is \$2000 and the local rock group can be hired for \$660 plus 10% of gate receipts. Meal costs are \$26 per couple. The senate expects to set a price of \$40 per couple. At that price, estimated minimum ticket sales are 180 and maximum ticket sales are 400. The treasurer argues that the price should be set at \$50 per couple at which price minimum sales are estimated at 100 tickets and maximum sales at 300.

(a) What is the number of couples that must buy tickets to break even at
(i) \$40 per couple? (ii) \$50 per couple?

(b) What is the variation between the maximum and the minimum expected profit
(i) at \$40 per couple? (ii) at \$50 per couple?

11. Eden Motels plan to build a motel complex that consists of 500 economy units, 300 deluxe units, and 200 luxury units. Rent is \$40 per night for economy units, \$60 per night for deluxe units, and \$90 per night for luxury units. The complex will be open year round and occupancy of the units is expected to be approximately proportional to the number of units of each type—that is, for every five economy units, three deluxe units and two luxury units will be rented. Annual fixed cost of the complex is estimated at \$4 489 500 while variable cost per night is \$15 per unit.

(a) At what percent occupancy level will the motel complex break even?

(b) How many units must be rented on average per night to generate an annual profit of \$2 993 000?

12. One type of insecticide costs retailers \$4.00 per package. The normal retail margin is 50% based on the retailer's cost. Total consumer spending on the product is expected to be \$9 600 000. The insecticide is sold to retailers by wholesale distributors at a margin of 25% of the wholesale selling price.

Chemie Inc. has developed a competing product to be marketed under the brand name Bio-Kill. Market research indicates that Chemie Inc. will be able to sell the product to wholesalers at the same price charged by manufacturers of the first product to wholesalers. Chemie's variable costs are estimated to be $33\frac{1}{3}\%$ of Chemie's selling price and fixed costs for the first year of production are estimated to be \$400 000. What market share must Bio-Kill attain for Chemie Inc. to break even on the product?

II.2 *Linear programming—the two-product case*

A. Basic concepts

Linear programming is a mathematical technique that helps managers make the best use of a firm's economic resources which are in limited supply, such as money, material, labour, machinery, space, etc. These limited resources have to be allocated among competing uses so as to maximize profits or minimize costs.

A typical problem of this type is the case of a manufacturer who produces four different products. Each requires a specified amount of time in each of five processes. In each of the five processes, only a limited number of hours are available per time period. Furthermore, the profit per unit of output is different for each of the five products.

The problem that must be solved requires optimizing output with the available resources. The optimal output in this context is the number of units of each product that should be produced to maximize the total profit.

Linear programming problems are of differing complexity. Simple linear programming problems involving two products only can be solved using two-dimensional graphs; multi-product problems require the use of more advanced algebraic techniques.

In this text, we are concerned only with introducing the concept of linear programming and solving the simplest cases. To deal with the two-product case graphically, we will take the following approach.

1. State the problem in algebraic terms.
   (a) Represent the number of units of each product by X_1 and X_2 respectively and organize the data in the form of a chart.
   (b) State the **objective function** in equation form. The objective function is a mathematical presentation of the goal to be achieved—either a profit to be maximized or a cost to be minimized.
   (c) List the **operational constraints** imposed on the objective function. The operational constraints state that the total amount of each type of economic resource used has to be consistent with the available amount of each resource.
   (d) List the **non-negative constraints**. These constraints state that X_1 and X_2 cannot be *less* than zero; that is, the number of units produced cannot be negative.
2. Graphically represent the algebraic relationships.
   (a) Represent the constraints graphically in a two-dimensional system of rectangular axes to obtain the **area of feasibility**. This area contains all points (X_1, X_2) that represent the *possible* combinations of X_1 and X_2 which can be produced consistent with the availability of the resources.
   (b) Introduce graphs of the objective function to identify the **optimal point**. The optimal point is the point (X_1, X_2) for which the profit will be maximized or the cost will be minimized. If a single solution exists, the optimal point is *always* a corner point on the boundary of the area of feasibility.
3. Algebraically determine the coordinates of the optimal point to find the optimal solution and the value of the objective function at that point.

B. Graphic solution

***Example* II.2a** A manufacturer markets two products. Each unit of Product A requires three hours in the molding department, four hours in the paint shop, and one hour in finishing. Each unit of Product B requires three hours in molding, two hours in painting, and two hours in finishing. Each week 210 hours are available in molding, 200 hours in painting, and 120 hours in finishing. Shipping can handle no more than 40 units of Product A per week. Each unit of Product A contributes $20 to profit while each unit of product B contributes $30. Determine how many units of each product should be manufactured per week to maximize profit.

Solution

STEP 1 **Algebraic statement of problem**

(a) Let the number of units of Product A be represented by X_1; let the number of units of Product B be represented by X_2.

	Data Summary		
	Resource quantity per unit for		*Available resource quantity*
Constraints	*Product A*	*Product B*	
1. Molding	3	3	210
2. Painting	4	2	200
3. Finishing	1	2	120
4. Shipping	1	N/A	40
Profit	$20	$30	Maximize

(b) *The objective function*
The goal is to maximize profit. The value of the total profit can be represented by P. For Product A the profit is $20 per unit or $\$20X_1$. For Product B the profit is $30 per unit or $\$30X_2$. The total profit is $20X_1 + 30X_2$. The objective function is $P = 20X_1 + 30X_2$ with X_1 and X_2 to be chosen so that P becomes as large as possible.

(c) *The operational constraints*
Production in the given situation depends on limited resources; the availability of time in the molding department, in the paint shop, and in finishing, as well as the ability of shipping to handle Product A.

Each constraint on the operations of the business can be expressed algebraically by relating the resource requirements per unit of product to the total resource available.

Each unit of Product A requires 3 hours in the molding department as does each unit of Product B. The total time used in the molding department to manufacture the two products must be less than or at most equal to 210 hours per week.

$$3X_1 + 3X_2 \leqq 210$$

Similarly with respect to the paint shop,

$$4X_1 + 2X_2 \leqq 200$$

and with respect to finishing,

$$X_1 + 2X_1 \leqq 120$$

As far as shipping is concerned, the total number of units of Product A must be less than or equal to 40.

$$X_1 \leqq 40$$

(d) *The non-negative constraints*
The minimum number of units of each product that can be produced is zero. This fact is represented by the inequalities $X_1 \geqq 0$ and $X_2 \geqq 0$, called the non-negative constraints.

(e) *General form of a linear programming problem*
The problem is now stated in the general form of a linear programming problem consisting of three parts.

(i) The objective function $\quad P = 20X_1 + 30X_2$

(ii) The operational constraints

1. Molding	$3X_1 + 3X_2 \leqq 210$
2. Painting	$4X_1 + 2X_2 \leqq 200$
3. Finishing	$X_1 + 2X_2 \leqq 120$
4. Shipping	$X_1 \leqq 40$

(iii) The non-negative constraints $\quad X_1 \geqq 0$, $\quad X_2 \geqq 0$

STEP 2 Graphic representation of the algebraic relationships

(a) *Preliminary considerations*

(i) The non-negative constraints

Use a set of rectangular axes with the horizontal axis representing values of X_1 and the vertical axis representing values of X_2. The constraint $X_1 \geqq 0$

describes the region to the right of the vertical axis while the constraint $X_2 \geqq 0$ describes the region above the horizontal axis.

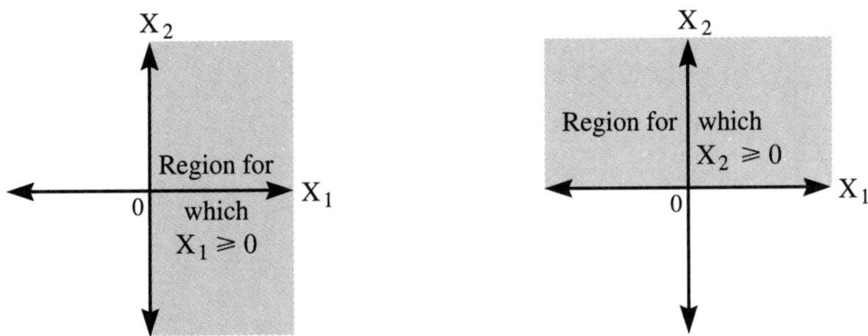

The region for which both conditions hold ($X_1 \geqq 0$ and $X_2 \geqq 0$) is the first quadrant. This is true for all linear programming problems.

(ii) Graphic representation of the objective function

The objective function may be represented graphically for various profit levels by assuming specific values for P.

Let $P_1 = 1500$.

Then the specific objective function becomes

$$20X_1 + 30X_2 = 1500$$

For $X_1 = 0 \longrightarrow X_2 = 50 \longrightarrow$ Graph point A(0, 50)
For $X_2 = 0 \longrightarrow X_1 = 75 \longrightarrow$ Graph point B(75, 0)

The line AB (see Figure II.6) joining the two points represents all combinations for which the profit is \$1500.

(0, 50) $\longrightarrow$ 0 units of Product A and 50 units of Product B
(75, 0) $\longrightarrow$ 75 units of Product A and 0 units of Product B
(45, 20) $\longrightarrow$ 45 units of Product A and 20 units of Product B
(15, 40) $\longrightarrow$ 15 units of Product A and 40 units of Product B

Let $P_2 = 3000$.

Then the specific objective function becomes

$$20X_1 + 30X_2 = 3000$$

For $X_1 = 0 \longrightarrow X_2 = 100 \longrightarrow$ Graph point C(0, 100)
For $X_2 = 0 \longrightarrow X_1 = 150 \longrightarrow$ Graph point D(150, 0)

The line CD joining the two points represents all combinations (X_1, X_2) for which the profit is \$3000.

Similarly, additional lines may be drawn for any convenient profit figure such as $P_3 = 4500$ (see line EF in Figure II.6) and $P_4 = 6000$ (see line GH).

FIGURE II.6 ***Graphic representation of the objective function***

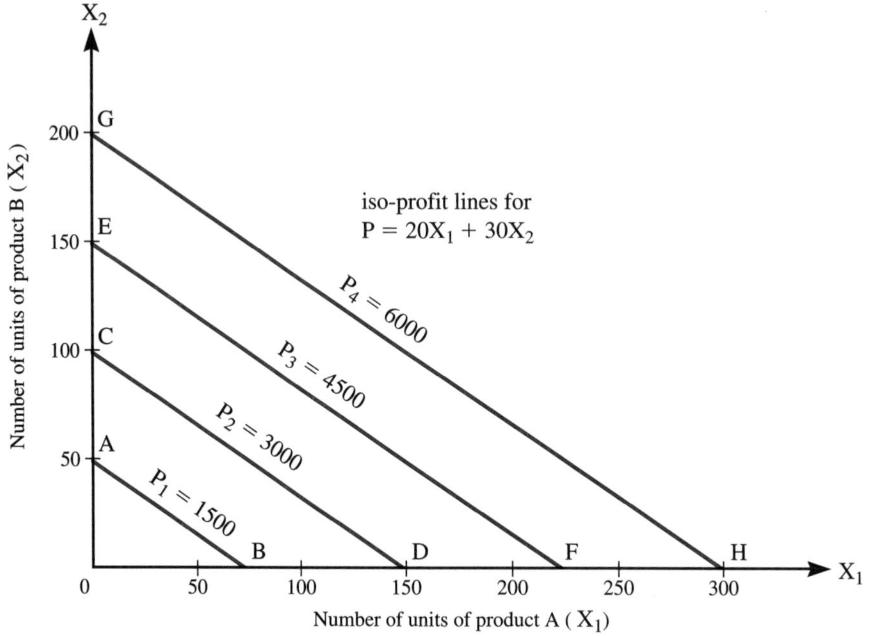

Note:

1. Each profit level results in a specific profit line. Since X_1 and X_2 cannot be negative the lines are not extended across the two axes.
2. The various combinations of X_1 and X_2 that satisfy the equation of a particular profit will be points on the line and will produce the same amount of profit. Such lines are called **iso-profit lines**.
3. The various iso-profit lines have the same slope and run parallel to each other. All the possible iso-profit lines for a particular objective function represent a family of parallel lines.
4. The total profit represented by each iso-profit line increases with increasing distance of the line from the origin.
5. The parallel nature of the iso-profit lines and the increase in profit with the increase in distance from the origin is of crucial importance in locating the optimal point graphically.

(iii) Graphing the operational constraints

Each constraint involves an inequality that, when graphed, represents a region called the area of feasibility for the resource represented by the inequality. Each inequality can be graphed by first graphing the associated equality and testing for the region.

For the molding department, the inequality $3X_1 + 3X_2 \leqq 210$ is associated with the equation $3X_1 + 3X_2 = 210$.

For $X_1 = 0, X_2 = 70 \longrightarrow$ Graph the point F(0, 70)
For $X_2 = 0, X_1 = 70 \longrightarrow$ Graph the point G(70, 0)

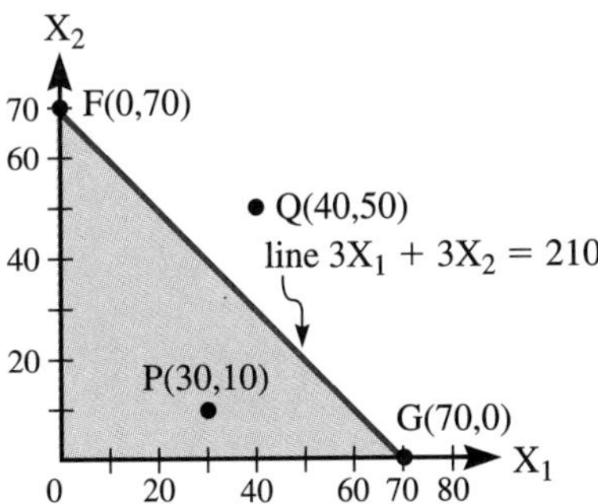

Test the point (0, 0)

$3X_1 + 3X_2 = 3(0) + 3(0) = 0 \leqq 210$

Since the coordinates (0, 0) satisfy the inequality, the point (0, 0) is a point in the region described by the inequality. Therefore, the region described by $3X_1 + 3X_2 \leqq 210$ is the area to the left of the line $3X_1 + 3X_2 = 210$. However, since X_1 and X_2 cannot be negative, the combinations (X_1, X_2) that are feasible are represented by the points inside the triangle OFG as shown in the diagram.

The point P(30, 10) lies inside the triangle OFG indicating that the combination (30, 10) is possible. The coordinates (30, 10) indicate a combination of 30 units of Product A and 10 units of Product B.

To produce 30 units of Product A requires 3(30) = 90 hours in molding; to produce 10 units of Product B requires 3(10) = 30 hours in molding. The combination requires a total of 120 hours in molding—less than the 210 hours available. The combination 30 units of Product A and 10 units of Product B is feasible.

The point Q (40, 50), representing a production of 40 units of Product A and 50 units of Product B, lies outside the area of feasibility. This combination is not possible.

To produce 40 units of Product A requires 3(40) = 120 hours in molding; to produce 50 units of Product B requires 3(50) = 150 hours in molding. The combination requires a total of 270 hours in molding; since only 210 hours are available, the combination 40 units of Product A and 50 units of Product B is not feasible.

For the paint shop, the inequality $4X_1 + 2X_2 \leqq 200$ is associated with the equation $4X_1 + 2X_2 = 200$.

For $X_1 = 0, X_2 = 100 \longrightarrow$ Graph point H(0, 100)
For $X_2 = 0, X_1 = 50 \longrightarrow$ Graph point J(50, 0)

The area of feasibility for the paint shop is the triangle OHJ as shown in the diagram below.

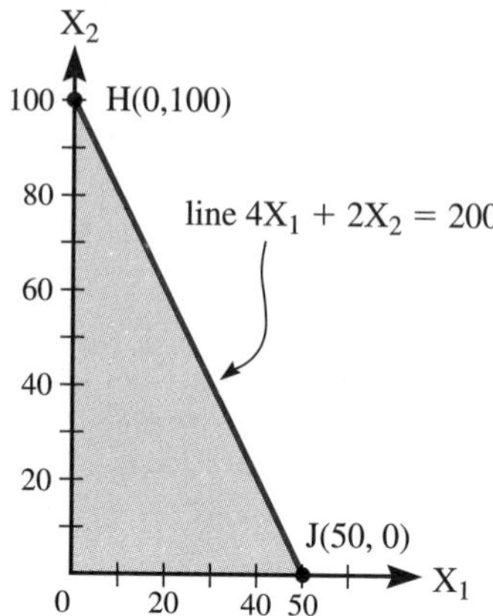

The area of feasibility for finishing, defined by the inequality $X_1 + 2X_2 \leqq 120$ and the non-negative constraints, is the triangle OAK as shown in the diagram below.

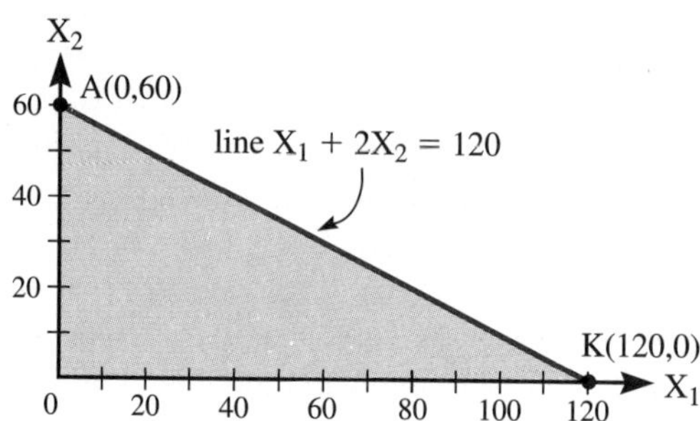

Finally, the area of feasibility for shipping, defined by the inequality $X_1 \leqq 40$ and the non-negative constraints, is the area between the X_2 axis and the line represented by $X_1 = 40$ as shown below.

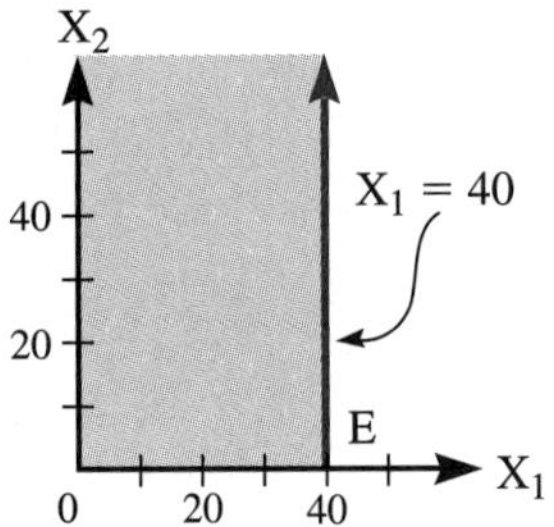

(b) *Graphing the area of feasibility*

The area of feasibility for the combined resources is the area containing the points that satisfy all operational constraints. This area is found by graphing the individual constraints on the same set of axes (see Figure II.7). For molding and painting combined, the area of feasibility is the intersection of the two triangles OFG and OHJ, that is, the area OFCJ as shown below.

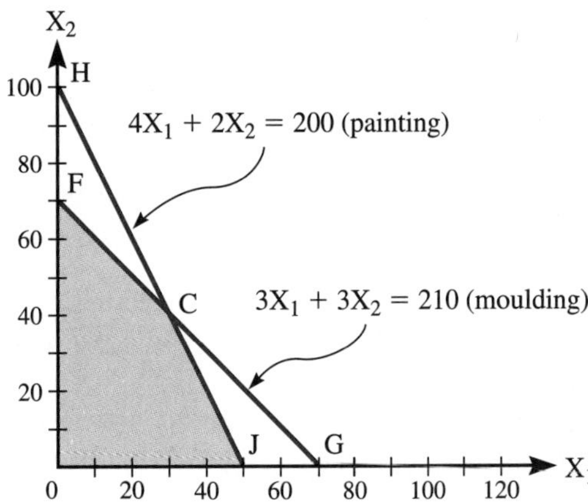

For molding, painting, and finishing combined, the area of feasibility is the area OABCJ as shown below.

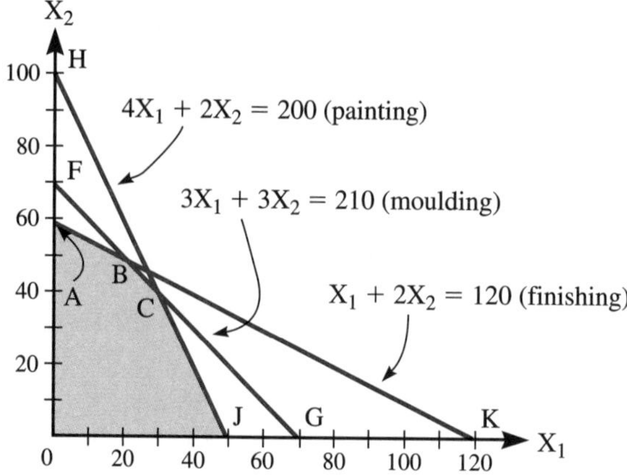

When shipping is also considered, the area of feasibility is reduced to the area OABCDE as shown in Figure II.7.

FIGURE II.7 ***Area of feasibility***

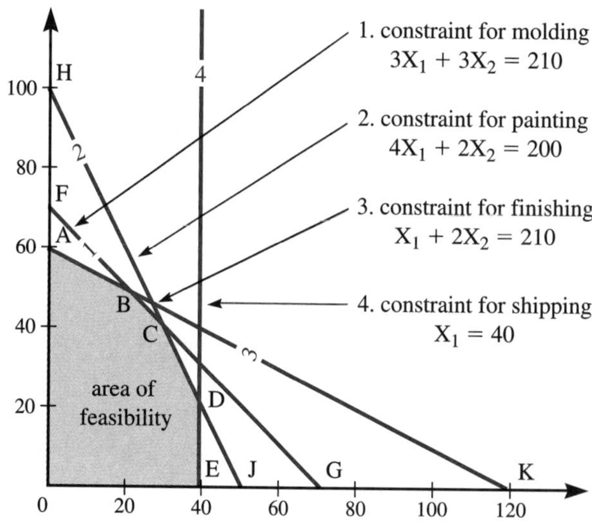

(c) *Locating the optimal point*

Once we have determined the area of feasibility by graphing the operational constraints, we need to locate the optimal point—the point whose coordinates are the combination (X_1, X_2) which generates the maximum profit. This is done by introducing graphs of the objective function $P = 20X_1 + 30X_2$ by the method previously explained.

In this case, a convenient value of P = \$1500.

For $X_1 = 0 \longrightarrow X_2 = 50 \longrightarrow$ Graph point S(0, 50).
For $X_2 = 0 \longrightarrow X_1 = 75 \longrightarrow$ Graph point T(75, 0).

Draw the profit line ST (see Figure II.8).

Part of the iso-profit line ST passes through the area of feasibility. Any combination (X_1, X_2) that represents the coordinates of a point on this line provides a profit of \$1500.

The line ST is one of the family of parallel lines defined by the equation $P = 20X_1 + 30X_2$. Some of the lines represent a profit lower than \$1500, others a profit greater than \$1500, depending on whether such lines are closer to the origin or farther away from the origin.

For example, a line parallel to ST through the point A(0, 60)—see Figure II.8—yields a profit of

$$P = 20(0) + 30(60) = 0 + 1800 = \$1800.$$

This particular iso-profit line passes through the area of feasibility and any combination of (X_1, X_2) falling on this line generates a profit of \$1800.

FIGURE II.8 ***Locating the optimal point***

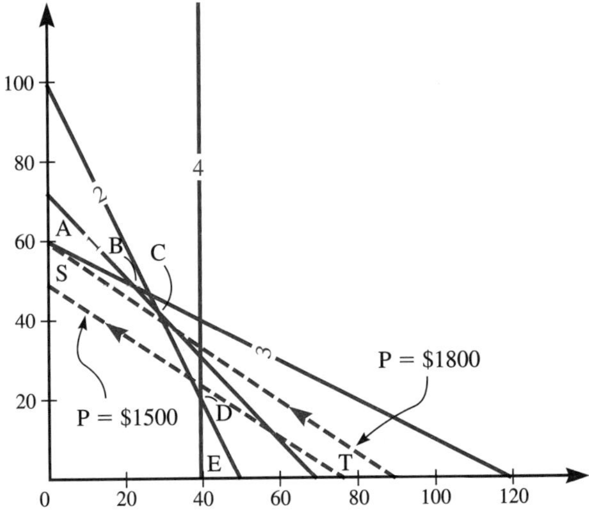

As long as a profit line passes through the area of feasibility OABCDE and is farther away from the origin, it will generate a profit higher than that which is obtainable from a profit line closer to the origin. However, for profit lines that do not pass through the area of feasibility, any combination (X_1, X_2) which represents a point on such a line does not satisfy all the constraints and is thus not attainable.

Therefore, the profit line that will generate the greatest possible profit is the line located farthest away from the origin such that at least one point on the line is still within the area of feasibility OABCDE.

When considering possible lines parallel to the two profit lines drawn in Figure II.8, it becomes apparent that the profit line farthest from the origin that still passes through the area OABCDE is a line drawn through the point B. The point B must be the optimal point representing the combination (X_1, X_2) for which the profit is the maximum amount attainable with the given combination of resources.

Note: The optimal point is a point on the boundary of the area of feasibility. This location is generally true for any linear programming problem.

STEP 3 **Finding the optimal combination (X_1, X_2) and the maximum amount of profit**

The coordinates of point B represent the number of units of Product A and Product B that should be produced to maximize the profit. This combination (X_1, X_2) provides for optimal utilization of the available resources; it can be found algebraically by solving the system of equations representing the two lines that form the point B.

From Figure II.7, it is apparent that point B is formed by the intersection of Line AK, represented by $X_1 + 2X_2 = 120$, and Line FG, represented by $3X_1 + 3X_2 = 210$.

Equation ① $\longrightarrow X_1 + 2X_2 = 120$
Equation ② $\longrightarrow 3X_1 + 3X_2 = 210$

To eliminate X_1,

multiply ① by 3 $\longrightarrow 3X_1 + 6X_2 = 360$
subtract ② $\longrightarrow 3X_1 + 3X_2 = 210$

$$3X_2 = 150$$
$$X_2 = 50$$

To find X_1, substitute $50 = X_2$ in ①

$$X_1 + 2(50) = 120$$
$$X_1 + 100 = 120$$
$$X_1 = 20$$

The solution to the system is $(X_1, X_2) = (20, 50)$.

For $(X_1, X_2) = (20, 50)$,
$P = 20X_1 + 30X_2 = 20(20) + 30(50) = 400 + 1500 = 1900.$

The optimal production is 20 units of Product A and 50 units of Product B for a maximum profit of $1900.

Note: The available resources are used as follows.

Molding $3X_1 + 3X_2 = 3(20) + 3(50) = 60 + 150 = 210$
Since the maximum time in molding is 210 hours, molding capacity is totally used.

Painting $4X_1 + 2X_2 = 4(20) + 2(50) = 80 + 100 = 180$
Since the maximum available time is 200 hours, 20 hours are unused.

Finishing $X_1 + 2X_2 = 20 + 2(50) = 20 + 100 = 120$
Since the maximum available time is 120 hours, finishing capacity is totally used.

Shipping $X_1 = 20$. Since capacity is 40 units, 50% of shipping's capability to handle Product A is used.

***Example* II.2b** A company makes two kinds of boots. X_1 is top quality; X_2 is ordinary quality. Producing top quality boots takes twice as long as ordinary quality. If only ordinary quality boots are made, 3000 pairs of boots can be made per week. Enough material is available to make 2400 pairs of boots. The top quality boots require a special zipper and enough zippers are available for 1100 pairs per week. Ordinary zippers are available to make 2200 ordinary pairs per week. Top quality boots give a profit of \$32 per pair and ordinary quality boots give a profit of \$24 per pair. Use the graphic method of linear programming to find the optimal production mix, the total contribution to profit of this mix, and the use of the available resources.

Solution

	Resource quantity required per pair of boots		*Available resource quantity*
Constraints	*Top quality*	*Ordinary quality*	
1. Time units	2	1	3000
2. Material	1	1	2400
3. Special zipper	1	N/A	1100
4. Ordinary zipper	N/A	1	2200
PROFIT	\$32	\$24	MAXIMIZE

STEP 1 **Statement of problem in algebraic form**

(a) Objective function $P = 32X_1 + 24X_2$

(b) Operational constraints
1. $2X_1 + X_2 \leqq 3000$
2. $X_1 + X_2 \leqq 2400$
3. $X_1 \leqq 1100$
4. $X_2 \leqq 2200$

(c) Non-negative constraints $X_1 \geqq 0;\ X_2 \geqq 0$

STEP 2 **Graphic solution**

Area OABCDE is the area of feasibility. The optimal point is C.

FIGURE II.9 ***Graphic solution***

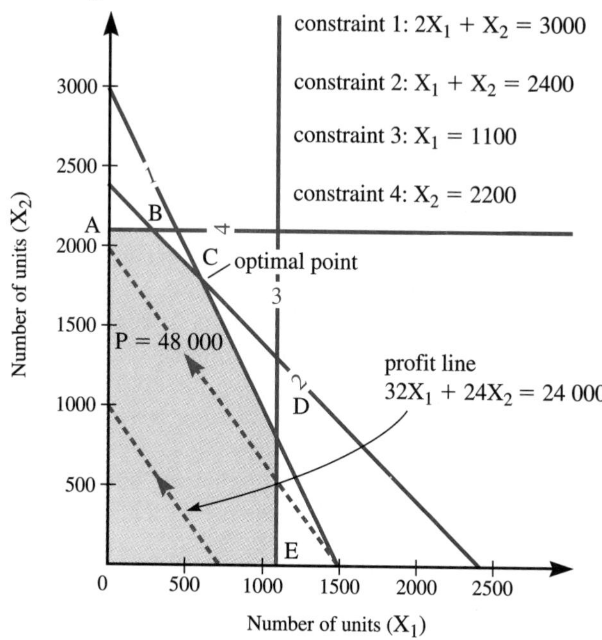

STEP 3 **Conclusion**

The optimal point C is formed by the intersection of

Constraint ①	⟶	$2X_1 + X_2 = 3000$ and
Constraint ②	⟶	$X_1 + X_2 = 2400$
subtract	⟶	$X_1 = 600$
		$X_2 = 1800$

The coordinates of the optimal point are (600, 1800).

The optimal solution requires producing 600 pairs of top quality boots and 1800 pairs of ordinary quality boots.

The maximum profit that can be generated is

$$P = 32(600) + 24(1800) = 19\ 200 + 43\ 200 = \$62\ 400$$

Resource use for the optimal production is as follows:

1. Time used — 2(600) + 1800 = 3000; since 3000 time units are available, time capacity is totally used.
2. Material — 600 + 1800 = 2400; since material for 2400 pairs is available, the supply of material is totally used.
3. Special zippers — 600 pairs used; 1100 pairs available; 500 pairs unused.
4. Ordinary zippers — 1800 pairs used; 2200 pairs available; 400 pairs unused.

Exercise II.2

A. Solve each of the following linear programming problems. Show in your answer

(a) an algebraic statement of the problem;

(b) a graph of the area of feasibility showing the optimal point;

(c) an algebraic computation of the optimal solution including the amount of profit and utilization of the resources.

1. A manufacturer produces two products. Product A contributes \$7 per unit to profit and Product B contributes \$5 per unit. The manufacturing process requires time on each of three machines. Product A requires eight hours on Machine I, two hours on Machine II, and four hours on Machine III. Product B requires five hours on each of Machines I and II, and six hours on Machine III. Machine I is available for 4200 hours, Machine II for 2000 hours, and Machine III for 2800 hours.

2. Swim Quip has production facilities for assembling and distributing residential pool heaters and pool filters. The facilities consist of departments for subassembly, final assembly, finishing, and testing. Each filter requires twelve hours in subassembly, two hours in final assembly, and one hour in finishing. Each heater requires thirty-six hours in subassembly, 3.2 hours in final assembly, four hours in finishing, and two hours in testing. Capacity is 3600 hours in subassembly, 480 hours in final assembly, 324 hours in finishing, and 100 hours in testing. Each filter contributes \$60 to profit whereas each heater contributes \$180 to profit.

B. Solve each of the following problems.

1. A manufacturer produces two types of product. Product A requires 3 units of material, 1 unit of time in fabricating, and 1 unit of time in finishing. Product B requires 1 unit of material, 3 units of time in fabricating, and 1 unit of time in finishing. Maximum daily resources are 24 units of material, 30 units of time in fabricating, and 12 units of time in finishing. Product A contributes \$30 per unit to profit while Product B contributes \$40 per unit.

   (a) State the problem in algebraic form.

   (b) Graphically solve the problem.

   (c) Find the optimal solution algebraically and determine the maximum profit.

   (d) Determine the utilization of resources for the optimal solution.

2. A manufacturer makes two types of brackets. Brackets of both types are formed in Department A from a piece of steel of which 750 are available for the time period. Each ordinary bracket requires four time units in Department A while each fancy bracket requires ten time units. The total number of time units available in Department A for the time period is 4800. The ordinary bracket is finished in Department B and requires four time units while the fancy bracket is finished in Department C and requires six time units. 2400 time units are available in each of the two finishing departments. The ordinary bracket contributes \$4 to profit and the fancy bracket contributes \$6.

(a) State the problem in algebraic form.

(b) Graphically solve the problem.

(c) Find the optimal solution algebraically and give the maximum profit and the utilization of the manufacturing facilities.

3. The Debris Company intends to market two types of containers. Each square container costs the company \$20 and each round container costs \$30. Each square container occupies 20 square units of floor space while each round container occupies 10 square units. \$12 000 is available per period to buy containers of either type and 8000 units of floor space is available to store them. Each container weighs 100 kg and the floor of the storage room will not support more than 45 000 kg. Each square container contributes \$30 to profit while each round container contributes \$20. Demand is such that no more than 350 round containers can be sold. Using the graphic method of linear programming, find the optimum product mix, the total contribution to profit of this mix, and the utilization of resources.

Summary of formulae used

Formula II.1

$TR = TC + NI$

TOTAL REVENUE = TOTAL COST + NET INCOME

Formula II.2

$TR = (X)(P)$

TOTAL REVENUE = VOLUME IN UNITS × UNIT REVENUE

Formula II.3

$TC = FC + TVC$

TOTAL COST = FIXED COST + TOTAL VARIABLE COST

Formula II.4

$TVC = (X)(VC)$

TOTAL VARIABLE COST = VOLUME IN UNITS × VARIABLE COST PER UNIT

Formula II.5

$TR = FC + TVC + NI$

TOTAL REVENUE = FIXED COST + TOTAL VARIABLE COST + NET INCOME

Glossary of terms used

Area of feasibility in a linear programming graph, the area containing all the points (X_1, X_2) that represent the possible combinations in the product mix

Break-even analysis a method of determining the level of output at which a business neither makes a profit nor sustains a loss

Break-even chart a graphic representation of cost-volume-profit relationships used to identify the break-even point

Break-even point the level of output at which net income is zero

Cost function an algebraic expression stating the relationship between cost and volume

Fixed costs costs that remain constant for the time period for all levels of output considered

Iso-profit line the line representing the various possible combinations in the product mix that yield the same amount of profit

Linear programming a mathematical technique used to determine the optimal allocation of limited resources

Non-negative constraints algebraic expressions stating that the variables used are limited to positive values

Objective function an algebraic representation of the goal to be achieved in a linear programming problem

Operational constraints an algebraic representation of the limitations imposed on operations because of the limited availability of various resources

Optimal point the point whose coordinates represent the product mix at which the profit is maximized or the cost minimized

Revenue function an algebraic expression representing the behaviour of revenue

Variable costs costs that are constant per unit of output regardless of volume; they fluctuate in total amount as volume fluctuates

Appendix III

Finding the rate of interest (i) *without preprogramming*

III.1 *Finding the conversion rate* i *for simple annuities*

A. *Finding the conversion rate* i *without preprogramming when the amount of a simple annuity is known*

Finding the periodic rate of interest when S_n, R, and n are known is a rather awkward problem. Substituting the known values in Formula 11.1 or the general solution of the formula for i results in an exponential equation that is difficult to solve.

For example, if $S_n = 25\,000.00$, $R = 500.00$, and $n = 32$, the substitution in Formula 11.1 gives

$$25\,000.00 = 500.00\left(\frac{[(1 + i)^{32} - 1]}{i}\right)$$

$$50.00 = \frac{[(1 + i)^{32} - 1]}{i}$$

$$50.00i = (1 + i)^{32} - 1$$

$$(1 + i)^{32} - 50.00i - 1 = 0$$

However, instead of trying to solve the equation, the value of i can be found by using an approximation method based on trial and error. A value for i is arbitrarily selected and the compounding factor $\frac{(1 + i)^n - 1}{i}$ is computed. The numerical value of the factor indicates whether the rate to be found is more or less than the selected rate. The process of choosing a rate, computing the compounding factor, and comparing this factor with the actual compounding factor is repeated until an approximation sufficiently close to the actual rate is obtained.

To avoid writing the accumulation factor repeatedly, the factor $\frac{(1+i)^n - 1}{i}$ is represented by the symbol $s_{\overline{n}|\,i}$ (read "*s* angle *n* at *i*").

$$\frac{(1+i)^n - 1}{i} = s_{\overline{n}|\,i}$$

$$S_n = Rs_{\overline{n}|\,i}$$

***Example* III.1a** Find the nominal rate of interest at which \$200.00 deposited at the end of each quarter for fifteen years will amount to \$20 000.00.

Solution

$$S_n = 20\,000.00; \quad R = 200.00; \quad n = 15(4) = 60$$

$$s_{\overline{n}|\,i} = \frac{(1+i)^{60} - 1}{i} = \frac{20\,000}{200} = 100.0000$$

We want to find the quarterly rate i for which the accumulation factor $s_{\overline{60}|\,i} =$ 100.0000. The first selection of i should allow for a reasonable range within which the nominal rate might be expected to fall. For most practical purposes, this range is 6% to 20%. Thus, we will try 12% as our initial selection.

$$\text{Try } i = \frac{12\%}{4} = 3\% = 0.03.$$

$$s_{\overline{60}|\,3\%} = \frac{(1.03)^{60} - 1}{0.03} = 163.05344$$

Since $s_{\overline{60}|\,3\%} = 163.05344$ is greater than $s_{\overline{60}|\,i} = 100.0000$, the selected rate of 3% is greater than the actual rate i. The actual nominal rate must be less than 12%.

We must now choose a second selection for i. This selection should allow for the relationship between the value of the actual compounding factor and the factor computed for the first selected value of i. It should preferably result in a compounding factor smaller than 100.00. A considerable drop in rate is indicated since $s_{\overline{60}|\,3\%}$ is considerably greater than $s_{\overline{60}|\,i}$.

Try a nominal rate of 6% where $i = 1.5\% = 0.015$.
$s_{\overline{60}|\,1.5\%} = 96.214651$
This means $s_{\overline{60}|\,1.5\%} < s_{\overline{60}|\,i}$, that is, $i > 1.5\%$.

By now we know that $1.5\% < i < 3\%$. The nominal rate lies between 6% and 12%. Furthermore, because of the closeness of $s_{\overline{60}|\,1.5\%}$ to $s_{\overline{60}|\,i}$, the actual nominal rate must be much closer to 6% than to 12%.

Try a nominal rate of 7% where $i = 1.75\% = 0.0175$.
$s_{\overline{60}|\,1.75\%} = 104.67522$
$1.5\% < i < 1.75\%$ and $6\% < \text{nominal rate} < 7\%$.

For a closer approximation, further rates can be used. In doing so, pay attention to the size of the computed accumulation factors relative to the actual accumulation factor.

For $i = 1.6\%$, $s_{\overline{60|}\,1.6\%} = 99.495336 \longrightarrow i > 1.6\%$

For $i = 1.62\%$, $s_{\overline{60|}\,1.62\%} = 100.16772 \longrightarrow i < 1.62\%$

For $i = 1.61\%$, $s_{\overline{60|}\,1.61\%} = 99.830835 \longrightarrow i > 1.61\%$

$1.61\% < i < 1.62\%$

$i = 1.615\%$ approximately

$6.44\% <$ nominal rate of interest $< 6.48\%$

The nominal rate of interest is 6.46% approximately.

Programmed solution

0	20 000	200	60				
PV	FV	PMT	N	CPT	%i	(Please wait)	1.6150267
		(or −200)					

The accuracy of the approximation becomes apparent when comparing the answer with the precise computed value of 1.6150267% or a nominal rate of 6.4601068%.

***Example* III.1b** A debt of $4000.00 is due in two years. An agreement was made whereby the debt could be paid off by making monthly payments of $145.00 at the end of each month for the next two years. What is the nominal rate of interest allowed on the payments?

Solution

$$S_n = 4000.00; \quad R = 145.00; \quad n = 24$$

$$s_{\overline{24|}\,i} = \frac{4000.00}{145.00} = 27.586207$$

Try a nominal rate of 12%. $i = 1\% = 0.01$

$s_{\overline{24|}\,1\%} = 26.973465 \longrightarrow i > 1\%$

Try a nominal rate of 18%. $i = 1.5\% = 0.015$

$s_{\overline{24|}\,1.5\%} = 28.633520 \longrightarrow 1\% < i < 1.5\%$

Try a nominal rate of 15%. $i = 1.25\% = 0.0125$

$s_{\overline{24|}\,1.25\%} = 27.788083 \longrightarrow 1\% < i < 1.25\%$

For $i = 1.15\%$, $s_{\overline{24|}\,1.15\%} = 27.458606 \longrightarrow 1.15\% < i < 1.25\%$

For $i = 1.19\%$, $s_{\overline{24|}\,1.19\%} = 27.589811 \longrightarrow i = 1.19\%$ approximately

The nominal rate of interest is approximately 14.28%.

Programmed solution

0	4000	145	24			
PV	FV	PMT	N	CPT	%i	1.1889046
		(or −145)				

The more precise computed value of i = 1.1889046% or a nominal rate of 14.266855%.

B. *Finding the conversion rate* i *without preprogramming when the present value of a simple annuity is known*

When A_n, R, and n are known, the periodic rate of interest can be found by a method similar to the one used for finding the rate of interest when S_n is known. The only difference is that the present value factor $\frac{1-(1+i)^{-n}}{i}$ is to be approximated.

To avoid writing the present value factor repeatedly, the factor $\frac{1-(1+i)^{-n}}{i}$ is represented by the symbol $a_{\overline{n}|\,i}$ (read "a angle n at i").

$$\frac{1-(1+i)^{-n}}{i} = a_{\overline{n}|\,i}$$

$$A_n = Ra_{\overline{n}|\,i}$$

However, take care to allow for the fact that the value of $a_{\overline{n}|\,i}$ is inversely related to i; that is, the greater i, the smaller will be $a_{\overline{n}|\,i}$.

Example **III.1c** What is the nominal rate of interest on a loan of $5000.00 repaid by payments of $425.00 made at the end of each quarter for four years?

Solution

$$A_n = 5000.00; \quad R = 425.00; \quad n = 16$$

$$a_{\overline{n}|\,i} = \frac{1-(1+i)^{-n}}{i} = \frac{A_n}{R}$$

$$a_{\overline{16}|\,i} = \frac{5000.00}{425.00} = 11.764706$$

For a nominal rate of 12%, i = 3% and $a_{\overline{16}|\,3\%} = 12.561102$.
Since $a_{\overline{16}|\,3\%} > a_{\overline{16}|\,i}$, $3\% < i$ due to the inverse relationship between $a_{\overline{n}|\,i}$ and i. Therefore, the next attempt should involve a rate *greater* than 3%.

For $i = 4\%$, $a_{\overline{16}|\,4\%} = 11.652296 \longrightarrow 3\% < i < 4\%$
For $i = 3.8\%$, $a_{\overline{16}|\,3.8\%} = 11.826111 \longrightarrow 3.8\% < i < 4\%$
For $i = 3.9\%$, $a_{\overline{16}|\,3.9\%} = 11.738726 \longrightarrow 3.8\% < i < 3.9\%$
For $i = 3.87\%$, $a_{\overline{16}|\,3.87\%} = 11.764841$

Thus, i = 3.87% (approximately) and the nominal rate is 15.48%.

Programmed solution

0	5000	425	16			
FV	PV	PMT	N	CPT	%*i*	3.870155

The more precise computed value of $i = 3.870155\%$ or a nominal rate of 15.48062%.

Example **III.1d** A car can be bought for \$8240.00 plus GST of 7%. A financing plan is available requiring a down payment of \$800.00 and monthly instalments of \$256.00 for three and a half years. What is the nominal rate of interest?

Solution

$$A_n = 8240.00 + 7\% \text{ of } 8240.00 - 800.00 = 8016.80$$

$$R = 256.00; \quad n = (3.5)(12) = 42$$

$$a_{\overline{42}|i} = \frac{8016.80}{256.00} = 31.315625$$

for $i = 1\%$, $a_{\overline{42}|1\%} = 34.158108 \longrightarrow i > 1\%$
for $i = 1.5\%$, $a_{\overline{42}|1.5\%} = 30.994049 \longrightarrow 1\% < i < 1.5\%$
for $i = 1.4\%$, $a_{\overline{42}|1.4\%} = 31.592375 \longrightarrow 1.4\% < i < 1.5\%$
for $i = 1.44\%$, $a_{\overline{42}|1.44\%} = 31.351073 \longrightarrow 1.44\% < i < 1.5\%$
for $i = 1.45\%$, $a_{\overline{42}|1.45\%} = 31.291160 \longrightarrow 1.44\% < i < 1.45\%$
for $i = 1.446\%$, $a_{\overline{42}|1.446\%} = 31.315105$

The value of $i = 1.446\%$ approximately and the nominal rate is approximately 17.352%.

Programmed solution

0	8016.80	256	42			
FV	PV	PMT	N	CPT	%*i*	1.4459134

The more precise computed value of $i = 1.4459134\%$ and the nominal rate = 17.35096%.

Exercise III.1 (same as Exercise 11.6)

A. Compute the nominal rate of interest for each of the following ordinary annuities.

	Amount S_n	*Present value* A_n	*Periodic rent*	*Payment interval*	*Term*	*Compounding period*
1.	\$9000.00		\$143.54	3 months	8 years	quarterly
2.	\$4800.00		\$ 49.00	1 month	5 years	monthly
3.		\$7400.00	\$119.06	1 month	7 years	monthly
4.		\$5540.00	\$800.00	6 months	5 years	semi-annually

B. Answer each of the following questions.

1. Compute the nominal rate of interest at which \$350.00 paid at the end of every three months for six years accumulates to \$12 239.76.
2. What is the nominal rate of interest if a four-year loan of \$6000.00 is repaid by monthly payments of \$171.58?
3. Réné contributed \$250.00 every three months into an RRSP for ten years. What was the nominal rate of interest earned by the RRSP if the balance in Réné's account just after he made his last contribution was \$19 955.40?
4. Rita converted a RRSP balance of \$119 875.67 into an RRIF that will pay her \$1800.00 at the end of every month for nine years. What is the nominal rate of interest?
5. A car valued at \$11 400.00 can be bought for 10% down and monthly payments of \$318.56 for three and a half years. What is the effective cost of financing?
6. A property worth \$40 000.00 can be purchased for 20% down and quarterly mortgage payments of \$1100.00 for 25 years. What effective rate of interest is charged?

III.2 *Finding the conversion rate* i *for annuities due*

A. Finding i *when the amount* S_n *(due) is known*

Since Formula 12.1 is awkward for finding i, we can develop the formula into a more suitable form.

$$S_n(\text{due}) = R(1+i)\left[\frac{(1+i)^n - 1}{i}\right] \longleftarrow \text{Formula 12.1}$$

$$= R\left[\frac{(1+i)^{n+1} - (1+i)}{i}\right] \longleftarrow \text{multiplying by } (1+i)$$

$$= R\left[\frac{(1+i)^{n+1} - 1 - i}{i}\right]$$

$$= R\left[\frac{(1+i)^{n+1} - 1}{i} - \frac{i}{i}\right]$$

$$\boxed{S_n(\text{due}) = R\left[\frac{(1+i)^{n+1} - 1}{i} - 1\right]}$$

Since the factor $\frac{(1+i)^{n+1} - 1}{i}$ may be represented by the symbol $s_{\overline{n+1}|\,i}$,

$$\boxed{S_n(\text{due}) = R(s_{\overline{n+1}|\,i} - 1)} \longleftarrow \textit{Formula } \textbf{III.1}$$

***Example* III.2a** At what nominal rate of interest compounded semi-annually will $320.00 deposited at the beginning of every six months for twelve years accumulate to $15 000.00?

Solution

$$S_n(\text{due}) = 15\,000.00; \quad R = 320.00; \quad n = 12(2) = 24$$

$$15\,000.00 = 320.00\left[\frac{(1+i)^{24+1} - 1}{i} - 1\right] \longleftarrow \text{substituting in Formula III.1}$$

$$\frac{15\,000.00}{320.00} = \frac{(1+i)^{25} - 1}{i} - 1$$

$$46.875 + 1 = \frac{(1+i)^{25} - 1}{i} = s_{\overline{25}|\,i}$$

$$s_{\overline{25}|\,i} = 47.875$$

Choose a reasonable nominal rate, such as 12%; $i = 6\%$.

For $i = 6\%$, $s_{\overline{25}|\,6\%} = 54.864512 \longrightarrow i < 6\%$

For $i = 4\%$, $s_{\overline{25}|\,4\%} = 41.645908 \longrightarrow 4\% < i < 6\%$

For $i = 5\%$, $s_{\overline{25}|\,5\%} = 47.727098 \longrightarrow 5\% < i < 6\%$

Since 47.727098 is much closer to 47.875 than 54.864512, i is much closer to 5% than to 6%; try a value of i very close to 5%, such as 5.1%.

For $i = 5.1\%$, $s_{\overline{25|}\,5.1\%} = 48.390405 \longrightarrow 5\% < i < 5.1\%$
For $i = 5.02\%$, $s_{\overline{25|}\,5.02\%} = 47.858911 \longrightarrow 5.02\% < i < 5.1\%$
For $i = 5.023\%$, $s_{\overline{25|}\,5.023\%} = 47.878720 \longrightarrow i = 5.023\%$ approximately

Since the semi-annual rate of interest is approximately 5.023%, the nominal rate of interest = 2(5.023%) = 10.046%.

B. Finding i *when the present value A_n(due) is known*

Formula 12.2 too is awkward to use when finding i and can be developed into a more suitable form.

$$A_n(\text{due}) = R(1+i)\left[\frac{1-(1+i)^{-n}}{i}\right] \longleftarrow \text{Formula 12.2}$$

$$= R\left[\frac{(1+i)-(1+i)^{-n+1}}{i}\right] \longleftarrow \text{multiplying by } (1+i)$$

$$= R\left[\frac{1+i-(1+i)^{-(n-1)}}{i}\right]$$

$$= R\left[\frac{i}{i}+\frac{1-(1+i)^{-(n-1)}}{i}\right]$$

$$A_n(\text{due}) = R\left[\frac{1-(1+i)^{-(n-1)}}{i}+1\right]$$

Since the factor $\frac{1-(1+i)^{-(n-1)}}{i}$ can be represented by the symbol $a_{\overline{n-1|}\,i}$,

$$A_n(\text{due}) = R(a_{\overline{n-1|}\,i}+1) \longleftarrow \textit{Formula } \textbf{III.2}$$

***Example* III.2b** A lease contract valued at $16 000.00 is to be fulfilled by making payments of $325.00 at the beginning of each month for ten years. What is the nominal rate of interest paid if interest is compounded monthly?

Solution

$$A_n(\text{due}) = 16\,000.00; \quad R = 325.00; \quad n = 10(12) = 120$$

$$16\,000.00 = 325.00\left[\frac{1-(1+i)^{-(120-1)}}{i}+1\right] \longleftarrow \text{substituting in Formula III.2}$$

$$\frac{16\,000.00}{325.00} = \frac{1 - (1 + i)^{-119}}{i} + 1$$

$$49.2306769 - 1 = \frac{1 - (1 + i)^{-119}}{i} = a_{\overline{119}|i}$$

$$a_{\overline{119}|i} = 48.230769$$

For a nominal rate of 12%, $i = 1\%$.

For $i = 1\%$, $\quad a_{\overline{119}|1\%} = 69.397527$

$$a_{\overline{119}|1\%} > a_{\overline{119}|i} \text{ and } 1\% < i$$

For $i = 2\%$, $\quad a_{\overline{119}|2\%} = 45.262496 \longrightarrow 1\% < i < 2\%$
For $i = 1.8\%$, $\quad a_{\overline{119}|1.8\%} = 48.906776 \longrightarrow 1.8 < i < 2\%$
For $i = 1.83\%$, $\quad a_{\overline{119}|1.83\%} = 48.330360 \longrightarrow 1.83\% < i < 2\%$
For $i = 1.835\%$, $\quad a_{\overline{119}|1.835\%} = 48.235357 \longrightarrow 1.835\% < i < 2\%$
For $i = 1.836\%$, $\quad a_{\overline{119}|1.836\%} = 48.216393 \longrightarrow 1.835\% < i < 1.836\%$

$$i = 1.835\% \text{ approximately}$$

The nominal rate of interest = 12(1.835%) = 22.02% (approximately).

Exercise III.2

A. Find the unknown value in each of the following annuities due.

	Amount	*Present value*	*Periodic payment*	*Payment period*	*Term*	*Int. rate*	*Conversion period*
1.	$70 000.00		$367.00	1 year	25 years	?	annually
2.		$42 000.00	$528.00	1 month	10 years	?	monthly
3.		$28 700.00	$2015.00	6 months	15 years	?	semi-annually
4.	$36 000.00		$235.00	3 months	12 years	?	quarterly

B. Answer each of the following questions.

1. What nominal rate of interest was paid if contributions of $250.00 made into an RRSP at the beginning of every three months amounted to $18 307.00 after ten years?

2. A vacation property valued at $20 000.00 was bought for fifteen payments of $2750.00 due at the beginning of every six months. What nominal rate of interest was charged?

3. What is the effective rate of interest on a lease contract valued at $13 500.00 if payments of $1500.00 are made at the beginning of every six months for seven years?

4. An insurance policy provides a benefit of $250 000.00 twenty years from now. Alternatively, the policy pays $4220.00 at the beginning of each year for twenty years. What is the effective rate of interest paid?

III.3 *Finding the rate of interest for deferred annuities when their present value is known*

A. *Finding the rate of interest of a deferred annuity without preprogramming*

The rate of interest for a deferred annuity can be determined by trial and error using a method similar to the one previously explained. We obtain a suitable formula for determining i by solving the general problem of finding the present value of a deferred annuity represented in Figure III.1.

FIGURE III.1 ***Graphic representation of the deferred ordinary annuity***

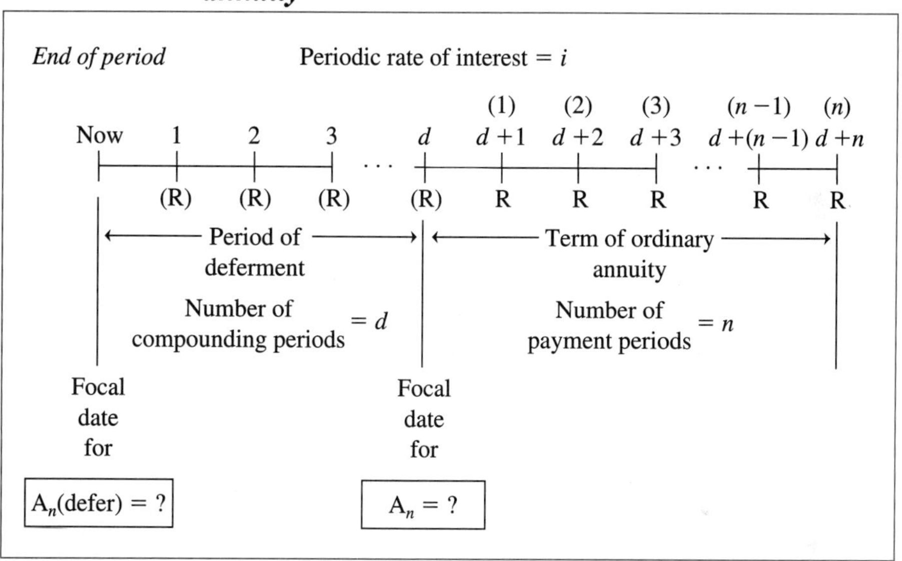

However, since this text uses only the original approach to finding the present value of a deferred annuity when finding R, n, or i, only the formula for this approach is developed.

STEP 1 Find the present value of the ordinary annuity at the end of the period of deferment.

$$A_n = R\left[\frac{1 - (1 + i)^{-n}}{i}\right] = Ra_{\overline{n|}\, i}$$

STEP 2 Find the present value of A_n at the focal point 'now.'

$$P = A_n(1 + i)^{-d}$$

STEP 3 Since P represents the present value of the deferred annuity,

$$\boxed{A_n(\text{defer}) = R(1 + i)^{-d}(a_{\overline{n|}\, i})} \longleftarrow \textit{Formula}\ \textbf{III.3}$$

Example **III.3a** Payments of \$900.00 are made at the end of every three months for fifteen years from a fund of \$8000.00 earning interest compounded quarterly. If the payments were deferred for ten years, what was the nominal rate of interest?

Solution

The payments form a deferred ordinary annuity. $A_n(\text{defer}) = 8000.00$;

$$R = 900.00; \quad n = 15(4) = 60; \quad d = 10(4) = 40$$

$$8000.00 = 900.00(1 + i)^{-40}\left[\frac{1-(1+i)^{-60}}{i}\right] \longleftarrow \text{using Formula III.3}$$

$$8.8888889 = (1 + i)^{-40}\left[\frac{1-(1+i)^{-60}}{i}\right]$$

$$a_{\overline{60}|i} \times (1 + i)^{-40} = 8.8888889$$

For a nominal rate of 12%, the quarterly rate $i = 3\%$.

For $i = 3\%$, $\quad a_{\overline{60}|3\%} \times (1 + .03)^{-40}$
$= (27.675564)(0.3065568) = 8.4841334$

Since $a_{\overline{60}|3\%} \times (1 + .03)^{-40} < a_{\overline{60}|i} \times (1 + i)^{-40} \longrightarrow 3\% > i$,

for $i = 2.9\%$, $\quad a_{\overline{60}|2.9\%} \times (1 + .029)^{-40}$
$= (28.278648)(0.3187022) = 9.0124664 \longrightarrow 2.9\% < i < 3\%$

for $i = 2.93\%$, $\quad a_{\overline{60}|2.93\%} \times (1 + .0293)^{-40}$
$= (28.095572)(0.3150076) = 8.8503199 \longrightarrow 2.9\% < i < 2.93\%$

for $i = 2.92\%$, $\quad a_{\overline{60}|2.92\%} \times (1 + .0292)^{-40}$
$(28.156390)(0.3162342) = 8.9040149 \longrightarrow 2.92\% < i < 2.93\%$

for $i = 2.923\%$, $\quad a_{\overline{60}|2.923\%} \times (1 + .02923)^{-40}$
$= (28.138123)(0.3158658) = 8.8878694 \longrightarrow i = 2.923\%$ approximately

The nominal rate of interest $= 4(2.923\%) = 11.69\%$ approximately.

B. *Finding the rate of interest of a deferred annuity with programming*

While no direct solution is possible with the current generation of preprogrammed pocket calculators, the preprogramming features can be used in the trial and error method.

Programmed solution for Example III.3a

First, substitute in Formula III.3 and determine the numerical value of the factor containing *i*.

$$8000 = 900(1 + i)^{-40}(a_{\overline{60}|i})$$
$$8.8888889 = a_{\overline{60}|i}(1 + i)^{-40}$$

Second, find approximations to the above factor using the following steps repeatedly.

STEP 1 Find $a_{\overline{60}|i}$.

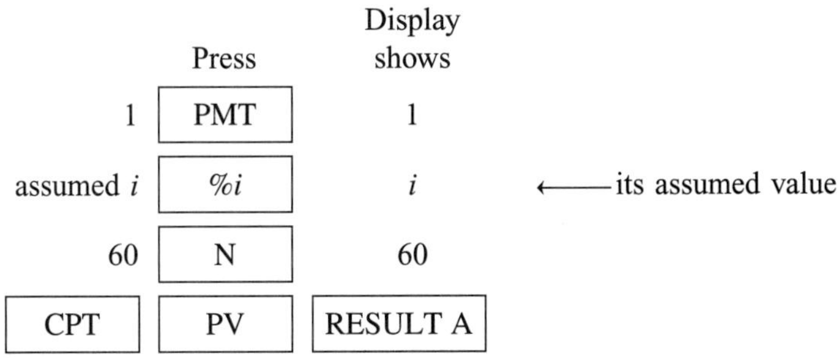

	Press	Display shows	
1	PMT	1	
assumed i	%i	i	⟵ its assumed value
60	N	60	
CPT	PV	RESULT A	

STEP 2 Find $(1 + i)^{-40}$.

Now use result A, the value of $a_{\overline{60}|i}$ for the assumed value of i, as the future value for finding $(1 + i)^{-40}$. Result A need not be keyed in; just press FV immediately after PV.

	Press	Display shows	
	FV	RESULT A	
0	PMT	0	
assumed i	%i	i	⟵ its assumed value
40	N	40	⟵ $d = 40$
CPT	PV	RESULT B	

Result B is the factor that is to be compared with 8.8888889.

Try $i = 3\%$.

	Press	Display shows	
1	PMT	1	⟵ start of Step 1
3	%i	3	⟵ assumed value of i
60	N	60	

CPT	PV	27.675564	⟵ result A
	FV	27.675564	⟵ start of Step 2
0	PMT	0	
3	%i	3	⟵ assumed value of i
40	N	40	⟵ $d = 40$
CPT	PV	8.4841334	⟵ result B

Since $a_{\overline{60}|3\%} \times (1 + 0.03)^{-40} < a_{\overline{60}|i} \times (1 + i)^{-40} \longrightarrow 3\% > i$,

try $i = 2.9\%$, Result A = 28.278648
Result B = 9.0124664
$2.9\% < i < 3\%$

try $i = 2.93\%$, Result B = 8.8503199
$2.9\% < i < 2.93\%$

try $i = 2.92\%$, Result B = 8.904149
$2.92\% < i < 2.93\%$

try $i = 2.923\%$, Result B = 8.8878694

$$i = 2.923\% \text{ quarterly (approximately)}$$

The nominal rate of interest = 4(2.923%) = 11.69%.

***Example* III.3b** Payments of $500 are to be made at the beginning of each month for four years starting two years after a contract valued at $12 000 was signed. What nominal rate of interest compounded monthly has been charged?

Solution

Since the payments are at the beginning of each month, the problem involves a deferred annuity due.

$$A_n(\text{defer}) = 12\,000; \quad R = 500; \quad n = 48; \quad d = 24$$

$$12\,000 = 500(1 + i)^{-24}(a_{\overline{48}|i})(1 + i)$$
$$24 = (1 + i)^{-23}(a_{\overline{48}|i})$$
$$24 = a_{\overline{48}|i}(1 + i)^{-23}$$

For $i = 1.5\%$, Result B = 24.171475 $\longrightarrow i > 1.5\%$
For $i = 1.55\%$, Result B = 23.646096 $\longrightarrow 1.5\% < i < 1.55\%$
For $i = 1.52\%$, Result B = 23.959776 $\longrightarrow 1.5 < i < 1.52\%$
For $i = 1.516\%$, Result B = 24.001949 $\longrightarrow i = 1.516\%$

The nominal rate of interest is 18.192% approximately.

Exercise III.3

A. For each of the following deferred annuities, find i.

	Present value	*Periodic payment*	*Made at*	*Payment interval*	*Period of deferment*	*Term*	*Compounding period*
1.	\$45 000.00	\$7250.00	end	6 months	7 years	16 years	semi-annually
2.	\$7 500.00	\$920.00	beginning	3 months	9 years	7 years	quarterly

B. Answer each of the following questions.

1. Andreas invested \$3500.00 in an annuity deferred for twenty-five years that paid him \$3000.00 at the end of every six months for twenty years. What rate of interest compounded semi-annually did Andreas receive on his investment?

2. A ten-year \$15 000.00 promissory note is redeemed by making semi-annual payments of \$6200.00 for fifteen years. If the first payment is due at the date of maturity of the promissory note, what is the effective rate if interest is compounded semi-annually?

3. Judith Ball invested \$10 000.00 on her 35th birthday in an annuity that will pay her \$5000.00 every six months for twenty years. If the first payment is due six months after her 60th birthday, what is the nominal annual rate of interest compounded semi-annually?

4. A lease can be bought for \$64 000.00. If the lease requires payments of \$4700.00 every three months for ten years and the first payment is due two years after the lease is purchased, what is the effective annual rate of interest based on quarterly compounding?

III.4 *Finding the conversion rate* i *for general annuities due and deferred general annuities without preprogrammed calculators*

A. Finding i *for general annuities without a preprogrammed calculator*

Finding the equivalent effective rate per payment period can be done by trial and error using the same method found in Section III.1. When the amount S_{nc} is known, use Formula 13.1; if the present value A_{nc} is given, Formula 13.2 applies.

***Example* III.4a** An ordinary annuity of \$500.00 per quarter accumulates to \$12 500.00 in five years. What rate of interest compounded monthly do the deposits earn?

Solution

$$S_{nc} = 12\ 500.00; \quad R = 500.00; \quad n = 5(4) = 20; \quad c = \frac{12}{4} = 3$$

The equivalent effective quarterly rate of interest

$$f = (1 + i)^3 - 1$$

$$12\,500.00 = 500.00\, s_{\overline{20}|f} \longleftarrow \text{substituting in Formula 13.1}$$
$$25.0 = s_{\overline{20}|f}$$

For $f = 3\%$, $s_{\overline{20}|3\%} = 26.870374 \longrightarrow f < 3\%$
For $f = 2\%$, $s_{\overline{20}|2\%} = 24.297369 \longrightarrow 2\% < f < 3\%$
For $f = 2.3\%$, $s_{\overline{20}|2.3\%} = 25.036609 \longrightarrow 2\% < f < 2.3\%$
For $f = 2.28\%$, $s_{\overline{20}|2.28\%} = 24.986482 \longrightarrow 2.28\% < f < 2.3\%$
For $f = 2.29\%$, $s_{\overline{20}|2.29\%} = 24.011530 \longrightarrow 2.28\% < f < 2.29\%$
For $f = 2.285\%$, $s_{\overline{20}|2.285\%} = 24.999002 \longrightarrow 2.285\% < f < 2.29\%$
For $f = 2.2854\%$, $s_{\overline{20}|2.2854\%} = 25.000004 \longrightarrow f = 2.2854\%$ approx.

$$(1 + i)^3 = 1.022854$$
$$1 + i = 1.022854^{\frac{1}{3}}$$
$$i = 1.0075607 - 1$$
$$i = 0.0075607 = 0.75607\%$$

The nominal rate of interest is 12(0.75607%) = 9.07284% compounded monthly.

***Example* III.4b** A twenty-year residential mortgage of $45 000.00 is repaid by making payments of $546.83 at the end of each month. What is the rate of interest compounded semi-annually on the mortgage?

Solution

$$A_{nc} = 45\,000.00; \quad R = 546.83; \quad n = 20(12) = 240; \quad c = \frac{2}{12} = \frac{1}{6}$$

The equivalent effective monthly interest

$$f = (1 + i)^{\frac{1}{6}} - 1$$

$$45\,000.00 = 546.83 a_{\overline{240}|f} \longleftarrow \text{substituting in Formula 13.2}$$
$$a_{\overline{240}|f} = 82.292486$$

For $f = 1\%$, $a_{\overline{240}|f} = 90.819416 \longrightarrow 1\% < f$
For $f = 1.2\%$, $a_{\overline{240}|f} = 78.574552 \longrightarrow 1\% < f < 1.2\%$
For $f = 1.14\%$, $a_{\overline{240}|f} = 81.943828 \longrightarrow 1\% < f < 1.14\%$
For $f = 1.13\%$, $a_{\overline{240}|f} = 82.529073 \longrightarrow 1.13\% < f < 1.14\%$
For $f = 1.134\%$, $a_{\overline{240}|f} = 82.294136 \longrightarrow f = 1.134\%$ approximately

$$(1 + i)^{\frac{1}{6}} = 1.01134$$
$$1 + i = 1.01134^6$$
$$i = 1.0699983 - 1$$
$$i = 0.069983 = 7\% \text{ approximately}$$

The interest rate on the mortgage is 14% compounded semi-annually.

B. *Finding the conversion rate* i *for general annuities due*

When finding the rate of interest for a general annuity due, first determine the equivalent effective interest per payment period f. Do this calculation using Formula 13.3 when the amount S_{nc}(due) is known or Formula 13.4 when the present value A_{nc}(due) is known.

The computation, however, is made easier by using the two alternate formulae

$$S_{nc}(\text{due}) = R\left[\frac{(1+f)^{n+1}-1}{f} - 1\right] \text{ or } S_{nc}(\text{due}) = R(s_{\overline{n+1}|f} - 1) \quad \longleftarrow \textit{Formula III.4}$$

$$A_{nc}(\text{due}) = R\left[\frac{1-(1+f)^{-(n-1)}}{f} + 1\right] \text{ or } A_{nc}(\text{due}) = R(a_{\overline{n-1}|f} + 1) \quad \longleftarrow \textit{Formula III.5}$$

***Example* III.4c** Deposits of $300.75 made at the beginning of every three months accumulate to $10 000.00 at the end of six years. What rate of interest compounded monthly has been earned by the deposits?

Solution

$$S_{nc}(\text{due}) = 10\,000.00;\quad R = 300.75;\quad n = 6(4) = 24;\quad c = \frac{12}{4} = 3;$$

$$f = (1+i)^3 - 1$$

$$10\,000.00 = 300.75(s_{\overline{24+1}|f} - 1) \longleftarrow \text{substituting in Formula III.4}$$
$$33.250208 = s_{\overline{25}|f} - 1$$
$$s_{\overline{25}|f} = 34.250208$$

For $f = 3\%$, $s_{\overline{25}|3\%} = 36.459264 \longrightarrow f < 3\%$
For $f = 2\%$, $s_{\overline{25}|2\%} = 32.030299 \longrightarrow 2\% < f < 3\%$
For $f = 2.5\%$, $s_{\overline{25}|2.5\%} = 34.157763 \longrightarrow 2.5\% < f < 3\%$
For $f = 2.52\%$, $s_{\overline{25}|2.52\%} = 34.246386 \longrightarrow 2.52\% < f < 3\%$
For $f = 2.521\%$, $s_{\overline{25}|2.521\%} = 34.250824 \longrightarrow 2.52\% < f < 2.521\%$
For $f = 2.5208\%$, $s_{\overline{25}|2.5208\%} = 34.249937 \longrightarrow 2.5208\% < f < 2.521\%$
For $f = 2.5209\%$, $s_{\overline{25}|2.5209\%} = 34.250381 \longrightarrow 2.5208\% < f < 2.5209\%$
For $f = 2.52086\%$, $s_{\overline{25}|2.52086\%} = 34.250203 \longrightarrow f = 2.52086\%$

$$(1+i)^3 = 1.0252086$$
$$1 + i = 1.0252086^{\frac{1}{3}} = 1.0083332$$
$$i = 0.0083332 = 0.83332\%$$

The rate of interest is 12(0.83332%) = 9.99988% or 10% compounded monthly.

***Example* III.4d** A property valued at $74 250.00 can be bought by making payments of $913.32 at the beginning of each month for fifteen years. What rate of interest compounded semi-annually is being charged?

Solution

$$A_{nc}(\text{due}) = 74\,250.00; \quad R = 913.32; \quad n = 15(12) = 180;$$

$$c = \frac{2}{12} = \frac{1}{6}; \quad f = (1+i)^{\frac{1}{6}} - 1$$

$$74\,250.00 = 913.32(a_{\overline{180-1}|f} + 1) \longleftarrow \text{substituting in Formula III.5}$$
$$81.296807 = a_{\overline{179}|f} + 1$$
$$a_{\overline{179}|f} = 80.296807$$

For $f = 1\%$, $a_{\overline{179}|1\%} = 83.154881 \longrightarrow 1\% < f$
For $f = 1.1\%$, $a_{\overline{179}|1.1\%} = 78.081342 \longrightarrow 1\% < f < 1.1\%$
For $f = 1.05\%$, $a_{\overline{179}|1.05\%} = 80.555264 \longrightarrow 1.05\% < f < 1.1\%$
For $f = 1.06\%$, $a_{\overline{179}|1.06\%} = 80.050665 \longrightarrow 1.05\% < f < 1.06\%$
For $f = 1.055\%$, $a_{\overline{179}|1.055\%} = 80.302340 \longrightarrow 1.055\% < f < 1.06\%$
For $f = 1.0551\%$, $a_{\overline{179}|1.0551\%} = 80.297295 \longrightarrow 1.0551\% < f < 1.06\%$
For $f = 1.05511\%$, $a_{\overline{179}|1.05511\%} = 80.296790 \longrightarrow f = 1.05511\%$

$$(1+i)^{\frac{1}{6}} = 1.0105511$$
$$1 + i = 1.0105511^6 = 1.0650002$$
$$i = 0.0650002 = 6.5\%$$

The rate of interest is 2(6.5%) = 13% compounded semi-annually.

C. *Finding the rate for deferred general annuities*

You can determine the rate of interest for a deferred general annuity by trial and error as previously explained. For deferred ordinary general annuities, use the formula

$$A_{nc}(\text{defer}) = R(1+f)^{-d}\left[\frac{1-(1+f)^{-n}}{f}\right] = R(1+f)^{-d}\, a_{\overline{n}|f}$$

where $f = (1+i)^c - 1$ and d is the number of deferred payment intervals $\longleftarrow$ ***Formula* III.6**

For deferred general annuities due, multiply Formula III.6 by $(1 + f)$.

***Example* III.4e** A retirement annuity of $12 000.00 payable at the end of each year for fifteen years is bought for $7560.73. If the payments are deferred for twenty-five years, what is the rate of interest compounded quarterly on the annuity?

Solution

$$A_{nc}(\text{defer}) = 7560.73; \quad R = 12\,000.00; \quad n = 15; \quad d = 25;$$

$$c = 4; \quad f = (1+i)^4 - 1$$

For a deferred ordinary general annuity, use Formula III.6.

$$7560.73 = 12\,000.00(1 + f)^{-25}\left[\frac{1 - (1 + f)^{-15}}{f}\right]$$

$$(1 + f)^{-25}\left[\frac{1 - (1 + f)^{-15}}{f}\right] = 0.6300608$$

We need to find the annual rate of interest f for which

$$a_{\overline{15}|f} \times (1 + f)^{-25} = 0.6300608$$

For $f = 12\%$, $a_{\overline{15}|\,12\%} \times (1 + 0.12)^{-25}$
$= (6.8108645)(0.0588233) = 0.4006376 \longrightarrow f < 12\%$

For $f = 10\%$, $a_{\overline{15}|\,10\%} \times (1 + 0.10)^{-25}$
$= (7.6060795)(0.0922960) = 0.7020107 \longrightarrow 10\% < f < 12\%$

For $f = 10.4\%$, $a_{\overline{15}|\,10.4\%} \times (1 + 0.104)^{-25}$
$= (7.4355148)(0.0842894) = 0.6267354 \longrightarrow 10\% < f < 10.4\%$

For $f = 10.38\%$, $a_{\overline{15}|\,10.38\%} \times (1 + 0.1038)^{-25}$
$= (7.4438978)(0.0846721) = 0.6302904 \longrightarrow 10.38\% < f < 10.4\%$

For $f = 10.381\%$, $a_{\overline{15}|\,10.381\%} \times (1 + 0.10381)^{-25}$
$= (7.4434783)(0.0846529) = 0.6301121 \longrightarrow 10.381\% < f < 10.4\%$

For $f = 10.3813\%$, $a_{\overline{15}|\,10.3813\%} \times (1 + 0.103813)^{-25}$
$= (7.4433525)(0.0846472) = 0.6300586 \longrightarrow f = 10.3813\%$

$$\text{Since } (1 + i)^4 = (1 + f) = 1.103813$$
$$1 + i = 1.103813^{\frac{1}{4}}$$
$$1 + i = 1.025$$
$$i = 0.025 = 2.5\%$$

The rate of interest is 4(2.5%) = 10% compounded quarterly.

***Example* III.4f** Payments of \$500 are to be made at the beginning of each month for four years starting two years after a contract valued at \$12 000 was signed. What nominal rate of interest compounded quarterly has been charged?

Solution

Since the payments are at the beginning of each month, the problem involves a deferred general annuity.

$$A_{nc}(\text{defer}) = 12\,000; \quad R = 500; \quad n = 48; \quad d = 24;$$

$$c = \frac{4}{12} = \frac{1}{3}$$

To find the equivalent monthly rate of interest f, substitute the given values in Formula 13.9, multiply by $(1 + f)$, and determine the factor for which f is to be computed.

$$12\,000 = 500(1 + f)^{-24}(a_{\overline{48}|f})(1 + f)$$
$$24 = (1 + f)^{-23}(a_{\overline{48}|f})$$
$$24 = a_{\overline{48}|f} \times (1 + f)^{-23}$$

We need to find the monthly rate f for which

$$a_{\overline{48}|f} \times (1 + f)^{-23} = 24$$

This is exactly the same problem as finding the monthly rate i in Chapter 12, Example 12.6e, except that we must now determine the quarterly rate of interest.

$$f = 1.516\%$$
$$(1 + i)^{\frac{1}{3}} = 1.01516$$
$$1 + i = 1.01516^3$$
$$1 + i = 1.046173$$
$$i = 0.046173$$
$$i = 4.6173\%$$

The nominal rate of interest compounded quarterly is 18.469%.

Exercise III.4

A. For each of the following ordinary general annuities, determine the nominal rate of interest.

	Amount S_{nc}	*Present value* A_{nc}	*Periodic payment* R	*Payment Interval*	*Term*	*Nom. rate of int.*	*Conversion period*
1.	\$39 200.00		\$1100.00	1 year	12 years	?	monthly
2.		\$9 600.00	\$1220.00	6 months	5 years	?	monthly
3.		\$62 400.00	\$5200.00	6 months	25 years	?	annually
4.	\$55 500.00		\$75.00	1 month	20 years	?	semi-annually

B. For each of the following general annuities due, determine the nominal rate of interest.

	Amount S_{nc}*(due)*	*Present value* A_{nc}*(due)*	*Periodic payment* R	*Payment interval*	*Term*	*Nom. rate of int.*	*Conversion period*
1.	\$6 400.00		\$200.00	6 months	9 years	?	monthly
2.	\$25 000.00		\$790.00	1 year	15 years	?	quarterly
3.		\$7 500.00	\$540.00	3 months	5 years	?	monthly
4.		\$60 000.00	\$725.00	1 month	25 years	?	semi-annually

C. 1. Compute the rate of interest compounded monthly at which \$400.00 paid at the end of every three months for eight years accumulates to \$20 000.00.

2. What is the rate of interest compounded quarterly if a loan of \$21 500.00 is repaid in seven years by payments of \$2500.00 made at the end of every six months?

3. A mortgage of \$27 500.00 is repaid by making payments of \$382.00 at the end of each month for fifteen years. What is the rate of interest compounded semi-annually?

4. A property worth \$35 000.00 is purchased for 10 percent down and semi-annual payments of \$2750.00 for twelve years. What is the effective rate of interest if interest is compounded quarterly?

5. What is the rate of interest compounded annually on a lease valued at \$21 600.00 if payments of \$780.00 are made at the beginning of each month for three years?

6. An insurance policy provides for a lump sum benefit of \$50 000.00 fifteen years from now. Alternatively, payments of \$1700.00 may be received at the beginning of each of the next fifteen years. What is the effective rate of interest if interest is compounded quarterly?

7. A business venture requiring an initial investment of \$5000.00 yields no returns for the first three years and net returns of \$950.00 at the end of every three months for the following seven years. What rate of interest compounded semi-annually does the venture yield?

8. A \$40 000.00 lease requires semi-annual payments of \$9750.00 for five years due in advance. If the payments are deferred for two years, what is the nominal annual rate of interest charged?

9. An annuity bought for \$32 000.00 provides ordinary annuity payments of \$8200.00 every three months for fifteen years. If the payments are deferred for ten years, what rate of interest compounded semi-annually is paid on the investment?

10. A leasing agreement with a cash value of \$24 500.00 requires semi-annual payments of \$6500.00 for five years. If the first payment is due three years from the date of the agreement, what is the effective rate of interest on the lease if interest is compounded monthly?

III.5 *Finding the accurate yield rate for bonds by trial and error*

A method of trial and error similar to the one used to find the nominal rate of interest can be used to obtain as precise an approximation to the yield rate as desired. When using this method, use the rate obtained by the method of averages for the first attempt by substituting in Formula 15.1

$$PP = S(1+i)^{-n} + R\left[\frac{1-(1+i)^{-n}}{i}\right] = S(1+i)^{-n} + Ra_{\overline{n}|\, i}$$

***Example* III.5a** Compute the yield rate for Example 15.4b (see page 636).

Solution

The approximate value of i by the method of averages is 5.48%; the quoted price is \$25 875.00.

Our aim is to find the value of i for which Formula 15.1 gives a purchase price equal to the quoted price of \$25 875.00.

$$S = 25\ 000.00; \quad R = 1437.50; \quad n = 20$$

$$PP = 25\ 000.00(1 + i)^{-20} + 1437.50a_{\overline{20}|i}$$

$$\text{For } i = 5.48\%, \ PP = 25\ 000.00(1.0548^{-20}) + 1437.50a_{\overline{20}|5.48\%}$$
$$= 8600.77 + 17\ 207.22$$
$$= \$25\ 807.99$$

Programmed solution

0	25 000	20	5.48			
PMT	FV	N	%i	CPT	PV	8 600.77
0	1437.50					
FV	PMT	CPT	PV			17 207.22

The purchase price is 25 807.99

Since the computed purchase price of \$25 807.99 is less than the quoted price of \$25 875.00, $i < 5.48\%$.

For $i = 5.46\%$, PP $= 8633.46 + 17\ 235.83 = 25\ 869.29 \longrightarrow i < 5.46\%$
For $i = 5.456\%$, PP $= 8640.01 + 17\ 241.56 = 25\ 881.57 \longrightarrow 5.456\% < i < 5.46\%$
For $i = 5.458\%$, PP $= 8636.73 + 17\ 238.70 = 25\ 875.43 \longrightarrow i = 5.458\%$

Note: Because the computed purchase price is almost exactly equal to the quoted price, $i = 5.458\%$ is a precise value.

The yield rate is 2(5.458%) = 10.916%.

Example **III.5b** Compute the yield rate for Example 15.4d (see page 637).

Solution

The approximate value of i by the method of averages = 4.75%; the quoted price on December 2, 1996, is \$5187.50.

We want to find the value of i for which Formula 15.1 gives a purchase price equal to the quoted price of \$5187.50.

When the date of purchase is between interest dates, we can approximate the precise value of i by using the theoretically correct number of interest conversion intervals in fractional form.

The number of days from the date of purchase (December 2, 1996) to the next interest payment date (January 15, 1997) is 44;

the number of conversion periods from December 2, 1996, to July 15, 2008, is

$$23 + \frac{44}{184} = 23.23913.$$

$$S = 5000.00; \quad R = 250.00$$

Substituting in Formula 15.1,

$$PP = 5000.00(1 + i)^{-23.23913} + 250.00a_{\overline{23.23913}|i}$$

For $i = 4.75\%$, $PP = 5000.00(1.0475^{-23.23913}) + 250.00a_{\overline{23.23913}|4.75\%}$
$= 1700.62 + 3473.03$
$= \$5173.65$

Programmed solution

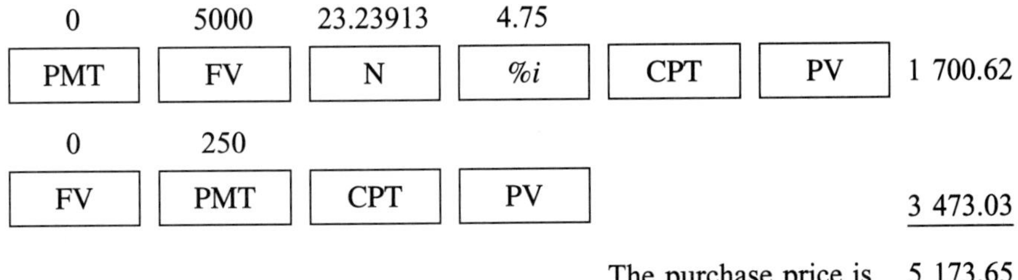

The purchase price is 5 173.65

Since the purchase price of \$5173.65 is less than the quoted price of \$5187.50, $i < 4.75\%$.

For $i = 4.73\%$, $PP = 1708.19 + 3479.72 = 5187.91 \longrightarrow 4.73 < i < 4.75\%$
For $i = 4.731\%$, $PP = 1707.81 + 3479.38 = 5187.19 \longrightarrow 4.73\% < i < 4.731\%$
For $i = 4.7305\%$, $PP = 1708.00 + 3479.55 = 5187.55 \longrightarrow i = 4.7305\%$

The yield rate is $2(4.7305\%) = 9.461\%$.

***Example* III.5c** A \$10 000.00, 11.5% bond with quarterly coupons redeemable at 106 on September 1, 2001, is bought on April 10, 1992, at $94\frac{1}{2}$. What is the yield rate?

Solution

The quoted price is $10\ 000.00(0.945) = \$9450.00$;

the redemption value is $10\ 000.00(1.06) = \$10\ 600.00$;

the average book value is $\dfrac{(9450.00 + 10\ 600.00)}{2} = \$10\ 025.00$.

The interest payment dates are December 1, March 1, June 1, and September 1; the interest date closest to April 10 is March 1.

Assuming that the price was quoted on March 1, 1992, the time to maturity is 9 years and 6 months; the number of interest payments to maturity is $4(9.5) = 38$;

the quarterly interest payment is $10\ 000.00\left(\dfrac{0.115}{4}\right) = \$287.50$;

the total interest payments are $38(287.50) = \$10\ 925.00$;

the discount is 10 600.00 − 9450.00 = \$1150.00.

$$\text{The average income per interest payment interval} = \frac{(10\,925.00 + 1150.00)}{38}$$

$$= \$317.76$$

$$\text{The approximate value of } i = \frac{317.76}{10\,025.00} = 0.0316968 = 3.17\%$$

The number of days from April 10 to June 1 is 52;
the number of days in the interest payment interval March 1 to June 1 is 92;
the exact number of interest payment intervals from April 10, 1992, to September 1, 2001, is $37 + \frac{52}{92} = 37.565217$.

$$S = 10\,600.00; \quad R = 287.50; \quad n = 37.565217$$

Substituting in Formula 15.1,

$$PP = 10\,600.00(1 + i)^{-37.565217} + 287.50a_{\overline{37.565217}|\,i}$$

$$\begin{aligned} \text{For } i = 3.17\%, \text{ PP} &= 10\,600.00(0.3096438) + 287.50(21.777797) \\ &= 3282.22 + 6261.12 \\ &= \$9543.34 \end{aligned}$$

Programmed solution

0	10 600	37.565217	3.17			
PMT	FV	N	%i	CPT	PV	3282.22
0	287.50					
FV	PMT	CPT	PV			6261.12

The purchase price is 9543.34

	Since 9543.34 > 9450.00	⟶ $i > 3.17\%$
For $i = 3.20\%$,	PP = 3246.57 + 6232.64 = 9479.21	⟶ $i > 3.20\%$
For $i = 3.22\%$,	PP = 3223.03 + 6213.76 = 9436.79	⟶ $3.20\% < i < 3.22\%$
For $i = 3.214\%$,	PP = 3230.07 + 6219.41 = 9449.48	⟶ $i = 3.214\%$

The yield rate is 4(3.214) = 12.856%.

Example **III.5d** Ram Snead purchased a \$5000, 10% bond with semi-annual coupons redeemable at par at $93\frac{3}{4}$ twenty years before maturity. He sold the bond nine years later at $100\frac{1}{2}$. What yield rate did Ram realize?

Solution

Ram's purchase price is 5000.00(0.9375) = \$4687.50 ⟵ original book value
Ram's selling price is 5000.00(1.005) = \$5025.00 ⟵ final book value

$$\text{The average book value is } \tfrac{1}{2}(4687.50 + 5025.00) = \$4856.25.$$

The semi-annual coupon is $5000.00\left(\frac{0.10}{2}\right) = \$250.00$;

the number of interest payments received by Ram is 9(2) = 18;

the total interest payments are 18(250.00) = \$4500.00;

the gain on the sale is 5025.00 − 4687.50 = \$337.50 ⟵ discount

$$\text{The average income per interest interval is } \frac{(4500.00 + 337.50)}{18} = \$268.75$$

$$\text{The approximate value of } i \text{ is } \frac{268.75}{4856.25} = 0.0553411 = 5.53\%.$$

Our aim is to find the value of i for which Formula 15.1 gives a purchase price of \$4687.50 given that

$$S = 5025.00; \quad R = 250.00; \quad n = 18$$

$$PP = 5025.00(1 + i)^{-18} + 250.00a_{\overline{18}|i}$$

$$\begin{aligned}\text{For } i = 5.53\%, \ PP &= 5025.00(1.0553^{-18}) + 250.00a_{\overline{18}|5.53\%} \\ &= 5025.00(0.3795186) + 250.00(11.220278) \\ &= \$4712.15\end{aligned}$$

Programmed solution

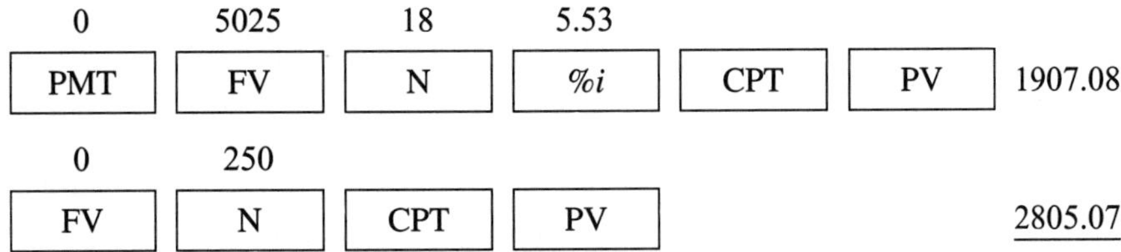

The purchase price is 4712.15

Since 4712.15 > 4687.50, $i > 5.53\%$.

For $i = 5.55\%$, PP $= 1900.59 + 2800.78 = 4701.37 \longrightarrow i > 5.55\%$
For $i = 5.57\%$, PP $= 1894.12 + 2796.51 = 4690.63 \longrightarrow i > 5.57\%$
For $i = 5.577\%$, PP $= 1891.86 + 2795.01 = 4686.87 \longrightarrow 5.57\% < i < 5.577\%$
For $i = 5.576\%$, PP $= 1892.18 + 2795.22 = 4687.40 \longrightarrow i = 5.576\%$

The yield rate is 2(5.576%) = 11.152%.

Exercise III.5

A. Use trial and error to find the yield rate for each of the following bonds.

1. A $1000, 11.5% bond with semi-annual coupons redeemable at par on November 15, 2004, is bought on April 5, 1991, at $96\frac{3}{4}$.

2. A $5000, 16% bond with interest payable quarterly redeemable at 110 on July 1, 2003, is bought on October 26, 1990, at $101\frac{7}{8}$.

3. A $10 000, 15% bond with semi-annual coupons was bought seventeen years before maturity at $102\frac{1}{4}$ and sold at $99\frac{1}{2}$ five years later.

4. Four $1000, 10.5% bonds with interest payable semi-annually redeemable at 101 on August 15, 2011, were bought on October 14, 1994, at $87\frac{3}{4}$ and sold on May 25, 1998, at $91\frac{1}{2}$.

   (a) What would have been the yield rate if held to maturity?

   (b) What was the yield rate realized by selling the bond on May 25, 1998?

5. A $25 000, 9.5% bond with semi-annual coupons redeemable at par is bought sixteen years before maturity at $78\frac{1}{4}$.

6. A $10 000, 15% bond with quarterly coupons redeemable at 102 on October 15, 2007, is bought on May 5, 1995, at $98\frac{3}{4}$.

Supplementary formulae

Formula III.1

$S_n(\text{due}) = R(s_{\overline{n+1}|\,i} - 1)$ Alternate form of the formula for finding the amount of an annuity due

Formula III.2

$A_n(\text{due}) = R(a_{\overline{n-1}|\,i} + 1)$ Alternate form of the formula for finding the present value of an annuity due

Formula III.3

$A_n(\text{defer}) = R(1 + i)^{-d}\, a_{\overline{n}|\,i}$ Finding the present value of a deferred ordinary annuity using the symbol $a_{\overline{n}|\,i}$ for the discount factor

Formula III.4

$S_{nc}(\text{due}) = R(s_{\overline{n+1}|f} - 1)$

Alternate form of the formula for finding the amount of a general annuity due

Formula III.5

$A_{nc}(\text{due}) = R(a_{\overline{n-1}|f} - 1)$

Alternate form for finding the present value of a general annuity due

Formula III.6

$A_{nc}(\text{defer}) = R(1 + f)^{-d}\, a_{\overline{n}|f}$

where $f = (1 + i)^c - 1$ and d is the number of deferred payment intervals

Alternate form for finding the present value of a deferred ordinary general annuity

Answers to Odd-numbered problems, Review exercises, and Self-tests

Chapter 1

Exercise 1.1

A. 1. 14 **3.** 53 **5.** 23 **7.** 24 **9.** 1.3333333 **B. 1.** 1.375 **3.** 1.6666667 **5.** 1.8333333 **7.** 1.0833333 **C. 1.** 0.6666667 **3.** 0.0833333 **5.** 1.3333333 **7.** 0.5555556 **D. 1.** 3.375 **3.** 8.3333333 **5.** 33.3333333 **7.** 7.7777778 **E. 1.** 5.63 **3.** 18.00 **5.** 57.70 **7.** 13.00 **F. 1.** 720 **3.** 630.85 **5.** 1911 **7.** 220 000 **9.** 4000

Exercise 1.2

A. 1. $409 062.50 **3.** $1147.50 **5.** $176.00 **B. 1.** $0.41 **3.** 2.9

Exercise 1.3

A. 1. (a) $955.50 **(b)** $12.25 **(c)** $1157.63 **3. (a)** $7.26 **(b)** $1185.50 **5. (a)** $16.47 **(b)** $875.94 **7.** $1568.06 **9. (a)** $225.00 **(b)** $332.25 **11.** 9.25% **13.** $19 680 **15.** $425.21 **17.** $5.95

Review exercise

1. (a) 29 **(b)** −8 **(c)** 11 **(d)** 8 **(e)** 1000 **(f)** 0.15 **(g)** 340 **(h)** 950 **(i)** 625 **(j)** 1250 **2. (a)** 20.2083333 kg **(b)** $24.25 **(c)** 5.05 kg **(d)** $6.06 **3.** $35, $150, $147, $252; Total $584 **4. (a)** $11.1875 **(b)** $9.60 **5.** $13 875 **6.** $13 680 **7. (a)** $9.24 **(b)** $918.61 **8. (a)** $1456.00 **(b)** $9.60 **(c)** 16.5 hours **9. (a)** $845.52 **(b)** $10.84 **(c)** $1048.77 **10. (a)** $367.50 **(b)** $8.55 **11. (a)** $387.45 **(b)** $26.65 **12.** $1924.25 **13. (a)** $398.65 **(b)** $11.39 **14.** 4.25% **15.** $21 750 **16.** $8.44 **17. (a)** $8.40 **(b)** 13 **18.** $5945.00 **19.** $10.56 **20.** 41.5 hours

Self-test

1. **(a)** 4417.2 **(b)** 94.5 **(c)** 2606.4 **(d)** 4560 **(e)** 4800 **2.** \$7080 **3.** \$203 **4.** \$7.35 **5.** \$299 250 **6.** \$650 **7.** 15.5% **8.** \$2382.41 **9.** \$788.50 **10.** \$8.90 **11.** \$687.00 **12.** \$9.00

Chapter 2

Exercise 2.1

A. **1.** 19a **3.** $-a - 10$ **5.** $0.8x$ **7.** $1.4x$ **9.** $-x^2 - x - 8$ **11.** $x - 7y$ **13.** $-2a^2 - 6ab + 5b^2$ **15.** $14 - 9x + y$ **B.** **1.** $-12x$ **3.** $-10ax$ **5.** $-2x^2$ **7.** $60xy$ **9.** $-2x + 4y$ **11.** $2ax^2 - 3ax - a$ **13.** $35x - 30$ **15.** $-20ax + 5a$ **17.** $3x^2 + 5x - 2$ **19.** $x^3 + y^3$ **21.** $7x^2 + 3x + 39$ **C.** **1.** $4ab$ **3.** $4x$ **5.** $10m - 4$ **7.** $-2x^2 + 3x + 6$ **D.** **1.** -5 **3.** 378 **5.** 3000 **7.** 902 **9.** 1400

Exercise 2.2

A. **1.** 81 **3.** 16 **5.** $\frac{16}{81}$ **7.** 0.25 **9.** 1 **11.** $\frac{1}{9}$ **13.** 125 **15.** $\frac{1}{1.01}$

B. **1.** 2^8 **3.** 4^3 **5.** 2^{15} **7.** a^{14} **9.** 3^{11} **11.** 6 **13.** $\frac{3^{11}}{5^{11}}$ **15.** $\frac{(-3)^{11}}{2^{11}}$ **17.** 1.025^{150} **19.** 1.04^{80} **21.** $(1 + i)^{200}$ **23.** $(1 + i)^{160}$ **25.** a^5b^5 **27.** $m^{24}n^8$ **29.** 16 **31.** $\frac{b^8}{a^8}$

Exercise 2.3

A. **1.** 72 **3.** 3 **5.** 1.0758857 **7.** 1.0132999 **B.** **1.** 55 **3.** 12.25 **5.** 1.0711221 **7.** 0.6299605 **9.** 163.05343

Exercise 2.4

A. **1.** $9 = \log_2 512$ **3.** $-3 = \log_5 \frac{1}{125}$ **5.** $\ln 18 = 2j$ **B.** **1.** $2^5 = 32$ **3.** $10^1 = 10$ **C.** **1.** 0.6931472 **3.** -2.2537949 **5.** 10.66

Exercise 2.5

A. **1.** 3 **3.** 80 **5.** 18 **7.** -35 **9.** -4 **11.** -8 **13.** 5 **15.** 20 **17.** 200 **B.** **1.** $x = 4$; L.S. = 17 = R.S. **3.** $x = 0$; L.S. = -7 = R.S.

Exercise 2.6

A. **1.** $x = -10$; L.S. = 320 = R.S. **3.** $x = -3$; L.S. = -15 = R.S. **B.** **1.** 20 **3.** -1 **5.** $\frac{1}{2}$ **C.** **1.** -1 **3.** $\frac{5}{6}$

Exercise 2.7

A. 1. \$28.28 **3.** 192 **5.** \$670.00 **7.** \$23 500.00 **9.** 18 **11.** 20 dimes; 56 nickels; 16 quarters

Review exercise

1. (a) $-2x - 7y$ **(b)** $1.97x$ **(c)** $6a - 7$ **(d)** $x + 3y$ **(e)** $9a^2 - 4b - 4c$ **(f)** $-x^2 + 3x + 1$ **2. (a)** $-15a$ **(b)** $28mx$ **(c)** -7 **(d)** $-3ab$ **(e)** $36xy$ **(f)** $24abc$ **(g)** $-12x + 20y + 4$ **(h)** $x - 2x^2 - x^3$ **(i)** $-6x + 4$ **(j)** $7a - 4$ **(k)** $26a - 29$ **(l)** $14ax - 2a^2 + 10a$ **(m)** $2m^2 - 7m + 5$ **(n)** $3a^3 - 8a^2 - 5a + 6$ **(o)** $-14x^2 + 34x + 36$ **(p)** $-26am^2 + 26am + 37a$ **3. (a)** -47 **(b)** $6\frac{1}{3}$ **(c)** 0.16 **(d)** 200 **(e)** 644.40 **(f)** 2500 **4. (a)** -243 **(b)** $\frac{16}{81}$ **(c)** 1 **(d)** $\frac{-1}{3}$ **(e)** $\frac{625}{16}$ **(f)** 1 **(g)** $-19\,683$ **(h)** 1024 **(i)** 59 049 **(j)** m^{12} **(k)** $\frac{16}{81}$ **(l)** $\frac{25}{16}$ **(m)** 1.03^{150} **(n)** $(1 + i)^{80}$ **(o)** 1.05^{150} **(p)** $16x^4y^4$ **(q)** $\frac{81}{a^8b^4}$ **(r)** $\frac{1}{(1 + i)^n}$ **5. (a)** 0.96 **(b)** 1.0121264 **(c)** 1.07 **(d)** 0.9684416 **(e)** 1.0986123 **(f)** -2.9957323 **(g)** 11.849186 **(h)** 98.291653 **6. (a)** -7 **(b)** 880 **(c)** -21 **(d)** -18 **(e)** 3 **(f)** -11 **(g)** 250 **(h)** 40 **(i)** -5 **(j)** 7 **(k)** 39 **(l)** 56 **7. (a)** $x = -7$; L.S. $= -203 =$ R.S. **(b)** $x = 5$; L.S. $= -32 =$ R.S. **(c)** $x = -3$; L.S. $= \frac{-23}{14} =$ R.S. **(d)** $x = -\frac{7}{12}$; L.S. $= \frac{11}{9} =$ R.S. **(e)** $x = 7$; L.S. $= 25 =$ R.S. **(f)** $x = -\frac{1}{3}$; L.S. $= -1 =$ R.S. **(g)** $x = -\frac{1}{2}$; L.S. $= -\frac{31}{6} =$ R.S. **8. (a)** 138 **(b)** \$63 350 **(c)** \$117 **(d)** \$44 500 **(e)** heat \$814; power \$1056; water \$341 **(f)** \$37 500 **(g)** Machine A, 17; Machine B, 25; Machine C, 35 **(h)** superlight, 27; ordinary, 45 **(i)** 164 **(j)** \$1400; \$1680; \$3200

Self-test

1. (a) $-2 - 8x$ **(b)** $-2x - 9$ **(c)** $-16a - 7$ **(d)** $-6x^2 + 6x + 12$ **2. (a)** -7 **(b)** $18\frac{2}{3}$ **(c)** 0.192 **(d)** 0.40 **(e)** 1474.00 **(f)** 1450.00 **3. (a)** -8 **(b)** $\frac{4}{9}$ **(c)** 1 **(d)** 2187 **(e)** $\frac{9}{16}$ **(f)** $-x^{15}$ **4. (a)** 1.0253241 **(b)** 23.114772 **(c)** 0.024926 **(d)** -2.995723 **5. (a)** $n = 6$ **(b)** $n = 5$ **6. (a)** -36 **(b)** 9.00 **(c)** 20 **(d)** -3 **(e)** 3 **(f)** 35 **(g)** 25 **(h)** 2 **7. (a)** \$240 **(b)** 4600 **(c)** 55 **(d)** \$4500

Chapter 3

Exercise 3.1

A. 1. (a) 3:8 **(b)** 3:2 **(c)** 5:8:13 **(d)** 3:6:13 **3. (a)** 5:16 **(b)** 2:7 **(c)** 2:7:11 **(d)** 23:14:5 **(e)** 5:4 **(f)** 25:21 **(g)** 9:16:18 **(h)** 28:40:25 **(i)** 8:15 **(j)** 9:10 **B. 1.** 8:7 **3.** 2:3:12 **C. 1.** \$2295; \$510; \$255 **3.** \$5250; \$2800; \$1400

Exercise 3.2

A. 1. 4 **3.** 56 **5.** 7.4 **7.** 2.4 **9.** $\frac{7}{10}$ **11.** 1 **B. 1.** 21 months **3.** 600 km **5. (a)** $3600 **(b)** $9000 **7.** $100 800

Exercise 3.3

A. 1. 0.64 **3.** 0.025 **5.** 0.005 **7.** 2.5 **9.** 4.5 **11.** 0.009 **13.** 0.0625 **15.** 0.99 **17.** 0.0005 **19.** 0.005 **21.** 0.09375 **23.** 1.625 **25.** 0.0025 **27.** 0.0175 **29.** 1.375 **31.** 0.00875 **33.** $0.33\frac{1}{3}$ **35.** $0.16\frac{2}{3}$ **37.** $1.83\frac{1}{3}$ **39.** $1.33\frac{1}{3}$ **B. 1.** $\frac{1}{4}$ **3.** $\frac{7}{4}$ **5.** $\frac{3}{8}$ **7.** $\frac{1}{25}$ **9.** $\frac{2}{25}$ **11.** $\frac{2}{5}$ **13.** $\frac{5}{2}$ **15.** $\frac{1}{8}$ **17.** $\frac{9}{400}$ **19.** $\frac{1}{800}$ **21.** $\frac{3}{400}$ **23.** $\frac{1}{16}$ **25.** $\frac{1}{6}$ **27.** $\frac{3}{400}$ **29.** $\frac{1}{1000}$ **31.** $\frac{5}{6}$ **33.** $\frac{4}{3}$ **35.** $\frac{5}{3}$ **C. 1.** 350% **3.** 0.5% **5.** 2.5% **7.** 12.5% **9.** 22.5% **11.** 145% **13.** 0.25% **15.** 9% **17.** 75% **19.** $166\frac{2}{3}$% **21.** 4.5% **23.** 0.75% **25.** 1.125% **27.** 37.5% **29.** $133\frac{1}{3}$% **31.** 65%

Exercise 3.4

A. 1. 36 **3.** 300 **5.** 18 **7.** 6 **9.** 0.50 **11.** 2 **13.** 7.50 **15.** 17.50 **B. 1.** $16 **3.** $1950 **5.** $9 **7.** $200 **9.** $600 **11.** $49 **13.** $135 **15.** $60 **C. 1.** $15.60 **3.** $1.62 **5.** $48.40 **7.** $22.42 **D. 1.** 20 **3.** 440 **5.** 36 **7.** 30 **E. 1.** 60% **3.** 115% **5.** 5% **7.** 600% **9.** $166\frac{2}{3}$% **F. 1.** $200 **3.** $3.60 **5.** $3.06 **7.** $200 **9.** $1.10 **11.** $240 **13.** 500% **15.** $300 **G. 1.** $28 **3.** $1500 **5.** $45 000 **7.** 45 000

Exercise 3.5

A. 1. 168 **3.** $1140 **5.** $88 **B. 1.** 50% **3.** 200% **5.** 2% **C. 1.** 32 **3.** $130 **5.** $4.40

Exercise 3.6

A. 1. 27 **3.** 12.5% **5.** $4320 **7. (a)** $180 000 **(b)** $225 000 **B. 1.** $14.52 **3.** $150 **5.** $79.18 **7.** $5000 **9.** $83\frac{1}{3}$% **11.** 325% **13.** $96.69 **15.** $680 **17.** $44 800 **19.** $900

Review exercise

1. (a) 5:6 **(b)** 6:1 **(c)** 9:40 **(d)** 6:1 **(e)** 240:20:1 **(f)** 15:4:3 **2. (a)** 3 **(b)** 18 **(c)** 1.61 **(d)** 2.70 **(e)** $\frac{9}{5}$ **(f)** 2 **3. (a)** 1.85 **(b)** 0.075 **(c)** 0.004 **(d)** 0.00025 **(e)** 0.0125 **(f)** 0.0075 **(g)** 1.625 **(h)** 0.1175 **(i)** $0.08\frac{1}{3}$ **(j)** $0.83\frac{1}{3}$ **(k)** $2.66\frac{2}{3}$ **(l)** 0.10375 **4. (a)** $\frac{1}{2}$ **(b)** $\frac{3}{8}$ **(c)** $\frac{1}{6}$ **(d)** $\frac{5}{3}$ **(e)** $\frac{1}{200}$ **(f)** $\frac{3}{40}$ **(g)** $\frac{3}{400}$ **(h)** $\frac{1}{160}$ **5. (a)** 225% **(b)** 2% **(c)** 0.9% **(d)** 12.75% **(e)** 125% **(f)** 137.5% **(g)** 2.5%

(h) 28% **6. (a)** 210 **(b)** 7.20 **(c)** 195 **(d)** 3.60 **7. (a)** \$112 **(b)** \$930 **(c)** \$1155 **(d)** \$1320 **8. (a)** \$6.66 **(b)** \$8.30 **(c)** \$90.00 **(d)** \$27.72 **9. (a)** 62.5% **(b)** 175% **(c)** \$0.48 **(d)** \$22.50 **(e)** \$280 **(f)** \$440 **(g)** 2% **(h)** 500% **(i)** \$132 **(j)** \$405 **10. (a)** \$18 **(b)** \$1955 **(c)** $16\frac{2}{3}\%$ **(d)** 550% **(e)** \$56 **(f)** \$340 **(g)** \$140 **11.** \$1200; \$1800; \$1500 **12.** \$2400; \$4200; \$4800 **13.** \$63 000; \$47 250; \$70 875; \$7875 **14.** \$75 000; \$50 000; \$60 000 **15.** 16 minutes **16.** \$182 000 **17. (a)** \$14 700 **(b)** \$36 750 **18.** 540 **19. (a)** 59 250 **(b)** 19 750 **20.** \$56 250; \$84 375; \$9375 **21. (a)** \$42 600 **(b)** \$8520 **22. (a)** \$400 000 **(b)** \$280 000 **23. (a)** 50.00%; 22.22%; 27.78% **(b)** 125% **24. (a)** 7.5% **(b)** $16\frac{2}{3}\%$ **25. (a)** 8% **(b)** 92% **26. (a)** $166\frac{2}{3}\%$ **(b)** $266\frac{2}{3}\%$ **27.** \$350 000 **28.** \$165 **29.** \$84 000 **30.** \$15 000 **31. (a)** \$300 000 **(b)** \$23 400 **(c)** \$17 550 **(d)** 37.5% **32. (a)** \$80 000 **(b)** \$250 000 **(c)** 312.5%

Self-test

1. (a) \$350.00 **(b)** \$76.05 **(c)** \$145.00 **(d)** \$13.20 **2. (a)** 20 **(b)** 3 **3. (a)** 1.75 **(b)** 0.00375 **4. (a)** $\frac{1}{40}$ **(b)** $\frac{7}{6}$ **5. (a)** 112.5% **(b)** 2.25% **6.** 45% **7.** \$4800 **8.** \$10 000 **9.** \$72 **10.** \$16 875; \$11 250; \$6750; \$5625 **11.** 14% **12.** \$17.50 **13.** 5% **14.** 180 **15.** \$72 000

Chapter 4

Exercise 4.1

A. 1. A(−4, −3) B(0, −4) C(3, −4) D(2, 0) E(4, 3) F(0, 3) G(−4, 4) H(−5, 0)

3. (a)

x	−5	−4	−3	−2	−1	0	1	2	3
y	−3	−2	−1	0	1	2	3	4	5

(b)

x	3	2	1	0	−1	−2
y	5	3	1	−1	−3	−5

(c)

x	3	2	1	0	−1	−2	−3
y	6	4	2	0	−2	−4	−6

(d)

x	−5	−4	−3	−2	−1	0	1	2	3	4	5
y	5	4	3	2	1	0	−1	−2	−3	−4	−5

B. 1.

x	0	3	2
y	−3	0	−1

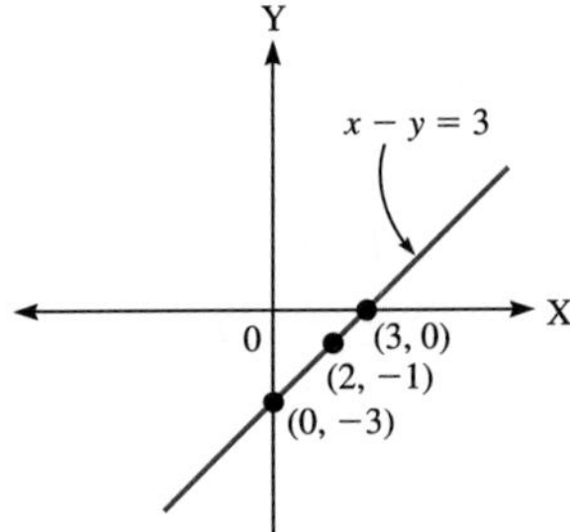

3.

x	0	−2	2
y	0	2	−2

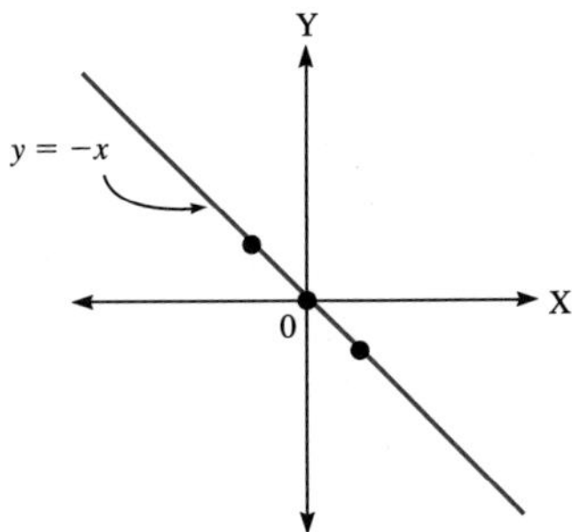

5.

x	0	4	−4
y	−3	0	−6

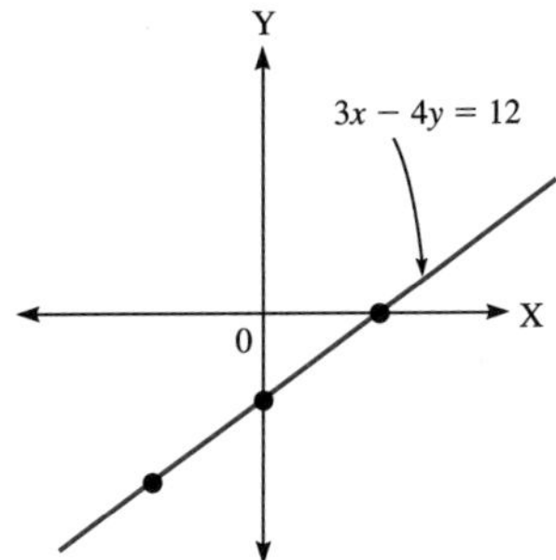

7.

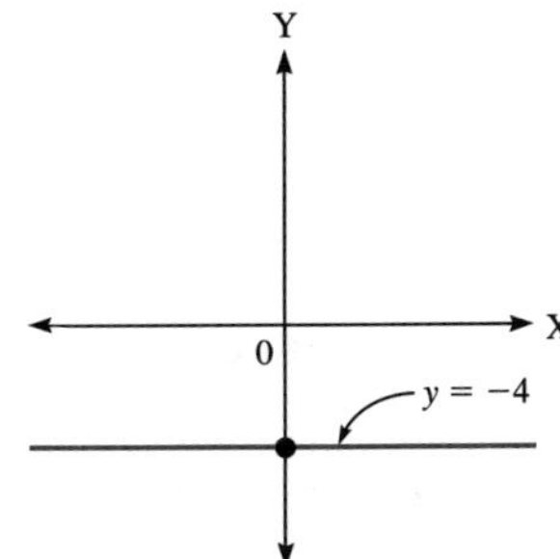

Exercise 4.2

A. 1. For $x + y = 4$

x	0	4	2
y	0	0	2

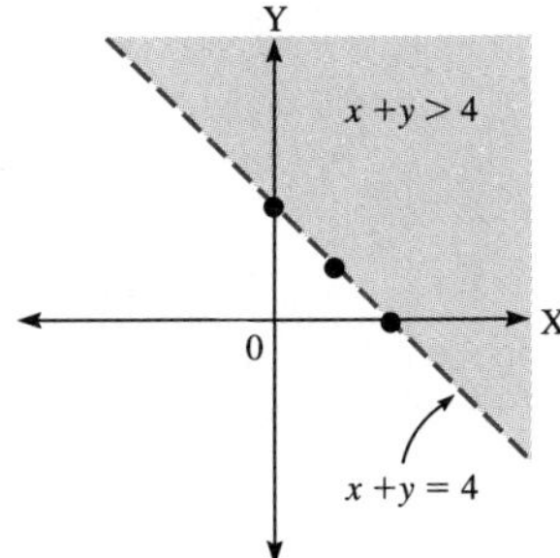

3. For $x - 2y = 4$

x	0	4	−4
y	−2	0	−4

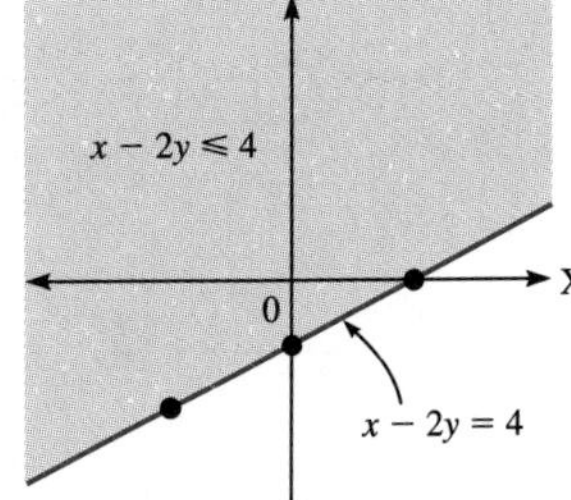

5.

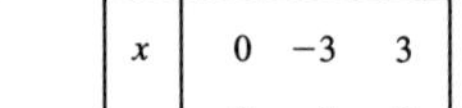

Graph $2x = -3y$

x	0	−3	3
y	0	2	−2

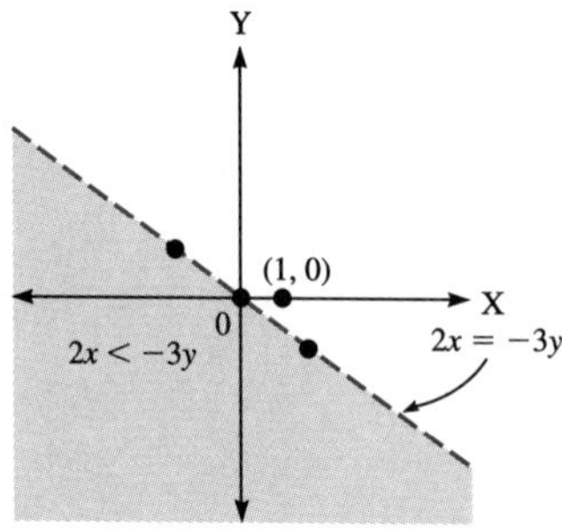

7.

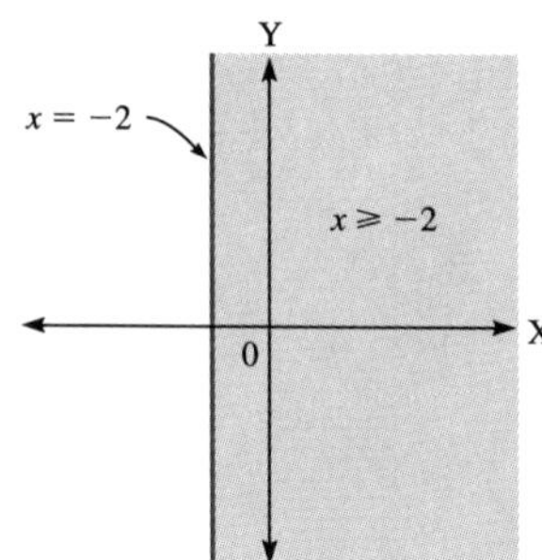

Exercise 4.3

A. 1.

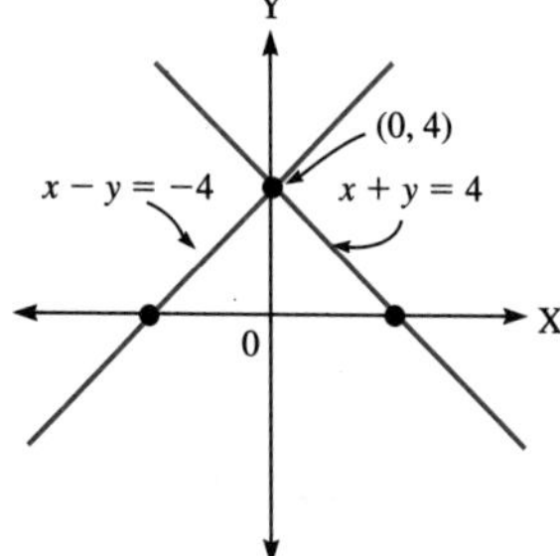

3.

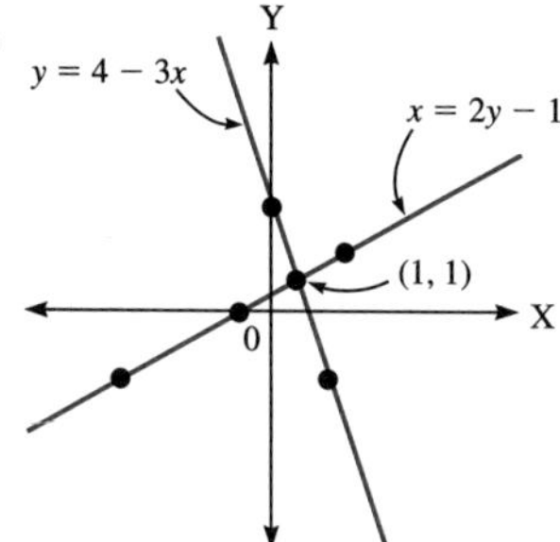

5.

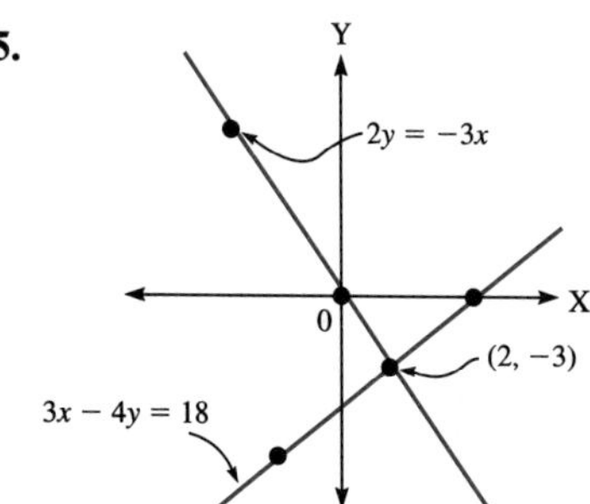

7.

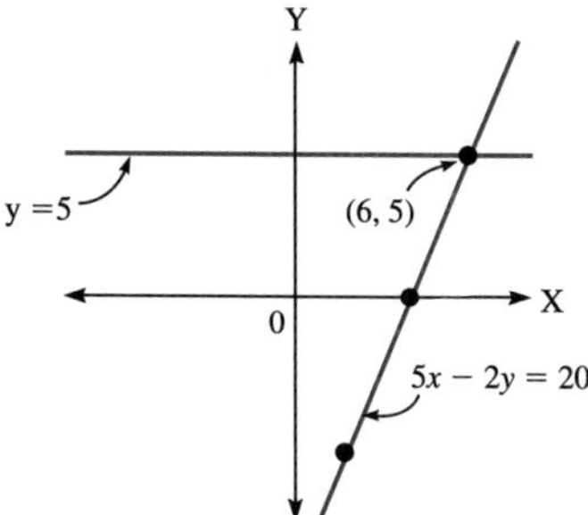

B. 1.

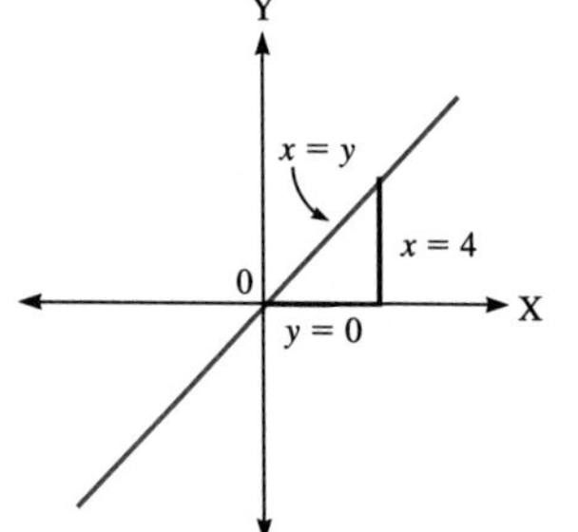

3.

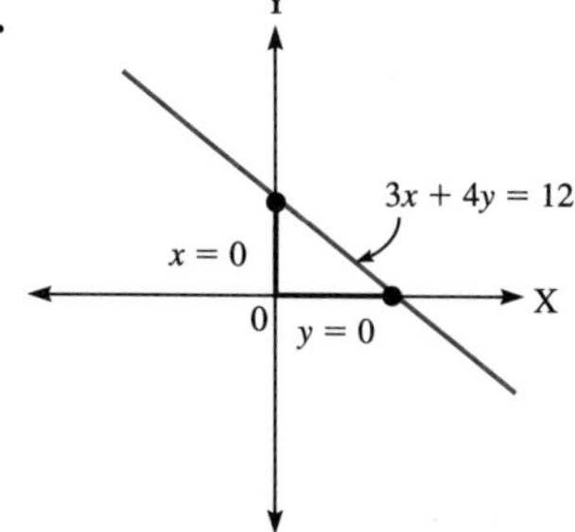

C. 1.

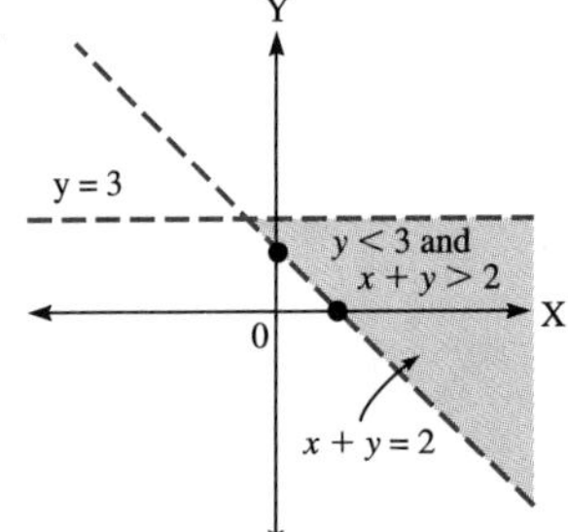

3.

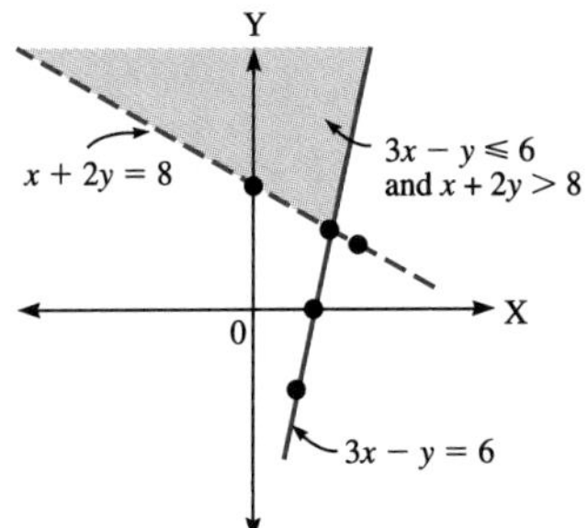

5.

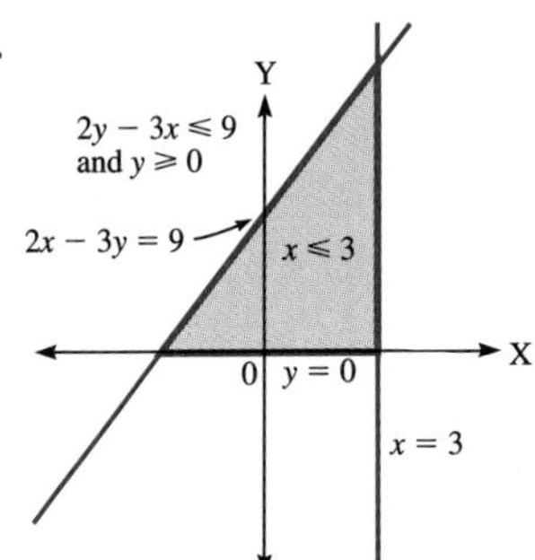

7.

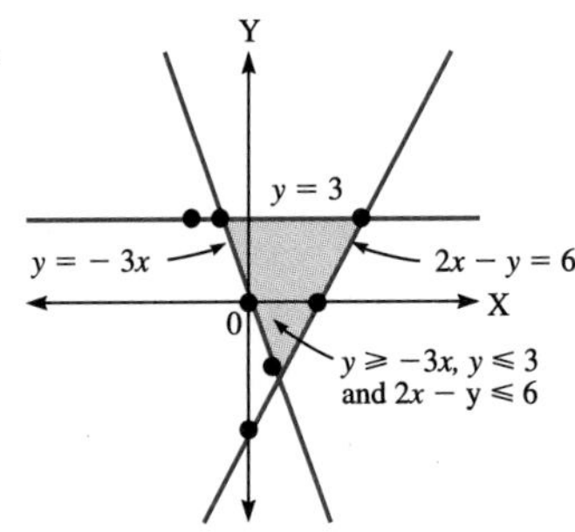

Exercise 4.4

A. 1. $x = -8, y = -1$ **3.** $x = 10, y = 12$ **5.** $x = -3, y = 3$
B. 1. $x = -4, y = 3$ **3.** $x = -1, y = 3$ **5.** $x = 4, y = 3$
C. 1. $x = 12, y = 8$ **3.** $x = 1.5, y = 2.5$ **5.** $x = 6, y = 10$ **7.** $x = \frac{1}{2}, y = \frac{3}{4}$

Exercise 4.5

A. 1. $x = -5, y = 4, z = 3$ **3.** $a = 10, b = 12, c = 15$
5. $m = 0.8, n = 0.6, k = 1.2$

Exercise 4.6

A. 1.

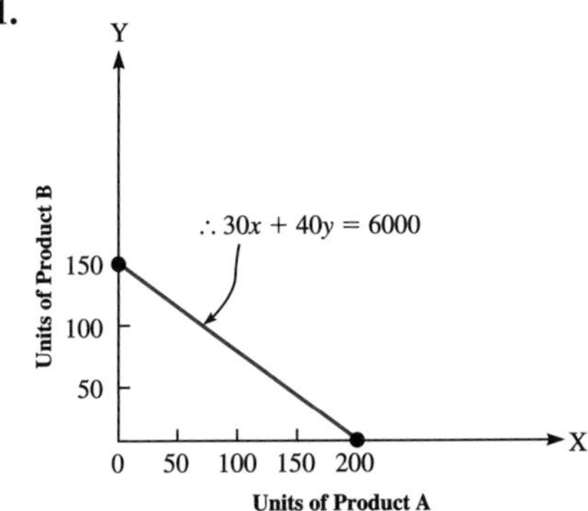

3.

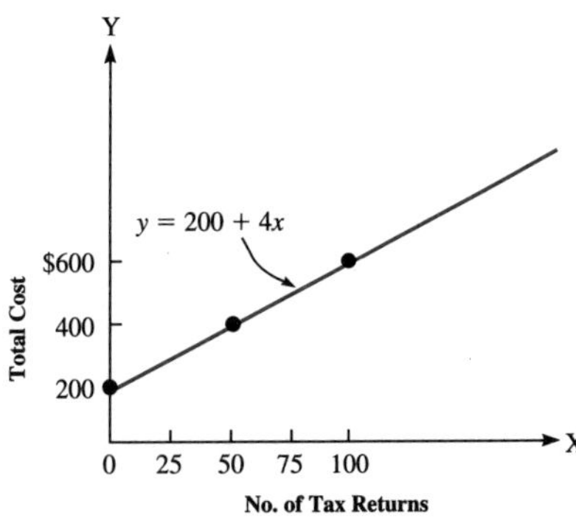

B. 1. 15; 9 **3.** Brand X, 90; No-name, 50 **5.** Kara, $31 500; Fred, $23 500
7. Type A, 42; Type B, 18 **9.** 20 dimes; 56 nickels; 16 quarters

Review exercise

1. (a)

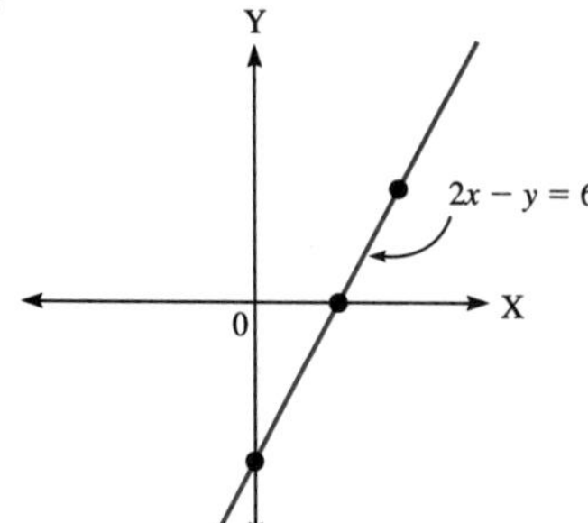

(b)

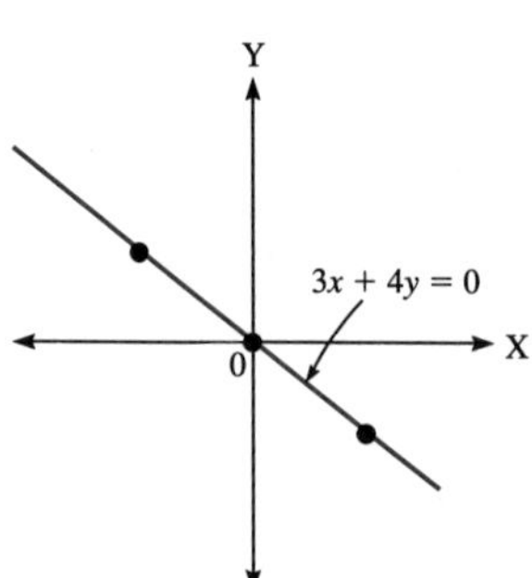

(c)

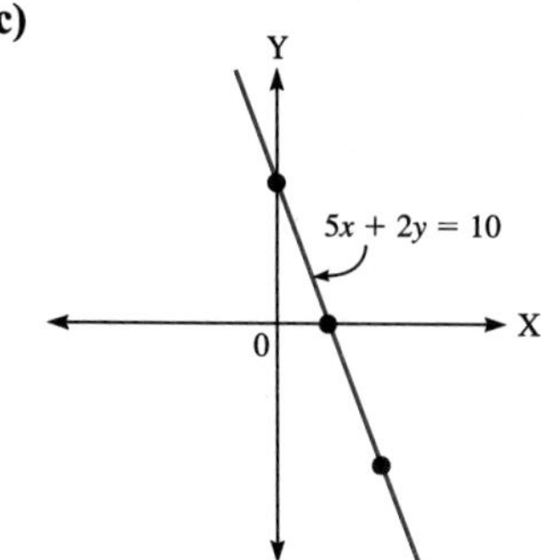

(d)

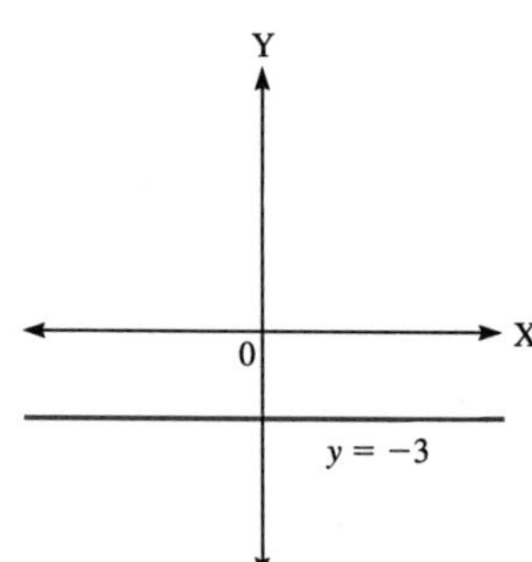

(e)

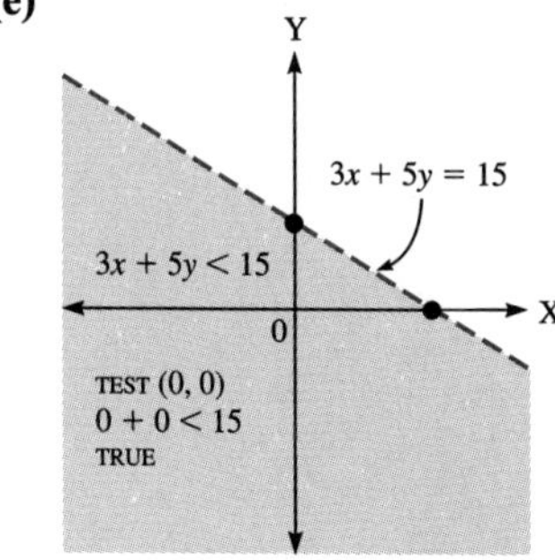

(f)

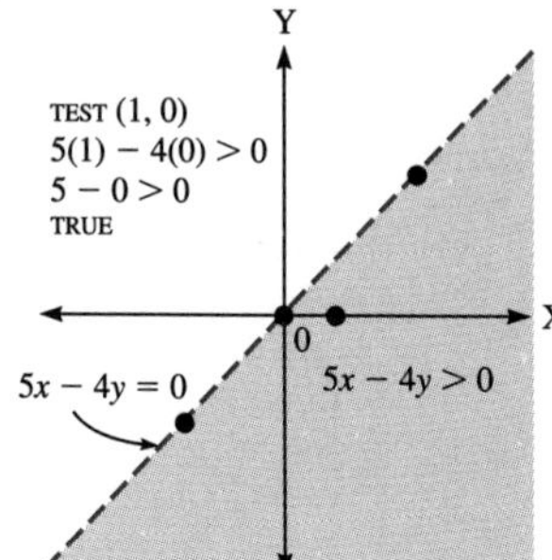

(g)

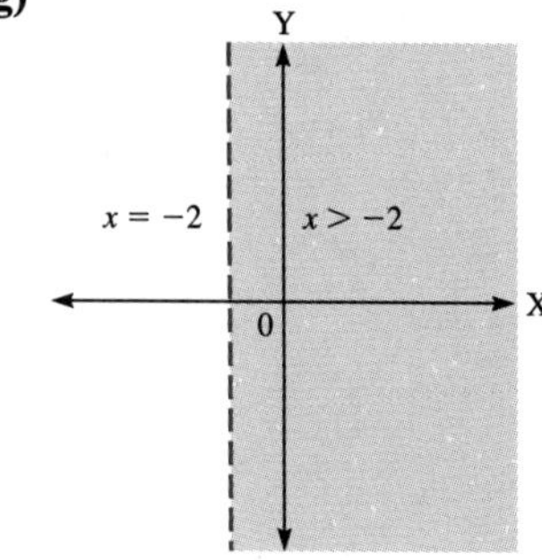

(h)

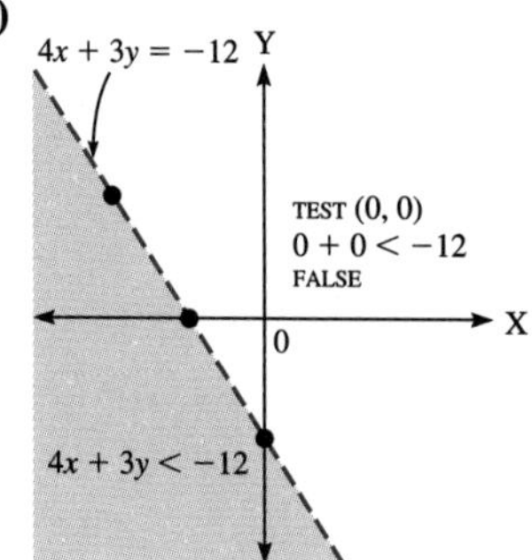

2. (a)

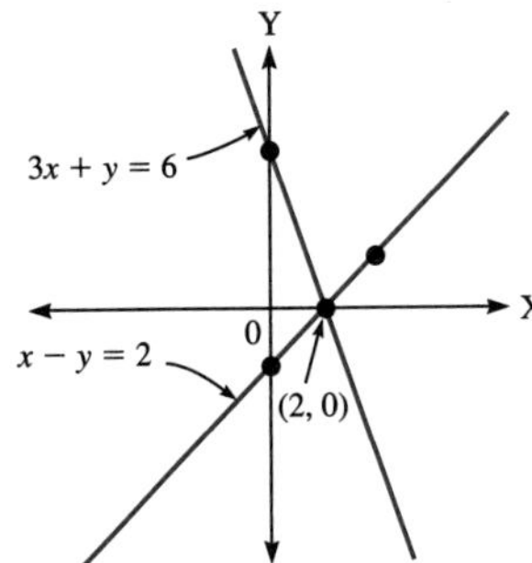
Y
X
0
3x + y = 6
x − y = 2
(2, 0)

(b)

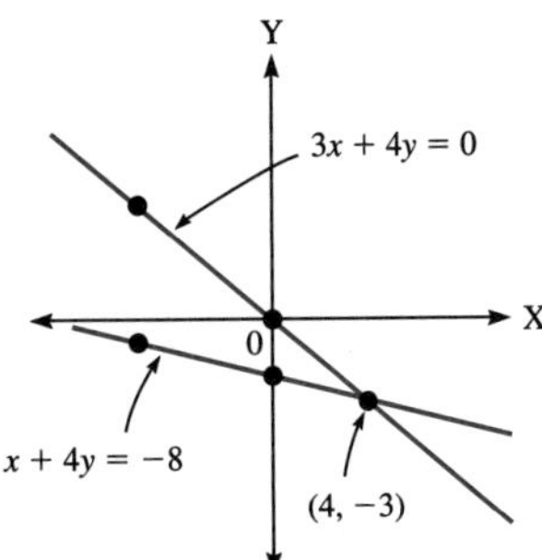
Y
X
0
3x + 4y = 0
x + 4y = −8
(4, −3)

(c)

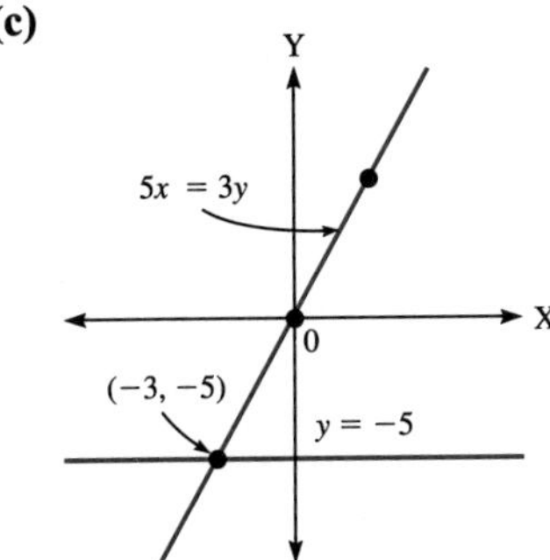
Y
X
0
5x = 3y
(−3, −5)
y = −5

(d)

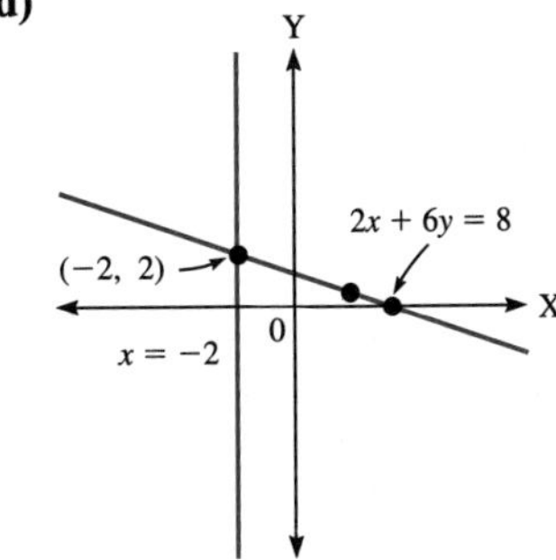
Y
X
0
2x + 6y = 8
(−2, 2)
x = −2

3. (a)

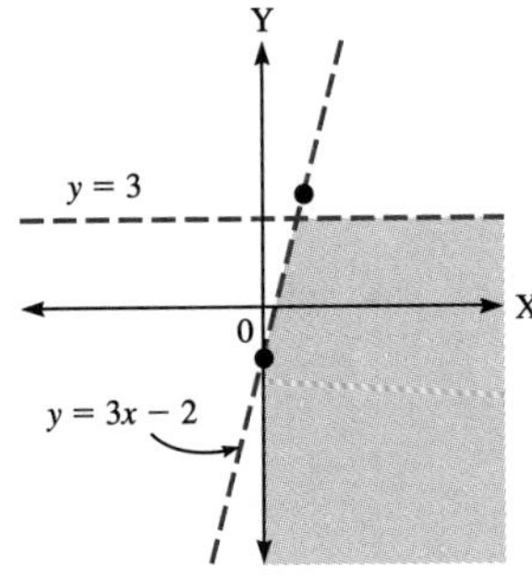
Y
X
0
y = 3
y = 3x − 2

(b)

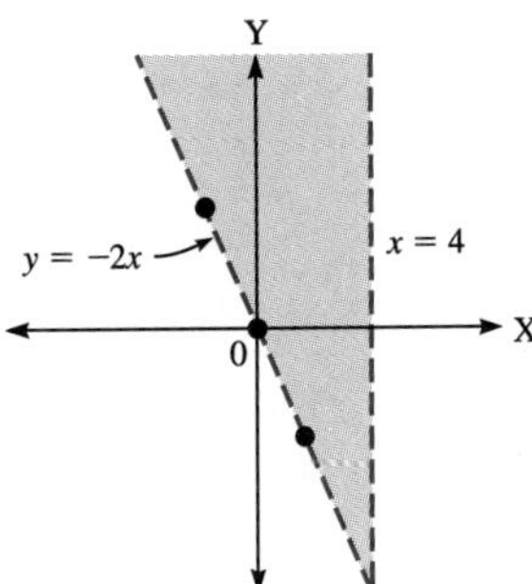
Y
X
0
y = −2x
x = 4

(c)

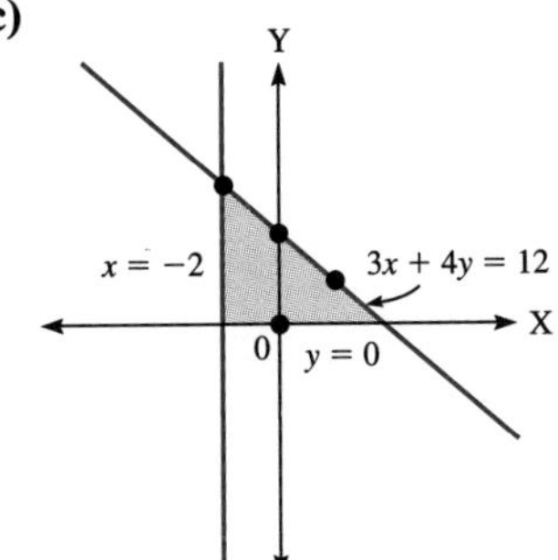
Y
X
0
x = −2
3x + 4y = 12
y = 0

(d)

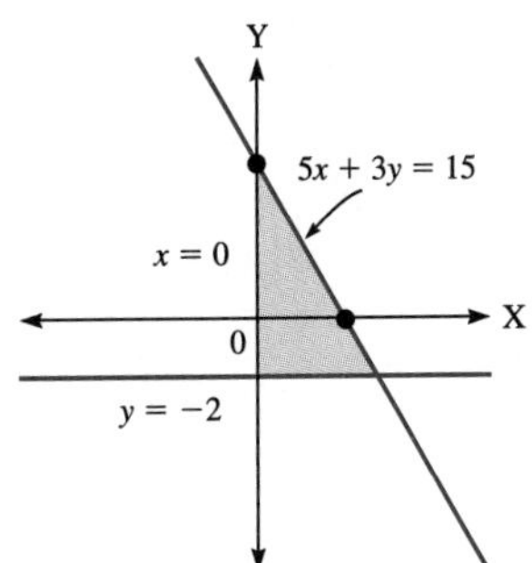
Y
X
0
5x + 3y = 15
x = 0
y = −2

4. (a) $x = -1, y = 1$ **(b)** $x = 5, y = -1$ **(c)** $x = -1, y = 10$
(d) $x = -3, y = 4$ **(e)** $x = 2, y = -3$ **(f)** $x = -4, y = 1$
(g) $a = 4, b = -2, c = 2$ **(h)** $a = 10, b = 6, c = -20$
(i) $a = 1, b = -3, c = +2$ **(j)** $a = -2, b = 1, c = 3$
(k) $m = 6, n = 8, k = 10$ **(l)** $m = \frac{2}{3}, n = \frac{2}{5}, k = \frac{3}{4}$

5. (a) **(b)**

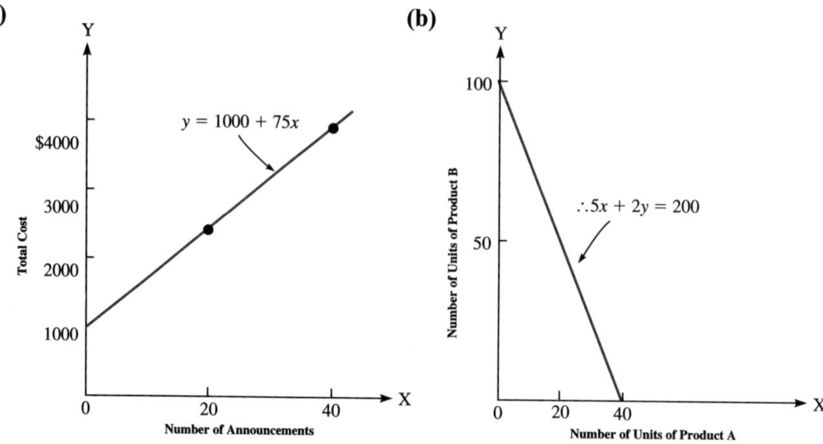

6. (a) first number 8; second number 9 **(b)** 275 at \$2.50; 175 at \$3.50 **(c)** \$105
(d) white \$36; red \$66 **(e)** 17, 25, 35 **(f)** heat \$814; power \$1056; water \$341
(g) direct selling \$37 500; TV advertising \$37 750; newspaper advertising \$12 250
(h) 164 quarters; 16 50¢ coins; 25 \$1 coins

Self-test

1. (a)

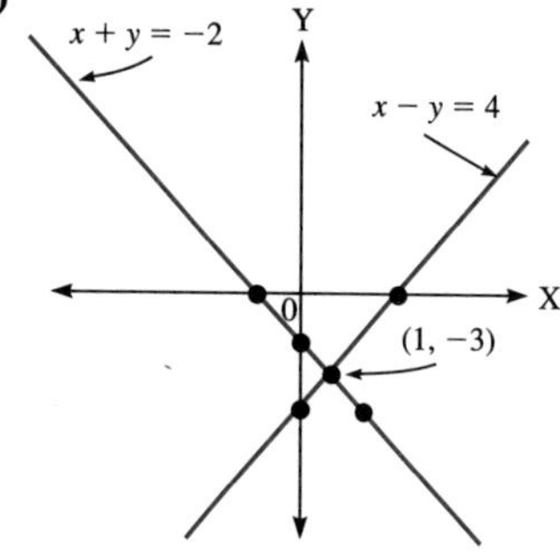

(b)

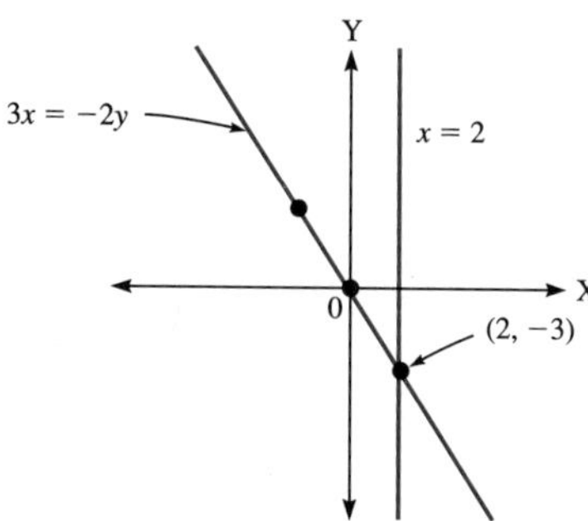

2. (a)

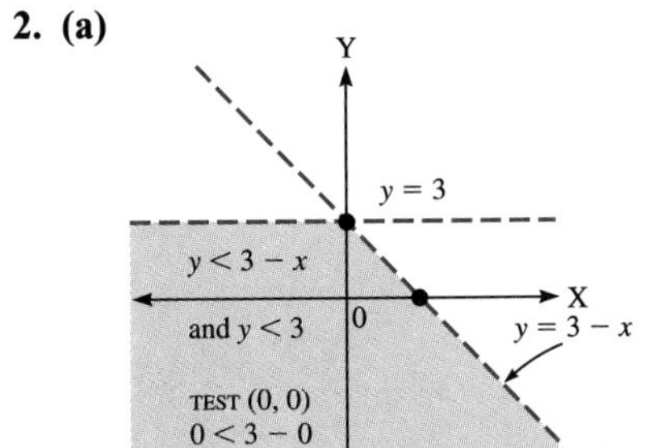

(b)

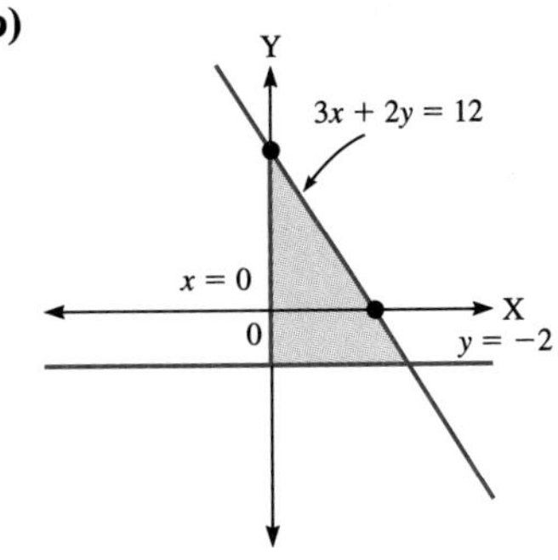

3. (a) $x = 4, y = -3$ **(b)** $x = 0, y = 3$ **(c)** $a = 3, b = 2, c = -2$ **(d)** $a = 2, b = -2, c = 5$ **4.** \$8000; \$4000 **5.** \$7500 **6.** \$1400; \$1680; \$3200

Chapter 5

Exercise 5.1

A. 1. (a) annual depreciation \$3500 **(b)** depreciation year 1 to 4, \$3705.75; year 5 to 7, \$3477.00; year 8 to 10, \$3248.25 **(c)** depreciation per unit \$0.35; year 1 to 4, \$3762.50; year 5 to 7, \$3430.00; year 8 to 10, \$3220.00 **(d)** constant part 636.3636; year 1, \$6363.64; year 10, \$636.35 **(e)** rate 20%; year 1, \$8000.00; year 10, \$368.71 **(f)** rate 18.77476%; year 1, \$7509.90; year 10, \$1155.72 **(g)** rate 20%; year 1, \$8000; year 10, \$1073.74 **B. 1. (a)** \$375 500; \$12 300 **(b)** \$263 000; \$15 000 **(c)** \$259 443.09; \$12 972.15 **(d)** \$253 985.20; \$13 041.02

Exercise 5.2

A. 1. (a) (i) Revenue = $120x$ **(ii)** Cost = $2800 + 50x$

(b)

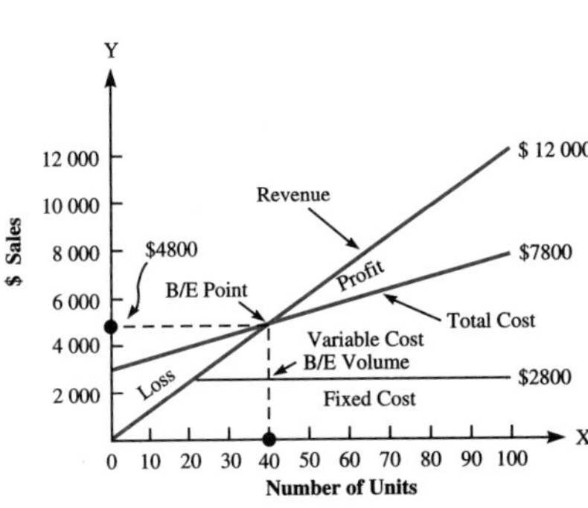

(c) (i) 40 **(ii)** 40% **(iii)** \$4800

3. (a) (i) Revenue $= x$ **(ii)** Cost $= 220\ 000 + 0.45x$

(b)

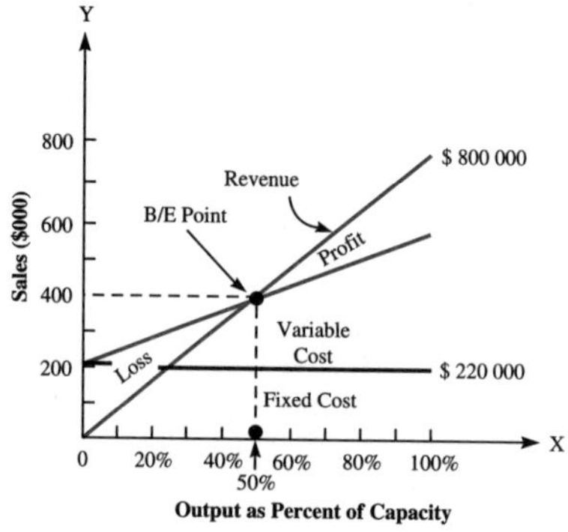

(c) (i) not applicable **(ii)** 50% **(iii)** \$400 000

Review exercise

1. (a) constant value \$265; depreciation year 1, \$2120; year 8, \$265 **(b)** rate 25%; depreciation year 1, \$3000; year 8, nil **(c)** rate 17.97066%; depreciation year 1, \$2156.48; year 8, \$538.93 **2. (a)** \$6784.00; \$1260.80 **(b)** \$1934.77; \$484.92 **(c)** \$6038.19; \$483.06 **(d)** \$1111.79; \$171.92 **3.** constant part is 330; depreciation year 1, \$1980; year 6, \$330 **4.** \$22 903.79 **5.** \$1974.82

6. (a)

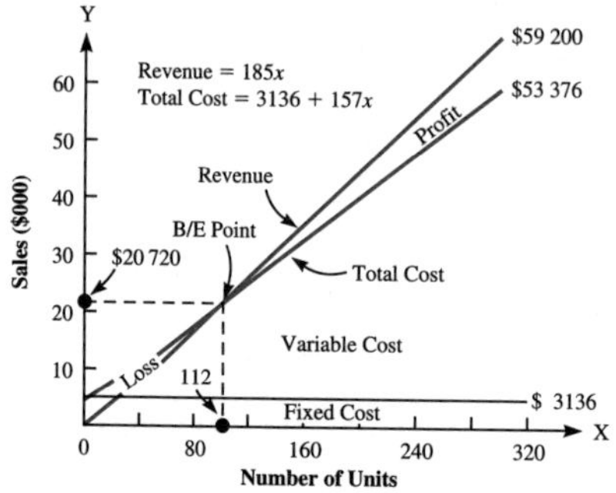

(b) (i) 112 **(ii)** 35% **(iii)** \$20 720 **(c)** (i) 30% **(ii)** 38.75% **(iii)** 70%

7. (a) Revenue $= x$; cost $= 4800 + 0.70x$

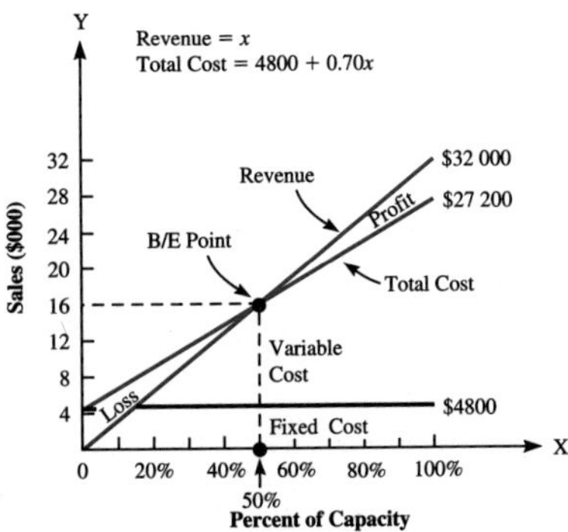

(b) (i) \$16 000 **(ii)** 50%
(c) (i) 43.75% or \$14 000 **(ii)** 39.375% or \$12 600

8. (a)

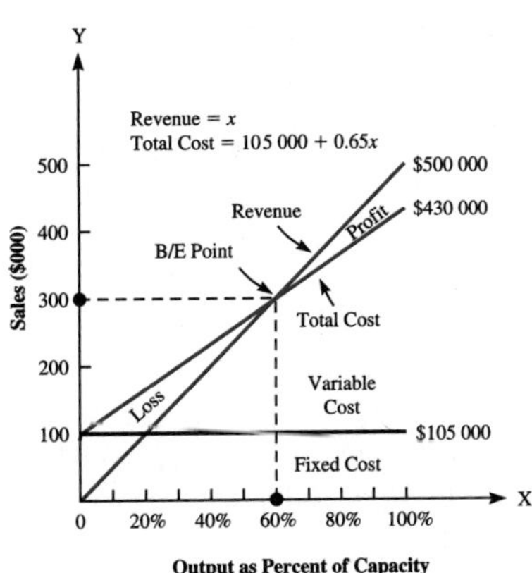

(b) (i) 60% **(ii)** \$300 000 **(c)** \$335 000
9. (a) (i) 96 **(ii)** 64% **(iii)** \$61 440 **(b)** \$73 600 **(c)** 62%

Self-test

1. \$35 000 **2.** \$6100 **3.** \$800.65

4. (a)

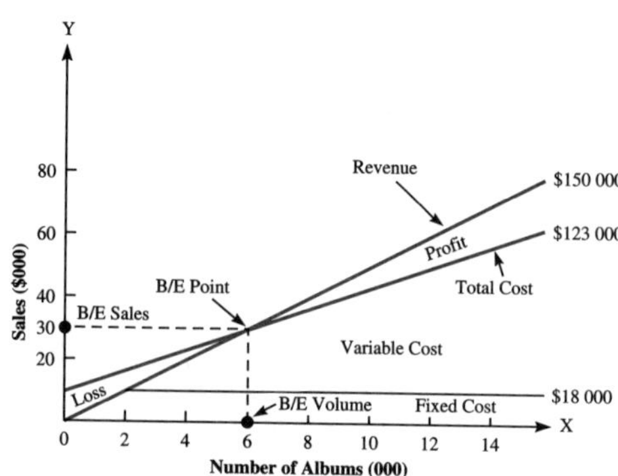

(b) (i) 6000 **(ii)** 60 000 **(iii)** 40% **(c)** 5600 **(d)** 5500
5. (a) (i) \$500 000 **(ii)** 62.5% **(b)** \$525 000

Chapter 6

Exercise 6.1

A. 1. \$13.53 **3.** \$134.96 **5.** $33\frac{1}{3}$% **7.** \$30.24; 32.5% **9.** \$137.89; 48.55%; **11.** \$1583.33; 61% **B. 1. (a)** \$127.68 **(b)** \$112.32 **(c)** 46.8% **3.** 15.9% **5. (a)** 38.75% **(b)** $48.26\frac{2}{3}$% **7.** \$74.10 **9.** 15% **11.** \$426.00 **13.** \$180.00

Exercise 6.2

A. 1. \$640.00 **3.** \$776.11 **5.** \$1136.80 **7.** \$4581.50 **B. 1.** \$582.00; \$850.00 **3.** \$564.50; \$536.28 **5.** \$810.00; \$810.00 **C. 1. (a)** Sept. 10 **(b)** \$5276.85 **(c)** \$103.20 **3.** \$2507.19 **5.** \$2184.00 **7. (a)** \$1164.00 **(b)** \$733.54 **(c)** \$600.00 **9. (a)** \$1925.00 **(b)** \$3400.00

Exercise 6.3

A. 1. (a) \$6.00 **(b)** \$3.84 **(c)** \$2.16 **(d)** 25% **(e)** 20% **3. (a)** \$35.00 **(b)** \$31.50 **(c)** \$3.50 **(d)** $66\frac{2}{3}$% **(e)** 40% **5. (a)** \$10.50 **(b)** \$12.75 **(c)** −\$2.25 **(d)** $38\frac{8}{9}$% **(e)** 28% **B. 1.** \$6.25; 25%; 20% **3.** \$102.40; 60%; 37.5% **5.** \$75.95; \$21.70; 28.6% **7.** \$44.24; \$22.12; $33\frac{1}{3}$% **9.** \$78.10; \$46.86; 150% **11.** \$111.30; \$133.56; 20% **C. 1.** \$5.12 **3. (a)** \$75.00 **(b)** \$63.00 **(c)** \$8160 **(d)** 147.14% **5. (a)** 120% **(b)** 54.55% **7. (a)** \$22.80 **(b)** \$26.22 **(c)** 13.04% **9. (a)** \$53.25 **(b)** 28.57% **11. (a)** \$32.00 **(b)** 150%

Exercise 6.4

A. 1. \$68.00; \$85.00; \$62.90 **3.** 200%; \$120.00; 37.5% **5.** \$45.50; 24.36%; \$96.25
B. 1. \$51.00; \$59.00; −\$8.00 **3.** \$96.40; \$30.65; \$7.91 **5.** \$160.00; 12%; \$124.20
C. 1. (a) \$228.69 **(b)** 54% **3.** \$70.00 **5. (a)** 40% **(b)** −\$8.00 **(c)** 10.294% **(d)** $9\frac{1}{3}$% **7.** −\$6.50 **9. (a)** \$19.00 **(b)** \$4.00 **(c)** 21.05% **11.** −\$97.50 **13.** −\$82.50

Review exercise

1. (a) \$31.92 **(b)** \$24.08 **(c)** 43% **2.** 37.5% **3.** 45.66% **4.** \$2.16 **5.** 15% **6.** \$465.00 **7.** \$30.00 **8. (a)** June 10 **(b)** \$2584.00 **9.** \$2520.67 **10. (a)** \$1940.00 **(b)** \$2813.00 **11. (a)** \$2000.00 **(b)** \$9310.00 **12. (a)** \$1645.00 **(b)** \$1500.00 **13. (a)** \$7.92 **(b)** \$3.12 **(c)** 39.4% **(d)** 65% **(e)** \$6.96 **(f)** −\$0.96 **14. (a)** \$90.00 **(b)** \$58.50 **(c)** 53.85% **(d)** \$74.88 **(e)** −\$6.48 **15. (a)** \$6.60 **(b)** 25.9% **16. (a)** \$77.50 **(b)** 42.86% **17. (a)** \$1217.70 **(b)** 32% **18.** \$240.00 **19. (a)** 25% **(b)** \$3.06 **(c)** 25% **20. (a)** −\$0.60 **(b)** 21.25% **21. (a)** \$253.00 **(b)** \$189.75 **(c)** 25% **22. (a)** −\$13.20 **(b)** 25% **23.** 12.5% **24. (a)** \$189.00 **(b)** 21.25% **(c)** $133\frac{1}{3}$% **25. (a)** \$154.00 **(b)** 27.27% **(c)** \$138.95 **(d)** 21% **26. (a)** \$2152.40 **(b)** 69.43% **(c)** 40.98%

Self-test

1. \$295.77 **2.** 37.5% **3.** 50.5% **4.** 6.5% **5.** \$1635.04 **6.** \$1940.00 **7.** \$1450.00 **8.** \$1587.50 **9.** \$240.00 **10.** \$1010.00 **11.** \$348.36 **12.** \$1360.00 **13.** 180% **14.** \$110.00 **15.** 23.4% **16.** \$1130.00 **17.** −\$660.45 **18.** −\$94.77

Chapter 7

Exercise 7.1

A. 1. 0.125; 1.25 **3.** 0.1025; $\frac{165}{365}$

Exercise 7.2

A. 1. 112 days **3.** 166 days **B. 1.** 244 days **3.** 341 days

Exercise 7.3

A. 1. \$945.00 **3.** \$215.80 **5.** \$75.34 **B. 1.** \$10.87 **3.** \$31.71

Exercise 7.4

A. 1. $1224.00 **3.** $10.75% **5.** 14 months **7.** 144 days **B. 1.** $3296.00 **3.** 9.5% **5.** 11 months **7.** $876.00

Exercise 7.5

A. 1. $516.16 **3.** $892.26

Exercise 7.6

A. 1. $266.00; $39.90 **3.** $517.50; $547.17 **5.** $2025.00; 292 days
B. 1. $1222.00 **3.** $1704.60

Exercise 7.7

A. 1. $829.33 **3.** $617.50 **5.** $1108.24 **7.** $885.05 **9.** $622.41 **11.** $1161.61 **B. 1.** $1156.80 **3.** $519.17 **5.** $1438.68 **7.** $943.21

Review exercise

1. (a) 172 days **(b)** 186 days **2. (a)** $63.98 **(b)** $67.15 **3. (a)** $1160.00 **(b)** $601.77 **4. (a)** 7.5% **(b)** 265 days **(c)** 11% **(d)** 10 months **5. (a)** $640.00 **(b)** $5709.97 **6.** $1225.03 **7.** $1175.06 **8.** 9.25% **9.** 16.25% **10.** 7 months **11.** 196 days **12.** $4642.75 **13.** $1661.77 **14.** $1440.00 **15.** $3200.00 **16.** $3467.89 **17.** $1736.47 **18.** $3127.53 **19.** $2682.09 **20.** $1022.07 **21.** $3474.83 **22.** $2351.17 **23.** $1559.86 **24.** $3544.91 **25.** $961.50 **26.** $1056.12 **27.** $1694.41 **28.** $1850.98

Self-test

1. $64.20 **2.** 9 months **3.** 12.5% **4.** $9797.92 **5.** $5901.04 **6.** $4781.68 **7.** $4484.94 **8.** 14% **9.** 359 days **10.** $1372.91 **11.** $7293.39 **12.** $51.47 **13.** $1163.85 **14.** $2942.86 **15.** $1959.52 **16.** $1335.77

Chapter 8

Exercise 8.1

A. 1. December 30, 1994 **3.** $530.00 **5.** 154 days **7.** $560.19
B. 1. (a) March 3, 1996 **(b)** 155 days **(c)** $42.81 **(d)** $882.81 **3. (a)** April 4, 1997 **(b)** 63 days **(c)** $22.65 **(d)** $1272.65

Exercise 8.2

A. 1. $644.61 **3.** $837.19

Exercise 8.3

A. 1. $455.00 **B. 1.** $1166.60 **3.** $1622.66

Exercise 8.4

A. 1. $978.68; $21.32 **3.** $857.48; $12.43

Exercise 8.5

A. 1. $33.75 **3.** $603.91 **B. 1.** $1980.49 **3.** $449.94

Exercise 8.6

A. 1. Totals are $1267.29; $67.29; $1200.00

Review exercise

1. (a) November 2 **(b)** $79.45 **(c)** $1679.45 **2.** $1316.34 **3.** $750.00 **4.** $3029.62 **5.** $5251.51 **6.** $940.00 **7.** $824.74 **8.** $1899.36; $29.84 **9.** $1259.04 **10.** $712.18; $19.23 **11.** $932.04 **12.** $187.56 **13.** Totals are $3168.05; $168.05; $3000.00

Self-test

1. $31.79 **2.** $1169.77 **3.** $1160.00 **4.** $1747.34 **5.** $1638.54 **6.** $353.21 **7.** $700.69 **8.** Totals are $4149.24; $149.24; $4000.00

Chapter 9

Exercise 9.1

A. 1. 0.12; 5 **3.** 0.03375; 36 **5.** 0.0775; 27 **7.** 0.0125; 150 **9.** 0.06125; 9
B. 1. 1.7623417 **3.** 3.3033821 **5.** 7.5035457 **7.** 6.4454727 **9.** 1.7074946
C. 1. (a) 48 **(b)** 3.5% **(c)** 1.035^{48} **(d)** 5.2135890

Exercise 9.2

A. 1. $713.39 **3.** $2233.21 **5.** $5468.38 **7.** $17 519.84 **9.** $815.99
B. 1. $9167.68; $4167.68 **3.** $2075.07 **5. (a)** $305.90 **(b)** $318.08 **(c)** $324.80 **(d)** $329.55 **7. (a)** $198.98; $98.98 **(b)** 395.93; $295.93 **(c)** $1567.57; $1467.57 **(d)** 161 **11. (a)** Bank $9721.46; Credit union $9783.23 (preferred) **(b)** $61.77 **C. 1.** $4513.28 **3.** $1714.21 **5.** $3942.41 **7.** $1102.13 **9.** $2830.30

Exercise 9.3

A. 1. $574.37 **3.** $245.31 **5.** $409.16 **7.** $500.24 **B. 1.** $721.65; $878.35 **3.** $762.84 **5.** $3129.97

Exercise 9.4

A. 1. $1494.52; $505.48 **3.** $2603.25; $1527.78 **5.** $1830.33; $493.70 **B. 1.** $3681.95 **3.** $1084.96 **5.** $4222.77 **7.** $1532.09

Exercise 9.5

A. 1. $7153.84 **3.** $2537.13 **5.** $1742.51 **7.** $641.36 **9.** $2421.79 **B. 1.** $4226.45 **3.** $1536.03 **5.** $1022.56 **C. 1. (a)** $2269.71 **(b)** $2847.12 **(c)** $4000.00 **(d)** $7049.37 **3.** $6805.32 **5.** $693.04 **7.** $2653.87 **9. (a)** $3113.90 **(b)** $1847.95 **11. (a)** $646.41 **(b)** $946.41

Review exercise

1. (a) $1198.28 **(b)** $1221.61 **(c)** $1227.05 **2. (a)** $15 191.84 **(b)** $24 317.66 **(c)** $80 919.18 **3. (a)** $2890.09 **(b)** $890.09 **4. (a)** $6519.80 **(b)** $6530.25 **5. (a)** 15 190.57; $13 390.57 **(b)** $9363.67; $8113.67 **6. (a)** $1770.06; $1829.94 **(b)** $6424.27; $2575.73 **7.** $9791.31 **8.** $5537.42 **9.** $643.23 **10.** $3190.62 **11.** $8855.18 **12.** $15 636.83 **13.** $5051.70 **14.** $1344.92; $2655.08 **15.** $641.28 **16.** 43 059.20 **17.** $3680.65 **18.** $14 417.83 **19.** $109 067.46 **20. (a)** $2294.73 **(b)** $2743.63 **(c)** $3922.02 **21.** 3950.07 **22.** $5000.01 **23.** $3036.21 **24.** $1857.55 **25.** $3271.60 **26.** $3574.57

Self-test

1. $898.83 **2.** $2027.06 **3.** 2.7118780 **4.** $11 078.60 **5.** $7941.94 **6.** $15 714.67 **7.** $775.07 **8.** $4504.29 **9.** $833.11 **10.** $18 715.77 **11.** $3251.23 **12.** $2971.97

Chapter 10

Exercise 10.1

A. 1. (a) $4152.58 **(c)** $3820.34 **2. (a)** $429.44 **(c)** $1120.13 **B. 1.** $6625.24 **3.** $1102.89 **5.** $34 961.66

Exercise 10.2

A. 1. (a) $155.03 **(c)** $4344.21 **2. (a)** $3050.92 **(c)** $250.75 **B. 1.** $856.46 **3.** $8452.52 **5.** $2346.36

Exercise 10.3

A. 1. \$2604.43 **3.** \$2642.50 **5.** \$1056.70 **7.** \$2201.49 **B. 1.** \$3150.53 **3.** \$1997.42 **5.** \$2174.95 **7.** \$1830.97

Exercise 10.4

A. 1. (a) 9.726% **(c)** 16.075% **(e)** 15.419% **2. (a)** 12.5% **(c)** 16.2% **(e)** 9.778% **3. (a)** 13.4 years **(c)** 117.8 months **(e)** 20.149 quarters **B. 1.** 9.237% **3. (a)** 10.402% **(b)** 7.585% **5.** 6.991% **7.** 17.998% **9.** 9.329 years **11.** 17.501 years **13.** 2.818 years **15.** November 1, 1997 **17.** 21 months

Exercise 10.5

A. 1. (a) n = 10 quarters (2.5 years) **(c)** n = 1.2068263 (37 days) **2. (a)** 12.891% **(c)** 14.974% **3. (a)** \$608.78 **(c)** \$2316.07 **4. (a)** \$1487.00 **(c)** \$3038.52 **5. (a)** 25.232% **B. 1.** n = 32.282417 months (2 years, 252 days) **3.** n = 7.137049 half-years (3 years, 208 days) **5.** 7.385% **7.** \$5.88 **9.** \$2470.63 **11.** 5.031% **13. (a)** 11.552453 years (11 years, 202 days) **(b)** 4.5 years **15.** 13.76%

Review exercise

1. \$9548.77 **2.** \$11 102.50 **3.** \$10 681.77 **4.** \$6913.53 **5.** \$55 276.80 **6.** \$30 851.84 **7.** \$996.10 **8.** \$4194.33 **9.** \$1040.76 **10.** 14.072% **11.** 6.03% **12.** 10.665 months (325 days) **13.** \$1269.12 **14.** \$690.09 **15.** 22.571 half-years (11 years, 95 days) **16.** 18.235% **17. (a)** \$14 772.44 **(b)** \$23 450.65 **18. (a)** \$6703.20 **(b)** \$3576.00 **19. (a)** 13.08% **(b)** 14.35% **(c)** 8.833% **(d)** 16.99% **(e)** 17.35% **20. (a)** 11.02% **(b)** 13.32% **(c)** 9.417% **21. (a)** 18.22% **(b)** 18.65% **22. (a)** n = 16 half-years (8 years) **(b)** n = 24.958883 quarters (6 years, 88 days) **(c)** n = 39.576737 months (3 years, 109 days) **(d)** n = 5.3319014 (5 years, 122 days) **23.** n = 3.1637199 months (97 days) **24.** n = 3.5228126 half-years (1 year, 278 days) **25.** n = 15.289101 quarters (3 years, 301 days—September 28, 1997) **26.** \$2013.35 **27.** \$6324.34 **28.** 42.6 months **29.** 7.742 years (7 years, 271 days) **30.** 6.880%

Self-test

1. 63 months **2.** \$2177.36 **3.** 16.07545% **4.** 12.7932% **5.** 19 months **6.** 13.456508% **7.** 9.7134 years **8.** 10.0% **9.** \$24 253.31 **10.** \$12 984.30 **11.** \$756.81 **12.** \$1494.03

Chapter 11

Exercise 11.1

A. 1. (a) annuity certain **(b)** annuity due **(c)** general annuity **3. (a)** perpetuity **(b)** deferred annuity **(c)** general annuity **5. (a)** annuity certain **(b)** deferred annuity due **(c)** simple annuity

Exercise 11.2

A. 1. 54 193.60 **3.** $59 185.19 **5.** 17 915.08 **B. 1.** $22 413.48 **3.** $73 587.28 **5. (a)** $41 220.21 **(b)** $4500.00 **(c)** $36 720.21 **7.** $62 177.25

Exercise 11.3

A. 1. $9515.19 **3.** $24 213.90 **5.** $6019.47 **B. 1.** $6897.00 **3. (a)** $9906.20 **(b)** $2093.80 **5. (a)** $2399.98 **(b)** $495.90 **7.** $4245.42 **9. (a)** $12 000.00 **(b)** $1570.82 **(c)** $12 928.59 **(d)** $928.59 **(e)** $48.38

Exercise 11.4

A. 1. $821.39 **3.** $2002.75 **5.** $272.73 **B. 1.** $207.87 **3.** $868.95 **5.** $271.34 **7.** $3141.41 **9.** $614.89

Exercise 11.5

A. 1. n = 14.6023569 years (14 years, 8 months) **3.** n = 247.77343 months (20 years, 8 months) **5.** n = 12.298243 half-years (6 years, 2 months)
B. 1. n = 74.4983386 months (6 years, 3 months) **3.** n = 17.531631 quarters (4 years, 5 months)

Exercise 11.6

A. 1. 16% **3.** 9% **B. 1.** 12.5% **3.** 13% **5.** 16.765%

Review exercise

1. (a) $26 734.60 **(b)** $17 280.00 **(c)** $9454.60 **2. (a)** $53 090.08 **(b)** $85 500.00 **(c)** $32 409.92 **3.** $554.81 **4.** $374.80 **5.** $722.62 **6.** $4446.79 **7.** 12.73 half-years (6 years, 5 months) **8.** 10.43% **9.** 16.94% **10.** $232.12 **11.** n = 19.770076 half-years (9 years, 11 months) **12.** n = 157.83982 months (13 years, 2 months) **13.** 6.05% **14.** 9.65%

15. $101 517.64 **16.** $3386.22 **17.** $188.56 **18.** n = 12.5 half-years (6 years, 3 months) **19.** 14.43% **20.** $24 418.00 **21.** $34 031.63 **22.** 5.881% **23.** $26 945.42 **24.** 24.97 quarters (6 years, 3 months) **25.** $910.15 **26.** $4964.12 **27.** **(a)** $12 591.67 **(b)** $3208.64 **(c)** $15 015.80 **(d)** $208.64 **28.** $6446.13 **29.** n = 28.811254 months (2 years, 5 months) **30.** **(a)** 9.725% **(b)** n = 97.758303 months (8 years, 2 months)

Self-test

1. $540.36 **2.** $18 277.44 **3.** $7882.30 **4.** 10.90% **5.** n = 38.37 **6.** $12 562.27 **7.** 5.704% **8.** $12 308.20 **9.** $60 946.71 **10.** $5231.73 **11.** $6056.04 **12.** $837.27 **13.** $2460.25 **14.** $937.19

Chapter 12

Exercise 12.1

A. 1. $135 334.71; $71 813.10 **3.** $140 009.31; $23 083.77 **5.** $43 738.24; $7278.61 **B. 1.** $39 593.70 **3.** $33 338.44 **5.** **(a)** $1238.56 **(b)** $1575.00 **(c)** $336.44 **7.** **(a)** $47 435.50 **(b)** $28 235.50 **9.** $1899.50

Exercise 12.2

A. 1. $80.80 **3.** $1448.69 **5.** n = 112.5892 months (9 years, 5 months) **7.** n = 7.7784905 years (7 years, 10 months) **9.** 13.495% **11.** 12.5% **B. 1.** $352.61 **3.** n = 27.916189 quarters (7 years) **5.** 7.0% **7.** $2568.82 **9.** n = 109.48123 months (9 years, 2 months) **11.** 16.165%

Exercise 12.3

A. 1. $5048.76 **3.** $1325.85 **5.** $150.35 **B. 1.** $91 086.44 **3.** **(a)** $6265.33 **(b)** $19 200.00 **(c)** $12 934.67

Exercise 12.4

A. 1. $576.10 **3.** $5239.14 **5.** n = 42.75398 quarters (10 years, 9 months) **B. 1.** $10 203.89 **3.** n = 39.878728 months (3 years, 4 months) **5.** $8822.89 **7.** $4880.66 **9.** n = 54.465762 months (4 years, 7 months)

Exercise 12.5

A. 1. $73 529.41 **3.** $12 029.76 **B. 1.** $27 951.82 **3.** $331.04

Review exercise

1. **(a)** \$11 223.39; \$5799.35 **(b)** \$11 728.44; \$6060.33 **2.** **(a)** \$6172.13; \$3823.78 **(b)** \$6141.42; \$3804.76 **3.** \$28 344.35 **4.** \$50 236.74 **5.** **(a)** \$411.57 **(b)** \$403.50 **6.** **(a)** \$201.34 **(b)** \$202.85 **7.** \$538.40 **8.** **(a)** \$1226.81 **(b)** \$1211.66 **9.** n = 89.05638 months (7 years, 6 months)
10. n = 11.320563 half-years (5 years, 8 months) **11.** 12.33% **12.** 25.10%
13. 124 638.48 **14.** \$16 932.74 **15.** \$361.31 **16.** \$1184.68 **17.** \$134 615.38
18. \$92 210.53 **19.** **(a)** \$2638.84 **(b)** \$3444.00 **(c)** \$805.16
20. **(a)** \$12 743.59 **(b)** \$7200.00 **(c)** \$5543.59 **21.** n = 16.502949 years (16 years, 7 months) **22.** n = 106.15677 months (8 years, 11 months)
23. \$32 695.51 **24.** \$46 807.18 **25.** **(a)** \$15 749.42 **(b)** 3149.42 **(c)** 432.91 **(d)** \$8179.68 **26.** **(a)** \$85 882.89 **(b)** \$118 117.11 **(c)** \$196.16 **(d)** \$168 691.20 **27.** n = 31.367147 months (2 years, 8 months)
28. n = 53.47007 quarters (13 years, 5 months)
29. n = 83.065997 quarters (20 years, 10 months)
30. n = 146.61299 months (12 years, 3 months)

Self-test

1. \$84 209.75 **2.** \$153 600 **3.** 180 months **4.** \$43 360.62 **5.** \$56 023.13
6. \$9207.27 **7.** 15.6% **8.** 285 months **9.** \$1258.38 **10.** 19.91%
11. \$625.42 **12.** \$2012.54

Chapter 13

Exercise 13.1

A. **1.** \$45 855.46 **3.** \$38 312.27 **5.** \$64 166.42 **7.** \$38 545.95
B. **1.** \$23 268.48 **3.** \$2326.66 **5.** **(a)** \$13 265.50 **(b)** \$3265.50
7. \$77 934.83

Exercise 13.2

A. **1.** \$47 853.23 **3.** \$35 530.59 **5.** \$3993.29 **7.** \$34 627.57
B. **1.** \$6281.74 **3.** \$31 736.56 **5.** **(a)** \$25 786.03 **(b)** \$9213.97
7. \$80 000.00 **9.** \$15 592.21

Exercise 13.3

A. **1.** \$702.87 **3.** n = 80.878233 (half-years) **5.** 16.94% **7.** \$271.68
9. n = 58.307344 (months) **11.** 17.0% **B.** **1.** \$330.63 **3.** \$117.26
5. n = 105.21875 (months) **7.** n = 147.86752 (months) **9.** 10.778% **11.** 9.24%

Exercise 13.4

A. 1. \$62 800.18 **3.** \$11 304.61 **5.** \$716.80 **7.** \$903.61
9. $n = 24.27752$ (half-years) **11.** $n = 22.559972$ (quarters) **13.** 11.28%
15. 4.89% **B. 1.** \$70 213.74 **3.** \$21 677.07 **5.** \$459.47
7. $n = 52.541832$ (quarters) **9.** 14.97%

Exercise 13.5

A. 1. \$10 272.72 **3.** \$3135.48 **5.** \$147.55 **7.** $n = 12.400424$ (years)
B. 1. \$40 000.51 **3.** \$2361.32 **5.** $n = 12.359779$ (years)

Exercise 13.6

A. 1. \$91 027.09 **3.** \$88 446.04 **B. 1.** \$132.86 **3.** \$96 147.23 **5.** \$1393.91

Review exercise

1. (a) \$19 792.33 **(b)** \$20 392.06 **2. (a)** \$28 435.42 **(b)** \$28 552.68
3. (a) \$42 902.49 **(b)** \$39 344.62 **(c)** \$18 913.98 **(d)** \$24 739.60
(e) \$49 140.05 **(f)** \$52 640.05 **4. (a)** \$22 492.54 **(b)** \$20 000.05
(c) \$6407.77 **(d)** \$4668.08 **(e)** \$23 632.98 **(f)** \$23 872.98 **5. (a)** \$16.44
(b) \$500.37 **6. (a)** \$61.82 **(b)** \$1261.46 **7. (a)** \$576.59 **(b)** \$985.49
(c) \$3855.55 **(d)** \$2808.55 **(e)** \$438.51 **(f)** \$1570.68 **8. (a)** \$796.00
(b) \$2563.40 **(c)** \$1198.61 **(d)** \$18 231.17 **(e)** \$222.27 **(f)** \$2455.83
9. (a) $n = 148.05199$ (months) **(b)** $n = 147.28515$ (months)
10. (a) $n = 34.2738$ (years) **(b)** $n = 27.9824$ (half-years)
11. (a) $n = 5.5811165$ (quarters) **(b)** $n = 5.8560171$ (half-years)
(c) $n = 50.201572$ (months) **(d)** $n = 11.721502$ (quarters)
12. (a) $n = 7.8316936$ (half-years) **(b)** $n = 10.513419$ (years)
(c) $n = 16.395667$ (quarters) **(d)** $n = 13.77754$ (half-years) **13.** 6.21%
14. 8.57% **15.** \$75 962.59 **16.** \$17 367.81 **17.** \$29 122.52 **18.** \$68 849.58
19. \$12 885.42 **20.** \$17 072.87 **21.** \$105.30 **22.** \$28 089.24 **23.** \$1320.05
24. \$4079.07 **25.** \$1338.04 **26.** \$8908.36 **27.** \$1.24 **28.** \$5972.06
29. $n = 90.10018$ (months) **30.** $n = 28.4623$ (years)
31. $n = 420.01797$ (months) **32.** $n = 19.302708$ (half-years)
33. $n = 59.909808$ (quarters) **34.** $n = 28.605079$ (quarters)

Self-test

1. \$108 276.76 **2.** \$8738.42 **3.** \$1081.13 **4.** \$153.98 **5.** \$21.97
6. 60 months (5 years) **7.** 12% **8.** 32 quarters (8 years) **9.** \$15 666.17
10. \$744.25

Chapter 14

Exercise 14.1

A. 1. (a) $588.56 **(b)** $5858.52 **(c)** $175.76 **(d)** $412.80 **3. (a)** $1103.73 **(b)** $4913.61 **(c)** $196.54 **(d)** $907.19 **5. (a)** $170.31 **(b)** $4336.50 **(c)** $75.89 **(d)** $94.42 **B. 1. (a)** $n = 19.47532$ **(b)** $2493.97 **3. (a)** $n = 21.415917$ **(b)** $14 987.48 **C. 1. (a)** $1282.84 **(b)** $18 232.24 **(c)** $80 970.40 **(d)** $44 970.40 **3.** Payment $2403.60; total paid $16 825.25; interest paid $6825.25 **5.** Total paid $14 943.16; interest paid $5743.16 **7.** $1029.33 **9.** $1160.09 **11. (a)** $5062.87 **(b)** $2667.24 **(c)** $2856.83 **(d)** Totals $162 011.89; $77 011.89; $85 000.00 **13. (a)** $n = 20.750427$ **(b)** $1808.32 **(c)** $958.57 **(d)** Totals $51 895.03; $27 895.03; $24 000.00

Exercise 14.2

A. 1. (a) 1829.69 **(b)** $20 286.42 **(c)** $819.57 **(d)** $1010.12 **3. (a)** $200.22 **(b)** $5010.15 **(c)** $60.76 **(d)** $139.46 **5. (a)** $5164.01 **(b)** $39 844.31 **(c)** $4371.02 **(d)** $792.99 **B. 1. (a)** $n = 22.61883$ **(b)** $3952.19 **3. (a)** $n = 14.894792$ **(b)** 1585.00 **C. 1. (a)** $396.87 **(b)** $35 259.23 **(c)** $13 546.55 **(d)** $446.08 **3. (a)** $n = 20.1335$ **(b)** $5716.23 **(c)** $7116.23 **5.** Payments $4487.21; total paid $31 410.44; interest paid $15 410.44 **7.** $1916.06 **9. (a)** $318.15 **(b)** $3323.12 **(c)** $259.36 **(d)** $364.44 **(e)** Balances $37 056.14; $36 913.71

Exercise 14.3

A. (using Method 1) **1.** $725.07 **3.** $73.74 **5.** $700.62 **7.** $312.17 **B. 1. (a)** $n = 37.656744$ **(b)** $237.92 **3.** $511.30 **5.** $591.61 **7.** $1809.15 **9. (a)** $n = 61.523813$ **(b)** $724.48 **(c)** $84 599.48 **(d)** $68 599.48

Exercise 14.4

A. 1. (a) $558.24 **(b)** $6399.60 **3. (a)** $9.14 **(b)** $1964.15 **5. (a)** $495.27 **(b)** $9598.44 **B. 1. (a)** $700.00 **(b)** $265.25 **(c)** $965.25 **(d)** $10 868.38 **3. (a)** $62.50 **(b)** $143.33 **(c)** $205.83 **(d)** $2246.16 **5. (a)** $4275.00 **(b)** $1123.59 **(c)** $5398.59 **(d)** $36 997.28 **C. 1. (a)** $2699.00 **(b)** $64 776.00 **(c)** $10 024.00 **3.** Deposits $1835.31; totals $12 847.17; $7152.80; $19 999.97 **5.** $2755.03 **7. (a)** $128.71 **(b)** $11 879.62 **(c)** $368.76 **(d)** $984.72 **(e)** Totals $23 167.80; $76 833.29; $100 001.09 **9. (a)** $54 750 **(b)** $2760 **(c)** $57 510 **(d)** $10 096 **(e)** $163 172 **(f)** Totals $55 161; $244 839; $300 000

Review exercise

1. **(a)** \$1958.20 **(b)** \$27 662.40 **(c)** \$18 377.85 **(d)** \$782.16 **(e)** \$1375.81 **(f)** Totals \$62 662.40; \$27 662.40; \$35 000.00 **2.** **(a)** \$190.32 **(b)** \$3419.20 **(c)** \$6189.46 **(d)** \$50.81 **(e)** \$161.94 **(f)** Totals \$11 419.20; \$3419.20; \$8000.00 **3.** **(a)** $n = 37.656744$ **(b)** \$35 433.72 **(c)** \$1250.38 **(d)** \$1006.34 **(e)** Totals \$75 321.78; \$35 321.78; \$40 000.00 **4.** **(a)** \$549.15 **(b)** \$6528.08 **(c)** \$411.02 **(d)** \$692.38 **(e)** Totals \$74 491.80; \$73 708.73; \$783.07 **5.** **(a)** \$1114.86 **(b)** \$152.15 **(c)** \$25 493.06 **(d)** \$1478.18 **(e)** Final balance \$16 869.77; Totals \$37 029.20; \$26 398.97; \$10 630.23 **6.** **(a)** $n = 16.294188$ **(b)** \$7464.05 **(c)** \$707.75 **(d)** Totals \$46 478.84; \$28 978.84; \$17 500.00 **7.** **(a)** $n = 9.3198366$ **(b)** \$1139.87 **8.** **(a)** $n = 160.53831$ **(b)** \$485.59 **9.** **(a)** $n = 21.888956$ **(b)** \$3832.80 **10.** **(a)** $n = 19.700707$ **(b)** \$14 240.01 **11.** **(a)** \$7327.06 **(b)** \$23 960.63 **(c)** \$3817.84 **(d)** Totals \$73 270.60; \$36 729.37; \$109 999.97 **12.** **(a)** \$1201.97 **(b)** \$17 570.15 **(c)** \$2443.36 **(d)** Totals \$38 463.04; \$26 536.90; \$64 999.94 **13.** **(a)** \$13 750.00 **(b)** \$8279.90 **(c)** \$22 029.90 **(d)** \$72 194.23 **(e)** \$5989.29 **(f)** Totals \$66 239.23; \$33 760.07; \$100 000.00 **14.** **(a)** \$28 875 **(b)** \$2201 **(c)** \$50 152 **(d)** \$266 560 **(e)** \$11 317 **(f)** Totals \$66 017; \$233 983; \$300 000 **15.** **(a)** \$180.90 **(b)** \$2183.20 **(c)** \$5218.47 **(d)** \$38.03 **(e)** Totals \$8683.20; \$2183.20; \$6500.00 **16.** **(a)** $n = 13.75176$ **(b)** \$1699.63 **(c)** Totals \$61 924.49; \$29 924.49; \$32 000.00 **17.** **(a)** \$2014.91 **(b)** \$19 701.80 **(c)** \$18 565.84 **(d)** \$1474.26 **18.** **(a)** \$711.87 **(b)** Totals \$4983.09; \$5016.91; \$10 000.00 **19.** **(a)** \$1032.37 **(b)** \$3839.26 **(c)** \$26 996.81 **(d)** \$1058.30 **20.** **(a)** $n = 26.995779$ **(b)** \$995.86 **21.** **(a)** $n = 38.468063$ **(b)** \$8318.12 **22.** **(a)** \$13 920.00 **(b)** \$5211.80 **(c)** \$19 131.80 **(d)** \$70 723.83 **(e)** Totals \$52 117.95; \$43 882.05; \$96 000.00

Self-test

1. \$6027.52 **2.** \$58 197.77 **3.** \$71.90 **4.** \$371.86 **5.** \$20 081.81 **6.** \$620.82 **7.** \$1297.87 **8.** \$622 192.28 **9.** Totals \$16 788.06; \$8211.95; \$25 000.01 **10.** Balance after 3rd \$11 867.56; Balance after 40th \$9754.86; Totals \$23 232.00; \$11 232.00; \$12 000.00

Chapter 15

Exercise 15.1

A. **1.** \$107 592.94 **3.** \$27 477.23 **5.** \$53 909.88 **7.** \$9706.28 **9.** \$11 939.29 **11.** \$9294.84 **B.** **1.** \$403.02 **3.** \$937.89 **5.** \$4 278 802 **7.** \$39 020.77 **9.** **(a)** \$19 656.14 **(b)** \$792.35 **(c)** \$18 863.79 **11.** \$5449.01

Exercise 15.2

A. 1. (a) $3822.93 (discount) **(b)** $21 177.07 **3. (a)** $1773.12 (discount) **(b)** $8628.88 **5. (a)** $9837.48 (discount) **(b)** $54 962.51 **7. (a)** $194.24 (discount) **(b)** $880.01 **B. 1. (a)** $30 384.99 (discount); $69 615.01 **(b)** $18 481.46 (discount); $81 518.44 **3. (a)** $269.95 (premium); $5469.95 **(b)** $199.89 (premium); $5399.89 **5. (a)** $3098.85 (discount) **(b)** $9362.53 **(c)** $9007.10 **7.** $4 630 385

Exercise 15.3

A. 1. (a) $967.90 (discount); $4032.10; totals $1575.00; $2542.90; $967.90 **3.** $49.18 (premium); $1079.18; totals $420.00; $370.82; $49.18 **B. 1.** $976.84 (gain) **3.** $64.02 (loss) **5.** $313.43 (gain)

Exercise 15.4

A. 1. 11.83% **3.** 12.12% **5.** 13.28%

Exercise 15.5

A. 1. (a) $83 059.44 **(b)** $69 652.79 **(c)** $1420.23 **3.** $659 919.33

Review exercise

1. (a) $5336.73 **(b)** $4550.35 **2. (a)** $9443.35 **(b)** $8927.93 **3.** $24 894.85 **4.** $746.05 **5. (a)** $929.50 (premium); $20 929.50 **(b)** $148.72 (premium); $21 548.72 **6. (a)** $2243.20 (premium); $11 243.20 **(b)** Nil; $9000.00 **(c)** $883.64 (discount); $8116.36 **7. (a)** $9962.95 (discount) **(b)** $93 969.33 **(c)** $90 115.74 **8. (a)** $225.87 (premium) **(b)** $43 556.85 **(c)** $42 624.98 **9.** $4527.64 **10.** $1071.17 **11. (a)** −$3469.30 (discount) **(b)** $24 625.42 **(c)** $23 330.78 **12.** 12.56% **13.** $72 356.00 **14.** −$72.73 (discount); $927.27; totals $870.00; $942.73; $72.73 **15.** $272.16 (discount); $4727.84; totals $4287.50; $4559.66; $272.16 **16.** $381.32 (premium); $21 381.32; totals $9300.00; $8918.68; $381.32 **17.** $6124.75 (loss) **18.** $993.69 (gain) **19.** 12.18% **20.** 15.20% **21.** 12.38% **22.** 14.40% **23. (a)** $46 906.73 **(b)** $20 770.01 **(c)** $298.05 (loss) **24.** $256 678.26 **25.** $92 388.48 **26.** 15.24% **27.** $977.39 (loss) **28. (a)** $8857.03 **(b)** $7879.25 **(c)** $351.27 (loss)

Self-test

1. $9269.44 **2.** $1110.97 **3.** $304.02 (premium) **4.** $51 806.82 **5.** $21 459.38 **6.** $4613.34 **7.** −$327.27 (discount); totals $2300.00; $2627.27; $327.27 **8.** 12.46% **9.** $1 110 226.27 **10.** $2062.19 **11.** $1707.25 (loss) 12. 12.92%

Chapter 16

Exercise 16.1

A. 1. (a) annual charge $7723.82; depreciation year 1, $1723.82; year 10, $6064.24 **(b)** assumed payment $1723.82; depreciation year 1, $1723.82; year 10, $6064.25 **B. 1. (a)** $536 089.36; $3510.66 **(b)** $536 089.54; $3510.64

Exercise 16.2

A. 1. $78 339.71 **3.** $217 799.60 **5.** 17.18% **7.** 18.76% **B. 1.** $242 514 **3.** 14.16% **5.** 19.47% **7.** $2479.28

Exercise 16.3

A. 1. $9522.57 **3.** $34 126.41 **5.** $104 872.03 **B. 1.** $1237.93; $1997.02; $4777.70; $4973.38 **3. (a)** $116 363.64 **(b)** $124 921.08 **5.** $23 045.65 **7.** $1944.03 **9.** $10 168.60 **11. (a)** Machine A $12 038.70, $1444.64; Machine B $12 342.73, $1481.13 **(b)** Machine A $10 399.58; $1871.92; Machine B $10 241.33, $1843.44 **13.** $13 480.74 **15.** $4.21; $3.99; difference $0.22 **17.** IH Tractor; $713.30 **19.** Model A; $1013.38

Review exercise

1. (a) annual charge $2589.94; depreciation year 1, $669.94; year 8, $1893.39 **(b)** assumed payment $669.94; depreciation year 1, $669.94; year 8, $1893.39 **2. (a)** $21 320.39; $2193.13 **(b)** $21 319.58; $2193.29 **3.** $936 556.85 **4.** $3575.02 **5.** $67 276.81 **6.** $2761.59 **7.** $420 222.93 **8.** $1287.32 **9. (a)** $197 350.04 **(b)** $29 602.51 **10.** 16.48% **11. (a)** 13.43% **(b)** $513 356.67 **12. (a)** $30 752.22 **(b)** $4127.72 **13.** $489.09 **14. (a)** Machine 1 $31 987.50, $4158.38; Machine 2 $32 079.63, $4170.35 **(b)** Machine 1 $27 943.37, $5588.67; Machine 2 $26 856.03; $5371.05 **15.** $2026.14 **16. (a)** Machine B **(b)** $0.11 **17.** $21 743.55 **18. (a)** Yes **(b)** $10 116.63

Self-test

1. Assume payment $7023.87; totals $42 143.22; $14 856.78; $57 000.00 **2.** $68 575.56 **3.** $1 052 879.80 **4.** 10.33% **5.** $37 997.99 **6.** $100 178.44 **7.** $15 089.77 **8.** $0.01 **9.** $14 230.15

Chapter 17

Exercise 17.1

A. 1. Alternative 2; present values are $44 634; $53 448 **3.** Alternative 1; present values are $48 569; $46 604 **B. 1.** Offer 2; present values are $52 138; $54 262 **3.** Lease; present values are $88 167; $86 379

Exercise 17.2

A. 1. Reject; NPV is −$5367 **3.** Alternative 1; NPV's are $234; $203 **B. 1.** Project B; NPV's are $1787; $2568 **3.** No; NPV is −$8561 **5.** Yes; NPV is $5696 **7.** Yes; NPV is $5142

Exercise 17.3

A. 1. 25.3% **3.** 20.7% **B. 1.** at 18%, NPV = $6101; at 20%, NPV = −$292; R.O.I. = 19.9% **3.** at 18%, NPV = $1286; at 20%, NPV = $104; R.O.I. = 19.9% **5.** at 22%, NPV = $148; at 24%, NPV = −$1538; R.O.I. = 22.2%

Review exercise

1. Alternative B; present values are $51 624; $52 161 **2.** Alternative 1; present values are $73 559; $74 653 **3.** Alternative 1; NPV's are $3916; $3597 **4.** Yes; NPV = $508 **5.** −$22 227 **6.** $404 **7.** at 26%, NPV = $370; at 28%, NPV = −$1939; R.O.I. = 26.3% **8.** at 18%, NPV = $135; at 20%, NPV = −$673; R.O.I. = 18.3% **9.** at 16%, NPV = $47 272; at 18%, NPV = −$22 227; R.O.I. = 17.4% **10.** at 14%, NPV = $404; at 16%, NPV = −$4383; R.O.I. = 14.2% **11.** at 24%, NPV = 2035; at 26%, NPV = −$184; R.O.I. = 25.8% **12.** at 12%, NPV = $3307; at 14%, NPV = −$2876; R.O.I. = 13.1% **13.** Project B; present values are $22 256; $22 909 **14.** Project B; NPV's are $3510; $4862 **15.** −$1215 **16.** at 24%, NPV = $1023; at 26%, NPV = −$1690; R.O.I. = 24.8% **17.** Yes; NPV = $28 940 **18.** at 14%, NPV = $36 347; at 16%, NPV = −$7635; R.O.I. = 15.7%

Self-test

1. Alternative A; present values are $13 552; $10 856 **2.** $3887 **3.** at 16%, NPV = $3466; at 18%, NPV = −$4368; R.O.I. = 16.9% **4.** Present values are $5939; $6040; purchase **5.** Proposal B, net present values are $701; $1427 **6.** at 26%, NPV = $356; at 28%, NPV = −$7526; R.O.I. = 26.1%

Index